INTERNATIONAL BACCALAUREATE

DESIGN AND TECHNOLOGY
Diploma Course

Peter Metcalfe
Roger Metcalfe

Copyright ©IBID Press, Victoria.

First published in 2011 by IBID Press, Victoria,

Library Catalogue:

1. Design and Technology

2. International Baccalaureate. Series Title: International Baccalaureate in Detail

Peter Metcalfe, Roger Metcalfe

ISBN: 978-1-921917-00-4

Cover design by Key-Strokes.

Published by IBID Press, 36 Quail Crescent, Melton, 3337, Australia.

Printed by KHL Printing

PREFACE

This text has been developed primarily to meet the syllabus requirements of the International Baccalaureate Design and Technology Syllabus. However, it also goes beyond the syllabus to deliver background knowledge and support for the concepts and principles underpinning the program.

In a rapidly changing technological world, texts like this must reinforce the changing nature of design and the role of designers. Designers have both an opportunity and a responsibility to shape our future. Courses such as the International Baccalaureate support and encourage the principles of sustainable design, creativity, problem solving and ethical decision making. It is hoped this text goes some way to supporting these goals.

It is intended that the added depth will provide students of design with a better understanding of the complex relationships between technology, humankind and the environment. On occasions, historical notes have been provided to show the origins of current practice but, in general, the information is as contemporary as possible.

Peter and Roger Metcalfe

Acknowledgements

The authors would like to thank the following for their help and assistance in the creation of this text.

Karen Scott

Chang (Cindy) Liu for research assistance on the Food and Energy chapters.

Alan Jacques, Richard Harper research and illustration.

Tamara Bell and Cate Scott.

Bard Australia Pty Ltd., W.L. Gore & Associates (Australia) Pty Ltd.

Cook Medical, Vasctek Terumo for the supply of vascular graft samples for the Medical textiles section

and Elesevier for permission to reprint Figure 4.4.10b from: Modern Physical Metallurgy and Materials, Engineering, 6th Ed., R.E. Smallman and R.J. Bishop. (1999). Butterworth Heinemann.

TABLE OF CONTENTS

DESIGN PROCESS

CONTENTS

1

Designing can involve people working as individuals or as part of a team; pooling their knowledge of mathematics, science and technology to generate creative and practical solutions to problems. The skills designers possess and the tasks they complete include:

- designing, making and operating the many systems, services and products that make up our everyday lives
- producing new innovative products or developing current products
- developing sustainable or green products to make the world cleaner, safer and healthier.

Designers use a variety of approaches to help them solve problems in the most efficient and effective way. The process chosen is as much a function of the type of project as it is the designer's individual or preferred style.

1.1 THE DESIGN CYCLE MODEL AND THE DESIGN PROCESS

> 1.1.1 Describe how designers use design cycle models to represent the design process.
>
> © IBO 2007

The design cycle is often represented graphically to show the structural elements of the design process and how they interact. The variety of design models is only matched by the range of applications they find.

The design process is commonly used in: product design, engineering, architecture and marketing. It is however, just as appropriate to the fields of webpage design, medicine, dentistry and robotics.

An architectural design process model may employ the following stages - schematic design, design development, presentation and evaluation, detail development and construction documentation.

A product design process model may vary from the previous and contain the following elements - market need, clarification of task, specification, conceptual design, concept, embodiment design, layout, detail design and manufacturing instructions.

However the design process is modelled, it usually consists of a series of interrelated stages contrived to focus and refine the designer's efforts towards a final solution in response to a predefined problem or need and most often contains the following elements:

- identifying needs or clarifying a need or opportunity
- analysing, researching and specifying requirements
- generating ideas and possible solutions
- developing and refining a chosen solution
- realizing or manufacturing the chosen solution
- testing and evaluating the chosen solution against the specification.

1.1.2 List the stages in the IB design cycle model (DCM).

The IB design cycle model consists of six interrelated stages and includes:

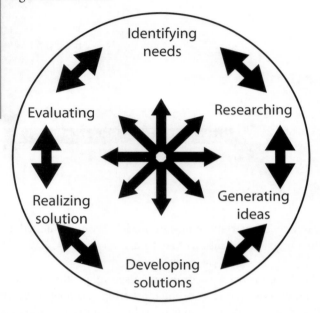

Figure 1.1.2 IB Design cycle model © IBO 2007

1.1.3 Describe a design brief.

A design brief is most often the written starting part of any new design. The intention of a design brief is not to provide answers or unnecessarily constrain investigation but to provide a framework for the solving of a problem.

A well-written design brief establishes:

- design goals (such as a functioning prototype)
- context (intended market and/or environment)
- major restrictions, constraints or requirements (materials or legislative demands etc.)
- criteria by which an effective response would be judged or evaluated (such as: improved functionality, environmental friendliness, reduced operating costs).

1.1.4 Describe the identifying or clarifying a need or opportunity stage of the IB design cycle model.

Well-designed products don't just happen by accident, but by careful design. Successful designs and designers, start with a clear understanding of product context. Product or design context is a combination of factors including:

- characteristics of the target market
- purpose, goal or need for the product
- situation or environment within which the product will perform
- capabilities and limitations of appropriate technologies and materials.

Products that meet contextual needs have a better chance of being successful. Using this general information, a designer is better informed when developing a precise design specification.

1.1.5 Describe a design specification.

1.1.6 Describe the analyzing, researching and specifying requirements stage of the IB design cycle model.

A product specification should consist of information related to the product. This information should not just list design requirements but provide justification for their inclusion. This list should not direct the design but help focus the designer's attention towards fruitful investigations through the statement of a series of relevant restrictions. The nature of design requires that these statements need to be very specific and not include any vagaries that may lead to misinterpretation of the brief.

Specifications must be carefully developed through communication between designers, manufacturers and consumers. Product design specifications are produced after thorough investigation. This research process may use a variety of techniques including: market research, consumer surveys, patent investigations, literature searches and competition or SWOT analyses.

A design specification must be flexible enough to evolve throughout the design process. The final product design specification (PDS) can then be successfully used to evaluate the final product.

1.1.7 Describe the generating ideas and solutions stage of the IB design cycle model.

© IBO 2007

The idea generation phase involves the search for alternative solutions. This creative component of the design process uses the specification as a starting point. Designers here deal more with design concepts rather than complete and detailed solutions. Designers will seek a range of sources for inspiration and choose from a variety of approaches to support the generation of ideas. These approaches are sometimes grouped loosely under the heading of cognitive organizers. Examples of creativity tools include:

TRIZ
SCAMPER
mindmapping
brainstorming
concept maps
six thinking hats
morphological analysis.

Sketching and note taking is key to the successful documentation of ideas. During this stage all of the creative alternatives should be evaluated before the most promising solution is selected.

1.1.8 Describe developing the chosen solution stage of the IB design cycle model.

© IBO 2007

In this stage, previously under-developed ideas start to take form and evolve using both the research previously uncovered and specification requirements. Design decisions are also made on the basis of information gained through testing and evaluative procedures.

The final part of the development stage is the proffering of a final design solution and production of engineering drawings sufficient to allow production. The type of project undertaken will determine the style of drawing chosen and the level of supporting documentation required.

1.1.9 Describe the 'testing and evaluating the chosen solution' stage of the IB design cycle model.

© IBO 2007

The last stage of the design process involves assessing

the degree to which the project achieved its preset goals. These goals were of course established in the earliest part of the design cycle. A measure of the project's degree of success is determined here. Suggestions are also made recommending modifications or improvements in production methods (manufacturing processes) and design (functionality, aesthetics). This process can be repeated in an endless loop of review and improvement.

Negative evaluations do not always indicate a product's potential market success. The iconic Alessi Juicy Salif lemon squeezer, designed by Frenchman Philippe Starck, is hailed as a design classic. Yet, when evaluated under performance-based criteria, the retro-style rocket ship device is notoriously difficult to use successfully. When fielding criticism of his creation Starck is alleged to have said, "My juicer is not meant to squeeze lemons; it is meant to start conversations".

Figure 1.1.9 Starck-designed juicer

Image by Niklas Morberg [Creative Commons Attribution-Share Alike 2.0 Generic], via Wikimedia Commons

1.1.10 Explain why the IB design cycle model is not linear and why it is iterative in practice, thus making it representative of design thought and action.

© IBO 2007

The design process requires an integrated, interrelated approach involving: research, testing and evaluation. Many consider design to be an iterative process, a stepwise refinement from the general to the specific. This iterative, or repetitive, approach allows designers to take large amounts of untested research and innovative ideas and evaluate improvements for their effects incrementally.

Using this technique designers are able to focus on improvements one at a time, testing their feasibility as the overall project continues to evolve.

If the IB design cycle model were to adopt a linear mechanism for development of solutions the production of optimal results would be severely hampered.

> 1.1.11 Explain the role of the designer in the design process.
>
> © IBO 2007
>
> 1.1.12 Describe how designers interact with others and how the emphasis of the design process varies depending on the designer's role.
>
> © IBO 2007

The role of the designer is ever-changing. A diversity of contexts requires a range of approaches. Depending on the outcome, the role of the designer will change, e.g. design briefs may call for an ergonomic overhaul, prototype creation, energy or materials revisions for efficiency etc. Each of these problems would require a different skill set and plan of attack.

Designers may be required to confer with; marketing people, manufacturers, clients and, in some instances, the public (if conducting their own market research, or user trials).

> 1.1.13 Explain why elements of the model may differ in importance according to the particular design context.
>
> © IBO 2007

The design process must be both dynamic and flexible. Application of one particular rigid model can never be suitable in all contexts. Depending on the desired outcome, various components of the process require more attention, time or repeated cycling to provide a suitable solution.

> 1.1.14 Define incremental design, radical design, convergent thinking and divergent thinking.
>
> © IBO 2007

Incremental design is the process of taking an existing product and making it better. It can allow designers to focus on particular features for development. Followed by frequent testing, incremental design can improve the chances of success. Wholesale design changes can generate numerous unpredictable problems that cascade or propagate throughout a design and may be difficult to trace back to the source.

In the 1960s, the radical design movement emerged. It rejected the traditional principles of good design and pursued a more anti-establishment approach. Much of the work was inspired by urban design, alternative lifestyles and environmental issues. Today, radical design refers more to innovation-driven creativity. Radical designers have intuitive skills that anticipate the emergence of design trends not currently evident. In some cases, the innovation itself creates the trend and thus generates its own market niche. Radical design is also often referred to 'breakthrough' design.

Convergent thinking is the application of knowledge or research gathered, and then applied, to 'converge' or focus on arriving at the single best solution to a proposed problem. Convergent thinking is an analytical, logical approach that is not necessarily very creative. Convergent thinkers acquire knowledge that they consider may be useful for future problem solving. When evaluating a product currently on the market convergent thinking allows designers to break a design up into its component parts or examine its functionality to determine how well it meets the designer's intention.

Divergent thinking is a more creative approach to problem solving where a range of alternative, creative, unusual or innovative solutions to a problem are considered. When using divergent thinking the approach to solving a problem is different every time. In the design process it is most evident when generating ideas.

Radical design involves the development of an entirely new approach to solving a design problem. The solution may be the result of gathering existing technologies and applying them in new ways, or may be the result of a technological breakthrough. Radical designs are marked by their widespread acceptance and impact in terms of accrued benefits. They often lead to new fields of design, are subject to copying and start a new cycle of incremental development.

Apple computing is recognized for its radical design concepts leading to the successful introduction of new ideas, refined, and then developed, over time. Apple's 1998 iMac, (Figure 1.1.14), available as a single, (gumdrop shaped and coloured), monitor and processor unit was sold with built-in speakers, 'puck' style mouse and no floppy disk drive. This was a clear example of radical design in action. The popular market alternative 'beige box' continued as separate monitor and processor components, and for some time included floppy disk drives.

Figure 1.1.14 Apple's radical iMac design

1.1.15 Describe the relationship between incremental design and convergent thinking.

Incremental design allows for the development of a product in a series of evolutionary stages. Convergent thinking plays an important part in this role, by focusing the designer's attention on one particular feature at a time for analysis, modification and improvement.

1.1.16 Describe the relationship between radical design and divergent thinking.

Divergent thinking allows designers to extend their investigations beyond the 'normal' range. This may generate ideas that although implausible may spark a relationship to another 'radical' response that would not normally be considered or exposed to any degree of development.

1.1.17 Explain how elements of the design model reflect convergent and divergent thinking.

A combination of convergent and divergent thinking occurs when designers are developing ideas. Testing for functionality, or materials appropriateness, employs convergent thinking, while making creative adjustments to designs to improve their performance employs more divergent thought processes.

1.1.18 Explain how design work is often a combination of incremental and radical thinking.

The Apple iPod (Figure 1.1.18) is an example of both radical and incremental design. At the time of inception there were numerous portable music playing and/or MP3 devices.

Starting with a small, rectangular, white MP3 player with a text view screen, standard 5GB capacity and an innovative mechanical click wheel for navigation, the first iPod was an instant success. Not to rest on its laurels, however, Apple continued to develop their product over the years by reducing, and on occasions increasing its physical size. More importantly it continued to innovate through shape, capacity, colour, navigation mechanisms (touch screens etc.) and media access, (MP3, video, WIFI internet).

This product was borne out of radical design and continued to develop incrementally until emerging technologies allowed for additional radical redevelopment. A whole market has since developed around the supply of iPod related accessories.

Figure 1.1.18 Apple iPod design variations

Incremental design is far more commonplace than radical design. It relies on improving an existing product through a series of development changes often in response to market demand or technological change. Radical design by its nature is new and ground breaking. As such, it is often opening untested niches in the marketplace. Additionally, it tends to be more risky in terms of commercial viability.

Further reading

Gray, P., *Design is the Differentiator, The Changing Role of Industrial Design*.

Lloyd, P., and Snelders, D. (2003) *What was Philippe Starck thinking of?* Design Studies, Vol. 24, No. 3, May.
Wallace, K., & Clarkson, J. (1999). *An Introduction to the Design Process*. Cambridge University Engineering. Cambridge.

1.2 GENERATING IDEAS

1.2.1   Define constructive discontent.

1.2.2   Identify a design context where constructive discontent has been the primary generator of ideas.

© IBO 2007

Constructive discontent is the process of generating alternative solutions to existing products in need of improvement. These improvements may be related to functionality, cost, efficiency of performance or any other identified need.

1.2.3   Define adaptation.

1.2.4   Identify a design context where adaptation has been the primary generator of ideas.

© IBO 2007

Adaptation involves the transferring of successful design solutions, or parts thereof, to provide new solutions for design problems in entirely different fields. Biomimicry is an approach to design and innovation that involves transferring successful designs from nature into new design contexts. Development of Japan's Shinkansen bullet train uses solutions found in nature to enhance the efficiency of its design. The nose-cone section of the train, shown in Figure 1.2.4, is modelled on the beak of a Kingfisher bird. The bird's beak is designed to absorb sudden changes in pressure caused by diving into water. A similar situation was observed by Japanese designers when trying to avoid low-level sonic booms caused when their super-fast trains exited tunnels.

Figure 1.2.4a Shinkansen bullet train nose-cone

Image by Parag.naik [CC-Attribution 3.0 Unported], via Wikimedia Commons

1.2.5   Define analogy.

1.2.6   Identify a design context where analogy has been the primary generator of ideas.

© IBO 2007

Analogy invokes likeness or similarity. Analogous design therefore involves the transfer of an idea from one situation to another. Compact fluorescent lamps are an example of analogous design. Inspired by the need to reduce energy during the energy crisis of the 1980s, designers transferred and modified existing technologies and processes and translated these into a different context within the same field to generate an entirely new product.

1.2.7   Define brainstorming.

1.2.8   Identify a design context where brainstorming has been the primary generator of ideas.

© IBO 2007

During brainstorming, several engineers and/or designers will meet to propose possible solutions to the design brief. Brainstorming is a 'free-for-all' where any idea, no matter how unusual, is considered and recorded. Extreme, impractical ideas may lead to the development of innovative and feasible solutions.

A whiteboard is a simple tool often used during this process, allowing quick sketches or notes of ideas to be recorded. Due to the broad scope of participants' experiences, each person involved in a brainstorming session will come up with quite different ideas and solutions. From a brainstorming session, (a single project may require several brainstorming sessions), the most feasible solutions are agreed upon and taken into the next phase – conceptual design. These ideas are sometimes analysed and ranked using a weighted decision matrix where design considerations such as cost, ease of use, effectiveness and safety are considered.

Brainstorming is an integral and regular part of innovation and the design process. The earliest occurrences of brainstorming occurred when NASA was developing ideas for the exploration of space. Specifically, the development of early spacesuits benefitted from the gathering of scientists from a variety of disciplines charged with developing a suit for astronauts. The group was asked to freely express their ideas and interestingly the most appropriate concept was proposed by a biologist. Figure 1.28 shows astronaut Gordon Cooper in his 1963 Mercury Program suit.

Figure 1.2.8 Early NASA spacesuit design

Image by NASA [Public domain], via Wikimedia Commons

1.2.9 Define attribute listing.

1.2.10 Identify a design context where attribute listing has been the primary generator of ideas.

Attribute listing is a de-constructive process of reducing an idea, product or process to its constituent parts and analysing each of these components rather than the whole. This allows designers to concentrate on the key features of the design and examine ways to adjust or improve individual attributes, one by one. As a process for the generation of ideas, the systematic development of alternatives to these design attributes could involve the application of convergent or divergent thinking.

Attribute listing is most suitable for product development where the general concept for the product has been established and fine tuning, improvement or efficiencies are required.

1.2.11 Define morphological synthesis.

1.2.12 Identify a design context where morphological synthesis has been the primary generator of ideas.

The word morphology comes from the Greek concept morphé, meaning shape or form. Morphological analysis deals with the organisation of this 'shape or form' and how components interact to create a whole.

In creative problem solving it is easy to get stuck in conventional thinking or in the ruts of any given train of thought. Morphological analysis is one of the creative tools that is available to stimulate designers into considering many other possibilities. As a problem-solving tool, morphological analysis is designed to assist with creativity. Similar to attribute listing, it uses the same basic technique but offers the generation of a new product by mixing components in new ways. Working backwards from the product or outcome, inwards, towards the system components, the problem under consideration is broken down into components and possible alternatives proposed for each. These alternatives are then recombined in various combinations of these values in a 'what if' analysis to consider the benefits of associating the chosen elements. For the purposes of convenience, a simple grid or matrix is created with two axes representing the components and the variables. In some situations, this matrix can be constructed as a cube with the variables listed separately over the z-axis. The power of this approach is evident when considering that a simple analysis with four component parts and five variables for each would generate a staggering 625 possible solutions for evaluation.

This technique is designed to provide a structured approach to producing creative alternatives that may not be considered in a more conventional approach. This process is particularly useful when searching for new product concepts dealing within the configuration of a total design solution, evaluating existing products or reviewing competing designs in the marketplace.

1.2.13 Discuss why designers use a variety of techniques to develop ideas.

Designers use a range of idea development strategies so as not to restrict the creative process. Selection of processes can be as simple as personal preference, past success, time, design context or even the need to break with convention.

Further Reading

Jin, S. T., Kim, Y. S. K. & Kim M. H. (2005). *Diverse Characteristics in Design Problem Solving: A Case Study of Disciplinary Comparisons*. IDC International Design Conference, National Yunlin University of Science and Technology. Taiwan.

Ritchey, T. (1998). *General Morphological Analysis A general method for non-quantified modeling*, The Swedish Morphological Society. Adapted from the paper 'Fritz Zwicky, Morphologie and Policy Analysis', presented at the 16th EURO Conference on Operational Analysis. Brussels.

Eggermont, M., *Biomimetics as Problem Solving,.Creativity and Innovation Tool*. Schulich School of Engineering. University of Calgary.

1.3 COMMUNICATING IDEAS

1.3.1   Define freehand drawing.

© IBO 2007

As a part of their everyday operations, designers need to acquire the skills associated with graphical communication. The quick and easy nature of sketching as a tool provides the designer with a great deal of flexibility whether in the field or a design studio. The only tools required are paper and a pencil. Used in the early stages of the design process pencil sketches allow designers to quickly jot down ideas that may influence the final design.

1.3.2   Describe the importance of annotating freehand drawings.

© IBO 2007

Annotations accompany drawings to improve the communication of information. They also help with the creative process documenting fleeting thoughts before they are forgotten. Designers use annotations in a variety of ways including the need to:

- identify problems for future resolution
- clarify obscure or difficult-to-sketch concepts
- note a range of related thematic variations or alternatives
- record their thoughts about particular features for later reference.

1.3.3   Explain the purpose of two- and three-dimensional (2D and 3D) freehand drawings.

© IBO 2007

3D sketches provide designers with a sense of form, proportion and aesthetics while 2D sketches are able to isolate and detail more structural features. At some later stage, these sketches may need to be translated into a more formal and accurate representation.

1.3.4 Define orthographic drawing.

© IBO 2007

1.3.5 Explain the purpose of an orthographic drawing. © IBO 2007

© IBO 2007

Orthographic drawing uses lines of sight that are always perpendicular to the viewing plane to produce a projected image, hence the name orthographic projection (Figure 1.3.4a).

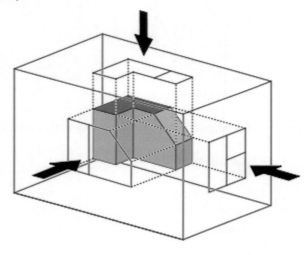

Figure 1.3.4a Orthographic drawing

Varieties of different forms of orthographic projection are named depending on the positioning of the object and the observer in relation to the plane or planes of projection. Different styles, such as first and third angle projections are identified by the one of four quadrants or angles they enclose, (Figure 1.3.4b).

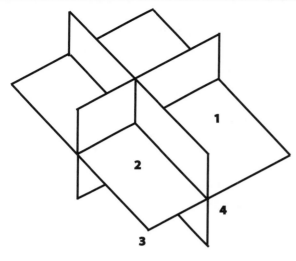

Figure 1.3.4b Drawing planes

In third angle projection, the front and horizontal planes of projection are perpendicular to each other, however, using the line of intersection of the two projection planes as a hinge, the top view is swung directly above the front view. Frequently the folding line between the views is drawn on the paper. Above the folding line, an HP notation indicating a horizontal plane appears while below the folding line the letters VP may appear indicating a vertical plane (Figure 1.3.4c).

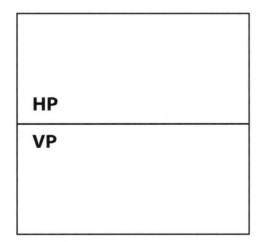

1.3.4c Third angle projection planes

The first and third angle projections are both used extensively throughout the world. When the first quadrant is used, the lines of sight travel from the observer's eye to the object and then to the plane of projection. When the third angle of projection is used, the lines of sight travel from the observer's eye through the plane of projection to the object (Figure 1.3.4d). In each type of projection the views are obtained in a similar way but their relative positions vary.

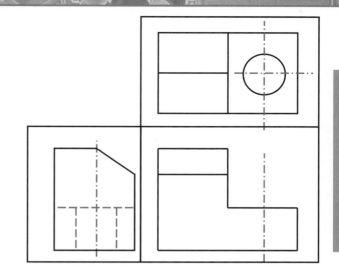

Figure 1.3.4d Third-angle projection view placement

In first angle projection, the top view is on the bottom, drawn below the front view whereas, in third angle projection, the top view is drawn above the front view. Australia, Canada and the United States all use third angle of projection. The standard symbol identifying a third angle orthographic projection drawing appears as show in Figure 1.3.4e.

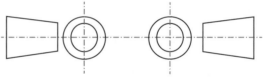

Figure 1.3.4e First angle and third-angle projection symbols respectively

In a conventional third angle orthographic projection, the views will always appear in the positions shown. The top view is projected directly onto the horizontal plane of projection and shows the width and depth dimensions. The front view is projected directly onto the vertical frontal plane of projection and shows the width and height dimensions. The left-side view is projected directly onto the vertical left plane of projection. The side view of an object shows the depth and height dimensions. In most cases, three views convey all of the information to adequately describe an object. In product design, orthogonal drawing usually refers to accurate line drawings used to convey dimensional and/or assembly details. These may be manually drawn using drafting equipment or now, more commonly, using CAD software.

General assembly is an orthogonal drawing that communicates the functional detail of a design by indicating the size and relative position of all parts, fastening details and functional relationships between parts.

Views are carefully selected, and sectioning and other conventional representations used to successfully communicate the complete design. Critical overall dimensions may be shown along with accompanying notes explaining details for overall assembly and function.

Sub-assembly drawings are used for large or highly complex products. Product assembly may also have to be broken down into sub-assemblies to allow a sufficient level of detail to be shown. In this situation a hierarchy of assembly drawings may be required to relate each part to the functioning of the whole.

> 1.3.6   Identify the stage of the design process where orthographic drawings are relevant.
>
> © IBO 2007

An orthographic drawing, (commonly referred to as an engineering or working drawing), shows precise details and dimensions. It is most often used as a workshop or production drawing. Generated in the final stage of the design process, and fully dimensioned, they provide valuable information to manufacturers and engineers relating to: dimensions, tolerances, construction methods, materials, surface finishes and assembly. Patent applications such as the one shown in Figure 1.3.6 show a sample of an engineering drawing.

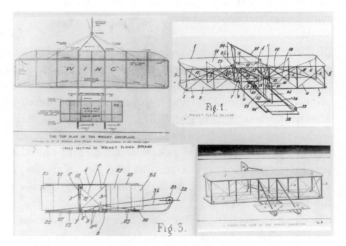

Figure 1.3.6 Wright Brothers 1908 engineering drawing patent application

Image by unknown author [Public domain], via Wikimedia Commons

> 1.3.7   Define isometric drawing.
>
> 1.3.8   Explain the purpose of an isometric drawing.
>
> © IBO 2007

Isometric drawing is a 3D pictorial style of drawing where an object is viewed from a corner. Derived from the Greek 'equal measurement' this style of drawing uses actual measurements taken from the object or orthogonal drawings.

Parallel 30° lines ensure that near and far objects are given equal emphasis. As a final touch for realism, sketches may be rendered to enhance depth perception. Surface textures may also be added to indicate different materials.

Isometric drawing has found acceptance by engineers and drafters when choosing a style of pictorial drawing for: technical drawings, workshop manuals, patent illustrations and machine components. This is particularly the case when components require assembly. Figure 1.38 shows a drawing of what is perhaps the first rendered, 30° isometric drawing.

Figure 1.3.8 Isometric optimal-grinding engine

Image by William Farish (1759 – 1837) [Public domain], via Wikimedia Commons

1.3.9 Define exploded isometric drawing.

1.3.10 Explain the purpose of an exploded isometric drawing.

Exploded assembly is usually an isometric drawing with all parts displaced (exploded) along a central axis. This type of drawing is more visually descriptive showing actual assembly configurations and fastening details. Exploded drawings serve to clearly identify parts for assembly and maintenance procedures.

1.3.11 Define perspective drawing.

1.3.12 Explain the purpose of perspective drawing.

Perspective drawing is based on observation from a single point, the eye, which produces images similar to that of a camera. Perspective drawings create the illusion of an object's size diminishing the further it retreats from a fixed viewpoint. Early artists employed the technique of perspective. A contemporary of da Vinci, German artist Albrecht Durer further perfected the technique of perspective in use at the time. Durer developed several machines designed to 'capture' an image that would maintain spatial relationships of objects, varying in distance from the observer. 'Durer's window' as shown in Figure 1.3.11 used a piece of glass acting as a picture plane to accurately create a perspective image. These concepts of picture planes, vanishing points and spatial relativity are equally relevant today.

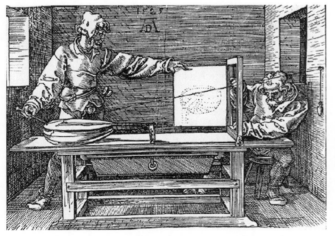

Figure 1.3.11 1525 woodcut showing use of Durer's perspective machine

Image by unknown author [Public domain art], via Wikimedia Commons

The natural appearance of perspective drawings makes them popular choices with artists and architects. The receding lines give emphasis to objects in the foreground and less prominence to those in the background.

1.3.13 Define computer-aided design (CAD) and computer modelling.

1.3.14 Outline two advantages and two disadvantages of using CAD instead of traditional drawing methods.

CAD stands for computer-aided design. CAD drawings exist as electronic data files that are created using specialist software.

Advantages of CAD drawings include their ability to be:

- stored in a variety of formats
- corrected or altered very quickly
- created as 2-D or 3-D representations
- rescaled, zoomed, cropped etc. for detail
- presented as paper printouts, virtual models or rapid prototypes
- electronically distributed for collaboration as part of a group project
- used in conjunction with numerical control machinery for CAD/CAM production.

Disadvantages of CAD drawings include:

- staff training required
- initial cost and upgrading of software
- high level of skill required to be competent
- compatibility between software and hardware
- skills constantly require upgrading as software updates
- steep learning curves associated with early stages of uptake.

1.3.15 Define algorithm.

1.3.16 Describe how an algorithm can be used to communicate a process.

An algorithm is a chronological sequence of steps used to complete a task. Algorithms may be presented in words, as a flowchart or in structured code. A computer program is an algorithm written for a computer in a particular style or programming language. In mathematics and computing algorithms are used to solve problems.

Known by a variety of names including, but not limited to: flow diagram, process chart, process model, process flow diagram or work flow diagram; in every case, they provide a graphical representation of a process or procedure. Actions, sequencing and links are easily visible. Each step is marked by a standardized symbol representing an action or process. The three most commonly used symbols are graphics representing; terminator, process and decision. Symbols are linked by arrows showing the direction or flow of the chart. Figure 1.3.18 shows a simple process constructed as a flowchart. Notice the use of the three principle symbol types.

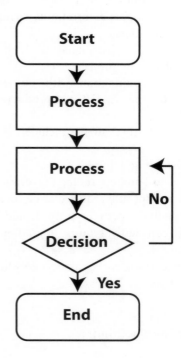

Figure 1.3.18 Simple flowchart

Flowcharts assist in communication by arranging tasks into logical sequences and actions. This allows the viewer to see a concise set of operations and the interrelationships between the component stages.

A flow chart is a way of showing an algorithm in graphical or diagrammatic form.

Models have a range of styles but essentially they all present a simplified representation of reality. They may be categorized in a variety of fashions but for simplicity are often broken up into two categories:

- physical - such as scale architectural models or product prototypes
- symbolic - including mathematical models, graphics and diagrams.

Graphs and tables could be classed as simple mathematical models and are often employed to document operations and processes or predict performance.

Clay modelling is a very traditional technique used by car designers to produce physical models. Some design studios have transferred their modelling activities to the CAD department while others maintain that clay is still the best way to visualise the development of 3D designs. Clay scale models such as the one shown in Figure 1.3.23a may be produced to examine aesthetics, while full-size models allow for wind tunnel testing, fitting of hardware and components such as door handles, glass etc. Physical models can also be digitized using 3D scanners. The process of 3D scanning allows engineers to virtually manufacture panels, add powerplants and drivetrains towards the development of a simulated working prototype.

*Figure 1.3.23a
Car modelled
in clay*

*Image by
Monash
University,
Faculty of
Art & Design,
Australia
2010*

As a design tool architectural models are a quick and inexpensive way for architects to visualize space, consider the relationship between buildings and landscape/environment and assist when discussing revisions with clients. Landscape models of large developments may use a scale of about 1:100 while, for individual buildings (requiring greater detail), a scale of 1:20 would be more appropriate. Models such as the one shown in Figure 1.23.b may use a variety of materials including: illustration board, foamcore, medium density fibreboard, corrugated cardboard, balsa wood and acrylic.

Figure 1.3.23b Single dwelling architectural model

Image by Wasily at nl.wikipedia [Public domain], from Wikimedia Commons

Models produced through the process of rapid prototyping may be made from a variety of materials including: polymers, metals, ceramic or wax. Rapid prototype models provide tactile feedback. They may even be produced to replicate the look and function of a real object. Made within hours and easily modified without the use of extensive tooling these models may quickly demonstrate the evolution of a model through a range of iterations. (For greater detail on rapid prototyping, see Option C).

1.3.24 Define mathematical model.

Mathematical or computational models are a means of representing essential aspects of reality (process, phenomenon, object, element, system, etc.) with the help of mathematical equations. They may also be used as predictive tools to help designers make critical decisions. Mathematical models are most often only valid within the particular ranges of their parameters. Conclusions drawn from these models should always be used in context.

1.3.25 Describe the role of spreadsheet software in the development of mathematical models.

Spreadsheet-driven mathematical models allow users to easily change input variables. The use of spreadsheets allow designers to quickly adjust parameters that can result in the testing of new designs through materials changes, dimensional variations or the review of 'what if' scenarios. Linked to CAD packages, spreadsheet-driven design tables allow for the creation of libraries of configured parts, (units of varying sizes for modular assemblies). This operation is easily achieved requiring no programming or specialist knowledge.

1.3.26 Outline the advantages and disadvantages of graphical, physical and mathematical models.

Graphical models such as sketches and freehand drawings are quickly generated and useful for communicating initial design concepts. Drawings of a more technical nature take longer and require a degree of expertise not only to correctly construct but also to interpret. CAD drawings such as 3D models, while requiring significant knowledge and skill to produce, are very user friendly when interpreting and manipulating.

Physical models have the advantage of tangibility. They may be physically handled and viewed from a variety of perspectives. Models can also be constructed to exhibit particular features of the design. Unfortunately they may not always be easily or quickly modified and in some cases may require complete reconstruction.

Mathematical models typically offer convenience and cost advantages over the alternatives. They can be extremely powerful, enabling predictions to be made about a system or process. Predictions inform designers of possible developments that are worthy of further investigation or may be employed to optimize use of: materials, strength, materials choice, performance etc. Mathematical modelling allows for the testing and development of optimal solutions using simple mathematical processes or complex techniques such as matrix algebra. Manufacturers may use mathematical models to optimize profits through the calculation and manipulation of such variables as: inventory, production time, plant capacity, warehousing constraints and transportation timings. Unfortunately, mathematical models cannot be entirely reliable in predicting real world situations and are only as good as their programming allows.

> **1.3.27** Describe three advantages of using models as part of the design process.
>
> © IBO 2007

Model making or the construction of a physical prototype has distinct advantages for designers, manufacturers and clients, including:

- opportunity for user trials
- client input into developing models
- speeding up product development cycles
- possibility of testing production methods and materials prior to production tooling
- reducing development costs by avoiding costly mistakes and false starts in production runs
- functionality of the design becomes more obvious when reviewing physical models and prototypes
- proof of concept when examining interacting or moving components or internal mechanisms.

> **1.3.28** Describe three limitations of the use of models in the design process.
>
> © IBO 2007

The exclusive use of models in the design process may cause problems in the form of:

- performance - models may not always be representative of final product
- functionality - models are not always able to replicate in-service use
- predictions - models may not always provide a true indication of the final product; materials, performance or interaction with the environment.

Further Reading

Simmons, C., Maguire, D., Phelps, N. (2009). *Manual of Engineering Drawing Technical Product Specification and Documentation to British and International Standards.* Butterworth-Heinemann.

Exercises

1. Identify the term that best suits the following definition; 'the transfer of a design or idea from one context to another.'

   A. analogy
   B. adaption
   C. adoption
   D. anathema

2. The design process is:

   A. iterative
   B. repetitive
   C. regressive
   D. progressive

3. A design specification provides a:

   A. solution to a problem
   B. clear design direction
   C. framework for the solving of a problem
   D. list of relevant restrictions upon which to focus research

4. The most appropriate style of communication for early concept designs would be a:

   A. physical model
   B. freehand sketch
   C. functional prototype
   D. orthographic drawing

5. Explain the difference between first and third angle projection.

6. Explain why a variety of design process models exist.

7. Create a flowchart for the process of getting out of bed in response to an alarm clock.

8. Explain why perspective is an important means of communication and identify a situation where it would be appropriate.

9. Identify and justify a design context where a designer would choose each of the these models: graphic, physical and mathematical.

10. Explain how flow charts may assist designers.

PRODUCT INNOVATION

CORE

There are many theories on the nature of, and mechanisms that bring about invention and innovation. These theories range from the 'lone genius', to coincidental discovery and cultural maturation. Most consider the role factors such as chance and serendipity may play in the process.

While some of these theories are contradictory and others sit comfortably beside each other, the debate over market demand versus technological opportunism continues to rage. Since 1934, when Schumpeter claimed entrepreneurial activities were driven by a technological push, the debate has swung both ways. Today's consensus is with the theories of Schmookler, who in 1962 decided user needs or market pull were the most influential drivers of innovation.

More recent research is swinging the pendulum back towards technology push theories where technological breakthroughs with strong intellectual property protection act as the driving force.

Regardless of the style of approach or driving forces, it is generally agreed innovation is the lifeblood of economic growth.

2.1 DESIGNERS AND THE PRODUCT CYCLE

2.1.1 Describe the product cycle.

© IBO 2007

New products progress through a series of stages from: development to introduction, growth to maturity, and finally decline. This sequence of events is known as the product cycle or product life cycle and describes the dynamic relationship between product changes and sales. Figure 2.1.3 shows a typical product cycle graph where sales are plotted against strategic product development stages. All of the various stages of the product cycle have implications for marketing.

2.1.2 Discuss the role of the designer in the product cycle.

© IBO 2007

Designers clearly have a role in the product cycle in many stages. Early in the cycle, designers are busy generating ideas and testing alternative solutions before settling on a final concept ready for testing and, eventually, introduction to the marketplace. Designers re-enter the cycle to bolster flagging product sales through the introduction of new products developments, modifications and/or improvements. Throughout the process, designers are working with multidisciplinary teams including: manufacturers, accountants, machinists, marketing staff etc.

2.1.3 Outline the product cycle in terms of early, mature and late stages of development.

© IBO 2007

In the early stages of the product cycle, manufacturers seek to raise product awareness. Pricing could be aggressive to capture market share and the product may be positioned in a premium price range to recoup research and development costs. At this point the target market is early adopters.

In the growth stage, product changes and modifications take place to stimulate the market. Increasing demand sees little need to modify pricing.

During the mature stage competition may appear and the pace of sales growth may slow. Market penetration should be good and manufacturers attempt to differentiate their product. Pricing may also be reduced to attract consumers away from competing products.

In the late stage, the product begins to decline in need, (due to competition or obsolescence), and therefore in sales, heavy discounting may occur, some new features may be added to recover flagging sales or the product may be discontinued.

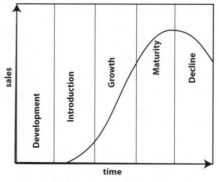

Figure 2.1.3 Product lifecycle stages

2.1.4 Identify products that are at the early, mature and late stages of their product cycle.

© IBO 2007

3D televisions and portable tablet computing devices are still in the early stages of development. In this phase we see rapid incremental changes as new technologies become available and fashions change. Figure 2.1.4 shows some of the changes in mobile phone technologies. This market is still in the growth stage, as competitors continue to make changes well past the models shown.

Figure 2.1.4 Mobile phone developments

Products such as the steam iron, ballpoint pen, reading glasses and scissors fall within the mature stage. These products are still in demand by consumers but see only minor changes in design and features.

VCRs, floppy discs, cassette tapes and cheque books are in the late stage, as they have all been overtaken by successive generations of products, technologies and systems.

2.1.5 Compare the design cycle with the product cycle.

© IBO 2007

The design cycle is concerned with identifying and clarifying problems or needs before arriving at a solution based on cycling through the testing and development of a range of alternatives. The product cycle is more concerned with the commercial development of a product based on market sales.

2.1.6 Discuss why for many products the product cycle has shortened.

© IBO 2007

The rapid pace of technological change, fashion trends and global competition are factors that have affected the length of the product cycle. Manufacturers are always looking for a competitive edge. Incremental change through the incorporation of new technologies also continues to drive innovation. Additional to these forces are manufacturers' interests in planned obsolescence and society's propensity towards disposing of consumer items on a regular basis.

Sustainable growth however can only come through new products and radical design.

Products using microchip technologies have seriously shortened product cycles due to the regular availability of faster, smaller, more powerful and lighter processors. These developments continue to revolutionize product design, making previous models (sometimes only months old) no longer competitive.

Figure 2.1.6 Microprocessor

Image by Rama (Own work) [CC-BY-SA-2.0-fr (www. creativecommons.org/licenses/by-sa/2.0/fr/deed.en)], via Wikimedia

Further Reading

Komninos, I. (2002) *Product Life Cycle Management.* Aristotle University of Thessaloniki.

2.2 INVENTION AND INNOVATION

2.2.1 Define invention and innovation.

© IBO 2007

Invention is broadly defined as the act of creating something new or the significant improvement of something already in existence. It most often involves creating something that has not existed before. Inventions may take the form of a product, service or system.

Innovation refers to the successful commercialization of an invention. An invention with no commercial viability would not be classed as an innovation.

2.2.2 Outline the stages of innovation.

© IBO 2007

The innovation cycle is a complex series of interactions between design and manufacturing considerations, market demands and business imperatives.

In simple terms, the innovation cycle may be loosely categorized into the following stages:

- developing a viable concept or idea into a market ready product
- manufacturing the product
- development of marketing strategies
- improving the product through design evolution.

2.2.3 Discuss the importance of science to invention and innovation.

© IBO 2007

Scientific theory or law provides the basic principles of how things work. Invention and innovation rely largely on the application of scientific advances and the understanding of cause and effect gained through research and development. Scientific gains lead to invention and finally innovation through the meeting of identified market needs.

2.2.4 Discuss the importance of technology to invention and innovation.

Frequently, new or at least improved technology is required as a precondition for innovative design. The primary challenge for design is the integration of new technologies and market research to produce user-friendly and attractive products. Advances in technology also uncover new possibilities for materials, manufacturing techniques and processes, all of which present new design opportunities.

2.2.5 Explain why the majority of inventions fail to become innovations.

2.2.6 Explain the relevance of design to innovation.

Design allows innovations to be successfully brought to the market and (re)developed over the product's life.

For continued innovation, products are constantly updated, (redesigned) to make them more commercially viable and to give consumers choice and improved products. Size and duration of market demand will eventually determine the financial market success of an invention.

The chances of an invention being developed into a market-successful innovation may be influenced by the following factors:

- expectations of demand
- magnitude of user needs
- expectations of profitability
- degree of positivity of market perception
- amount of intellectual property protection afforded by patents.

Innovation, through the redesigning of a product is a requirement for sustained market share or product growth. Without continual evolution through innovation products can saturate market demand. Design stagnation can also be the cause of products being surpassed by their competitors whose designs may continue to evolve.

2.2.7 Define dominant design, diffusion into the marketplace, market pull and technology push.

Dominant design is the emergence of a product design that achieves market dominance through the provision of a particular feature set that is seen as essential to the product category. Emergence of dominant design late in the product cycle can hamper early market growth as consumers wait for the right feature set to emerge.

In the recent past, industry experts have been used to identify the emergence of dominant design features in fields as diverse as automobiles, televisions and calculators. Prior to adopting this method it was generally agreed a dominant design was one that captured more than 50% of the product market and held it for four consecutive years.

Diffusion into the marketplace refers to the rate of acceptance of a product within the market. Diffusion is a dynamic process encompassing early adopters, cautious consumers and latecomers to the market looking for value or finally accepting the inevitability of change.

Marketing staff use 'S'-shaped product diffusion curves to predict which market segment their campaigns should be targeting.

Market pull is the action of consumers creating a need or market for a product or service that is then targeted by manufacturers when developing new products.

Technology push is evident when innovative technological breakthroughs occur and companies then search for marketable applications to then make them commercially viable. Technology push supporters agree that predicting market needs for products that do not yet exist is near impossible. They do however concede the role market pull has in developing or improving existing products.

2.2.8 Describe a design context where dominant design is relevant.

In the 1970s in the early stages of the introduction of video cassette recorders (VCRs) to the market, two competing systems existed, VHS and Beta.

During '70s the VCR became the best selling consumer electrical product, surpassing even television sales. Sony was the first to introduce its Betamax system followed by JVC a year later with its VHS system. The systems differed considerably and were quite incompatible with each other due to variations in tape-handling, encoding and physical cassette sizes.

The Beta system was originally the industry leader backed by the Sony Corporation. It was also seen as the technically superior device. Despite all this, the VHS system proved to be the survivor and soon achieved market dominance.

While JVC was the major producer of the VHS format technology, it licensed other companies to produce VHS machines while Sony continued to 'go it alone' before managing to strike deals with other companies. Coupled with a reduced recording time, (less than the length of a movie), and manufacturing issues associated with a more complex machine, Sony's system soon lost ground to the manufacturers of VHS systems. Even though Sony continued to innovate, (slow motion, hi-fi sound, wireless remotes), and develop its product further, it was unable to recover lost ground as VHS manufacturers assimilated and reproduced each of the Sony innovations within months. At the end of the 1980s Sony no longer manufactured a Beta system VCR.

JVC and its design department were clearl;y able to discern important dominant design features as they evolved and were even able to dominate the market with, arguably, a technically inferior product.

In more recent times digital technologies have now made VCRs all but obsolete.

The Apple® iPad® is an example of the early stages of market dominance in a new, innovative and highly competitive design field. Having established a market, other companies are now introducing their own tablet-based computer systems to try and capture market share. Apple® has started with the largest share of this developing market but as the field matures an essential set of design features will emerge. The company that markets a product encapsulating these features will assume market dominance.

> **2.2.9** Explain the difficulties of getting a product to diffuse into the marketplace.
>
> © IBO 2007

There is a direct relationship between total market potential and price. Before developing effective marketing strategies, accurate information must be obtained about the market size. This has a considerable effect on market diffusion predictions. Marketing strategies based on inaccurate information can lead to wrongful predictions for future market sales and create production problems causing either under or oversupply of product.

Speed of product diffusion is based on market acceptance by individual consumers and while their size and behaviours may prove difficult to predict, there are identified product factors that influence diffusion rates. Faster diffusion will occur if consumers can readily obtain answers to the following questions:

- what advantages does the new or modified product provide over alternative offerings?
- how difficult is the device to operate or maintain?
- can I easily see the product operational either in demonstrations or in the marketplace?
- is the product compatible with other related technologies?

> **2.2.10** Explain why it is difficult to determine whether market pull or technology push is the impetus for the design of new products.
>
> © IBO 2007

While these terms apply to the creation of an original product concept, these forces are still at play during the entire product lifecycle. As noted previously, the role market pull has in developing or improving existing products is well recognized and technological breakthroughs regularly play a role in product modifications. Most products however, are a combination of market pull and technology push. Even for an innovative technologically-based product to be successful there must be a degree of market readiness or acceptance otherwise the product will be a commercial failure.

> **2.2.11** Define lone inventor.
>
> © IBO 2007

The concept of 'lone inventor' was popularized by journalists during the Industrial Revolution, when inventors were associated with the development of significant discoveries such as Alexander Graham Bell and the telephone, Thomas Edison and the light bulb or gramophone (Figure 2.2.11) and, later, the Wright Brothers and flight.

During the 20th century, the notion of the lone inventor has gradually disappeared with the emergence of multi-national companies and research and development teams.

These groups are now mostly credited with major product developments.

Figure 2.2.11 Thomas Edison C1882 — lone inventor

2.2.12 Discuss why it is becoming increasingly difficult to be a successful lone inventor.

© IBO 2007

The majority of products today are very complicated. Materials technology, manufacturing processes and testing procedures are now so complex no one person has the knowledge, skills or resources to successfully bring a product to the market. Once an initial concept is proposed, multidisciplinary teams of experts are required to develop and market the successful product.

2.2.13 Explain why lone inventors often find it difficult to work in the design departments of large companies.

© IBO 2007

Lone inventors often have significant emotional investment and ownership issues surrounding their work and, as such, may have difficulty working with others who may wish to take design development in other directions. The nature of their working style may also indicate they are used to working independently and not part of larger teams where they are just one voice among many.

2.2.14 Define product champion.

2.2.15 Compare the lone inventor with the product champion.

© IBO 2007

Most often working with, and even coordinating teams, product champions are passionate about driving particular

products to market. They 'champion' the product both within, and outside, their organization. Product champions have a vision for their passion that, if successful, meets the needs of consumers and the manufacturer.

2.2.16 Explain why innovators may have difficulty in obtaining financial support for an invention.

© IBO 2007

Investing in innovation is about risk taking. Innovation tends to be more risky from technological, financial and market success standpoints. Market research is also less reliable for innovative products. Design teams and researchers have to rely on gathering as much feedback as possible from prototypes rather than generations of market-successful product developments. Early markets are also volatile and unpredictable places, characterized by high technological and customer uncertainty. Until customers form clear preferences about what constitutes a successful, marketable product, there is a great deal of variation in design and technologies on offer, not all of which can survive in a competitive marketplace.

Redevelopment of an existing product is more common due to the fact that market demand has already been established. Redevelopment may only involve incremental adjustments to form or features of an existing product.

Further Reading

Åstebro, T. et al. (2003). *Opportunity Knocks.*

Fry, A. (2002). *Creativity, Innovation and Invention: A Corporate Inventor's Perspective*, Creative Problem Solving Group Communiqué. Vol. 13, p.1-5.

Haggblom, T. A. (1996). *A Dynamic Product view of Diffusion.*

Miettinen, R. (1996). *Theories of Invention and Industrial Innovation.* Science Studies. Vol.9

Rising, L. 2003. *The Product Champion*, Software Testing and Quality Engineering. May/June.

Srinivasan, R., Lilien, G. L. & Rangaswamy A. (2006). *The Emergence of Dominant Designs*, Journal of Marketing. Vol. 70. 1–17.

Steffen, D. Design (2007). *Semantics of Innovation, Product language as a reflection on technical innovation and socio-cultural change.* 2007.

2.3 PEOPLE AND MARKETS

2.3.1 Define technophile, technocautious and technophobe.

2.3.2 Explain how people can be broadly classified according to their reactions to technological change.

Technophiles are early adopters of technology. They are often just as fascinated with the technology of the device as they are with its features and functions. They are prepared to pay a price premium for early entry into the market just to acquire the latest product.

Technocautious individuals however, tend to wait for technologies to prove themselves in the marketplace. They are often adopters at second-generation level of product development. They may also wait for market leaders to appear, improved features and price reductions.

Technophobes are more than cautious in their adoption of new technologies. They may not feel comfortable with new ways of working and often subscribe to the theory that what they currently have is, and will always be sufficient for their needs.

These categories classify people based on their reactions to technology. An individual's reaction may be based on a number of factors and may change over time, determined by the technology in question.

2.3.3 Define corporate strategy.

Corporate strategy refers to a company's planned approach for the future. It often involves an assessment of the current situation and mapping of policies and procedures to achieve predetermined goals. These goals may be; long or short term production-based, environmental, financial or deal with external factors such as competition. In simple terms, a corporate strategy is a company's strategic vision for the future.

2.3.4 Describe the corporate strategy referred to as 'pioneering'.

2.3.5 Describe the corporate strategy referred to as 'imitative'.

A pioneering strategy, as the name suggests, involves charting a new or innovative course. Many manufacturers believe there is a competitive advantage to being 'first to market', with a product or service. It is this approach that drives the pioneering strategy. Market pioneers not only need to carefully identify their market, in some cases they need to create one where none exists due to the ground-breaking nature of their product. They must generate sales as quickly as possible to justify the often large research and development costs involved in bringing a product to market.

Markets early in the product cycle are very volatile. Until a clear set of parameters are determined as to what constitutes a successful and marketable design, many companies will hold off entering. This is how the imitative or market colonizing strategy comes into play. In new markets it takes time for dominant designs to emerge and it is often the imitators or market colonizers that wait to capitalize on the research and development work of other firms. As the market matures and customer preferences develop, imitators enter and product development and improvement continues.

Dominant designs with associated market-driven features now appear. Corporations applying an imitative strategy to entering the market regularly avoid the high level of risk associated with innovation and side-step the large costs associated with early research and market development. The financial advantages and technological benefits here may be considerable.

Unfortunately, research shows that the majority of product and service pioneers rarely reach market dominance. Examples abound in industry of market innovators being unable to capitalize on their early entry to the market to produce a dominant design from a significant innovation. The Xerox Corporation is an example of such a company unable to reap the benefits in the PC market after developing a personal computer operating system interface, at its PARC research centre. Sony's Betamax failure to capture market dominance is another high profile example of an imitator achieving success as documented in section 2.2.8.

2.3.6 Explain the benefits for a company of using a hybrid strategy.

Companies adopting a hybrid pioneering and imitative strategy hope to combine the benefits of both approaches to building their sales and profitability. Adopting innovation while at the same time imitating market competitors, hybrid strategists plan to reduce research and development costs while at same time capturing market share with unique or innovative features within what may already be a market-familiar product.

2.3.7 Define market penetration.

2.3.8 Describe a strategy that a company would use to enhance market penetration.

Market penetration is a tool used to determine the potential growth available for product sales. It is often reduced to a simple mathematical calculation:

$$\frac{\text{product sales}}{\text{total market potential}}$$

A range of product promotion strategies may be employed including: discounts, celebrity endorsements, bonus offers etc.

Company acquisition is also a strategy employed by companies to improve their market penetration. Along with increased sales, additional technologies, personnel and intellectual property may also be acquired.

2.3.9 Define market development.

2.3.10 Describe how a company would undertake market development.

Market development is the process of developing: sales, new products or new markets. It is designed to grow a business in a variety of ways including:

- introducing new products or services to existing customers
- generating new products and/or services to new customers
- establishing a greater market base by attracting new customers

- educating consumers, particularly when introducing new product lines
- creating new applications for existing product; for example, nylon was originally developed for parachutes.

2.3.11 Define product development.

Product development involves product evolution through the addition of new features and technologies. Product development is mostly aimed at the existing customer market but may also attract new or first time purchasers.

2.3.12 Describe one example of how a company undertakes product development.

Household cleaning products are dominated by a small number of multi-national companies such as Proctor and Gamble, Unilever and SC Johnson etc. Cream, liquid and spray delivery systems continue to be the most popular modes of delivery. In recent times, these and other companies have identified market segments that require product development to meet the market. The introduction of cleaning wipes (disposable, cleaner-impregnated cloths) have been developed for busy households where cleaning time is considered the factor motivating purchasers. Other developments include anti-bacterial cleaning products designed to sterilize surfaces as well as remove dirt.

Figure 2.3.12 Product development

2.3.13 Define diversification.

2.3.14 Describe one example of diversification.

2.3.15 Define market sector and market segmentation.

2.3.16 Outline two ways in which markets may be segmented.

A product diversification strategy involves the modification of an existing product so that its market potential can increase. Its aim is to attract a new customer base and thus increase sales. It can be done by leveraging the reputation of existing products as well as developing new platforms to be able to produce and eventually sell the modified or the innovative products.

The premium accommodation provider, Marriot, have diversified through the mechanism of product extension. The generation of the 'Courtyard by Marriott' group has leveraged the brand recognition associated with Marriot hotels, but targeted business and budget travellers to widen their market appeal.

In another case, product diversification has taken the form of producing a new but related product, on sale to the same target market group. The Reebok shoe company has entered the bottled water market through its 'Reebok Fitness Water™' product.

Nike™, has also ventured out from its original core business of manufacturing sports shoes to generate sales in the areas of: fashion, sporting equipment and associated technologies such as pulse monitoring watches (Figure 2.3.14).

The product diversification strategy is different from product development in that it involves creating a new larger customer base, designed to expand the market potential of the original product. Effective product diversification requires accurate market targeting and careful attention to product differentiation in order to prevent cannibalizing of existing product markets. Its aim is to increase overall sales and profits of the company.

Figure 2.3.14 Nike™ watch product diversification

Market sectors are particular subsets of markets that share specific characteristics. Sectors are often large and could include such diverse fields as: pharmaceutical, household and automotive groupings.

Market segmentation involves the break up of markets into smaller divisions or segments. Consumers within market segments are identified as having similar characteristics. It is these characteristics that allow for careful targeting of goods and services. Traditionally markets have been divided using demographic characteristics such as age, gender, lifestyle or ethic background. Also, attributes such as: location, income, marital status, children and even physical characteristics such as height or quality of hearing may be used.

Products targeting specific market segments create new customers in existing markets. This approach often builds on a well-known brand names or market sectors. Examples include:

- sports cars or off-road vehicles
- Dyson vacuum cleaners marketing to pet owners
- automotive insurance packages tailored to 'mature' drivers.

2.3.17 Define robust design and product family.

2.3.18 Discuss an example of a robust design that evolved into a product family.

Robust product design uses the concept of standardized specifications for components or assemblies within a product family or associated brands, allowing companies to create a competitive advantage. Often based around a 'product platform' or 'standardized architecture', robust design gives manufacturers the opportunity to produce customized or alternative designs through the addition, subtraction or substitution of a range of components or assemblies. These variable configurations generate enormous flexibility and are often developed to target specific, previously identified markets

The automotive industry is a prime example of a market sector employing the principles of robust design to be competitive on a global scale. Examples of carmakers taking advantage of common platform architecture include:

- Porsche's, Cayenne, sharing the Volkswagen Touareg PL71 platform
- Ford employing a shared platform between its Focus and the Ford C-MAX
- Proton Inspira using a Mitsubishi Lancer platform.

The development of common product platforms brings important competitive advantages to a company including:

- increased modularity
- reduced design effort
- easier mass customizing
- reduced time-to-market for products
- lower research and development costs
- reductions in the number of suppliers.

Further Reading

Caulkins, J.P. et al., (2005). *Explaining Fashion Cycles: Imitators Chasing Innovators in Product Space*. Vienna, Austria.

Martin, M. V. & Ishii, K. *Design for Variety: Developing Standardized and Modularized Product Platform Architectures*, Research in Engineering Design. Volume 13. Number 4. pp 213-235.

Simpson, T. W. (2004). *Product Platform Design and Customization: Status and Promise*. AI EDAM: Artificial Intelligence for Engineering Design, Analysis and Manufacturing. 18, pp 3-20.

Shimokawa, K. (2000). *Reorganization of the Global Automobile Industry and Structural Change of the Automobile Component Industry*. Presented at 8th Annual Gerpisa Conference, Paris.

1. The product cycle stage where prices are at their highest is most likely:

   A. introduction
   B. growth
   C. maturity
   D. decline?

2. Lone inventors operate best when working:

   A. independently
   B. leading teams
   C. consulting for organisations
   D. as part of a large multi-skilled team?

3. Robust design is characterized by:

   A. its strength
   B. quality assurance testing
   C. shared product platforms
   D. independent product architecture?

4. Market penetration is best described as:

   A. how far a product reaches
   B. how quickly a product sells
   C. product sales as part of the total market.
   D. how successfully a product targets its niche?

5. Dominant designs:

   A. are the highest in quality
   B. are always first to market
   C. have recognized essential features
   D. imitate the best features of other designs.

6. Why do some products have extended product lives, while others have very short lives?

7. Explain the difference between product development and product diversification.

8. Explain why companies adopt an imitation strategy rather than developing new products of their own.

9. Identify the factors that have led away from lone inventors and towards research and development teams.

10. Explain why successful inventions do not always translate into innovations.

GREEN DESIGN

CONTENTS

3

Designers and manufacturers are increasingly considering the relationship between their products and the environment. Products on shelves everywhere exclaim their environmental credentials using terms such as 'environmentally friendly', 'sustainable', 'eco friendly' and 'green'. Quotes of international standards and certification abound.

What does it mean to be environmentally friendly? Is it an absolute term? How can the environmental friendliness of a material or product be measured or compared to other similar items? What are the relative effects and merits of green product design, manufacture, use and disposal? What are the economic considerations surrounding green design? The study of green design considers these and other questions.

3.1 PRINCIPLES OF GREEN DESIGN

3.1.1 Define green design, renewable resources and non-renewable resources

© IBO 2007

Green design refers to products that have a benign or reduced affect on the environment for their entire life cycle. More specifically, it refers to the minimizing of environmental impacts associated with product design, materials extraction, manufacturing, use, maintenance and end of life disposal. Other terms associated or interchangeable with green design include; sustainable, environmentally friendly and eco-design.

Renewable resources are those that are consumed at a lesser rate than they are replaced by natural processes. Renewable resources may take the form of energy or commodities. Some resources require careful management such as: geothermal power, plantation timber and water. While others such as wind, solar and tidal energies are perpetual in that they are deemed inexhaustible.

Non-renewable resources include materials that, due to their rate of depletion and the extreme time scales involved in their formation, are finite and therefore exhaustible. Fossil fuels such as coal, oil and natural gas are all non-renewable. Mineral and ore resources such as iron, diamond and bauxite are also considered non-renewable.

3.1.2 Outline the reasons for green design.

© IBO 2007

There are many forces acting on consumers and manufacturers alike to encourage the development of environmentally sustainable products. In many countries government policy now mandates manufacturing and production requirements based on legislation. European and national legislation is shifting responsibility for discarded products more and more to the producer. The need is thus generated for more efficient processes and procedures to design, develop and assess products with regard to their environmental impact. Examples of existing government policies include the EU 'take back' program and the US Clean Air Act.

Consumers are now also better informed about the environmental impact some products and their manufacturing practices have on the environment.

This increased environmental awareness translates into consumers making purchases based on this additional criterion. Many companies now promote their 'green' credentials through advertising campaigns, product information sheets and web links explaining their policies. Companies must respond to legislation and market demands but an increasing number also have a social conscience and may even see financial benefit when developing product lines.

Eco–labeling is a legislated requirement within the EU. In 1992 this program was introduced to certify products that met stringent criteria relating to the production and disposal of manufactured goods. Originally, the eco-label program was designed to assist with sustainable development but inclusion of an environmental rating on products is now perceived as a competitive, marketing advantage.

The International Standards Organization (ISO) is a network of national standards institutes spanning the globe. It is the largest producer and publisher of standards in the world. ISO 14000 is a group of management standards developed to deal with a range of environment related procedures including: environmental management systems, labeling, life cycle analysis, auditing etc. Adherence to these environmental management standards may make companies eligible for certification. This may then in turn be a requirement of their suppliers and thus certification could become a prerequisite for doing business in some fields.

3.1.3 List design objectives for green products

Their are many interpretations of green design, however, the World Business Council for Sustainable Development has developed a list of criteria designed to reflect the principles or objectives associated with the development of green products and includes:

- reducing toxic dispersion
- extending product durability
- enhancing material recyclability
- maximizing sustainable use of renewable resources
- increasing the serviceability of goods and services
- reducing the material and energy intensity of goods and services
- potentially requiring certification to become a prerequisite for doing business in some fields.

3.1.4 Discuss the impact of 'take back' legislation on designers and manufacturers of cars, refrigerators and washing machines.

Historically, disposal of discarded packaging, refrigerators, cars and electronic products has long been the responsibility of governments. Traditionally these unwanted items have been buried in landfill or incinerated with little consideration given to reuse or recycling. Not only is this process wasteful of many materials that may be recycled but also has serious impacts on the environment.

Suitable landfill sites close to the source of waste materials are increasingly difficult to find and consume land that would otherwise be public space. Even when appropriate sites are found, the burying of community and/or industrial waste generates its own set of problems including:

- risk of subsidence
- generation of odours, flammable and toxic gases
- attraction of scavenging bird and vermin populations
- release of pollutants into the atmosphere in the event of a fire
- pollution of surface and groundwater through run-off and leaching.

'Take-back' legislation or extended product responsibility (EPR) requires manufacturers to either manage their own waste or engage a third party to be responsible for managing waste products and packaging over the entire product life cycle.

The product life cycle starts with materials acquisition and finishes with product end-of-life and waste disposal. This period is often referred to as 'cradle to grave'. Legislation now requires a product specific approach, however, one immediate result is the reduction or elimination of landfill and incineration as the primary means of dealing with product end-of-life waste.

'Take-back' policy has implications for manufacturers and designers across the entire product life cycle. The legislation essentially aims to reduce environmental impacts through a three-stage process:

- increasing recycling rates
- reducing or eliminating pollution at every stage
- reducing the volume and toxicity of waste disposal.

Typically, EPR strategies used by designers and manufacturers include:

- producing more durable products
- identifying materials to aid recycling
- choosing materials that recycle more easily
- reducing the amount of materials used in products
- eliminating toxic materials in the product design stage
- developing and managing recovery, reuse and recycling systems
- designing modular or component-based construction, assisting repair or maintenance
- improving ease of recycling through design for disassembly approaches e.g. using clips.

Because manufacturers are financially responsible for management of their products' entire life cycles, these costs must be included within the retail price. To remain competitive in the market, companies, and therefore designers, have to make this process as efficient as possible. Consequently, there is an incentive for innovation as designers and manufacturers strive to reduce toxic waste materials while incorporating recyclable and recycled materials into their products.

It should be noted, waste management programs can add to production costs if not carefully integrated into designs that incorporate recyclable materials or reusable components that may lower future product costs and, in some cases, even generate an income.

Automakers and end-of-life vehicle legislation

For many years some 75% of the weight of end-of-life vehicles (ELVs) have been recycled. These figures are amongst the highest of any product group, and were previously seen as successful. These efforts mostly focused on the recovery of metals. Figure 3.1.4a shows an example of vehicle bodies gathered for recovery and recycling.

In 2000 the EU introduced the ELV directive (the first product of the European Commission's priority waste streams program) that was produced in response to the amount of hazardous emissions, toxic materials and non-recyclable components, primarily polymers, in vehicles.

The challenge was to address the waste stream generated during the production of vehicles, from the extraction of the raw materials to the assembly of a finished car. Vehicle production consumes a tremendous amount of resources and results in significant release of pollutants. As much as 13,000 kilograms of waste may be created from the production of a single vehicle.

In terms of recycling, the greatest opportunities for increased materials recovery rates involve plastics, rubber, glass, and electronic components. Plastics have traditionally been the largest proportion of non-recycled materials in vehicles.

Creating a 'cleaner, greener car' involves:

- review of painting and coating practices
- elimination of heavy metals and other damaging substances
- design of vehicles for recyclability and maximum use of recycled materials.

Specifically, manufacturers have removed the toxic heavy metals cadmium and chromium (VI) from vehicle production lines. Mercury content is already very low and continues to be phased out, while lead (as a component of solder) remains, but only in negligible amounts. These changes alone reduce the amount of hazardous waste handled during vehicle recovery and simplify the recycling process. More efficient production systems and improved electronic inventory management and materials handling systems have all helped to contribute to a 5% decrease in CO_2 emissions over the 2005–2007 period.

In 2009, the 'End-of-Life Vehicle Directive and Directive on Reusability, Recyclability and Recoverability,' set new requirements for automakers. New vehicles are now mandated to exhibit 'reusability and/or recyclability of at least 85%, and reusability and/or recoverability of at least 95% by weight, if measured against the international standard ISO 22620.' The auto industry has been able to meet these specifications by developing new recycling technologies, materials management through re-processing and better information management systems.

The amount of waste per vehicle continues to decline as manufacturers reuse a variety of production wastes and recycle material from scrapped vehicles, therefore using less landfill disposal and requiring smaller amounts of virgin materials.

Through the implementation of water reuse and re-circulation technologies, water consumed during vehicle production has been reduced by 23% per vehicle over the 2005–2007 period.

Through the application of water-based paints, emissions of volatile organic compounds (VOCs) have also been significantly reduced per vehicle. VOCs are organic solvents that serve as the carrier for pigments in paint. Their volatility means they easily become vapours or gases, thus causing the paint to dry.

Figure 3.1.4a Vehicle recovery and recycling

Whitegoods and the Waste Electronics and Electrical Equipment Legislation (WEEE)

Directive 2002/96/EC of the European Parliament and of the Council on Waste and Electronic Equipment noted the pace at which consumer electrical and electronic products were growing. This was happening without sufficient concern for waste management and recycling. The council, "insisted on the need for promoting waste recovery with a view to reducing the quantity of waste for disposal and saving natural resources, in particular by reuse, recycling, composting and recovering energy from waste and recognized that the choice of options in any particular case must have regard to environmental and economic effects".

'Take-back' schemes for WEEE items now exist throughout the EU and non-member countries. These programs place the responsibility of end-of-life waste management on manufacturers. The legislation has the intention of reducing the quantity of toxic waste, increasing recyclability of products and reducing pollution at its source.

Targets set in 2003 required manufacturers of washing machines and refrigerators (Category1) to recover a minimum of 80% by weight of every appliance and reuse, or recycle, 75% by weight.

Recovery minimum	80%
Reuse and recycling minimum	75%
Incineration for energy maximum	5%
Disposal maximum	20%

Figure 3.1.4b shows discarded household appliances; such as refrigerators, stoves, washers, dryers etc., gathered at one site ready for recycling and disposal by the EPA.

> 3.1.5 Explain how people can be broadly classified according to their attitudes to green issues.
>
> © IBO 2007

Many ancient cultures express a belief that they are part of nature, and live in harmony with it, taking only what they need to survive. The impact of these cultures is therefore generally taken as being sympathetic with the local ecosystem and the principles of environmental sustainability. If this is true, these cultures may represent only those civilizations that have faced environmental issues of their making, and found a solution. There is much evidence to suggest that many ancient civilizations collapsed from the ecological change brought about by their own actions and ignorance of its environmental consequences.

Until recently, most modern cultures have seen themselves as separate from nature and that, through technology, they have been liberated from such primitive concerns. With the onset of the Industrial Revolution, this mastery over nature was becoming more evident. At that same time, a small number of people also began to express disquiet at both the rate of change of society and the local environment. Authors, such as the Englishman Thomas Malthus (1766–1834), warned that population growth, if unchecked would exceed the capacity of the earth to provide food, a position again proposed by Paul Ehrlich in his 1968 publication, 'The Population Bomb'. Projections of the date at which such calamities would occur were averted however, by technological changes that increased food production. The American author, Henry David Thoreau (1817–1862), promoted the benefits of a simple life and advocated the conservation of virgin forest as a standard by which change could be measured. Industrialization as a rule, however, proceeded with little regard for its impact on the environment.

Widespread concern for the environment is a relatively recent consideration. The origins of popular awareness and understanding of environmental degradation probably lie with the publishing of 'Silent Spring' by the biologist Rachel Carson in 1962. Carson noted the effects of the use of DDT to control mosquitoes, on the environment and the food chain. Expanding on the theme, 'The Closing Circle: Nature, Man & Technology', by Barry Commoner (1971), detailed a number of instances of environmental degradation by industrial pollution. Commoner also proposed what he called the four laws of ecology:

- nature knows best
- everything must go somewhere
- there is no such thing as a free lunch
- everything is connected to everything else.

In 1971, Greenpeace was established, initially to oppose US atomic bomb tests, and subsequently became involved in the environmental movement more generally. Greenpeace rapidly became a focus group for protests against environmental pollution. Environmental concerns were further raised by a number of revelations regarding the disposal of toxic waste and the inadequacy of many safety control systems, among them: Minamata (1968), The Love Canal (1978), Three Mile Island (1979), Bhopal (1984), Chernobyl (1986), and the Exxon Valdez (1989).

In 1979, scientists James Lovelock and Lynn Margulis published 'Gaia: A new look at life on Earth', in which they proposed a controversial hypothesis that the Earth could be considered to be a superorganism that could respond to changes using a self-regulatory, or homeostatic, process. This hypothesis added support to the suggestion that human activity might not only change the local environment, but might set in train changes on a worldwide basis that might be irreversible. About this time, concerns about a rise in atmospheric carbon dioxide and its possible influence in global warming began to appear in the popular press. Today, we categorize people based on their attitudes to green issues.

Eco-warriors are individuals who take a proactive role in championing causes for the environment by caring for the natural world in their daily lives and decision-making. The Eco-warrior movement in Australia developed a flag, (Figure 3.1.5), symbolizing their ethical stance. The flag has fours colours. Red, yellow and black represent indigenous cultures worldwide, while green is indicative of nature and the environmental movement. In the centre of the flag is a tripod symbol representing unity. This flag first appeared

in the late 1990s when environmental activists gathered to protect an area of high ecological value.

3.1.5 Eco warrior flag

Image by Ecopeter at en.wikipedia (Transferred from en.wikipedia) [CC-BY-SA-3.0 (www.creativecommons.org/ licenses/by-sa/3.0)], from Wikimedia Commons

Eco-champions are individuals who promote awareness of environmental issues within organizations. As an example, Cardiff University (Wales), encourages members of staff to embrace sustainable practices. The university's website outlines a program inviting staff to nominate an eco-champion whose responsibility is to, "To promote and encourage the reduction in unnecessary energy and water consumption, minimise waste production and ensure efficient recycling of unwanted resources."

Eco-fans are defined by their enthusiasm to adopt environmentally friendly practices as consumers. They seek to help others in applying these same principles. Eco-fan groups around the world aim to spread the practice of environmentally friendly consumption and lifestyle.

Eco-phobes objectify the environment and see it as a machine that produces resources and energy for the use and control of mankind. Eco-phobes champion technological solutions to problems and see environmentalists as resisting progress. In these terms, environmental protection is seen as an inefficiency that only increases company costs, causes delays and reduces profitability.

Further reading

Williams, L. & Shu, T. (2000). *Murayama, Current Status of Extended Producer Responsibility Legislation and Effects on Product Design*. Proceedings of ASME Japan-USA Symposium on Flexible Automation. MI, USA.

Toffel, M. W. (2003). *Corporate Environmental Strategy*: International Journal of Corporate Sustainability, Vol. 10, Issue 9.

3.2 LIFE CYCLE ANALYSIS

In the 1960s concerns were appearing over the future supply of raw materials based on their current and projected usage. Companies and governments around the world started to develop numerical projections in an effort to predict the future availability of materials and resources.

Over the next decade multiple studies considered:

- rising demand
- availability of finite resources
- effects of increasing populations
- environmental impacts of traditional and alternative energy sources.

In 1969 The Coca Cola Company developed a system, (a precursor to life cycle inventory analysis), that compared environmental impacts of different drink containers. Other companies started following suit. In the United States the process became known as Resource and Environmental Profile Analysis (REPA) while in Europe it was called Ecobalance.

Acceptance of the developing LCA process was fostered by the oil crisis of the 1970s. As concerns over the supply of oil faded, the focus of LCAs shifted to hazardous waste management. In Europe in the late 1980s, the creation of the Environment Directorate (DG X1) adopted processes similar to those used in the USA. The Liquid Food Container Directive of 1985, by the EC, required companies to monitor energy and raw materials consumption as well as the solid waste generated by the containers themselves.

During the 1990s lack of standardization, and some spurious claims being made by manufacturers, led to the creation of the LCA standard series ISO 14000 by the International Standards Organisation (1997 through 2002).

Launched jointly by the United Nations Environment Program (UNEP) and the Society of Environmental Toxicology and Chemistry (SETAC) in 2002, the Life Cycle Initiative consisted of three complementary programs: Life Cycle Management, Life Cycle Inventory and Life Cycle Impact Assessment. The program aimed to improve the LCA process by promoting the exchange of quality data and expert opinions internationally.

LCA is a complex process and redirecting waste away from landfill and incinerators creates its own set of environmental impacts. Even when materials are 100%

recyclable they need to be transported for sorting and processing. Each of these alternatives have their own environmental impacts. It is this interconnected web that makes a full life cycle analysis such complex procedure.

> **3.2.1 Define life cycle analysis.**
>
> © IBO 2007

Life Cycle Analysis is a tool to support decision making for manufacturers when assessing the impact a product or process has on the environment. Specifically, the process involves the consideration of all stages of product development including: extraction of raw materials, production, packaging, use, maintenance and ultimately disposal, relative to the environment.

LCA is a relatively young technique; it became popular in the early nineties. Initially many thought that LCA would be a suitable tool to support environmental claims that could directly be used in marketing. Over the years, it has become clear that this is not the best application for LCA, although, it is clearly important to communicate LCA results in a careful and well-balanced way.

In recent years, life cycle thinking (LCT) has become a key focus in environmental policy making. A clear example is the concept of IPP (Integrated Product Policy) as communicated by the EU, but also in Asia and the Americas, many countries develop strategies that promote life cycle thinking as a key concept.

Another development is the sustainability reporting movement. "The majority of the Fortune 500 companies now report on the sustainability aspects of their operations." (PRé Consultants, Introduction to LCA with SimaPro, 2008)

Life cycle analysis is just one way companies are becoming more responsible for manufacturing-based emissions and retrieving product waste. It also forces designers to think about changing product design to favor the environment i.e. developing sustainable product designs considering energy, materials efficiencies, manufacturing processes, in-service use and finally product disposal.

> **3.2.2 Describe how life cycle analysis provides a framework within which clean production technologies and green design can be evaluated holistically for a specific product.**
>
> © IBO 2007

Products are made from a number of components and materials. All of these have their own individual set of accompanying environmental impacts. How can designers and manufacturers assess the myriad of combinations of changes to processes and materials to provide reliable data in a useful form? Life cycle analysis may be the answer.

Starting with the mining of raw materials, through the design, manufacturing and user stages, the LCA finishes with end-of-life waste disposal. Producing an accumulating numerical score, the LCA allows manufacturers and designers to analyse hypothetical changes and examine the impact-transfers and final environmental advantages or disadvantages based on the modification of these complex interactions.

The LCA process assists decision makers to quantitatively compare processes and materials. A simple analysis of the comparison between using locally supplied PVC, compared to an imported, recycled PVC product involving consideration of long distance transport and the accompanying emissions is an example of just one of many choices an effective LCA could address.

The LCA process must be very accurately defined for it to generate useful data for analysis. On occasions, a more simplified process may be employed or even an analysis conducted around only one specific stage or process. The LCA process can easily become too complex and bogged down in minutiae as researchers gather LCA data for suppliers of suppliers. This never-ending descent into detail can be alleviated to some degree as more companies adopt external certification for their processes and conform to internationally agreed conventions and standards.

Modified or simplified approaches to LCAs are used to reduce the time and expenses associated with a more detailed analysis. This approach also encourages more companies and manufacturers to adopt these principles for production reviews.

3.2.3   List the key stages in life cycle analysis.

© IBO 2007

The key stages in product life cycle analysis include: raw materials, manufacturing, distribution and end of life disposal. The purpose of the life cycle analysis process is to highlight areas where opportunities may occur to reduce energy or materials inputs and examines environmental consequences at every point in the product life cycle.

The process may be broken down into four component parts listed and arranged graphically in Figure 3.2.3:

- goal definition and scope – clearly specifying context, constraints and breadth of the review process
- inventory analysis – collecting and documenting data on energy, materials inputs and emissions
- impact assessment – analyzing environmental impacts associated with the above inputs and emissions
- interpretation – preparing interpretation of analysis for management.

N.B. LCA approaches are assistive devices in the decision-making process; the LCA itself makes no decisions.

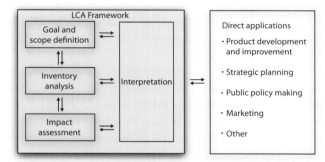

Figure 3.2.3 Phases of a LCA Study (ISO14040: 2006)

3.2.4   List the major environmental considerations in life cycle analysis

© IBO 2007

Every stage of product development has its own associated environmental impacts. These impacts can be broken down into inputs and outputs. Inputs include energy and raw materials, while outputs consist of energy, emissions and waste. The creation of these inputs and outputs can have a variety of direct and indirect environmental affects including but not limited to: climate change, ozone depletion, soil contamination and erosion, loss of biodiversity and habitat, reduction in water quality, depletion of finite resources and noise pollution. A detailed life cycle analysis incorporates every stage of a product's life, the so-called 'cradle-to-grave' span. To be successful the analysis must include environmental assessment of the impacts associated with:

- pre-production; incorporating mining of raw materials, processing and transportation
- manufacturing processes; including energy requirements, waste, cooling and lighting
- packaging and transportation; counting fuels, emissions, inks, size and density
- in-service use; encompassing power requirements, maintenance and in-use emissions
- end-of-life-disposal; involving waste recovery, recycling, reuse and landfill.

3.2.5 Describe how the life cycle stages and the environmental considerations can be organized into an environmental impact assessment matrix.

3.2.6 Analyse the environmental impact of refrigerators, washing machines and cars using an environmental impact assessment matrix.

A matrix simply provides a way of assisting with organizing and presenting data for analysis. An LCA matrix allows researchers to identify, collect and value individual environmental impacts over the entire product life cycle.

A numerical scale (0-4) is used to record the degree of environmental impact associated with each variable. The simplified life cycle analysis matrix shown in Figure 3.2.6a identifies product life cycle stages on the horizontal axis and the form of environmental impact on the horizontal.

The completed SLCA matrix shown in Figure 3.2.6b compares a variety of engine types. Relative values in each category have been awarded within the range of 1–4, where the lower values signify a greater impact on the environment. The final numerical result is shown in the bottom right hand corner of the table.

The authors of the table shown in Figure 3.2.6b indicate; "by a slim margin, the results of the Streamlined Lifecycle Analysis show that Gasoline is the fuel of choice. However, the SLCA weighs the importance of each life stage equivalently, which cannot be the case in a real world scenario. The environmentally-harmful emissions in each life stage differ greatly, and so life stages should be proportionally levied to account for this. If such were the case, and the use phase of the product were weighed to be of higher significance, Hydrogen fuel would have been the clear winner." Excerpt and Figure 3.2.6b provided by; http://en.wikiversity.org/wiki/DFE2008_Internal_Combustion_Engines#Economic_Input_Output_Life_Cycle_Assessment (Transferred from en.wikipedia) [CC-BY-SA-3.0].

Inventory Category/Life stage	Premanufacture	Product manufacture	Product delivery	Product use	Refurbishment, recycling disposal
Materials choice					
Energy use					
Solid residues					
Liquid residues					
Gaseous residues					

Figure 3.2.6a Simplified life cycle assessment matrix

3.2.7 Explain why elements of the matrix may differ in importance according to the particular design context.

The complex nature of individual product requirements including: materials sourcing and processing, energy inputs, emissions, production techniques, transportation and in-service energy needs, mean the nature and the number of elements in the matrix will vary wildly. The notion of a 'one size fits' all approach will not suffice.

In an effort to reduce the complexity of an LCA some of the minor components or indirect activities within a product's development may be removed from consideration when establishing the scope of the analysis. These components may however have a cumulative yet significant impact on the environment. If omitted from the parameters for consideration when developing the scope of an LCA then the result can be misleading.

Many occasions will also require the weighting of the separate matrix elements to produce results truly reflecting the environmental impact of the product over its entire life-cycle. Life cycle analysis using a balanced equivalency for each of the matrix elements when analyzing motor vehicles could produce an extraordinarily skewed result. This fact was highlighted in section 3.2.6, where an LCA was conducted comparing the relative performances of internal combustion engines.

An overwhelming majority of reports document the imbalance of environmental impact between production and in-service use. Clearly, the weighting process must be carefully considered. If some elements of the life cycle are inappropriately prioritised and weighted, then the final result can be even more distorted. Results obtained in this fashion could potentially change the emphasis for future product development from the in-service phase to the manufacturing phase, or erroneously recommend one product over another.

In a document commissioned by the British Motor Industry, research showed a bias towards vehicle operation compared to manufacturing of 9 to 1, i.e. 90% of all energy consumed was in the operational phase. Although lower for vehicles such as the Toyota Prius, a 2006 study delivered a figure of 75% of energy use in the operational stage. The remaining 25% was derived from a combination of fuel production, manufacturing and end-of-life disposal. This type of information is critical to the construction of an accurate LCA matrix.

In contradiction to the previous example, when considering electronic equipment for environmental impacts, research

Life Stage	Fuel	Material Choice	Energy Use	Solid Residues	Liquid Residues	Gas Residues	Total Score
FUEL							
Premanufactuirng	Gasoline	1	0	4	3	2	10
	Gasoline - Ethanol	3	2	3	1	3	12
	Hydrogen	1	1	1	2	2	7
Manufacturing	Gasoline	1	2	3	2	1	9
	Gasoline - Ethanol	3	1	4	2	3	13
	Hydrogen	2	0	3	3	3	11
Packaging Distribution	Gasoline	2	2	3	3	2	12
	Gasoline - Ethanol	2	1	3	2	1	9
	Hydrogen	2	1	3	3	1	10
ENGINE							
Premanufactuirng	Gasoline	3	2	2	3	3	13
	Gasoline - Ethanol	1	1	2	2	3	9
	Hydrogen	2	2	2	2	2	10
Manufacturing	Gasoline	2	1	3	3	2	11
	Gasoline - Ethanol	2	1	2	3	3	11
	Hydrogen	3	0	3	2	3	11
Packaging Distribution	Gasoline	3	3	3	4	3	16
	Gasoline - Ethanol	3	2	3	3	2	13
	Hydrogen	3	2	2	3	2	12
Product Use	Gasoline	0	4	4	3	0	11
	Gasoline - Ethanol	3	2	3	3	3	14
	Hydrogen	4	4	4	4	4	20
Recyling/Disposal	Gasoline	3	3	3	3	4	16
	Gasoline - Ethanol	3	2	3	3	1	12
	Hydrogen	3	2	2	3	3	13
Total (Fuel & Engine)	Gasoline	15	17	25	24	17	98
	Gasoline - Ethanol	20	12	23	19	19	93
	Hydrogen	20	12	20	22	20	94

Figure 3.2.6b Life cycle analysis matrix

identifies the in-use phase of lesser importance. Therefore assessments in this category, based only on energy use, could lead to wrong or grossly inaccurate conclusions.

When assessing consumer electronics, it is argued that consumers' patterns of energy use have a greater environmental impact than the replacement of older less efficient models and extended use of an older product is a more environmentally friendly choice than replacement.

3.2.8 Identify the roles and responsibilities of the designer, manufacturer and user at each life cycle stage of a product.

© IBO 2007

Product designers are charged with the responsibility of bringing products all the way from the conceptual stage through to the consumer. They must precisely predict, target and capture market segments through the continued development of innovative designs. These designs all start with a clearly defined brief. The role of a product designer is to find the solution of best fit and encompasses many of the skills and characteristics associated with marketing, manufacturing, materials engineering, aesthetics and ergonomics. Constantly in search of a competitive edge, designers play a crucial part in differentiating their products from others in the market. Companies also require designers to trim costs by minimizing packaging and generating designs that use fewer materials, produce less waste and contain more recycled and recyclable materials.

Research shows the overwhelming percentage (80% to 90%) of committed costs (including manufacturing, distribution and servicing) are locked-in at the design stage. Clearly, the role of the designer is of paramount importance when considering the financial aspect of every stage of product development.

Manufacturers have an important role to play in the selection of production processes. They have responsibilities for both quality control and the speed at which products are produced. They must specify standards for components and outsourced sub-assemblies.

Manufacturers are also responsible for product warranties and may even provide after-sales service or technical training in repair procedures. Manufacturers have a role to play in minimizing energy requirements, emissions, water contamination etc. through the adoption of waste management programs designed to recycle or reuse waste products. These measures reduce environmental impacts but can also make sound economic sense.

Users provide the demand for products. They have the right to purchase products that will perform to advertised expectations. Their patterns of spending, determine whether a more durable product is purchased over a disposable device. Responsible use of products can also reduce power requirements through such facilities such as the use of low power or sleep modes. Thoughtful disposal of products and packaging can increase recycling and reduce landfill. Consumers have the power to encourage designers and manufactures to pursue both creative and green developments of new and existing products through their buying patterns. Product sales clearly drive the process of design and innovation. Consumers also have opportunities to provide feedback to manufacturers and designers when completing warranty or product surveys on the purchase of a new product.

3.2.9 Describe one example of a situation where life cycle analysis identifies conflicts that have to be resolved through prioritization.

© IBO 2007

The LCA can help analysts examine how changes in design, materials, processes and use have an impact on the overall environmental impact of a product. It is this transfer of environmental impacts that the LCA measures. Decision makers are then able to compare competing scenarios and prioritize choices based on overall benefit.

Vehicle manufacturing: When making decisions based on its LCA analysis, automaker Toyota considered the implementation of carbon fibre in their vehicles. The high strength and lightweight properties would seemingly make carbon fibre an excellent choice for structural members in cars. On examination of the LCA it was found the energy used to produce carbon fibre was more costly than the fuel efficiencies gained when the vehicle was in use. Clearly the energy cost transfer between the manufacturing and end user stages was inappropriate.

3.2.10 Explain that life cycle analysis is targeted at particular product categories.

© IBO 2007

The use of the LCA process is beneficial when informing designers and manufacturers of the environmental impacts of their products at every stage of their life. Every product has some impact on the environment at some stage of its life cycle. The LCA process is best targeted to large volume product runs where even a small improvement has an effect due to the scale of manufacturing. Also, some products, currently in production may still employ dangerous or toxic materials, thus producing a higher level of environmental impact. It is these products that should be targeted due to their harmful effects. Using these two principles of production, volume and degree of harm, many products would be self-identifying.

Even products that generate low environmental impacts can benefit from a targeted or restricted LCA to further refine gains in energy inputs, emissions or materials processing.

> 3.2.11 Explain why life cycle analysis is not widely used in practice.
>
> © IBO 2007

Full scale LCAs are extraordinarily detailed and as such are both time consuming and expensive. It is indeed the overly complex nature of the data and the fact that much of it is open to interpretation, generating results that may be too unreliable for designers to apply directly.

Many issues appear when designers use data for the purposes of comparison. How can designers compare the environmental impacts between competing alternatives when variations occur in amount, toxicity, scarcity, ease of containment etc? Even when two items are almost identical in nature, very different LCA results can still be obtained. There are so many opportunities for small cumulative variables to affect the data that an identical result is nearly impossible. The interpretation of the data tends to be more subjective than scientific, to the point where similar products may generate very different responses for designers to pursue. Work is currently underway to try to standardize the approach to the interpretation of gathered data.

Ultimately, a LCA is a tool best used to inform decision makers and should be employed in conjunction with other approaches to arrive at a balanced decision.

> 3.2.12 Describe the reasons for the introduction of eco-labeling schemes.
>
> © IBO 2007

Eco-labeling programs first appeared in Europe in the late 1970s, targeting the promotion of products and packaging designed to minimize their environmental impact while maintaining high standards of performance. The use of the EU Ecolabel logo is a trusted brand and allows consumers to quickly and easily identify products meeting its stringent quality and environmental criteria.

Eco-labeling is also a method of testing, certifying and communicating environmental performance of products or services based on life cycle considerations. Due to the independent nature of the certifying bodies, eco-labeling differs from so called 'green' labels developed by manufacturers. The vagaries of manufacturer's claims such as; natural, safe, environmentally friendly and green have now been replaced through the use of third party, verifiable certification which in turn has improved consumer confidence in eco-labeling.

Eco-label programs have been developed and implemented worldwide. Large ranges of eco-labels exist that take a variety of forms including: logo style stamps of approval, performance indicators and certifying statements. Environmental labeling can be a determining factor when deciding whether items are suitable for import or export. Using ISO-based labeling programs and benchmarks makes it easier for governments to grant approval and for consumers to make informed buying choices. Eco-labeling allows manufacturers to promote their green credentials measured against a set of well-known independent standards through the use of highly recognizable symbols such as the EU Ecolabel (Figure 3.2.12). The EU Ecolabel is affixed to household appliances, garments, services and even accommodation.

Figure 3.2.12 EU Ecolabel

The EU's Integrated Product Policy supports industry in its efforts to design products with more efficient water use, extended life and increased use of recycled and recyclable materials. The program is aimed at developing greater consumer awareness and growing market demand for green products. Advantages associated with eco-labeling programs include the ease by which consumers can:

- compare products across a range
- obtain a measure of quality assurance
- identify environmentally friendly products.

Eventually the EU aims to extend this program to have companies report to the public in a fashion modelled after the principles of the 'triple bottom line' (see unit 12.1.1). This reporting style would have companies include information on environmental impacts, economic performance and social sustainability.

Manufacturers are increasingly recognizing the advantages in pursuing green design not just from legislative or social concerns but also in an effort to capture the growing 'green consumer' market.

3.2.13 Explain how eco-labeling reflects life cycle analysis of certain product categories.

The International Organization for Standardization (ISO) recognizes three types of voluntary eco-labels.

Type I ISO 14024: Environmental label suitability determined by product category life-cycle analysis based criteria assessment.

Type II ISO 14021: Information based, self-regulated environmental claims. The danger with self-regulated schemes is that, even though they may be based on genuine life cycle analyses, companies may choose to ignore phases of the life cycle where their product underperforms and only report on the more favourable aspects. This leads to inaccuracies where labeled products may not necessarily be class leaders in overall life cycle performance. In this case, comparison between products in the same category could prove difficult.

Type III ISO 14025: Quantified environmental information and data based around predetermined guidelines conforming to life cycle assessment conforming with ISO 14040. Certified by authorized independent third party.

The eco-labeling program is both well established and ever expanding. It covers twenty three major areas from product manufacturing categories through to campsite services. Product groups under development include buildings and wooden furniture. Items specifically excluded from the eco-labeling program include:

- pharmaceuticals
- foodstuffs and drinks
- specified medical devices
- materials classified as dangerous
- products developed using techniques harmful to the environment or individuals.

3.2.14 Compare the objectives of two different eco-labeling schemes.

Australia employs The Environmental Choice product label program. Administered by the Australian Environmental Labeling Association this non-profit organization certifies local and imported goods selling in the Australian market. The Australian eco-label system operates under guidelines comparable to ISO 14024. This voluntary program is the first of its type in Australia and fills a gap in consumer knowledge that has been available overseas for a number of years. A simplified life cycle assessment approach is used to identify the areas of greatest environmental impact. Specific criteria are then selected to judge environmental performance. Criteria used in this product assessment program are based on similar protocols to those in use by Australia's major trading partners.

The North American eco-labeling scheme, EcoLogo™, was founded in 1988, has widespread acceptance in the USA and is recognized worldwide. Over 7,000 products and services from 120 categories bear the EcoLogo™ trademark. The EcoLogo™ program is a Type I eco-label and thus meets or exceeds the criteria outlined in ISO 14024.

Figure 3.2.14 EcoLogo™ seal

In Europe, eco-labels are awarded to products (including packaging) and services that have been investigated for their environmental impact throughout their entire life cycle including their manufacturing, transport, in use and end-of-life disposal phases. An independent body must verify the results of these investigations before the eco-label can be attributed to the product. The EU eco-label is the only validated environmental impact program using life-cycle analysis to assess goods and services.

Household appliances awarded the European eco-label not only use energy and water more efficiently than standard unlabeled products, but the manufacturer also backs them in terms of durability and future parts supply.

3.2.15 Explain how eco-labeling and energy-labeling schemes can help consumers to compare potential purchases.

Eco-labels give consumers confidence in the knowledge that products thus certified have met or surpassed stringent life cycle performance standards. This guarantees the manufacturers' efforts to minimize environmental impacts at every stage of product life.

Energy rating labels assist consumers when comparing relative energy efficiencies of appliances within specific product categories.

The Energy Rating Label scheme in operation in Australia conforms to Australian standards. Labels are only awarded to products tested for minimum energy performance guidelines and typical energy consumption. The program is mandatory across Australia for domestic appliances including; refrigerators and freezers, clothes washers and dryers, dishwashers and air-conditioners. The program has two major components: a visual graphic rating system (using stars) that quickly allows consumers to compare efficiencies of items within a product group and an estimate of annual energy use with details relating to typical product use. The Australian energy label scheme provides:

- energy labeling on all electrical products
- comparative operating costs between products
- objective test information showing relative energy efficiency
- opportunities for manufacturers to develop more energy efficient products.

The Australian energy label scheme does not provide:

- verification of product safety
- indications of product durability
- energy efficiency seals of approval
- government-backed guarantees of quality
- actual amounts of energy consumed (consumer use and climatic conditions may vary).

Further Reading

Curran, M. & Notten, P. (2006). *Co-Chairs, Summary of Global Life Cycle Inventory Data Resources.*

Hochschorner, E. & Finnveden G. (2003). *Evaluation of Two Simplified Life Cycle Assessment Methods*, LCA Methodology. International Journal of LCA.

3.3 STRATEGIES FOR GREEN DESIGN

3.3.1 Define design for manufacture (DfM).

Design for manufacture is an important tool in reducing production costs through considerations of efficiencies of design, manufacturing and assembly. DfM is a process of refining the product by optimizing its design to improve rates of production and/or quality.

3.3.2 Describe why DfM can be a dominating constraint on the design brief and state that it can be conveniently split into design for materials, design for process and design for assembly.

It has always been possible for designers to create products on the drawing board that cannot be produced or require processes and materials that make them uneconomical to manufacture. Successful product design through the application of the principles of DfM takes into account the economic constraints of production. Research indicates that decisions made in the design phase determine 70 percent of the product's development, manufacturing and use costs. These figures show the significance DfM can play in designing or re-designing products. Carefully constructed briefs can focus a designer's attention on the importance of these constraints. The DfM process may be deconstructed into three complimentary components incorporating design for: materials, processes and assembly.

3.3.3 Define design for materials, design for process and design for assembly.

Design for materials is a mechanism by which designers select appropriate materials with the aim of reducing toxic substances, hazardous waste, polluting emissions and the quantity of materials required. Wherever possible single component materials are specified for moulding and recyclable materials are specified and marked for later identification. Similar specifications are then also applied to packaging.

Design for process involves reductions in: the amount of energy consumed, number of production processes employed, waste generated and emissions produced. The number of parts that require additional operations including: plating, painting, printing, labeling, insertion of screws, caulking, riveting and welding is decreased.

Design for assembly is an approach used by designers to analyze components and sub-assemblies with the goal of reducing costs through the reduction in the number of parts and maximizing the efficiency of assembly processes. Consideration of tools to be used during assembly may also be important. Reduction in the number and variety of tool types used during assembly is preferable.

> **3.3.4   Discuss three strategies that designers could employ for DfM.**
>
> © IBO 2007

Strategies for DfM are associated with: the number of parts in products, specification of surface finishes and final product assembly.

Reducing the number of parts by combining the function of multiple pieces into a single standardized component or module. This will not only simplify product design, but can also result in assembly efficiencies and lower inventories. Reduced part numbers frequently reduces the overall weight of a product. Reducing or minimizing the number of parts also applies to fasteners. One commonly used method is to replace a fabricated sub-assembly, utilizing many fasteners, with a single casting. A reduction in fasteners not only reduces costs but also assembly and repair times. If fasteners are specified, standard types and sizes should be used making supply easier and avoiding the need for specialized tooling.

Surface finishes should not be specified any smoother than necessary, the smoother the surface, the greater the machining costs.

Effective and efficient product assembly minimizes the axes of assembly. Wherever possible, assembly operations should ideally be in one direction, thus reducing handling, time consuming movement and re-orientation of the product. The item should be easy to assemble manually and where scale of production warrants with automation. Automated assembly processes are more consistent, produce a more reliable product and generate a consistently higher build quality. To assist with assembly, locating pins should be chamfered or tapered.

> **3.3.5   Describe how designers can modify the environmental impact of the production, use and disposal of their product through careful consideration at the design stage.**
>
> © IBO 2007

Stephanie Watson (Design Program Director of the Australian International Design Awards 2009) makes a very strong point when she claims that up to 80% of a product's environmental impact is determined at the design stage. This places design and designers in the unique position of having the greatest influence over environmental impacts.

To assist designers in the process of reducing environmental impacts a technique known as; 'design for environment', (DfE), is often employed. It entails the consideration of environmental impacts in the earliest stages of product design and development. Manufacturers employ these principles not just because they are environmentally responsible, but also because when applied appropriately they provide cost reductions, innovative products and processes, as well as a competitive edge.

Through the elimination of the use of toxic materials and their replacement with alternatives that do not compromise the functioning of the product, designers are able to remove harmful substances. If the removal of hazardous materials is not possible then measures must be put in place for end-of-life recovery and/or recycling.

DfE strategies are incorporated into every stage of a product's life cycle, i.e. preproduction, manufacturing, packaging, transportation, in-service use and disposal. Typically DfE involves: the reduction of energy and materials requirements, improved durability and product life, opportunities allowing for repair and upgrading and greater use of recycling and recycled materials in both packaging and the product.

DFE strategies can be as simple as replacing one process with another. Some manufacturers have switched drilling operations for mechanical punching procedures, the waste punch-blanks being more easily recovered and recycled than the shavings produced by machining.

In an effort to maintain consistency of application, continuous improvement and measurable outcomes, companies may also integrate standardized quality management systems such as ISO 9001, using certified environmental management systems e.g. ISO 14001.

3.3.6 Define reuse, repair, reconditioning and recycling.

3.3.7 Describe how reuse, repair, reconditioning and recycling contribute to the optimization of resource utilization.

Reuse involves the repeated use of components or products employing the same or an alternative purpose than that originally specified. Examples include: glass containers, plastic drink bottles, fabric bags etc.

The mechanism of repair relates to restoring a product or component to a good or sound working condition after deterioration or damage. Repairs may be functional or cosmetic. Examples include: mending clothes, repairing damage to vehicle bodywork, replacing faulty computer components.

Reconditioning or remanufacturing is the process by which used products may be returned, (or close), to their original manufactured specification. Reconditioning is aimed at extending product life until it is no longer commercially viable to continue. It may also refer to upgrading of components as new technologies become available. Reconditioned products generally come with a renewed warranty guaranteeing their quality. Examples include: reconditioned car engines, retreaded tyres, upgrading computers with replacement modules etc.

Recycling is often defined as the series of activities, including collection, separation and processing, by which products or other materials are recovered from the waste stream for use in the form of raw materials in the manufacture of new products. Recycled products may be reprocessed back into their original form e.g. used glass jars recycled back into new bottles, or, it may involve materials being reprocessed into a new product e.g. waste paper being recycled into cardboard (Figure 3.3.6). This reprocessing excludes the recovery of materials for energy. Thus it does not include reclaiming materials for use as fuel for producing heat or power by combustion.

Figure 3.3.6 Baled paper ready for recycling

Not only do reuse, repair, reconditioning and recycling make economic and environmental sense, within the EU it is a legislated requirement for electronic and electrical equipment. Directive 2002/96/EC of the European Parliament and the Council on waste electrical and electronic equipment (WEEE) states, "Where appropriate, priority should be given to the reuse of WEEE and its components, sub-assemblies and consumables. Where reuse is not preferable, all WEEE collected separately should be sent for recovery, in the course of which a high level of recycling and recovery should be achieved. In addition, producers should be encouraged to integrate recycled material in new equipment."

WEEE goals set for achievement by December 2006 show how the EU has had a program of gradually setting incremental targets.

"For WEEE falling under categories 2 (vc), 5, 6, 7 and 9 of Annex IA, the rate of recovery shall be increased to a minimum of 70% by an average weight per appliance, and component, material and substance reuse and recycling shall be increased to a minimum of 50% by an average weight per appliance."

Through the mechanisms of repair and reuse, the sourcing of new resources for the production of virgin materials and components and the associated environmental impacts are avoided, or at least delayed. The energy requirements required for repair for reuse are also significantly less than those for replacement.

Reuse and reconditioning activities also provide reconditioned products at reduced costs. The use of these secondhand products is increasingly becoming more socially acceptable across a range of socioeconomic groups within communities.

Aluminium cans provide an excellent example of the resource savings that can be made through recycling and product redesign. The energy required to produce one aluminium can from virgin materials is the same as that required to produce 20 cans from recycled materials. At the same time every kilogram of aluminium recycled reduces the production of greenhouse gases by 20kg. Since 1980, the redesigning of aluminium cans has also seen their weight reduced by 30%, thus reducing materials and energy consumption as well as the production of greenhouse gases.

Green product development involves the specification of environmentally friendly materials and production processes along with product designs that incorporate:

- extended product lives
- energy saving features
- highly efficient resource use
- ease of reuse, repair and recycling.

3.3.8 Describe how the strategies of reuse, repair, and recycling can be applied to the design of products, including packaging.

© IBO 2007

The following paragraphs provide examples of various technologies where designers have employed strategies to improve, reuse, repair or recycling.

The technological development of the one-time-use-camera (OTUC) by Kodak in 1987 saw a new freedom introduced into the world of photography. Although meeting all the design specifications and being a financial success, the camera met with opposition from environmentalists concerned about efficient use of resources and the subsequent environmental impacts around their disposal. To encourage consumers to continue to purchase the product, Kodak deliberately designed the camera so it could not be reloaded and reused. Designers, however, modified the camera to improve market acceptability by making it more environmentally

friendly. Kodak still did not want consumers reloading the cameras, but did make camera components reusable. Designers used the principles of design for disassembly (see 3.3.12) and DfE to replace plastic welded joints with snap fittings. This feature alone made the camera easier to reload at the factory. At the same time however Kodak also re-engineered the internals to make it difficult for consumers to reload the camera for reuse, thus ensuring continued sales, but with reduced costs.

Further modification to the original models came through efforts to make the cameras recyclable. Using the snap fittings to quickly and easily disassemble the camera cases, the plastic covers can be removed and sent to be ground up, melted and remanufactured into new plastic camera parts. Kodak workers sort the internals that have been colour coded to assist with identification and recycling. All of the electronic components are designed with reuse in mind and have an integrated counter indicating when they have reached their end-of-life operational use. These modular sub-assemblies are tested before reuse in new cameras. Smaller mechanical and structural parts such as thumb wheels and frames are separated for reuse. Packaging is shipped out for recycling into paper.

Instead of mercury batteries, more environmentally friendly batteries are specified to power the device in the event the camera was discarded rather than recycled. Where polymers are used, thermosoftening plastics allow for recovery and re-forming. In total, 90% of the camera can be recovered and reused or recycled.

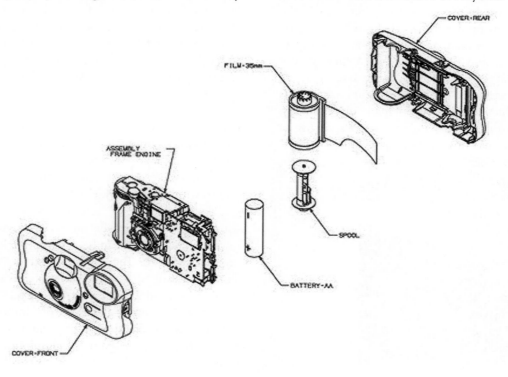

3.3.8 OTUC camera assembly image by Kodak

By 2004, this disposable camera design had won numerous international awards including: the Environmental Protection Agency (EPA) Program Champion Award (1998), the World Environment Center Gold Medal for International Corporate Environmental Achievement (1999), Queen's Award for Enterprise: Sustainable Development (2001) and the EPA Energy Star Award (2002). In 2008 the 84% recycle return rate in the U.S. far exceeded all other consumer products.

Refrigerators also provide opportunities for reuse, repair and recycling. In 2009, the 14 model Electrolux Refrigeration Collection won the award for Excellence in Sustainable Design in the Australian International Design Awards.

All of the models were designed to be highly energy efficient and consume only 51% of the energy used by comparable models ten years ago, through the use of low wattage defrost systems and high efficiency compressors. Iso butane, a non-synthetic refrigerant with a shorter life in the atmosphere, is also used in all of these models.

The judges were also impressed by Electrolux's commitment to product stewardship with a 'take-back' service for previously owned fridges, product package recycling and a product life expectancy of 20 years or more.

In 2009, one manufacturer of a popular portable vacuum cleaner redeveloped its product to use a minimum of 50% recycled plastic in its construction. This development shows the increasing trend towards greener design considering the previous model included recycled content of only 10%.

Additionally, cleaning solutions used in both upright and portable deep cleaners have now been re-formulated to remove phosphates, dyes and heavy metals. The chemicals are now based on biodegradable detergents, in line with design for environment certification standards. Plastic bottles containing these chemicals are blow-moulded from thermoplastic materials. To reduce waste, costs and recycle old product, manufacturers are now making these bottles with plastic from three sources: new resin, waste reclaimed from trimmings recovered during the manufacturing process and recycled bottles.

Manufacturers such as Dyson have their own recycling schemes allowing consumers to either leave their old cleaners at a designated recycling centre or have their old machines collected after purchasing a new cleaner.

In the area of tire manufacturing, opportunities for reuse and recycling of scrap tires continue to grow. In the USA alone, at the end of 2003, reprocessors existed sufficient to cope with 80% of scrap tires. This figure shows a dramatic increase from the 17% in 1990. This process allows tires, or their constituents, to be used in the following ways:

- retreaded and reused
- repurposed for civil engineering projects
- recycled into cut/stamped/punched products
- crumbed and used as a binder or aggregate substitute in rubber-modified asphalt.

3.3.9   List three material groups that can be easily and economically recycled.

© IBO 2007

Thermoplastics

Polymers are divided into two groups: thermosetting and thermosoftening. They consist of long chain molecules (see topic 4.5).

Not all polymers are recyclable. In thermosetting polymers the bonding between molecular chains is very strong and thus resists melting. When heated, thermosetting polymers decompose. These strong bonds also make thermosetting polymers impervious to solvents and thus resist dissolving. Recycling processes for polymers often involving remelting or dissolving the base material. Thermosetting polymers do not lend themselves to either of these processes and are thus difficult to recycle. Commonly recycled polymers include:

- polystyrene
- polypropylene
- polyvinyl chloride
- polyethylene - both high density and low-density polyethylene.

Metals

The most common metals recycled are steel and aluminium. Metals can be recycled indefinitely.

Steel is the most commonly recycled metal in the world. From the standpoint of energy consumption, the manufacture of steel from scrap is much more advantageous than manufacture based on iron ore. Recycled steel can be used in place of virgin iron, thus reducing iron ore extracted from mines. This results in about 75% energy saving and a reduction in associated environmental impacts.

Steel-making technologies such as the Basic Oxygen Furnace (BOF) and the Electric Arc Furnace (EAF) contribute to high rates of steel reusability. Typically the BOF uses 25% recycled steel while the EAF accepts 100% scrap steel.

Figure 3.3.9 Electric arc furnace

Image supplied by Alfred T. Palmer [public domain], via Wikimedia Commons

Aluminium is one of the most cost-effective materials to recycle. Recycled aluminium requires only 5% of the energy and produces only 5% of the CO_2 emissions associated with primary production processes. Aluminium cans collected for recycling need only be screened (for steel), washed and crushed before being packaged ready for transportation to a refinery for re-melting. Because aluminium can be recycled repeatedly, without any deterioration in quality, it is highly valued as a recyclable material.

Glass

Glasses as a material group are 100% recyclable. Glass may be recycled repeatedly and still produce a product of the highest quality. Recycled glass gathered and crushed is known as cullet. Use of cullet in the production of new glass is highly energy efficient. Almost any proportion of cullet can be added to a batch, provided it is in the right condition, i.e. free from impurities, especially metals and other ceramics. 'Green' glass is now commonly made from batches containing 95% cullet. Cullet mixed with virgin glass materials reduces temperatures required to melt the batch. Reduced temperatures translate into reduced energy production costs. Care must be taken, however, to only use clean recycled glass material, as small amounts of impurities can contaminate the melt. Glass suitable for recycling includes: clear, green or brown bottle glass. Because some glass is made to withstand higher temperatures these materials are unsuitable for recycling. They include: light globes, window glass, china,

mirrors, medical and laboratory glass. Cullet has also been successfully tested as an alternative for sand in the preparation of concrete.

> 3.3.10 Describe how many products comprise several different materials, and state that these materials have to be separated to enable recycling.
>
> ©IBO 2007

Common problems associated with recycling involve product assemblies, and even individual components, that are often made up of more than one kind of material or the inclusion some sort of fibre (as in composites). This adds to the difficulties of recycling. In a conscious effort to facilitate the recycling process, manufacturers have begun to design and make parts in a different way. Designers are limiting the variety of materials used and redesigning assemblies to facilitate their removal and separation when recycling. To aid in the identification, sorting and recovery of polymers, a coding system has been developed based on the 'Recycle Triangle' that uses a series of numbers and letters as shown in Figure 3.3.10a.

Figure 3.3.10a Polymer recycling triangle for polyethylene terephthalate (PET)

Before recycling, however, polymers need to be processed in the manner shown in Figure 3.3.10b.

Collection
⇓
Cleaning
⇓
Identification and Sorting
⇓
Size Reduction (shredding)
⇓
Extrusion/Pelletising
⇓
Manufacturing

Figure 3.3.10b Polymer recycling chart

Dismantling and recycling complex products such as cars, computers and washing machines containing a variety of metal types and polymers, can be an expensive and time-consuming process. Shredding of partially disassembled products results in particulate matter of mixed quality, yet, to be successful, the recycling of light metals such as aluminium and magnesium require high purity material due to their susceptibility to contamination.

Metal sorting technologies have increased in both speed and efficiency. Magnetic and eddy current separators can easily separate iron and ferrous alloys but with the advent of X-Ray technologies it is now possible to separate a variety of alloys and also distinguish composite materials and organic polymers.

3.3.11 Discuss the issues underpinning the economic recycling of materials.

One of the largest factors determining the economic viability of recycling relates to the degree and complexity of manufacturing processes involved in a materials manufacture. Newsprint, glass bottles, and cans (both aluminium and steel) are easily recycled because they are little more than the original materials from which they were made. More complex products such as composites or those heavily processed require more complicated and expensive process for recycling. However, even when materials are 100% recyclable they need to be transported for sorting and processing. The costs and energy consumed in collection, transportation, reprocessing and market redistribution add to the financial costs of recycling.

Critics of the economics of recycling also quote the loss of jobs in mining, logging and other related industries accompanying virgin production. Some materials suffer in quality when recycled and may only be recycled a limited number of times before material degradation renders them useless.

Market prices for recycled materials are particularly volatile. In times of economic recession factories require fewer raw materials due to reduced consumer demand. This places downward pressure on the price of recycled materials and can affect their profitability.

The economy of recycling however is not always about meeting break-even costs or competing with suppliers of virgin materials. The financial value of recycling can also be measured in the avoidance of waste management costs such as collection, sorting, transportation and landfill or incineration charges.

3.3.12 Define design for disassembly.

Design for disassembly (DfD) is a process that facilitates ease of repair, reuse, remanufacturing or recycling of a product. It has become increasingly popular with manufacturers as they strive to meet WEEE and RoHS legislative requirements while maintaining profitability. Manufacturers also see the benefits associated with DfD through the potential to reduce production costs.

3.3.13 Explain that design for disassembly is one aspect of design for materials and will facilitate recycling of products on disposal.

A range of tools and processes exist for designers that will assist them when attempting to facilitate recycling. Using these techniques, designers are able to create products that effectively minimize environmental impact. Approaches designers may employ include: design for disassembly, design for assembly or design for the environment.

To be effective, disassembly of a product into its component parts, in preparation for recycling can only be achieved if it is considered early in the design process through the application of appropriate guidelines. The adoption of the principles of DfD at the design stage provides a framework for selecting materials and fastening techniques as well as designing modular assemblies. This framework not only facilitates product disassembly but also assists with repair, recycling, salvage and reuse, thus, reducing the need for virgin resources required to manufacture a replacement product or component. Products that are easy to disassemble are not only easier to repair but also recondition or update.

On occasions, these design approaches may be in conflict. An example of such a conflict involves the following example. DfM or DfA systems may require the specification of rivets over bolted assemblies whereas DfD requirements may specify the reverse. In these situations a solution must be produced to generate the most environmentally responsible result.

3.3.12 Define design for disassembly.

Designers can employ a variety of strategies when considering DfD. These strategies may be broken down into three categories:

- materials selection
- fastening techniques
- design and specification of components, assemblies and sub-assemblies.

The choice of easily recycled materials streamlines future reprocessing operations when the product has reached the end of its useful life. Reduction in the variety of material types makes the sorting for recovery process much easier, as does the marking of polymers with recycling codes for ease of identification. Designers may also choose the most appropriate materials, giving consideration to the recycling methods available.

Careful choice of materials may also negate the need for coatings or inform the choice of coating, with ease of removal as a prerequisite. Coatings can contaminate a recycled resource and may therefore require costly, additional, removal processing.

Use of glues and adhesives needs to be eliminated or minimized. If necessary, the use of thermoplastic adhesives may be appropriate. Thermoplastic adhesives allow components or assemblies to be easily separated through the application of heat.

Incorporation of semi-permanent snap fittings, connectors, screws, bolts and clips instead of more permanent methods of securing such as welding, brazing and soldering also facilitate the disassembly process.

A major design consideration of DfD is the reduction in the number of parts. Fewer parts most often translates into faster assembly times. A by-product of part reduction is also smaller inventories and lower storage costs for manufacturers.

Better product value and longevity can be embedded at the design stage using the principles of modular design. Modular design involves the reduction of complex systems into sets of distinct independent components or sub-assemblies that may then be assembled together in a variety of ways. The use of these replaceable modules allows for these assemblies to be removed when part replacement, due to failure, or modification by updating is required. Waste can also be reduced if a large product

does not have to be scrapped because a small part fails or becomes obsolete.

Ease of access for removal and replacement of sub-assemblies means less technical expertise is required at a regional level. Localized servicing and customizing also becomes more possible if modifications become easier. Placement of sensitive, regularly replaced or items requiring regular maintenance in close proximity, means servicing schedules are easily synchronized.

Standardization of fasteners throughout the product means similar tools and skill sets are required for disassembly e.g. standard circlips of the same size used throughout an assembly would require only one tool for maintenance. Parts standardization also allows spare parts to be easily sourced.

Further reading

Directive 2002/96/EC of the European Parliament and the Council. (2003).

Product Innovation - The Green Advantage, Environment Australia. (2001). Commonwealth of Australia.

Dowie, T. & Simon, M. *Guidelines for designing for disassembly and recycling.*

Design for Environment Research Group, Department of Mechanical Engineering, Design and Manufacture. (1994). Manchester Metropolitan University.

Bogert, S. & Morris, J. (1993). *The economics of recycling, Resource Recycling.*

The economics of recycling, The CQ researcher, Congressional Quarterly Inc. (1998). Vol. 8 No. 12, pp. 265-268, .

How Producer Responsibility for Product Take-Back Can Promote Eco-Design, Clean Production Action. (2008).

Walker, S. (2008). *Extant objects: designing things as they are,* International Journal Sustainable Design. Vol. 1, No. 1.

Kurk, F. & McNamara, C. (2006). *Better by Design, an Innovation Guide: Using Natural Design Solutions,* Minnesota Pollution Control Agency.

Allen, D., et al. (2002). *Environmentally Benign Manufacturing: Trends in Europe, Japan, and the USA,* Journal of Manufacturing Science and Engineering. Vol. 124.

Exercises

1. Renewable resources are:
   A. easily purchased
   B. more expensive to obtain
   C. available in limited supply
   D. consumed at a lesser rate than natural processes replace them.

2. Green designs:
   A. always employ a LCA
   B. involve the choice of colours
   C. develop products with zero emissions
   D. reduce product impacts on the environment.

3. Design for dissassembly products would feature:
   A. welded parts, circlips, specific tooling requirements
   B. bolted sections, epoxy adhesives, soldered connections
   C. modular components, snap fittings, minimal axial lines of assembly
   D. all of the above.

4. Which of these combinations are not environmentally friendly:
   A. reuse, recycle, repair
   B. reduce, renovate, reclaim
   C. replace, repurchase, remake
   D. refurbish, restore, recondition.

5. Life Cycle Analysis:

   A. determines when to replace a product
   B. develops products with zero emissions
   C. identifies areas of environmental impact
   D. reduces product impacts on the environment.

6. List three reasons why green designs are becoming more common.

7. Explain how environmental design tools such as DfA and DfD may sometimes be in conflict.

8. Identify advantages provided to consumers through eco-labeling schemes.

9. Describe the role consumers play in green product development.

10. Discuss the advantages and disadvantages associated with recycling.

11. Explain how 'take back' legislation can assist designers and manufacturers.

12. What green design strategies can designers employ to improve a product's in-service use?

13. Compare eco-labeling schemes with energy labeling programs.

MATERIALS

CONTENTS

4

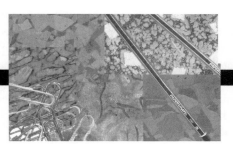

Knowledge of atomic structures is fundamental to the understanding of bonding and directly relates to engineering properties of materials. These materials are used in a wide variety of roles and applications based on the characteristic properties that suit them to the assigned role. These characteristics include their physical, mechanical and chemical properties. Standardized tests have been developed to measure and define the properties of materials in order that quality control in production is assured and to aid in the selection of appropriate materials for new and innovative designs.

Figure 4.1.1 Ernest Rutherford (1871—1937)

4.1 INTRODUCING AND CLASSIFYING MATERIALS

> 4.1.1 Define atom, molecule, alloy and composite.
>
> © IBO 2007

Atoms are defined as the smallest chemical unit, composed of protons, neutrons, and electrons, which cannot be further broken down by chemical means e.g. Hydrogen or Zinc.

Our modern concept of the atom begins with John Dalton (1766–1844). Dalton proposed that all matter was composed of small indivisible and indestructible particles he called atoms. In Dalton's concept of the atom, the elements were composed of atoms of unique size and shape. Later discoveries of the electron, (by Joseph Thomson in 1897), and the nucleus, (by Ernest Rutherford in 1911), showed that the atom was divisible into smaller sub-atomic particles. The Rutherford concept of atomic structure was close to that of today, consisting mostly of empty space with a positive nucleus surrounded by the negatively charged electron, as illustrated in Figure 4.1.1a. Rutherford, (Figure 4.1.1), won the Nobel Prize for Chemistry in 1908 and is widely regarded as the founder of nuclear physics.

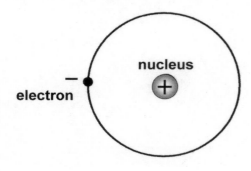

Figure 4.1.1a Rutherford model of the atomic structure

The positive charge of the nucleus arises from the presence of nuclear particles called protons. The number of protons in the nucleus is used to designate the atomic number of an element, sometimes represented by the capital letter 'Z'. The number of protons present determines the number of electrons orbiting the nucleus, such that the electrical charges are balanced resulting in an overall charge of zero .

Niels Bohr modified the Rutherford model in 1913, by proposing that the electrons orbiting the nucleus could only occupy certain energy levels. These energy levels formed shells or rings around the nucleus much like a sub-microscopic version of the solar system.

Within the nucleus is a second particle known as the neutron, discovered by the British physicist James Chadwick in 1932. The neutron carries no charge and therefore does not affect the balance of charges between the protons and electrons but is significant in explaining radioactivity. The modern electron cloud model of the atom explains that the exact location of the electron within its energy shell cannot be determined, but describes a probability cloud defining its location, as illustrated in Figure 4.1.1b.

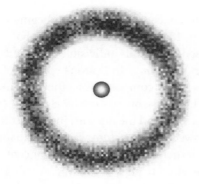

Figure 4.1.1b Electron cloud model of the atomic structure

Electrons first fill the lowest energy levels surrounding the nucleus before filling outer, higher energy shells. The first shell, closest to the nucleus, can contain only two electrons before it is complete. Subsequent shells can contain up to

$2n^2$ electrons, (where n is the shell number), as indicated in Figure 4.1.1.c, provided that the outermost shell contains a maximum of eight electrons. It is the outer electron shell that determines the chemical reactivity of the atom and is known as the valence shell. The Periodic Table arranges the elements in order of atomic number in such a way that the elements within each column contain the same number of valence electrons.

This last rule means that a lower shell may remain unfilled before the outer valency shell begins to fill, see Figure 4.1.1.d. Note for example the element Potassium. With nineteen electrons, the first and second shells are complete leaving nine electrons to be placed in a shell. The third shell can take up to eighteen electrons, but if all nine of the available electrons were placed in the third shell the rule that the outer shell can have only up to eight electrons would be violated. Therefore one electron moves into the fourth shell.

Shell	Electrons allowed per shell ($2n^2$)
1	2
2	8
3	18
4	32
5	50

Figure 4.1.1.c. Electrons per shell

Element	Atomic No.	Electron/Shell
hydrogen	1	1
helium	2	2
lithium	3	2-1
neon	10	2-8
sodium	11	2-8-1
argon	18	2-8-8
potassium	19	2-8-8-1
calcium	20	2-8-8-2
copper	29	2-8-18-1

Figure 4.1.1.d Electrons per shell for various elements

Within each shell, because there are interactions between the electrons present, there are sub-levels of energy or a hierarchy of energy levels known as 'orbitals'.

These sub-levels or orbitals are designated as s, p, d, f, g and h. The number of electrons or quantum states that can be present in each orbital is presented in Figure 4.1.1e.

Orbital	Quantum states
s	2
p	6
d	10
f	14
g	18
h	22

Figure 4.1.1.e Electron orbitals

This means that the electron structure shown in Figure 4.1.1.d can be further refined such that the electron structure of Calcium could be represented using the notation below:

Calcium: 2-8-8-2 becomes **1*s*2 2*s*2 2*p*6 3*s*2 3*p*6 4*s*2**

Note that in this representation, the shell number is the prefix, while the number of electrons present in each of the orbitals within the shell is shown as a postscript. Note also that as previously shown for Potassium the third shell could take up to eighteen electrons, but if all of the available electrons were placed in the third shell the rule that the outer shell can have only up to eight electrons would be violated. Therefore, instead of beginning to fill the 3*d* orbital, the two extra electrons in this case move into the *s* orbital of the fourth shell.

For a transition metal such as Iron, with an atomic number of 26 and a structure from Figure 4.1.1d of 2-8-14-2, the spread of electrons between the orbitals can be represented as shown below:

Iron: 2-8-14-2 becomes **1*s*2 2*s*2 2*p*6 3*s*2 3*p*6 3*d*6 4*s*2**

Note that since the p level of the third shell is full, the *d* level begins to fill. The *d* level, however, does not fill completely before the *s* level of the fourth shell begins to fill. It does this to maintain the condition indicated earlier that – shells can contain up to $2n^2$ electrons, (where n is the shell number), provided that the outermost shell contains a maximum of 8 electrons. By starting to fill the 4*s* shell before completing the 3*d* shell, the outermost shell (the valency shell) contains only 2 electrons, whereas if this had not occurred, and these outer two electrons went to the 3*d* shell, a total of 20 electrons would have been present in the outer shell. Therefore, the lower energy orbitals of the transition metals remain unfilled as the *s* orbital of the next shell begins to fill.

Note that Transition Metals, such as Copper, shown in bold type in Figure 4.1.1d, continue to fill a lower shell to completion before continuing to fill the outer shell.

A molecule is the simplest structural unit of an element or compound. It is a pure substance formed when two or more atoms of a single element share electrons, for example O_2. It can also refer to compounds, which are combinations of atoms of two or more different elements, for example H_2O.

Alloys are metals produced by mixing two or more metals. Alloys are developed in order to gain improved properties not available from the pure metal. While metal alloys occur in nature the industrial manufacture of an alloy allows the precise control of the alloy composition with consequential confidence in the material properties.

One of the oldest alloys developed was bronze (mostly an alloy of copper and tin), the widespread use of which ushered in the so-called Bronze Age. Complex alloys are increasingly common in fields as diverse as engineering and dentistry. Dental alloys combine Chromium, Cobalt, Molybdenum, and Titanium as an alternative to more expensive Gold implants. A Copper-Nickel alloy is commonly used for coins. Known as Cupro-nickel, (Figure 4.1.1f), this alloy is often composed of 75% Copper and 25% Nickel. The coins are surprisingly, a silver colour.

Figure 4.1.1f Cupro-nickel alloy photomicrograph

Composites are materials formed by combining two or more materials having quite different properties. Even though the constituent components work together to provide the composite with unique properties, within the composite the individual components are easily identifiable. The purpose of manufactured composites is to obtain superior mechanical properties to those of the individual original component parts.

Composite materials are not new. An early form of composite materials could be traced back to ancient Persia in the form of straw-reinforced bricks. At a much later time, cement, gravel, and steel bars were combined to form reinforced concrete.

Development of thin fibres and thermosetting polymers led to the creation of fibre-reinforced materials such as glass reinforced polymers (GRP). Much more recent examples are carbon-polymer and metal matrix composites.

Figure 4.1.1.g Transverse section through a tennis racquet (top), intersecting layers of carbon fibre and epoxy, and glass fibre (white) and epoxy

Image by Sarah Metcalfe

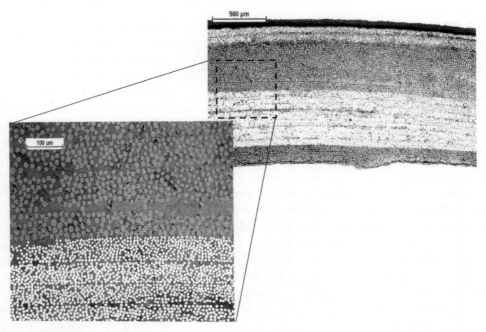

4.1.2 Describe a bond as a force of attraction between atoms.

© IBO 2007

An atom is able to join with other atoms in a number of ways through the force of attraction. The force or form of bonding depends on the number of valence electrons present. The primary methods of bonding are ionic, covalent and metallic bonds.

Ionic bonding occurs between metals (in Groups 1A and IIA) and non-metals (in groups VIA and VIIA). These groups have a valance shell that contains only one or two electrons (in the case of the metals), or are short of completion by one or two electrons (as is the case for the non-metals).

The metal loses (or transfers) an electron and the non-metal gains an electron. Following this transaction the metal atom contains more protons in its nucleus than orbiting electrons and therefore has a positive charge. The non-metal, having gained an electron, has more orbiting electrons than there are protons in its nucleus and therefore has a negative charge. In other words a positive

and negative ion has been created. These ions, having opposite charges, are attracted to each other, forming an ionic bond held together by electrostatic attraction.

The bonding between the two elements sodium and chlorine to form sodium chloride (NaCl) is a typical example of ionic bonding, illustrated in Figure 4.1.2a using electron dot, (or Lewis), notation.

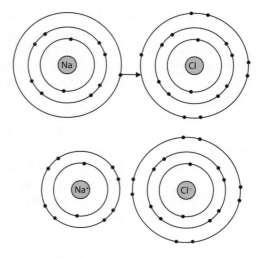

Figure 4.1.2a Ionic bonding of NaCl

Note that on bonding, the outer shells of both participants are complete. Ionic solids are typically:

- brittle
- transparent
- of a high melting point
- of moderate hardness
- non-conductors of heat or electricity (insulators) when solid
- electrical conductors when dissolved in solution allowing ions freedom to move.

Covalent bonding occurs between non-metals and between metals and non-metals. It is the strongest of the chemical bonds. A covalent bond results in the valence electrons being shared in order to complete the outer shells, as shown in Figure 4.1.2b. Silicon, Carbon, and Germanium are just a few examples of elements that form covalently bonded solids. In these elements there are four electrons in the half-filled- outer shell.

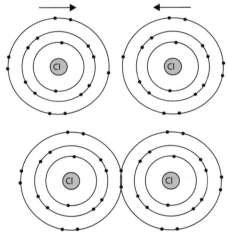

Figure 4.1.2b Covalent bonding of chlorine

Water, (H$_2$O), is another example of a covalently bonded molecule. Here two hydrogen atoms are needed to complete the outer valence shell of oxygen, (Figure 4.1.2c).

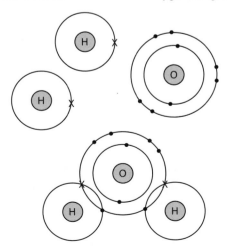

Figure 4.1.2c Covalent bonding of Water (H$_2$O) .

Covalently bonded materials are typically:

- insulators
- soft (graphite)
- of high or low MP
- hard (diamond)
- metallically lustrous (FeS$_2$).

Metallic bonds are typically characterized as atoms being arranged in a regular lattice, as illustrated in Figure 4.1.2d. A number of models have been proposed to explain the properties of a metal in terms of its bonding. The most familiar of these is the 'free electron' or 'electron sea' model. This view of metallic bonding proposed a regular lattice of positive atomic nuclei with the outer valence electrons available to move freely, see Figure 4.1.2d. Because the valence electrons can move freely among the nuclei these free electrons are described as being in an electron sea. These free valence electrons are essentially shared by all of the positive ions making up the metallic lattice in such a way that electrical neutrality is maintained. It is the non-localized and non-directional nature of metallic bonding that gives metals their tolerance to defects and their malleability.

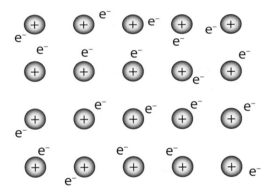

Figure 4.1.2d Free electron model of metallic bonding

4.1.3	Describe how materials are classified into groups according to similarities in their microstructures and properties.

Metallic solids typically have the following properties:

- malleable
- metallic lustre
- conductors of heat and electricity
- usually solid at room temperature.

Material classification can be undertaken using a number of criteria. One of the most common is to classify materials into the categories of metal or non-metal as shown in Figure 4.1.3a.

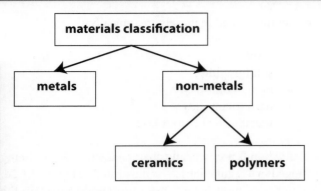

Figure 4.1.3a Classification of materials based on metals and non-metals

Material properties can also be used as a useful means of classifying materials. Such classifications could relate to properties such as conductivity as indicated in Figure 4.1.3b.

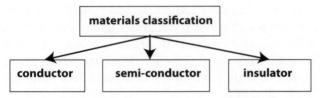

Figure 4.1.3b Classification of materials based on conductivity

4.1.4 Explain that several classifications are recognised but that no single classification is 'perfect'.

© IBO 2007

There is no one style of classification of materials that will suit every situation. If the health effects of ingesting various materials in dust form are the criteria, the materials may be divided into toxic or non-toxic. Resistance to corrosion within a specific environment may require the classification of materials into generic categories of excellent, good, fair and poor.

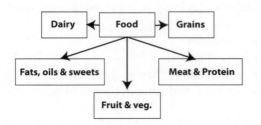

Many other methods of classification are possible and depend on the purpose for which classification is undertaken. Other common classifications are:

- natural and artificial
- solid, liquid and gas
- organic and inorganic
- crystalline and non-crystalline
- transparent, translucent and opaque.

4.1.5 Describe that for this course materials are classified into groups: timber, metals, plastics, ceramics, food and composites; and that some of these groups have subdivisions.

© IBO 2007

The IB classifies materials into six groups timber, metals, plastics, ceramics, food and composites. Examples of significant sub-groups, such as those shown in Figure 4.1.5a may be created. Each of these sub-groups can of course be further divided into a number of finer categories.

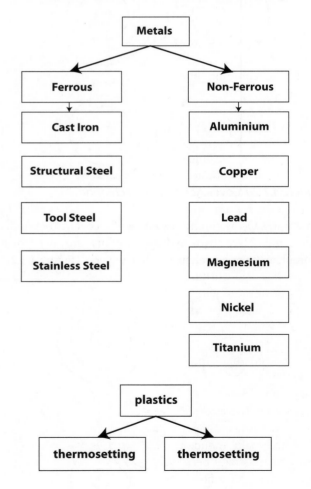

Figure 4.1.5a Classification of some materials into groups and sub-groups

4.2 PROPERTIES OF MATERIALS

Density

Density is a measure of the quantity of mass per unit volume. The SI units for measuring density are kilograms per cubic metre or kg/m^3.

Electrical Resistivity

Electrical conductivity (σ) and electrical resistivity (ρ) are measures of the ease with which free electrons move through a material and are inherent properties of a material. As might be expected, conductivity is inversely related to resistivity as indicated below:

$\sigma = 1/\rho$

This relationship is strictly true only when applied to metals. The values of resistivity and conductivity for a variety of common materials are presented in Figure 4.2.1a.

Resistivity in metals has been described in terms of resistance to the free flow of electrons. This resistance to motion was postulated to arise from the scattering of the electrons due to collisions with the positive ions of the metal lattice. According to this theory, resistivity arises from any phenomena that disturbs the motion of electrons, such as:

- collisions with lattice imperfections (e.g. caused by cold working)
- collisions with solute atoms (e.g. impurities)
- collisions with thermally-induced lattice vibrations (e.g. temperature).

Temperature has the greatest effect on resistivity. As temperature increases, thermally-induced lattice vibrations increase, raising the chance of interaction with an electron. Therefore, as temperature increases, so does resistivity. As the temperature approaches absolute zero, (0°K), thermally-induced lattice vibrations also approach zero and resistivity becomes a function of temperature-independent factors such as impurity content and microstructural effects such as lattice imperfections, precipitates and inclusions.

Material	Electrical Conductivity σ	Electrical Resistivity ρ
Silver	6.29×10^7	1.59×10^{-8}
HC Copper	5.98×10^7	1.67×10^{-8}
Gold	4.26×10^7	2.35×10^{-8}
Aluminium	3.77×10^7	2.65×10^{-8}
Tungsten	1.85×10^7	5.40×10^{-8}
Iron	1.02×10^7	9.76×10^{-8}
Platinum	9.43×10^7	10.6×10^{-8}
Titanium	2.38×10^7	42.0×10^{-8}
Graphite	10^5	10^{-5}
Magnetite	10^2	10^{-2}
Germanium	2.13	4.7×10^{-1}
Limestone	10^{-2}	10^2
Silicon	2×10^{-4}	5×10^3
Window Glass	2×10^{-5}	5×10^4
Granite	10^{-6}	10^6
Marble	10^{-8}	10^8
Bakelite	10^{-9} to 10^{-11}	10^9 to 10^{11}
Borosilicate Glass	10^{-9} to 10^{-15}	10^9 to 10^{15}
Mica	10^{-11} to 10^{-15}	10^{11} to 10^{15}
Polyethylene	10^{-15} to 10^{-17}	10^{15} to 10^{17}

Figure 4.2.1a Values of resistivity and conductivity for a variety of common materials

Thermal Conductivity

When a temperature gradient is present in a material, heat will flow from the region of higher temperature to the region of lower temperature. Thermal conductivity (K) is a measure of the efficiency with which thermal energy will travel through a material. The higher the thermal conductivity the greater is the rate at which heat will flow. The SI units for thermal conductivity are Weber/metre/°K ($Wm^{-1}K^{-1}$).

Metals typically have high thermal conductivity, while polymers and ceramics have a low thermal conductivity and are insulators rather than conductors of heat. The thermal conductivity of a number of materials at room temperature is provided in Figure 4.2.1b. Note, values are indicative only. For purposes of translation of values:

$$1 \ Wm^{-1}K^{-1} = 0.00239 \times Cal \ cm^{-1} \ s^{-1} \ K^{-1}$$
and
$$1 \ Btu \ hr^{-1}F^{-1}ft^{-1} = 1.731 \ Wm^{-1}K^{-1}$$

Material	Thermal Conductivity $Wm^{-1}K^{-1}$	Thermal Conductivity $Cal\, cm^{-1}s^{-1}K^{-1}$
Graphite	2000	4.8
Copper	380	20.9
Gold	310	0.74
Aluminium	230	0.55
Brass	109	0.26
Grey C I	55	0.13
Mild steel	54	0.13
Austenitic S/S	15	0.04
Glass	1	0.002
Oak	0.16	0.0004
Polyurethane	0.02	0.00005
Nylon 6,6	0.25	0.0006
PTFE	0.25	0.0006

Figure 4.2.1b Thermal conductivity of common materials at room temperature

Material	Mean Thermal Coefficient of Expansion ($10^{-6}\,K^{-1}$) at 20°C
Graphite	7.9
Copper	18
Aluminium	24
Brass	18.7
Mild Steel	11
Austenitic S/S	14.4–17.3
Grey Cast Iron	10.8
Glass–Pyrex	4
Glass–Plate	9
Bakelite	80
Polyurethane	57.6
Nylon 6,6	80

Figure 4.2.1c Thermal expansion values

ASM Metals Reference Book – 3rd Edition. (1993). and The Engineering Toolbox, www. Engineeringtoolbox. com/linear-expansion-coefficients-d_95.html

Thermal Expansion

When a material is heated, the thermal energy gained, results in an increase in atomic vibrations. This leads to an increase in atomic separation and an increase in the dimensions of the material overall. This increase in dimensions is typically quantified as the change in length per unit length per degree ($m\, m^{-1}\, K^{-1}$) for the coefficient of linear thermal expansion (α). Figure 4.2.1c shows α values for a number of materials from 20° to 100°C .

The coefficient of linear thermal expansion can vary with the introduction of phase changes within a material and is usually quoted for a specific temperature range.

Thermal Contraction Problem

A steel rod at a temperature of 600°C is measured to be 250mm long. What will the rod length be at 20°C?

$$\Delta l = \alpha\, \Delta T$$
$$= 11 \times 10^{-6} \times (600\text{-}20)$$
$$= 0.00638m \text{ or } 6.38mm$$

Rod length at 20°C will be 250-6.38
$$= 243.62mm$$

Shrink Fit Problem

A steel pin has been machined to a diameter of 150mm and is to be shrunk fit into a steel housing to create an interference fit of 0.15mm.

What temperature would the housing need to be heated to in order to position the pin in the housing and achieve the required interference? An insertion clearance on diameter of 1mm is to be used. Assume room temperature is 20°C and coefficient of thermal expansion for both the pin and housing is $11 \times 10^{-6}K^{-1}$.

Assume also uniform heating and no loss of temperature in removing heat from the housing and during insertion of pin.

Starting conditions –

Room temperature (20°C):
Pin diameter φ_p = 150mm
Shrink fit is to be 0.15mm

Therefore housing diameter φ_H must be machined to:

150 – 0.15 = 149.85mm

Coefficient of thermal expansion = $11 \times 10^{-6} K^{-1}$

$$\emptyset_H \times \alpha = 149.85 \text{ x} \times 11 \times 10^{-6}$$
$$= 0.00164835 mm^6 K^{-1}$$

This means that for every degree Kelvin, (or degree Celsius), that the temperature is raised, an expansion of 0.00164835mm should be obtained.

Accordingly, to expand the housing by 0.15 to 150mm plus a 1mm clearance, an expansion of 1.15mm is required.

Temperature = 1.15 / 0.00164835
= 698°C

Note that additional complications are introduced if the interference fit is between materials with differing coefficients of thermal expansion. In these situations, any changes in operating temperature that may increase or decrease the interference also need to be considered.

Hardness

Hardness refers to the resistance of a material to scratching or abrasion. It may also refer to resistance to indentation, penetration or cutting. The number of definitions for hardness, indicates that hardness may not be a fundamental property of a material, but rather a composite one including yield strength, work hardening, true tensile strength, modulus of elasticity, and others.

Hardness is routinely used as an indication of material condition. As a general guide, the greater the hardness of a material, the greater resistance it has to deformation and wear. As might be expected, a variety of tests have been developed to measure hardness. These tests fall into three broad groups, consisting of:

- scratch hardness (e.g. Mohs, Bierbaum, Pencil)
- static indentation hardness (e.g. Brinell, Rockwell, Vickers, Knoop, Janka, Durometer)
- dynamic hardness (Scleroscope, Leeb).

A selection of commonly used hardness tests are described below and the indentors used for some of these tests shown in Figure 4.2.1e. The requirements for surface preparation varies but all necessitate some preparation of the surface to ensure it is clean and free of debris.

Scratch Hardness

As the name implies scratch hardness tests involve the scratching of the test surface with a stylus/indentor.

The German mineralogist Friedrich Mohs developed one of the earliest measures of material hardness in 1812. The Mohs hardness as it has come to be known, is defined by how well a substance will resist scratching by another substance of known or defined hardness and a ranking from 1 to 10 assigned.

The scale contains ten minerals that Mohs proposed as exemplars of each position on the scale, starting with the mineral Talc at position 1, which can be scratched by a fingernail, to Diamond at 10, see Figure 4.2.1d.

The Mohs scale therefore is not linear; that is, each increment in the scale does not indicate a proportional increase in hardness. For instance, the progression from calcite to fluorite (from 3 to 4 on the Mohs scale) reflects an increase in hardness of approximately 25%, while the progression from Corundum to Diamond, on the other hand, (9 to 10 on the Mohs scale), reflects a hardness increase of more than 300%.

For this reason, the Mohs test, while greatly facilitating the identification of minerals in the field, is not suitable for accurately gauging the hardness of most materials, particularly industrial materials such as steel or ceramics.

Mohs Hardness	Mineral
1	Talc
2	Gypsum
3	Calcite
4	Flourite
5	Apatite
6	Orthoclase
7	Quartz
8	Topaz
9	Corrundum
10	Diamond

Figure 4.2.1d Mohs hardness scale

The Bierbaum test uses a standardised diamond indentor that is dragged across the test surface and the width of the scratch produced measured. This test is suited to a variety of materials, particularly plastics.

The pencil test uses a set of twenty pencils ranging from grades 9B to 9H. A pencil is placed in a holder at an angle of 45o to the test surface and the holder moved across the surface under a fixed force of 7.5N. The test is repeated until a pencil grade that just scratches/indents the surface is found and that grade recorded as the hardness. This test has found use in the testing of polymer coatings.

Static Indentation Hardness

Static hardness tests typically involve the penetration of an indentor into the test surface using low loading rates. The Barcol hardness test uses a cone-shaped steel indentor that is pushed into the test surface until a spring is completely depressed, resulting in the application of a fixed load. The depth to which the indentor has penetrated the surface is then read off a dial gauge calibrated from 0 to 100 and recorded as the Barcol number. This test is often used to determine the degree to which plastic resin has cured.

Brinell tests use a hardened steel or tungsten carbide ball typically of 10mm diameter to produce an indentation in the surface of the material using a standard load. The diameter of the impression is measured with a small portable microscope and the Brinell hardness read from a conversion table.

Rockwell tests use either a small steel ball or a diamond indentor ground to form a cone of 120°, to form an impression. Several Rockwell hardness scales are available (A, B, C, etc) using various combinations of indentor and applied load, depending on the material to be tested. The depth of the impression is related to a Rockwell hardness that is read of a dial gauge or LCD.

Vickers tests use variable loads and a diamond pyramid indentor. Because the same indentor is used and only the applied load varied, a comparable hardness is obtained when testing a range of materials. Because of this, the Vickers test is the standard method for the reliable measurement of metal and ceramic hardness. The impression diagonals are measured and related to a Vickers hardness number by reference to a table selected based on the applied load used in the test.

Knoop tests explore microhardness by making rhombohedral indentations, (one long and one short diagonal), with a pyramidal diamond indentor. The aspect ratio of the impression diagonals allows impressions to be placed closer together without concerns of previous impressions affecting later hardness results.

The Brinell, Rockwell, Vickers and Knoop hardness testers use a standardized indentor and fixed load to determine hardness and are used extensively in the testing of metals.

Figure 4.2.1e Commonly used indentors for hardness testing: Brinell (top), Rockwell (middle), Vickers (bottom)

The Janka hardness test is used for the testing of wood and is similar to the Brinell test in that a steel ball, this time of 11.28 mm, is impressed into the surface to a depth of 5.64mm (half the indenter diameter), leaving an impression of 100mm^2. The force required to create this impression is measured in kN and is reported as the Janka hardness (JH).

The Durometer hardness test (Figure 4.2.1f) is principally undertaken on polymers and involves the pressing of an indenter (consisting of a hardened steel rod) into the surface of the test piece. The indentation hardness is read from a dial gauge on the body of the instrument. If the indenter completely penetrates the sample, a reading of 0 is obtained, and if no penetration occurs, a reading of 100 results. This test is not a good predictor of other properties such as tensile strength, abrasion resistance or wear resistance and is generally used in concert with other tests for product specification.

Figure 4.2.1f Durometer Hardness tester

Dynamic Hardness

Dynamic hardness tests are rebound tests in which an indentor falls from a standard height and the change on rebound measured. These tests depend on elastic recovery of the test surface and use high rates of loading.

The Scleroscope or Shore Scleroscope tests measure the loss in kinetic energy from a falling diamond-tipped metal 'tup'. The tup is enclosed within a glass fronted graduated column and the bottom of the column placed against the surface to be tested. When the tup is released from the top of the column the tup falls, hits the test surface and rebounds. The height of rebound is recorded as the hardness (HSc). The test equipment is light and portable but must be held vertically and test access is restricted by the height of the column.

Figure 4.2.1h Summary of common hardness tests

The Leeb hardness test (Figure 4.2.1g) uses a small pen-shaped device containing a spring-loaded impact body. During testing a small permanent magnet within the impact body passes through a coil in the impact device inducing a voltage proportional to the velocity. The hardness calculated is a ratio of the velocities before and after rebound. Values can be displayed as Leeb hardness (HL) or more usually displayed as a Vickers, Rockwell or Brinell equivalent.

A summary of the hardness tests indicated above is provided in Figure 4.2.1h.

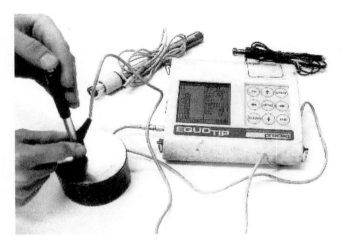

Figure 4.2.1g Equotip™ Hardness tester used to determine Leeb hardness

Load	Test Type	Test	Indentor	Measurement	Metal	Ceramic	Wood	Polymer	Minerals
		Brinell	10mm ø Steel or WC ball	Area					
		Rockwell	$^3/_{16}$' Steel ball or diamond cone	Depth					
		Vickers	Diamond pyramid	Area					
		Knoop	Diamond pyramid	Area					
Fixed		Barcol	Steel cone	Depth					
Load		Pencil	Pencils	Scratch					
		Bierbaum	Diamond	Scratch width					
		Slerescope	Diamond	Rebound height					
		Leeb	WC ball	Velocity change					
		Janka	11.28mm ø Steel ball	Force					
Variable	Static	Durometer	Steel rod	Depth					
Load		Mohs	Various	Scratch					
	Dynamic								

Many conversion tables are available that allow hardness measurements, undertaken with one method, to be compared with hardnesses obtained with a different method and to be equated approximately with tensile strength. These tables are developed from test data for a particular material such as Steel or Aluminium and cannot be extrapolated to include other materials not tested.,

---

4.2.2 Explain a design context where each of the properties in 4.2.1 is an important consideration.

Figure 4.2.2a Physical properties and design contexts

Property	Design Context
Density	This is important in relation to product weight and size (e.g. for portability). Pre-packaged food is sold by weight or volume and a particular consistency is required. Motor vehicle and aircraft components are required to be as low in density as possible to reduce overall weight and improve efficiencies.
Electrical Resistivity	This is particularly important when selecting materials as conductors or insulators in electronics products such as mobile phones and computers.
Thermal Conductivity	Important for objects that will be heated or which must conduct or insulate against heat. Building materials are rated for their conductivity or insulative properties.
Thermal Expansion	Very important when two dissimilar materials are joined. These may then experience large temperature changes while staying joined. Aircraft skins expand significantly due to both temperature and pressure variations and accurate specification is required to ensure structural integrity.
Hardness	This is important when resistance to scratching or penetration is required. Often used as a quality tool to confirm conformance to standard. Bearing surfaces such as those in motor vehicle brake systems are specifically designed considering hardness and extreme temperature properties. Even rubber braking systems in bicycles take into account the hardness of the brake block material.

4.2.3 Define tensile strength, stiffness, toughness and ductility.

Tensile strength

Tensile strength is a measure of a material's resistance to plastic deformation from a tensile or stretching type load. When the tensile strength of a material is quoted it is the maximum tensile strength, known as the ultimate tensile strength (ultimate tensile stress). This is one of the most often quoted mechanical properties for a material. The ultimate tensile strength, (UTS), represents the maximum applied tensile load that a material can sustain, divided by the material's original cross-sectional area. The tensile strength is therefore typically measured in kN/mm^2 or Mega Pascals (MPa), although, the non SI units; psi (lbf/in^2) and ksi are still used primarily in North America.

On the engineering stress-strain curve the tensile strength is represented by that position where the maximum stress is achieved as illustrated in Figure 4.2.3a.

Determine the Ultimate Tensile Stress (UTS) of a 15mm diameter rod if the maximum load it can withstand is 70kN.

Load	$= 70 \times 103$N
Diameter	$= 15 \times 10^{-3}$m^2
Area	$= \pi\, 152\, /4$
	$= 1.767 \times 10^{-4}$m^2
UTS	$=$ Load / area
	$= 70 \times 10^3 / 1.767 \times 10^{-4}$
	$= 396.1517$ MN/m^2
	$= 396$ MPa

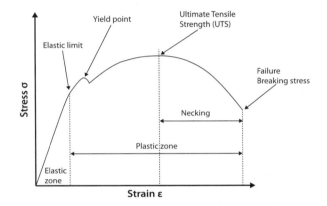

Figure 4.2.3a Engineering stress strain diagram

Stiffness

Stiffness is the resistance of an elastic body to deflection by an applied force. There are several measures of material stiffness depending on the stress state imposed. These include the modulus of elasticity (also known as Young's modulus), the shear modulus (also known as the Modulus of Rigidity), and the Bulk Modulus.

The most commonly quoted measure is the modulus of elasticity or Young's modulus, which is a measure of stiffness when a body is subjected to axial tensile or compressive stresses and is visible on the stress strain diagram as a straight line. The angle of the line (gradient) indicates the relative stiffness of the material, such that a stiff material will have a high Young's modulus. Young's modulus is represented by the capital letter E and is typically expressed in Giga-Pascals (GPa).

The gradients typical of a number of materials are presented in Figure 4.2.3b. In this Figure, it can be seen that a brittle material displays linear elastic behaviour and fails with little strain e.g. ceramics and glasses (1). A soft and tough material, on the other hand, exhibits a very small initial slope, but strain hardens and withstands larger strains before failure e.g. low carbon steel (2).

Materials such as Aluminium have no definite yield point (3). Elastomeric materials display non-linear elasticity e.g. natural and synthetic rubbers (4).

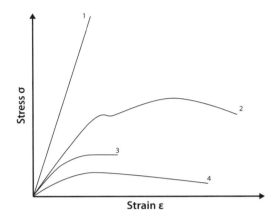

Figure 4.2.3b Typical Stress–strain curves for (1) ceramics and glasses, (2) low carbon steel, (3) Aluminium, (4) natural and synthetic rubbers.

The Young's modulus for a selection of common materials is presented in Figure 4.2.3c.

Material	Young's Modulus
Rubber	0.01–0.1
Nylon	24
Oak (along grain)	11
Glass	50–90
Aluminium	69
Copper	110–130
α–βTitanium	106–122
Carbon FRP	150
Cast Iron	170
Stainless Steel (300 series)	193–200
Structural Steel	190–210
Tungsten Carbide	450–650

Figure 4.2.3c Young's modulus for a selection of common materials

Adapted from ASM Handbook

Toughness

Toughness is the ability of a material to resist the propagation of cracks. A material's stress-strain curve can be used to give an indication of the overall toughness of the material. The area under the stress-strain curve, within the plastic range, is a measure of a material's toughness as illustrated in Figure 4.2.3d. The greater the area under the graph, the tougher the material, and the greater the amount of energy required to cause it to fail.

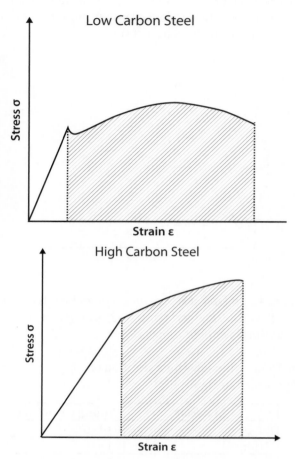

Figure 4.2.3d Comparison of stress-strain curves for low (above) and high (below) toughness materials.

Impact Toughness

A commonly employed method of testing the toughness of a material is to measure its resistance to impact. A number of standard tests are available, such as the Izod Impact test or the Charpy Impact test for metals. In these tests a test piece of standardized dimensions is obtained from the material to be evaluated and a notch machined into the surface to a 'V' or 'U' profile. The sample is subsequently fractured by impact with a pendulum and the swing height the pendulum attains following the sample fracture is used as a measure of the energy absorbed. Metals that are tough will generally undergo a ductile fracture in which plastic deformation occurs during crack propagation. Ductile fractures typically exhibit dull fibrous surfaces with obvious plastic deformation.

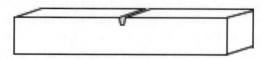

Figure 4.2.3e Illustration of a Charpy V-notch impact test piece.

The more plastic deformation required to advance the crack, the more energy is required and hence a tougher material. Low toughness metals will generally fracture in a brittle manner in which the crack is able to propagate without the absorption of additional energy. Little work is done in brittle fracture and hence the material fails catastrophically. Brittle fractures are usually characterized by bright crystalline features with no evidence of plastic deformation.

The toughness of a material will vary depending on the temperature. If tested at elevated temperatures, a material will show ductile fracture behaviour and consequently may be considered to have good toughness. If tested at low temperature the same material may fracture in a brittle manner and may be considered to have poor toughness.

Typically, a plot of absorbed energy versus test temperature for metals will produce a graph with a sigmoidal profile, in which the absorbed energy levels off past a certain temperature into what is known as the upper shelf energy (ductile) or the lower shelf energy (brittle). The inflection point between these two regions is known as the transition temperature and marks the position where one form of fracture begins to dominate over the other. Because of this, the appearance of the fracture can also be used to measure toughness by assessing the fracture appearance in terms of % Crystallinity or % Fibrosity. A typical Ductile-Brittle transition curve obtained by Charpy V-notch testing of steel is presented in Figure 4.2.3f. Representative fractures from each region are shown.

Historical note

Constance Tipper pioneered research into brittle/ductile transitions. Investigating the failure of Liberty ships during WWII, she discovered that there was a critical temperature below which fractures in steel change from ductile to brittle mode. The 'Liberty Ships' in the North Atlantic were subjected to such low temperatures that they would have been susceptible to brittle failure. These ships were the first all-welded, mass-produced, prefabricated cargo ships produced by the United States to assist in the war effort. The sudden and catastrophic failure of these vessels was a major problem for the Allies. Tipper demonstrated that the type of steel used, rather than the fact that the ships had been welded, was the cause of the fractures. The 'Tipper test' soon became the standard method for determining this form of brittleness in steel, although the test has now been largely superseded by the Charpy impact test.

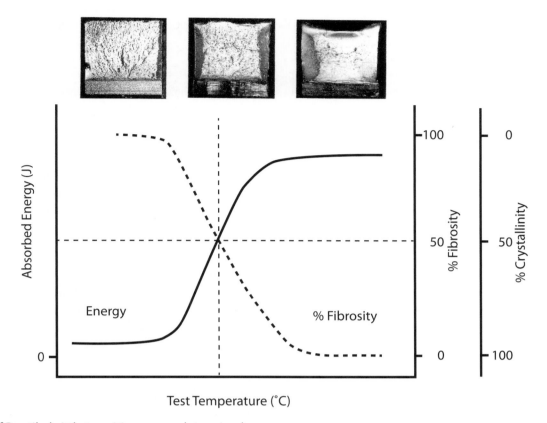

Figure 4.2.3f Ductile-brittle transition curves determined by impact testing of steel

The fracture toughness of a material relates to the size of crack that may be present before fracture will occur. Testing is performed using a notched specimen that is subjected to cyclic loading in tension or three point bending, in order to create a short fatigue crack as illustrated in Figure 4.2.3g. This pre-cracked sample is then fractured to determine a material constant known as the critical stress intensity or K_{1C}. This value is directly related to the energy for crack propagation within the material and to other material constants such as Young's modulus and Poisson's ratio. In this sense, the K_{1C} value provides a more fundamental measure of material toughness compared to the Charpy test, which includes not only the energy of crack propagation to fracture, but also the energy of crack initiation from the notch.

The limiting factor in the general use of fracture toughness tests lies in the difficulty and cost involved in producing a pre-cracked specimen compared with the ease of producing Charpy test pieces

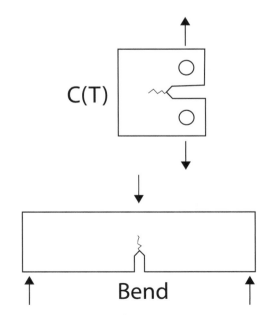

Figure 4.2.3g Fracture toughness test pieces

Ductility

Ductility is the ability of a material to undergo plastic deformation by extrusion or the application of tensile forces. Ductility should not be confused with the related concept of malleability, which is the ability of a material to be shaped plastically, generally by compressive forces.

The amount of cold work that individual metals can withstand without failure therefore depends on their ductility. Conversely, a material that is unable to undergo plastic deformation without failing is described as being brittle.

Both elongation and reduction of area determined from the stress-strain curve are measures of ductility.

4.2.4 Explain a design context where each of the properties in 4.2.3 is an important consideration.

© IBO 2007

Property	Design Context
Tensile Strength	Important when selecting materials for ropes and cables, e.g. in an elevator Although these devices are actually purchased based on a breaking strength of the rope, the tensile strength of the individual wires making up the rope is a critical factor.
Stiffness	Important when maintaining shape is critical to performance e.g. an aircraft wing.
Toughness	Important when materials are subjected to impact or must remain operational even when containing cracks, e.g. military equipment must be capable of resisting sudden impacts and have a rate of crack growth slow enough to allow detection and repair.
Ductility	Important when metals are extruded e.g. electrical wires (this is not to be confused with malleability which is the ability of a material to be shaped plastically).

Figure 4.2.4a Design context for a number of material properties

4.2.5 Outline the characteristics of taste, smell, appearance, texture and colour.

© IBO 2007

Aesthetic characteristics are those characteristics that relate to an appreciation of beauty and form and are commonly judged on information from our senses of sight, taste, hearing, smell and touch. Because these properties depend on the senses, responses to them can vary from one individual to another and from one context to another. Figure 4.2.5a lists the five senses and identifies typical material characteristics.

Senses	Materials Characteristics
Sight	Colour, reflectivity, contrast
Taste	Sour, sweet, salty, bitter
Hearing	Pitch, frequency, timbre, acoustic absorption
Smell	Odour, fragrance
Touch	Texture

Figure 4.2.5a Material characteristics identified by the five senses

4.2.6 Explain a design context where each of the properties in 4.2.5 is an important consideration.

© IBO 2007

Taste and smell have little design context for metals, with the possible exception that the fact that they do not contribute a smell or taste may be a requirement of their use, e.g. the processing and storage of food stuffs and production of office equipment. Other materials such as wood may be employed based on these very properties, e.g. oak barrels for the storage of wine and fragrant timbers for office panelling. The use of plastics and adhesives needs to be carefully considered, since although they can allow great freedom in design, they can potentially give off fumes that may be unpleasant or dangerous under particular conditions.

Sight or visual appearance is a particularly important material characteristic in architectural design. This can range from the application of coatings such as zinc or zincalume® that both protect the steel from corrosion and maintain a visually bright clean surface, to the deliberate use of 'weathering steels' that slowly form a tightly adherent oxide film on the surface, producing an attractive dark brown finish. Similarly, stainless steel and aluminium, (by anodizing), are often treated to produce various colours through the formation of an oxide on the surface.

Texture is often a consideration in the use of materials for architectural settings for the purposes of supplying a tactile element to the material as well as influences texture may have on lighting. Textural effects can range from polished, through brushed to grit blasted as well as textures created through etching, machining, rolling and stamping. Texture may also be applied to surfaces to either improve or reduce friction. The roughened surfaces may be an important feature for grip in such instances as hand held devices or car tires. Smoothly textured surfaces between moving parts would be specified to reduce drag and heat generated by friction.

Hearing or the influence that materials have on our sense of hearing are often a consideration, particularly in design of buildings where the reflection of sound from surfaces can result in poor acoustics. Material properties such as stiffness also have an effect on the pitch and frequency of sound. Acoustic, panels, glass and insulation all provide different ways of treating sound waves in architectural applications.

Further Reading

Beer Jr., F. Johnston, E. R. DeWolf, J. & Mazurek, D. (2011). *Mechanics of Materials.* McGraw-Hill Science/ Engineering/Math. USA.

Budinski, K. G. & M. K. Budinski. (2009). *Engineering Materials: Properties and Selection, 9th Edition.* Prentice Hall. USA.

Hibbeler, R. C. (2010). *Mechanics of Materials . 8th Edition,* (MasteringEngineering Series). Prentice Hall. USA.

Hummel, R. E. Hummel (2004). *Understanding Materials Science: History, Properties, Applications, Second Edition.* Springer. USA.

Newnham, R. E. (2005). *Properties of Materials: Anisotropy, Symmetry, Structure.* Oxford University Press, USA.

4.3 TIMBER

4.3.1 Describe the structure of natural timber.

© IBO 2007

Timber, (or wood), comes from trees and, being an organic material, is subject to the environment in which it grows. Its fundamental properties are subject to a great deal of variability. Due to the cellular nature of wood, its structure can be best likened to a collection of thin-walled tubes made of cellulose. These cellulose 'tubes' are bound together with a weak glue called lignin giving wood its 'grain' (Figure 4.3.1a). It is the direction of the cellulose tubes within wood that is commonly referred to as the grain.

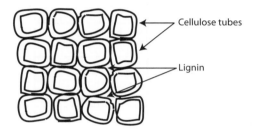

Figure 4.3.1a Cross-sectional cellular structure of wood

Wood can be described as an 'anisotropic material' i.e. it behaves differently in different directions or, more accurately, as an 'orthotropic material', having different properties in three mutually perpendicular directions (Figure 4.3.1b). These are generally described in terms of one direction parallel to the grain or growth rings and two directions perpendicular to the grain, one radial and the other tangential to the growth rings.

Wood is far stronger when loaded parallel to grain the than perpendicular to the grain. This difference can be as much as an order of magnitude.

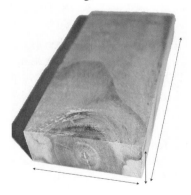

Figure 4.3.1b Orthotropic properties of wood

Some of the factors affecting the strength of timber (although by no means exclusive) are:

- moisture content
- duration of loading
- defects – knots, splits, shakes etc – act to reduce mechanical properties because they introduce a disruption to direction of grain flow
- chemical treatment – many chemical treatments have an adverse effect on mechanical properties although the effect is greatest for water-based preservatives compared to oil-based.

Wood has been used as a structural material for centuries.

The mechanical properties of wood species vary as indicated in Figure 4.3.1c.

Species	Condition (Moisture)	Modulus of Rupture (kPa)	Compressive strength parallel to grain (kPa)	Shear strength parallel to grain (kPa)	Modulus of Elasticity (MPa)
Western red Cedar	green (12%)	36,000 54,000	19,200 29,600	4,800 5,600	7,200 8,200
Radiata Pine	green (12%)	42,100 80,700	19,200 41,900	5200 11,000	8,100 10,200
Mahogany	green (12%)	62,100 79300	29,900 46,700	8,500 8,500	9,200 10,300
Oregon	green (12%)	52,000 88,000	24,200 41,600	8,300 12,300	7,800 9,400
Jarrah	green (12%)	68,300 111,700	35,800 61,200	9,100 14,700	10,200 13,000

Figure 4.3.1c Mechanical properties of various species of wood

4.3.2 Outline that timber can be classified according to the conditions needed for tree growth.

4.3.3 Outline that conifers are referred to as softwoods and that these grow only in temperate regions.

4.3.4 Outline that deciduous trees are referred to as hardwoods and that these grow both in temperate and tropical regions.

As timber comes from a living organism, it is perhaps not surprising that the classification system is not related purely to physical or mechanical properties, but to biological functions related to the way the tree grows.

Timber is therefore classified into two basic groups: hardwoods or softwoods.

These terms are perhaps unfortunate because they suggest a relationship with the physical property hardness, which is not intended. While 'softwoods' are often softer than 'hardwoods', the soft, light timber, Balsa wood, is classified as a 'hardwood', while the hard, heavy timber, Yew, is a 'softwood'.

The difference between hardwoods and softwoods lies in their structure. Softwoods have a simpler structure than hardwoods and under magnification it can be seen hardwoods contain both vessels and pores, while softwoods contain only pores. Vessels also have thinner walls than pore cells. Images produced from a scanning electron microscope (SEM), (Figure 4.3.3a), show the presence of pores in hardwoods (Oak, top) and absence in softwoods (Pine, bottom).

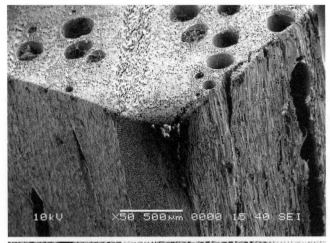

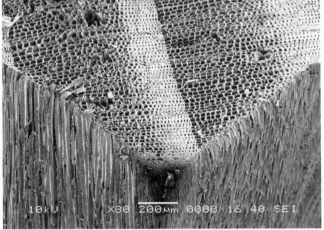

Figure 4.3.3b Conifer seed cone and needle-shaped leaves

Image by John Haslam from Dornoch, Scotland (Pine Cones - Scots Pine) [CC-BY-2.0 (www.creativecommons. org/licenses/by/2.0)], via Wikimedia Commons

Hardwoods are produced by broad leaved trees whose seeds are enclosed in fruit e.g. acorns. They have a variety of grains and a multitude of colours.

Hardwoods can originate from trees that are either the evergreen type (keeping their leaves all year round), or of the deciduous type which lose their leaves in winter. Hardwoods grow in all climatic conditions, wherever trees are found and bear seed-containing fruit. Classified as angiosperms, they are also called pored timbers based, on elements of their structure. The evergreen varieties are typically found in the tropical and sub-tropical regions of the world, such as South and Central America, Africa, India and South-East Asia. The deciduous varieties are typically found in the temperate regions such as Britain, Europe, Japan, USA and New Zealand.

4.3.5 Discuss issues relating to the consideration of timber as a renewable resource.

© IBO 2007

Reforestation is the process of restoring tree cover to areas where woodlands or forest once existed. If this area never returns to its original state of vegetative cover the destructive process is called deforestation. In order to maintain a sustainable forest industry reforestation is necessary.

Reforestation may take a variety of forms. In many temperate zones such as the eastern United States, reforestation occurs quite naturally as the native hardwood forests are so resilient, that those given any opportunity,

Figure 4.3.3a SEM showing hardwood and softwood structures

Image by Mckdandy [GFDL (www.gnu.org/copyleft/ fdl.html), CC-BY-SA-3.0 (www.creativecommons.org/ licenssoftwood climatees/by-sa/3.0/) or CC-BY-2.5 (www. creativecommons.org/licenses/by/2.5)], via Wikimedia Commons

Softwoods are typically conifers, meaning that they form a seed cone and have narrow needle like leaves, (Figure 4.3.3b), compared to hardwoods that typically have broad leaves. In softwoods, the cells are connected such that they allow the movement of nutrient throughout the length of the tree. Because of this, 'softwoods' grow much quicker than hardwoods, which do not have this arrangement. Classified as gymnosperms, they are also called non-pored timbers, based on elements in their structure. The trees grow in cooler climates and the timber is often light in colour.

quickly re-establish themselves. However, urban sprawl and agriculture require a permanently deforested land that is leading to forest reduction in the area. Artificial reforestation is required where poor logging practices and/or nutrient deficient soils generate erosion-prone environments.

In various arid, tropical, or sensitive areas, forests cannot re-establish themselves without assistance due to a variety of environmental factors. One of these factors is that, once forest cover is destroyed in arid zones, the land quickly dries out and becomes inhospitable to new tree growth. Other critical factors include overgrazing by livestock, especially animals such as goats, and over-harvesting of forest resources by native populations or outside businesses. Together, these forces may lead to desertification and the loss of topsoil. Without soil, forests cannot grow until the very long process of soil creation has been completed (if erosion allows this).

In some tropical areas, the removal of forest cover may result in a duri-crust or duri-pan that effectively seal-off the soil to water penetration and root growth. In many areas, reforestation is impossible because the land is in use by people. In these areas, reforestation requires tree seedling or tree planting programs. In other areas, mechanical breaking up of duripans or duricrusts is necessary. Careful and continued watering may be essential, and special protection, such as fencing, may also be required.

One debatable issue in artificial reforestation is whether the succeeding forest will have the same biodiversity as the original forest. If the forest is replaced with only one species of tree and all other vegetation is prevented from growing back, a monoculture forest similar to agricultural crops would be the result. However, most reforestation involves the planting of different seedlots of seedlings taken from the area. More frequently, multiple species are planted as well. Another important factor is the nature of the wide variety of plant and animal species that previously occupied a clearcut. In some regeneration areas the suppression of forest fires for hundreds of years has resulted in large single aged and single specie forest stands.

Reforestation need not be only used for recovery of accidentally destroyed forests. In some countries, such as Finland, the forests are managed by the wood products, pulp and paper industries. In such an arrangement, (like other crops), trees are replanted wherever they are cut. In such circumstances, the cutting of trees can be carefully controlled to allow easier reforestation. In Canada, the wood product, pulp and paper industries systematically replace many of the trees it cuts, employing large numbers of summer workers for tree planting.

The sustainable management of forest resources is called forestry. As commercial enterprises, managed plantations are established mostly as monocultures consisting of fast growing high-yield species such as shown in Figure 4.3.5.

Figure 4.3.5 Young Scots Pine stand (ca. 25 years of age) after the first thinning

Image by MPorciusCato [CC-BY-SA-3.0 (www.creativecommons.org/licenses/by-sa/3.0)], from Wikimedia Commons

4.3.6   List two examples of composite timbers.

A composite timber is one that has been man made, usually by recombining wood veneers or wood flakes with glues or resins to produce new wood products such as plywood, particle boards, and fibreboard.

Laminated Timber

As indicated earlier (see 4.3.1), wood is an 'orthotropic material' having different properties in three mutually perpendicular directions, with the strongest of these being when loaded parallel to grain. In order to take advantage of this, laminated timbers have been created in which layers of veneers are built up to create a timber with improved properties. In this instance, wood is cut into thin sheets in the order of 2-3mm thick, called veneers. These veneers are then glued back together using a phenolic resin adhesive with the grain of each sheet at right angles to the sheet above and below. When the desired thickness of the timber is achieved, the assembly is pressed together until the glue sets. Types of laminated timber include plywood, blockboard, and laminboard. An example of plywood is shown in Figure 4.3.6a. These products should not be confused with Laminated Board, which consists of a photographic image of timber, resin sealed and bonded to a core of high-density particleboard, followed by a backing board.

Advantages

- cheaper than solid timbers
- any thickness can be created
- stronger and more resistant to warping.
- decorative veneers can be applied to the surface
- laminates free of gross imperfections can be created.

Disadvantages

- cannot be made thinner
- if other than standard thicknesses are required extra sheets need to be glued in place
- glue lines at panel edges are subject to moisture ingress and the loss of interlaminate glue and must be protected.

Figure 4.3.6a Plywood sheets

Particle Board

Particle board is manufactured by glueing small flakes, chips or pieces of timber together under pressure, see Figure 4.3.6b. Chipboard is perhaps the best known example. Vulnerable to water, it may also be treated to be moisture resistant and covered in a plastic veneer to produce more serviceable surfaces for use in kitchens, bookcases, desktops etc.

Figure 4.3.6b Particle board sheets

> 4.3.7 Compare the characteristics of particle board, laminated woods (for example, plywood), pine wood (a softwood) and mahogany (a hardwood).
>
> © IBO 2007

Figure 4.37 Comparison table of timber and timber products

Wood type	Composition	Hardness (Janka)	Insect Resistance	Damp Resistance	Aesthetics, colour, grain
Particle Board	Wood flakes of various timber & flake size dependent on use.	2224	Addition of fungicide and insecticides to resin.	Must be sealed against moisture to avoid swelling	Mottled yellow flakes, no grain or knots
Laminated Board	Hardwood, resin sealed and bonded to core of high-density particleboard , followed by a backing board.	N/A Hard wearing surface	Highly durable	Very high	Warmth & beauty of timber. Various colours and simulated grains.
Plywood	Wood veneers arranged with grain of alternating layers oriented at 90°.	N/A	Durable	Should be sealed to avoid dimensional change	Warmth & beauty of timber. Various colours
Cyprus Pine	Solid Timber	6116	Highly durable	Should be sealed to avoid dimensional change	Warmth & beauty of timber. Golden brown & highlights. Dark knots.
Red Mahogany	Solid Timber	11997	Durable		Warmth & beauty of timber. Pale to dark red. Evenly textured.

4.3.8 Outline criteria for selection of timber for different structural and aesthetic design contexts.

© IBO 2007

Design Context	Selection Criteria
Buildings	Resistance to moisture and pest infestation. durability, hardness availability, cost
Furniture	Dimensional stability, strength, colour, grain, defect free
Children's Toys	Free of toxic chemicals, resistance to moisture

4.3.9 Describe the reasons for treating or finishing wood.

© IBO 2007

Green timber contains a high percentage of moisture (~85%) within its cells. Once cut, green timber will begin to lose moisture. The commercial drying of timber is called seasoning and is directed toward the controlled removal of moisture.

Before timber can be used commercially moisture must be removed in such a way that the structural integrity and yield strength of the timber is not affected by splitting or warping. Similarly, if moisture is not reduced to a level below about 20% the timber will be subject to decay and attack by fungus often referred to as dry rot. The drying of timber is not intended to remove all moisture but to achieve equilibrium with the environment. Known as the equilibrium moisture content or (EMC).

There are two primary methods used to season timber: air-drying and kiln-drying. Both methods involve the stacking of the sawn timber in such a way that movement is restrained during the drying process, while allowing air to freely circulate throughout the stack. In air-drying the stack is exposed to the general atmosphere, either in the open or stored in large sheds. In this situation there is little control over the drying process. Kiln drying, in contrast, places the stacks in a kiln, within which the drying environment is closely controlled. Temperatures within the kiln are typically controlled between 70° and 100° C.

The moisture within timber is contained either in the cell walls and is known as absorbed moisture, or within the cell cavities and intercellular spaces and is known as free moisture. During the initial drying of wood only the free moisture is removed and no structural changes

occur. Once the free moisture has been removed the loss of absorbed moisture begins. It is at this stage, when the moisture is below about 30%, that structural changes associated with shrinkage begin.

Figure 4.3.9a Timber seasoning

Drying proceeds from the surface into the centre. If the humidity is not controlled during the seasoning process, stresses develop between the surface of the timber and the centre that can lead to warping and splitting. Some of these effects are shown in Figure 4.3.9b.

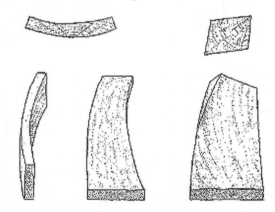

Figure 4.3.9b Common timber shrinkage and distortion defects

Softwoods are generally kiln-dried, while hardwoods, which can be subject to degradation during kiln drying, are usually air-dried.

Correctly seasoned timber exhibits the following features:

- strength
- stability
- resistance to decay
- easier to paint glue, nail, screw, and machine
- timber preservation processes require the removal of free water from wood.

Timber treatment

Timber is a natural product. Once the wood is taken from the natural protection of the bark, it is prone to attack from poor weather conditions, insects, fungus and moisture. To protect timber from these attacks it would be prudent to either treat the timber or apply a finish. Treatment can involve using solutions, which make the wood poisonous to insects, fungus and marine borers as well as protecting it from the weather. Finishes can also be applied but, generally speaking, timber that will be positioned outdoors should be treated, while an adequate finish should be applied to timber that will be positioned indoors.

Finished timber requires sanding, (to close up the grain leaving smaller gaps), with abrasive paper and the application of one of the following:

- oil
- stain
- paint
- shellac
- wax polish
- French polish
- plastic varnish.

4.3.10 Explain three differences in the selection of timbers for flooring if it were made of a hardwood, a softwood or a composite material.

© IBO 2007

Timbers for flooring should have a Janka hardness greater than 5kN to provide adequate resistance to damage. Above this, the selection of a timber for flooring is made on a number of criteria, three of which are indicated in Figure 4.3.10. below.

The Janka hardness test impresses a steel ball of 11.28 mm diameter into the surface to a depth of 5.64mm (half the indenter diameter), leaving an impression of $100mm^2$. The force required to create this impression is measured in kN and is reported as the Janka hardness (JH).

Figure 4.3.10 Timber flooring materials' properties

Wood Type	Material	Durability	Ease of Maintenance	Aesthetics
Hardwood	Red Mahogany	Durable	Good. Once sealed can be sanded and resealed over time.	Warmth and beauty of timber. Pale to dark red. Even, medium texture, interlocked grain.
Softwood	Cyprus Pine	Highly Durable	Good. Once sealed can be sanded and resealed over time.	Warmth and beauty of timber. Golden brown with highlights of pale yellow and dark knots.
Composite material	Plywood	Durable	Good. Once sealed can be sanded and resealed over time.	Warmth and beauty of timber. Various colours.
	Particle Board	Depends of addition of insecticides and fungicides	Must be sealed against moisture and traffic damage	Mottled pale yellow flakes. No grain or knots.
	Laminated Board	Highly durable	Very good but cannot be sanded and resealed.	Warmth and beauty of timber. Various colours. Can have simulated grain textures.

4.4 METALS

Metallic bonds

As previously indicated, (see section 4.1.2), the most familiar model of metallic bonding is the 'free electron' or 'electron sea' model, in which a regular lattice of positive atomic nuclei is present with the outer valence electrons available to move freely, see Figure 4.4.1a.

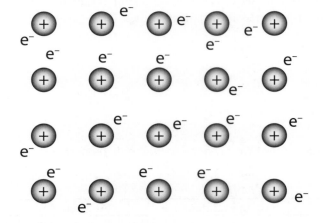

Figure 4.4.1a Free electron model of metallic bonding

The atomic lattice positions are each represented by the nucleus and the inner electron shells without the valence electrons. The lattice positions are essentially occupied by metal ions. The lattice maintains its shape as a balance between the attractive forces between the outer electrons and the lattice ions, and the repulsive force existing between the ions.

Because the outer-most shell (the valency shell) cannot contain more than eight electrons it is not uncommon for a lower energy shell to remain unfilled before the next (higher energy) shell begins to fill. This behaviour helps to explain the differences in physical properties, such as electrical conductivity, between metals.

The conductivity of a material is a measure of the ease with which it allows current to flow. Since current is created by the flow of electrons, a good conductor is one that allows electrons to flow freely and easily. The metallic bond is therefore particularly suited to good conductivity due to the sea of free electrons available.

Because the energy levels of the orbitals overlap in metallic bonding, with lower orbitals unfilled, several energy levels are available to the valence electrons. The availability of these unoccupied energy levels for valence electrons to move explains both the superior conductivity of metals and the relative conductivity between the metals.

When most solids form, (with the exception of glass and some polymers), they generally do so by arranging themselves in a regular three-dimensional pattern of atoms. This regular 3D arrangement is known as a crystal structure and all metals solidify as collections of crystals (also known as grains). If special care is taken, a metal can be made to solidify as a single large crystal, although metals are more commonly produced containing many crystals, being termed polycrystalline.

Three commonly encountered crystal structures for metals are shown in Figure 4.4.3a and represent the body centred cubic (BCC), face centred cubic (FCC) and close packed hexagonal (CPH) structures.

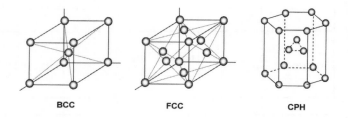

Figure 4.4.3a Common crystal structures

The crystal structure adopted by a metal will be the structure that results in the lowest energy state for the atoms of that metal. The crystal structure or lattice arrangement therefore reflects the properties of the metallic element. This arrangement can change depending on the temperature under consideration. For example at temperatures between 1410 and 1520°C pure iron has a BCC structure and is designated as delta (δ) iron. This structure transforms to FCC between 910-1410°C where it is known as gamma (γ) iron or austenite and then transforms again below 910°C to bcc where it is known as alpha (α) iron. While both delta (δ) iron and alpha (α) iron have a BCC structure, the interatomic distances differ, so that the size of the individual crystal cells is different. Figure 4.4.3b below gives an indication of the crystal structure of a number of common pure metals.

BCC	FCC	CPH
Chromium	Aluminium	Cobalt
Niobium	Copper	Magnesium
Iron (below 910° C)	Iron (910 -1400° C)	Titanium
Molybdenum	Nickel	Zinc
Tungsten	Silver	Zirconium

Figure 4.4.3b Crystal structure of a number of common pure metals

Alloying of a metal in which the alloying element substitutes for the atoms of the base metal can result in changes in the crystal lattice either throughout the alloy or locally, resulting in the presence of more than one crystal structure at a time. An example of this is brass, an alloy of copper with zinc. Common brass (70wt%Cu, 30wt%Zn) contains two 'phases', α and β, which are of differing crystal structure.

> **4.4.3   State that metals (pure or alloyed) exist as crystals.**
>
> © IBO 2007

As indicated above most metals are composed of many crystals, that is, they are polycrystalline. During the solidification of metals the atoms begin to arrange themselves in the crystal lattice. Because of variations in temperature and the presence of inhomogeneities of the mould surface and within the liquid, crystal growth will usually initiate (nucleate) at a number of positions, each of which has a different orientation from its neighbours. As solidification continues and each of these crystals (or grains) grows, a time arrives at which neighbouring crystals intersect. Because each crystal has initiated at a different position there will be a mismatch in the stacking order along the boundary between the crystals as shown in Figure 4.4.4a. This region of mismatch is known as the crystal or grain boundary.

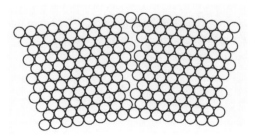

Figure 4.4.4 a Schematic representation of lattice mismatch at a boundary between two grains

If a finely polished metal surface is etched with an appropriate acid solution, the grains can be revealed. This occurs because the grain boundaries are selectively attacked. Etching is, in essence, a controlled corrosion process. Similarly various phases within the grains will also undergo differing rates of attack to reveal structure within the grains. The study of microstructural elements of metals and alloys is known as metallography.

When a metal is etched in an acid, atoms are chemically removed from the surface; the rate of removal of atoms from the surface depends on the orientation of the crystal that is facing the acid. Because each grain presents a different orientation, each grain etches down at a different rate as can be seen in Figure 4.4.4b, where the surface of a low carbon steel with a structure of ferrite and pearlite is shown following etching. The variation in level of attack of the various grains of ferrite, and differential attack of the cementite and ferrite lamella of the pearlite phase is clearly evident.

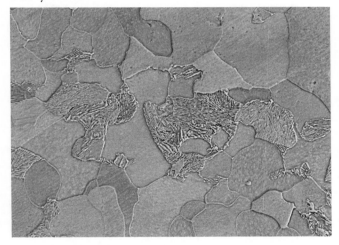

Figure 4.4.4 b Photomicrograph of the etched surface of a low carbon steel taken using a Scanning Electron Microscope and showing the different levels of attack obtained

Image by B Susanto

The grain size of a metal may be reported in a number of ways, such as number of grains per unit area or average diameter.

A simple rating of grain size, standardized by the American Society for the Testing of Materials (ASTM), and known as the ASTM grain size number, is often quoted when assessing grain size. In simplified form, this number is obtained by recording the number of grain boundaries that are intercepted by a line when viewing the microstructure at a magnification of ×100. The simple formula shown below is then used to produce the ASTM number. The grain size decreases as the grain size number increases.

$$N = 2^{n-1}$$

Where   N = the ASTM grain size number
n = number of grains per square inch at a magnification of ×100.

Figure 4.4.4 c A selection of microstructures, conforming to the indicated ASTM grain sizes 3, 4, 6 and 8

Standardized reference charts are available showing the grain size equivalent to each of the ASTM grain size numbers from 0 to 9, allowing an estimated grain size to be given without time consuming measurement. A selection of microstructures, conforming to the indicated ASTM grain sizes, is illustrated in Figure 4.4.c and represents the grain size when viewed at ×100 magnification.

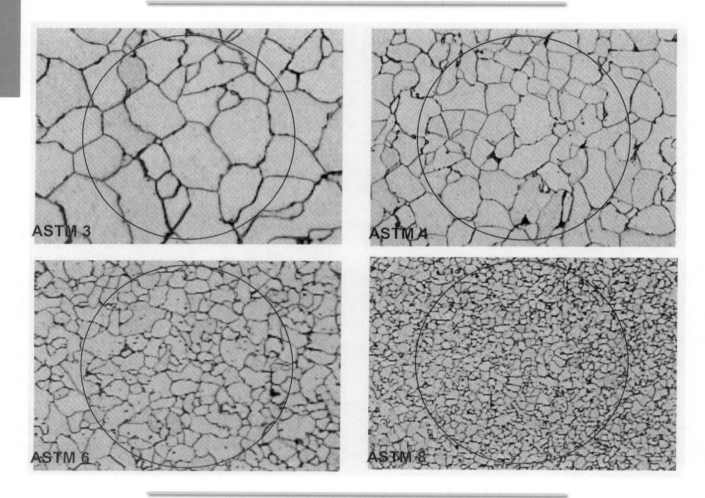

4.4.5 Explain how grain size can be controlled and modified by the rate of cooling of the molten metal, or by heat treatment after solidification.

© IBO 2007

Grain size is one of the most important characteristics of a material. In metals, the grain size influences the yield strength, impact toughness, elongation and creep resistance. The grain size of a metal can be influenced in a number of ways. One of the most fundamental of these is through control of the rate and direction of solidification.

With the appropriate control of the temperature gradients in a furnace and rate of cooling, large directionally

oriented grains can be grown, or indeed single crystals. High temperature nickel alloy turbine blades have been manufactured using these techniques in order to gain improvements in creep resistance. In this technique, solidification is directional from the bottom up.

Several techniques have been used to obtain directional growth. One of these, known as normal freezing, involves the placement of the metal charge in a small crucible arranged either horizontally or vertically and the charge melted in a furnace.

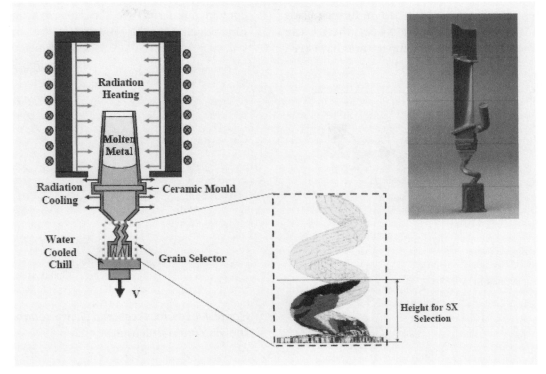

Figure 4.4.5 a Casting of a Single Crystal (SC) turbine blade.

From Dai, H. (2008). A Study of Solidification Structure Evolution during Investment Casting of Ni-based Superalloy for Aero-Turbine Blades. PhD thesis, University of Leicester.

If a crystal of preferred orientation is desired, a 'seed crystal' is placed at one end of the crucible. Heating of the crucible is then performed such that the charge and part of the seed crystal, if present, is melted. Either the crucible or the furnace is then slowly moved such that solidification begins from the seed crystal and follows its orientation as solidification gradually progresses. A variation on this technique has been used to produce single crystal nickel alloy aeronautical turbine blades as illustrated in Figure 4.4.5a.

In this case molten metal is introduced into the mould, which is itself surrounded by heating elements to maintain the metal within the mould in a molten state. At the bottom of the mould is a section known as the grain selector, consisting of a cavity at the top of which is a helical tube leading into the main body of the mould. A water-cooled plate is positioned at the bottom of the grain selector and promotes initial directional solidification, since heat is removed from the mould much faster from the preferentially cooled bottom, than through the ceramic walls of the mould. Numerous crystals are formed and grow toward the helical constriction, at which point only grains of a certain orientation will be able to progress. As solidification proceeds along the helix the number of grains with a suitable orientation is reduced until only one orientation remains and it is that orientation that finally enters into the main part of the mould containing what will become the turbine blade. Gradually lowering the mould or raising the heating coils maintains directional cooling of the casting.

An illustration of the grain structure obtained under normal casting conditions in which a polycrystalline structure is obtained, compared to that obtained through directional solidification and single crystal growth is shown if Figure 4.4.5 b.

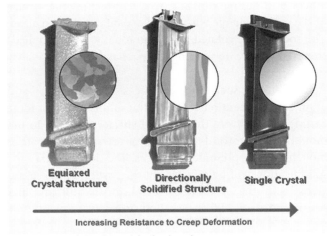

Figure 4.4.5 b Turbine blade development

Creep of Other Metals. DoITPoMs Teaching and Learning Packages, Dept of Materials and Metallurgy, University of Cambridge, UK. downloaded from www.doitpoms.ac.uk/tlplib/creep/other_metals.php

CORE

The effect these developments have had on turbine blade performance is illustrated in Figure 4.4.5c, where it can be seen that increasing operating temperatures have been obtained.

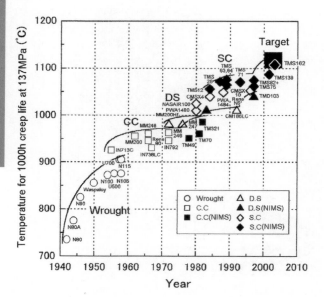

CC: Conventionally Cast; DS: Directional Solidification; SC: Single Crystal

Figure 4.4.5 c History of improvement in temperature capability of Ni base superalloys

From Koizumi, Y. et. al. (2003). Development of a next-generation Ni-base single crystal superalloy. Proc. International Gas Turbine Congress, Tokyo Japan.

A method known as crystal pulling or the Czochralski technique is often used to produce single crystals of Silicon and Germanium and involves touching the surface of the molten charge with a seed crystal attached to a rod. The rod is then rotated as it is gradually raised (pulled) from the surface developing a crystal as it goes.

Apart from the specialised instances of solidification and grain control mentioned above, the solidification of most casting will be from the external surface adjacent to the mould wall, in toward the centre, or toward a reservoir of molten metal represented by risers. The time required for solidification will be affected by the casting temperature along with the volume of metal to solidify and the provisions of any chills, cores and risers.

It is not unusual for large section castings to exhibit a range of grain sizes starting at the surface and consisting of a narrow zone of small 'chill' crystals, followed by a sometimes broad region of directionally oriented columnar crystals. The central zone of a large casting is often characterised by a region of equiaxed grains that have grown heterogeneously from a liquid that

contains numerous seed crystals resulting in no specific directionality in their growth.

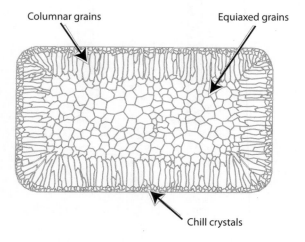

Figure 4.4.5d Cross sectional view through a casting showing grain structure

4.4.6 Define plastic deformation.

© IBO 2007

In polycrystalline materials slight deformation under load causes no permanent deformation, i.e. the atoms return to their original position on the removal of the deforming load. This is called elastic deformation and the matrix is obeying Hooke's Law. Plastic deformation is the condition in which permanent distortion of a body takes place. For most materials, plastic deformation will occur when a load is applied that exceeds the elastic limit (See section 4.2.3). Past this point, deformation is sufficient for irreversible slip to occur between the planes of atoms, such that the material will no longer return to its original shape on the removal of a load but will maintain some degree of distortion or permanent set.

Once the elastic limit has been passed and plastic deformation takes place, Hooke's Law no longer applies and stress is no longer directly proportional to strain.

4.4.7 Explain how metals work-harden after being plastically deformed.

© IBO 2007

During work hardening or strain hardening an increase in stress is required to continue deformation. This effect is considered to be the result of increasing resistance to slip within the grains of a polycrystalline material.

Slip occurs within the metal lattice when planes of atoms are able to move past each other. This movement of crystallographic planes is believed to be assisted by the movement of defects in the stacking order leaving local vacancies known as dislocations. Effectively, dislocations represent regions in which the regular lattice order has been locally disrupted. A number of different types of dislocations have been identified that help explain the different forms of plastic deformation encountered. This is outside the requirements of the IB and will not be treated further. In Figure 4.4.7a an illustration of a dislocation is presented. As can be seen the lattice is distorted and a stress field is associated with the dislocation.

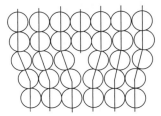

Figure 4.4.7a Dislocation in lattice arrangement

An illustration of the movement of a dislocation through the lattice is shown in Figure 4.4.7b.

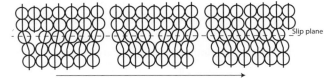

Figure 4.4.7b Dislocation movement through metal lattice

These dislocations can move through the metal lattice and will do so freely until they meet an obstacle. As dislocations pile up at grain boundaries, a back pressure is created that restricts the motion of dislocations in the lattice, making further deformation more difficult. A higher stress is therefore required to continue plastic deformation, which we identify as work hardening. The surface of a polished and etched sample of austenitic stainless steel is shown in Figure 4.4.7c, in which lines of slip can be seen within different grains.

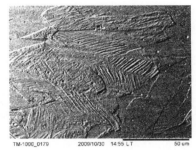

Figure 4.4.7c SEM surface image of plastically deformed austenitic stainless steel revealing slip lines

Image by Sarah Metcalfe

4.4.8 Describe how tensile strength of a metal is increased by alloying.

The alloying of a metal typically occurs in one of two ways depending on the size of atomic radius of the alloying element(s) relative to that of the base metal. A selection of atomic radii is presented in Figure 4.4.8a.

Element	Atomic Radii (pm)
H	37
N	73
O	74
C	77
B	88
S	102
Fe	124
Ni	125
Cr	125
Co	125
As	125
Cu	128
Zn	133
Mn	137
Pd	138
Al	143
Ti	145
Au	144
Ag	144
Sn	151
Pb	175

Figure 4.4.8a atomic radii

In those instances where the atomic radius of the alloying (solute) element, differs by no more than 15% from that of the base (solvent) metal, a substitution of one for the other can occur within the metal lattice. Such an alloy addition forms what is known as a substitutional solid solution. As the size difference between the substitutional atom and the lattice increases, an increasing strain is created in the lattice. This lattice strain acts as an impediment to dislocation movement, leading to an increase in strength, although above a difference of 15% substitutional solubility is limited. Therefore the larger the mismatch in atomic radii the greater is the strengthening effect of the alloy addition.

The arrangement of substitutional elements within the lattice can vary from disordered, meaning that there is no particular position or pattern within the lattice in which they may be found, to a clustered arrangement in which local groupings arise, to a highly ordered structure as illustrated in Figure 4.4.8b.

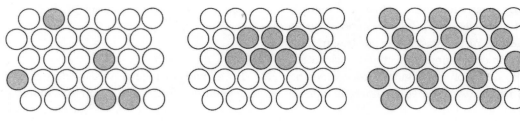

Figure 4.4.8b Illustration of a metal lattice containing substitutional alloying elements (grey)

An interstitial alloying element by contrast finds a position in the metal lattice in the spaces or interstices between the lattice positions of the base metal. Such an alloy addition is possible if the difference in atomic radii is greater than approximately 60%, although other factors also affect the ability and extent to which interstitial additions will occur. Such an alloy addition forms what is known as an interstitial solid solution.

As the size of the element taking up an interstitial site increases relative to the size of the vacancy within the lattice, an increase in lattice strain occurs. As may be seen from Figure 4.4.8a, Hydrogen, when present, would be an interstitial addition in most alloy systems. Hydrogen, Nitrogen, Oxygen, Carbon and Boron are present as interstitial additions in Iron, with most of the other elements being present as substitutional alloy additions. Lead (Pb) does not have any solubility (interstitial or substitutional) in the iron lattice due the exceptional difference in their atomic radii.

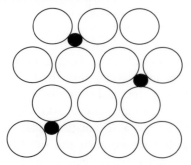

Figure 4.4.8c Illustration of a metal lattice containing interstitial alloying elements (dark)

By introducing strain into the lattice, both substitutional and interstitial alloying hinders the movement of dislocations and as a result increases the yield and tensile strength of the metal. This phenomenon is known as solution hardening.

Increasing the percentage of the alloying element leads to an increase in strength by increasing the number of regions of lattice strain, up to the point at which the solid solubility of the alloy is exceeded. At this point the

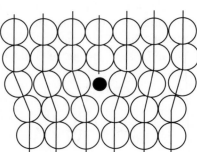

Figure 4.4.8d Illustration of a metal lattice with a dislocation, hindered in movement by the presence of substitutional and interstitial alloying elements

excess atoms often form in groups or clusters at the grain boundaries by diffusion, leading under conditions of slow cooling to the formation (precipitation) of a second phase consisting of a fine intermetallic compound. Substitutional and interstitial solutes can also interact leading to the formation of this second phase precipitation. The result is that some of the solute atoms are removed from the lattice and a decrease in solid solution hardening occurs, but a process known as precipitation hardening can occur.

If rapid cooling takes place, the precipitation of this second phase can be suppressed, but the alloy is unstable, and with time or under conditions of low temperature heat treatment (called an aging heat treatment) the second phase will precipitate as a fine dispersion throughout the matrix. If these clusters of atoms forming the intermetallic compounds remain coherent with the lattice, that is they maintain the same crystallographic orientation, they also act to impede dislocation movement and strengthening by precipitation, hardening is said to occur. The alloy Duralumin (Al-4wt% Cu) represents a common precipitation-hardening alloy. The time and temperature of the aging treatment needs to be closely controlled however, since if these precipitates grow too large they lose cohesion with the lattice, leading to a reduction in lattice strain and consequential loss of strength. At this point the alloy is said to have been over-aged.

Dispersion strengthening is similar to precipitation hardening in that a second phase is dispersed throughout the matrix, which restrains dislocation movement (slip). In dispersion hardening, however, the second phase dispersion is usually an oxide and powder metallurgy processes often produce the alloy. Thoria Dispersed Nickel (TD Nickel) is an example of this, in which Thoria (ThO_2) is dispersed within a Nickel matrix. Similarly, Sintered Aluminium Powders (SAP) consisting of ultra-fine powders of oxidised aluminium such that a thin oxide is formed on the particle surface and then sintered and pressed to create a fine dispersion of Al_2O_3 throughout the aluminium matrix.

4.4.9 Explain the effect of alloying on malleability and ductility.

© IBO 2007

As indicated previously, dislocation movement through the crystal lattice allows atoms to move past one another, or slip, along crystallographic planes during plastic deformation. By restricting the movement of dislocations, alloying elements restrict the degree of plastic deformation that can take place before fracture, as measured by a decrease in malleability and ductility.

4.4.10 Describe a superalloy.

© IBO 2007

The group of metal alloys known as superalloys all feature excellent high temperature strength and resistance to thermal shock, along with high temperature oxidation resistance. The superalloys are therefore particularly known for their ability to operate at high temperatures. Not only do they operate at high temperature, they achieve this by maintaining strength at temperatures approaching a high fraction of their melting point. A measure of this is known as the homologous temperature T_H, where T_H represents the ratio of operating temperature to melting temperature, expressed in degrees Kelvin. The superalloys typically have a $T_H > 0.7$.

The superalloys all exhibit a face centred cubic (FCC) structure and typically fall into three groups:

- Iron-Nickel based alloys
- Nickel based alloys
- Cobalt based alloys.

Most of the superalloys have a significant Chromium addition, which plays an important part in the formation of a tightly adherent oxide layer that restricts access of oxygen to the alloy surface, impeding further oxidation. Strengthening occurs by a combination of solid solution strengthening, precipitation hardening or dispersion hardening. The Iron-based grades are generally cheaper than the Nickel and Cobalt based alloys. Examples of several superalloys are provided in Figure 4.4.10a

Figure 4.4.10a Selection of Superalloys and an indication of the strengthening mechanism

Alloy Group	Common Name	% C	% Fe	% Co	% Ni	% Cr	% Mo	% W	% Ti	% Al	% Other
Iron-Nickel alloys	**Solid solution**										
	Incoloy 800	0.5	Bal.	—	32	21	—	—	0.4	—	
	Incoloy 900	0.5	Bal.	—	43	13	6	—	—	—	2.9 Ti, 0.2 Al
	Precipitation										
	Altemp A286	0.5	Bal.	—	26	15	1.25	—	2.5	0.2	0.003 B
Cobalt base alloys	**Solid solution**										
	HS 21	0.25	1	Bal.	3	27	5	—	—	—	
	HS 25	0.1	3	Bal.	10	20	1.5	15	—	—	
	Elgiloy	0.15	25	Bal.	15	20	7	—	—	—	0.4 Be
	MAR M322	1.00	—	Bal.		21	—	9	0.75	—	2 Zr, 4.5 Ta
	MP35N	—	—	Bal.	35	20	10	—	—	—	
	Solid solution										
	Hastelloy C276	0.02	5	2.5	Bal.	15	16	3.5	—	—	1 Mn
	Iconel 625	0.25	5		Bal.	22	9	—	—	—	3 (Nb + Ta)
	Precipitation										
	Iconel 601	0.5	14	—	Bal.	23	—	—	—	1.4	0.2 Cu
	Udimet 500	0.08	—	18	Bal.	19	4	3	3	3	0.005 B
	Waspaloy A	0.07	10	13	Bal.	19	4	—	3	1.5	0.006 B, 0.9 Zr
	Nimonic 90	0.1	3	18	Bal.	19	—	—	2.5	1.5	1.5 Si
	Rene 41	0.09	—	11	Bal.	19	10	—	3	1.5	0.01 B

Alloy additions made to the superalloys contribute to strength and oxidation resistance in a number of ways, summarised in Figure 4.4.10b. As can be seen from this table, carbide and gamma prime (γ') precipitation play a major role in the strengthening of the superalloys. The gamma prime phase represents an intermetallic precipitate such as γ'-Ni3Al or γ'-Ni3(Al,Ti). Through an understanding of the effects of the various alloying elements on the structure and properties of materials, such as the superalloys, metallurgists and materials engineers are able to design alloys for certain tasks.

Alloy additions	Solid solution strengtheners	γ' formers	Carbide formers	Grain boundary strengtheners	Oxide scale formers
Chromium	X	–	X	–	–
Aluminium	–	X	–	–	–
Titanium	–	X	X	–	–
Molybdenum	X	–	X	–	–
Tungsten	X	–	X	–	–
Boron	–	–	–	X	X
Zirconium	–	–	–	X	X
Carbon	–	–	–	X	X
Niobium	–	–	X		
Hafnium	–	–	X	X	X
Tantalum	–	–	X	X	X

Figure 4.4.10b Role of alloying elements in superalloys

4.4.11 List two design criteria for superalloys.

© IBO 2007

Creep Resistance: Elevated temperature creep resistance is one of the principal characteristics of super alloys. Creep is a process in which a material subjected to an applied load, lower than the yield strength, will over time, elongate or undergo strain. The rate at which creep will occur is dependent on both the applied stress and the operating temperature. Creep occurs as a result of thermal vibrations of the metal lattice, which over time allow obstacles to plastic flow to be overcome. This plastic flow typically occurs at the grain boundaries. In advanced stages of creep, grain boundary sliding leads to the development of cavities at grain boundary junctions, eventually resulting in fracture.

Oxidation Resistance: Due to the presence of additions such as Chromium, a tightly adherent oxide film is formed on the surface. This film restricts further access of Oxygen to the metal surface so that unless the oxide barrier is damaged the rate of oxidation is severely reduced.

4.4.12 Identify applications for superalloys.

© IBO 2007

Superalloys find particular application in high temperature service such as jet and rocket engines and chemical plants where mechanical strength at elevated temperature, and resistance to corrosive atmospheres and oxidation resistance is necessary.

The high corrosion resistance and biocompatibility of the Cobalt based alloys has also seen them used in biomedical applications. Some uses of a selection of superalloys are indicated in Figure 4.4.12.

General applications of superalloys based on sub groupings are shown below.

Iron-Nickel based superalloys find applications in:
- cryogenics
- jet engine components
- petrochemical processing machinery.

Cobalt based superalloys are employed in:
- turbine blades
- orthodontic wires
- biomedical implants
- food processing equipment.

Nickel based superalloys appear in:
- air scrubbers
- marine applications
- gas turbine components.

Alloy group	Common Name	Applications
Iron - Nickel based alloys	Incoloy 800	Applications requiring resistance to high temperature oxidation and carburization, e.g. Carbonizing equipment, heating element sheathing, heat treatment baskets, chemical and petrochemical processing equipment e.g. heat exchangers and piping equipment.
	Incoloy 901	Gas turbine parts including: rotors and compressor discs, high temperature fasteners, and cryogenic equipment.
	Altemp A286	Jet engine nacelles, parts and fasteners. Belleville springs and washers in oil-field and racing applications as well as cryogenics.
Cobalt based alloys	HS21	Turbine blades and vanes, biomedical implants.
	HS25	Turbine blades and vanes, combustion chambers, afterburner parts and biomedical implants.
	Elgiloy	Springs for oil-field applications and orthodontic wires.
	MAR M322	Jet engine turbine blades and vanes.
	MP35N	Aircraft fasteners, biomedical devices, chemical and food processing equipment, springs for oil-field applications.
Nickel based alloys	Hastelloy C276	Petrochemical processing equipment, heat exchangers, air scrubbers, flue-gas desulphurization equipment and cryogenic applications.
	Inconel 625	Heat exchangers and gas turbine components, reaction vessels and heat exchangers, valves, marine applications and cryogenics.
	Inconel 601	Chemical processing radiant tubes, steam superheater tube supports and heat treatment fixtures.
	Udimet 500	Gas turbine components e.g. vane guides.
	Waspalloy A	Gas turbine components e.g. discs, blades, seals and shafts. Missile components
	Nimonic 90	Gas turbine components e.g. valves, discs and blades. Hot working tools. High temperature springs.
	Rene 41	Jet and rocket engine parts: afterburner parts, turbine casings, wheels and fasteners. Space shuttle turbo pump seals.

Figure 4.4.12 Selection of specific superalloys

Further Reading

Donachie, M. J. & Donachie, S. J. (2002).*Superalloys - A Technical Guide Second Edition*. ASM International.

Donachie, M. J. & Donachie, S. J. (2006). *Selection of Superalloys for Design*. John Wiley & Sons.

Furrer, D. & Fecht, H. (1999). *Ni-Based Superalloys for Turbine Discs*. Journal of Materials.

4.5 PLASTICS

4.5.1 Describe a covalent bond.

As previously indicated (see section 4.1.2), covalent bonding occurs between non-metals and between metals and non-metals in which the valence electrons are shared, in order to complete the outer shells. The covalent bond is the strongest of the chemical bonds and like the ionic and metallic bonds, are examples of a primary bond.

The backbone of plastic is the carbon atom. In order to satisfy the octet rule and fill its outer shell, carbon can bond with up to four other atoms. With four (4) valence electrons, it is easier for Carbon to share electrons by bonding covalently than to gain or lose electrons, as occurs in ionic bonding. It is this ability to form so many bonds with other elements that results in the great diversity of carbon chemistry. The electron dot, or Lewis notation, for the carbon atom is presented in Figure 4.5.1a, along with the structural formula for the Carbon atom. Note that the Lewis notation shows the number of electrons present in the valency shell, while the structural formula shows the number of available sites for bonding.

Figure 4.5.1a Lewis diagram of a carbon atom (left) and structural diagram (right).

Two commonly encountered arrangements of a Carbon molecule are the linear chain, in which up to three bonds may be present in the Carbon-Carbon connection, and the ring, as illustrated in Figure 4.5.1b.

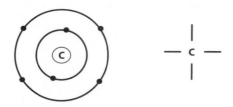

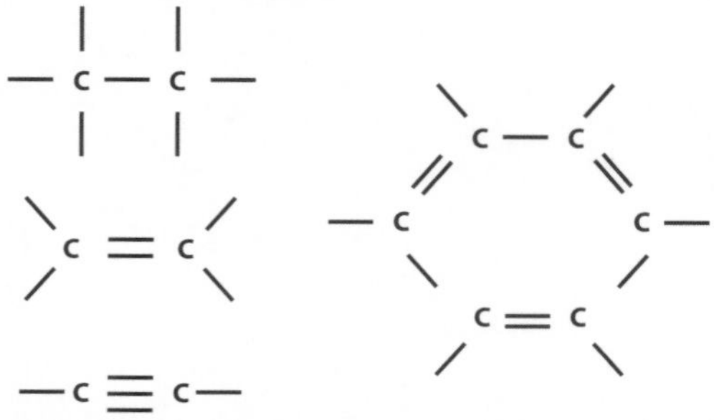

Figure 4.5.1b Two commonly encountered arrangements of a carbon molecule

Each of these arrangements can be considered as a molecular unit (or Mer) that can connect with identical units, to form a larger molecule, consisting of many mer-units or more commonly a polymer. All polymers have this feature, of consisting of many repeating mer-units, in common. The repeating mer-unit for a number of common polymers is indicated in Figure 4.5.1c.

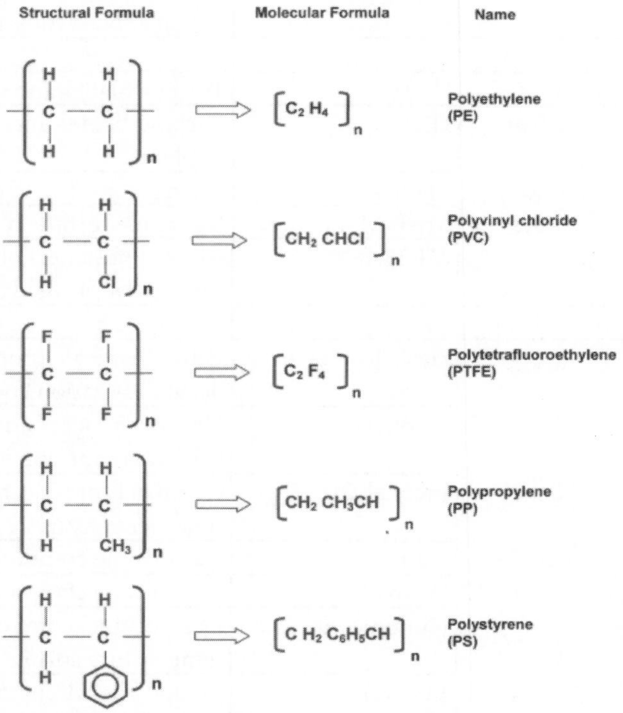

Structural Formula	Molecular Formula	Name
	$\left[C_2 H_4 \right]_n$	Polyethylene (PE)
	$\left[CH_2 CHCl \right]_n$	Polyvinyl chloride (PVC)
	$\left[C_2 F_4 \right]_n$	Polytetrafluoroethylene (PTFE)
	$\left[CH_2 CH_3 CH \right]_n$	Polypropylene (PP)
	$\left[C H_2 C_6 H_5 CH \right]_n$	Polystyrene (PS)

Figure 4.5.1c Representations of mer-unit polymers

It is the size of the mer and atoms bonded to the carbon atoms within individual mer-units that differentiate the structure and properties of the resulting polymer. As the length of the molecule increases, the properties of the polymer change, such that as the number of carbon atoms increases to several hundred, the material formed changes from a gas to a liquid and on to a solid. As this change occurs the degree of orderliness in which the chains are able to arrange themselves, or the crystallinity, of the polymer can be adjusted to produce different properties as illustrated in Figure 4.5.1d.

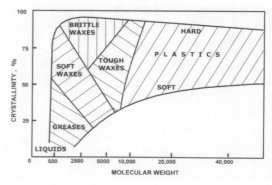

Figure 4.5.1d Effect of molecular weight and crystallinity on properties, Richards, J. (1951). Appl. Chem.,

4.5.2 Describe secondary bonds as weak forces of attraction between molecules.

A polymer, as we experience it, is a combination of many millions of polymer molecules joined together by both physical entanglement and intermolecular forces of attraction. These intermolecular bonds are not, however, achieved by a primary bond such as the covalent bond used to construct the molecules themselves, but rather by way of a weaker secondary type of bond. Two of these intermolecular bonds are the Hydrogen bond and van der Waals force.

Both of these bonds result from asymmetry in the electron clouds that can result in the molecule forming an electric dipole, in which one pole is positive and the other negative. The intermolecular attraction of these poles is the weak secondary bond formed between polymer molecules.

Figure 4.5.2a Model of the electrical dipole associated with a water molecule and resulting secondary bond attraction between molecules

Thermoplastic material consists of carbon atoms arranged in a single chain from which there may be many branches. Each chain is joined to its neighbour by van der Waal forces, which weaken on heating, allowing the material to become fluid.

As indicated in section 4.5.2 there is a large degree of physical entanglement between the molecules such that they can be visualized as a tangled mass as illustrated in Figure 4.5.3.

The properties of the thermoplastics are determined by structural features such as the degree of branching present and the length of individual chains, typically measured in terms of molecular weight. These factors determine the degree of crystallinity (regions with orderly chain packing) and density of the polymer, which in turn influence factors such as tensile strength, impact resistance, hardness and melting temperature.

The thermoplastics are available in a number of grades that typically involve blends of chains of differing density and molecular weight, such that they are defined in terms of a molecular weight distribution (MWD). The MWD determines the ease with which the polymer can

be processed such that as the MWD becomes broader the polymer becomes easier to process. The Melt Flow Index (MFI) is used as a measure of processability. This test involves the pushing of a measured amount of polymer through an orifice at a specified temperature and weighing the amount extruded over a ten minute period. The higher the MFI, measured in g/10min, the easier is the processability. Because of the presence of a distribution of densities and molecular weights, properties such as MFI and melting temperature are often expressed as a range.

Those polymers with an unbranched chain structure similar to that illustrated in Figure 4.5.3 (left) can form with relatively close alignment, leading to higher density and stronger secondary bonds. In contrast, the alignment of branched chains also illustrated in Figure 4.5.3 (right) is restricted, leading to lower densities and correspondingly lower secondary bond strength, with consequential effects on tensile strength and melting point.

Due to their linear structure thermoplastics can be drawn into fibres (nylon is an example). Typically, the characteristics of thermoplastics can be summarised as:

- ductile
- easily fabricated
- easily drawn into fibres
- can be injected into a mould
- can be remelted and remoulded.

Common thermoplastics are Polyvinyl chloride (PVC), Nylon, Perspex, Polytetrafluoroethylene (PTFE). These materials become plastic at elevated temperatures, allowing formation by a number of processes.

Figure 4.5.3 Schematic representation of the tangle of linear molecules comprising a thermoplastic. The individual molecules may be branched or non-branched

4.5.4 Describe the effect of load on a thermoplastic with reference to orientation of the polymer chain.

When a load is applied thermoplastic materials will undergo a certain amount of elastic deformation as the entangled molecules undergo a period of mechanical straightening. This movement is aided by the Carbon-to-

Carbon bonds, which can act as pivot points about which the chain can rotate. Once the applied load is removed the polymer returns to its original shape.

If the applied loadings exceed that required for mechanical straightening, the secondary bonds begin to be weakened, allowing the molecular chains to slide over each other. At this point plastic, non-recoverable, deformation has occurred and the material will not return to its original shape on the removal of the applied load.

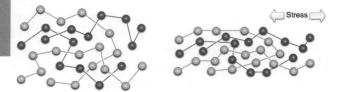

Stress

4.5.4 Effect of load on orientation of a thermosplastic

Image by LaurensvanLieshout [GFDL (www.gnu.org/copyleft/fdl.html) or CC-BY-SA-3.0-2.5-2.0-1.0(www.creativecommons.org/licenses/by-sa/3.0-2.5-2.0-1.0)], from Wikimedia Commons

4.5.5	Explain the reversible effect of temperature on a thermoplastic, with reference to polymer chains.

When thermoplastics are heated the weak bonds between chains are broken, allowing the molecular chains to move past each other. In this state, the thermoplastic can be plastically formed into a new shape. On cooling, the weak bonds between chains are re-established and the material stays in the new shape to which it was formed.

4.5.6	Explain how the reversible effect of temperature on a thermoplastic contributes to the ease of recycling of thermoplastics.

Because thermoplastics allow numerous cycles of heating and reforming into various shapes without deterioration these plastics are well suited to recycling.

4.5.7	Draw and describe the structure and bonding of a thermoset.

Thermosetting materials (also known as thermosets) are heated to a plastic state under pressure. Under these conditions of elevated temperature and pressure they are said to set, forming three-dimensional structures linked by covalent bonds. The thermosets therefore form a single large 3D network rather than the mass of molecular chains linked by secondary bonds, as is the case for the thermoplastics, as illustrated in Figure 4.5.7.

Figure 4.5.7 Schematic representation of the tangle of linear molecules comprising a thermoset in which a single 3D structure is formed.

4.5.8	Explain the non-reversible effect of temperature on a thermoset.

The thermosets are generally formed as part of a two part process in which linear chains are first formed, followed by a second step in which these chains are connected (or cross-linked) to neighbours by primary bonds, forming a three dimensional structure. Because the cross-link bonds formed between the chains are strong primary bonds, the chains cannot slide passed each other and are not easily broken. This rigid three dimensional structure leads to these materials exhibiting high strength but low ductility.

Thermoset materials cannot be reheated to a plastic state for reforming. On further heating the primary carbon bonds are broken, rather than the secondary bonds between the chains being weakened, and the material decomposes. The characteristics of thermosets can be summarised as:

- rigid
- cannot be remelted and remoulded
- higher strength than thermoplastics.

Common thermosets are; Bakelite (Phenol formaldehyde), Melamine and Diallyl Phthalate.

4.5.9	Discuss the properties and uses of polypropene and polyethene thermoplastic materials.

Both polypropene and polyethene are members of the polyolefin family of thermoplastics, having the general formula C_nH_{2n}. The various grades of these materials have similar properties. These materials typically have low density and negligible water absorbency, along with good resistance to chemicals. While mechanical properties are slightly lower than polyethene, polypropene has higher temperature resistance, allowing it to undergo sterilization by autoclave. This facility has allowed Polypropene to find extensive use in the medical environment as funnels, bottles, instrument jars etc.

Polyethene is also known as Polyethylene (PE) — [CH_2 – CH_2], and consists of a Carbon 'backbone' with each Carbon atom attached to two Hydrogen atoms, as illustrated in Figure 4.5.9a.

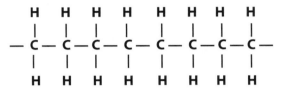

Figure 4.5.9a Configuration of the Polyethylene chain

Although the chemical formula is unchanged, Polyethylene is available in a number of grades, dependent on the length of the molecular chains from which it is made and the density of chain packing. Properties vary depending on chain length, density and the extent and type of branching and various combinations are blended together to produce specific properties. The polyethene product finally marketed is typically classified under one of the divisions indicated in the table Figure 4.5.9b.

ULMWPE and VLMWPE have long side branches along the molecular chain, that restricts the ability of the molecular chains to closely align. Because of this restriction in alignment, these regions have a lower density of chain packing. In addition, the greater separation of the chains in these regions leads to weaker van der Waals bonds. The ULMWPE and VLMWPE grades therefore have a relatively low density and melting temperature.

As the length of side chains decreases and the length of individual molecular chains increases, the packing efficiency also increases leading to an increase in density and secondary bond strength. Theses changes lead to greater strength, stiffness and melting point up to HDPE.

High Molecular Weight Polyethene (HMWPE) and Low Molecular Weight Polyethene (LMWPE) consist of a restricted molecular weight distribution (MWD) in which the MWD is confined either to long molecular chains, or short molecular chains respectively. These materials are usually blended in various proportions to modify the properties of the Polyethene grade being manufactured and can be used in LDPE, MDPE or HDPE.

A slight decrease in strength and density occurs on moving to UHMWPE, due to a restriction in the efficiency of packing resulting from the great length of the molecular chains.

Figure 4.5.9b Summary of Polypropene properties

	Tensile Strength MPa	Density g/cc	Hardness Shore D	MP °C	Structure	Properties	Uses
UHMWPE	20-40	0.930-0.935	68	138-152	Long chains no branching.	Very tough, low coef. of friction, wear resistant, non toxic.	Biomedical implants, ballistic vests, gears, skis, fishing line.
HDPE	21-53	0.940-0.960	59-64	125-135	Linear structure little branching.	Rigid, opaque, chemically inert.	Freezer bags, water pipes, cable insulation.
MDPE	12.4-19.3	0.926-0.940	50-64	104-127	Linear structure high degree of short branching	Shock resistance, stress cracking resistance.	Gas pipe and fittings, shrink film, carrier bags, geomembrane.
LDPE	9-14	0.910-0.930	38-50	98-118	Random long branching short side branching variable lengths.	Flexible, good resistance to acids/alkalis.	Sandwich bags, cling wrap,squeeze bottles, clothing, furniture.
LLDPE	20-24	0.915-0.925	48	120-160	Mix of no branches and uniform distribution	Tough, flexible, transparent	Cable covering, toys, lids, buckets, plastic film.
ULMWPE	5-25	0.904-0.912	62-66	104-115	Many short branches more evenly spread	Flexible at low temperatures.	Stretch wrap, hose, tubing, frozen food bags.
VLDPE		0.880-0.915					

Polypropene, also known as Polypropylene (PP) - [CH$_2$ – CH$_3$CH], is available in two general groups known as Polypropene Co-polymer (PP-C) or Polypropene Homopolymer (PP-H). The homopolymer form as the name implies consists only of Polypropene, while co-polymer utilises a second polymer such as ethene as an intermediary to connect Polyethene chains, leading to improved properties.

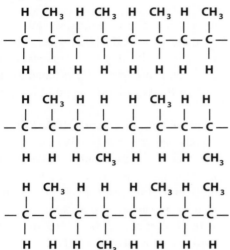

Figure 4.5.9c Configurations of the polypropene chain in the isotactic form (top), syndiotactic form (middle), and atactic form (bottom)

The homopolymer form of Polypropene contains a carbon 'backbone' in which one of the Carbon atoms is attached to two Hydrogen atoms, while the other carbon atom has one of the Hydrogen atoms replaced by a Methyl group [CH$_3$]. This asymmetry can affect the properties of Polypropene depending on the side of the chain on which the Methyl group is found. This variation in structure is known as the tacticity. If the methyl groups all occur on one side of the chain it is said to be isotactic. If they alternate from side to side in an orderly manner, the chain is said to be syndiotactic. While random positioning of the methyl group produces an atactic structure, as illustrated in Figure 4.5.9c.

The presence of the Methyl group side chain limits the packing obtained between chains. This packing decreases along with the properties as the regularity of the chain decreases, such that isotactic Polypropene has a melting point of approximately 160 -170° C, syndiotactic Polypropene has a melting point of approximately 125-135° C and atactic Polypropene has a melting point of <0° C.

The improved properties of the isotactic form of Polypropene, arising from the closer bonding with other chains, allowed by the regularity of the structure, has lead to the isotactic form being the most commonly used.

While more expensive than Polyethene the higher melting point of Polypropene allows autoclave sterilization.

As a general guide, Polypropene Homopolymer (PP-H) is stiffer than the co-polymer form, while the Polypropene Co-polymer (PP-C) has better impact resistance. A summary of Polypropene properties is provided in Figure 4.5.9d.

	Tensile Strength MPa	Density g/cc	Hardness Shore D	MP °C	Properties	Uses
PP Copolymer	< 70	0.700-0.905	70	120-170	Resistance to heat, (can be autoclaved), grease and oil.	Food containers, clothing, medicine bottles, brushes, prosthetics, disposable syringes.
PP Homo-polymer	60-70	0.899-0.948	80	155-170	Resistance to heat and stress cracking, grease and oil. Excellent insulating properties.	Food containers, chemical tanks, wet benches, prosthetics, plugs.

Figure 4.5.9d Properties of Polypropene

4.5.10 Discuss the properties and uses of polyurethane and urea–formaldehyde (methanal) thermoset materials.

These materials can be formed as either solid plastics or as foams. Foams are formed by the introduction of bubbles into the resin. Because of the presence of bubbles within the structure the foams are of low density. Depending on the polymer used these foams may be flexible, lending themselves to use in applications such as cushions, or rigid leading to use as light weight structural panels.

The term polyurethane, (PU), is a relatively generic term for a group of polymers with the common characteristic that they have a repeating sequence of the urethane molecule in their structure. This molecule is shown in Figure 4.5.10a and it will be noted that a free radical (symbol R) is attached to either end. A free radical is an atom or molecule that has at least one unpaired electron and so is available to form a bond. The asterisk associated with one of the free radicals in Figure 4.5.10a simply indicates that this free radical can be different to the free radical at the other end of the urethane molecule.

$$
\begin{array}{ccc}
& \text{H} & \text{O} \\
& | & || \\
\text{R} - & \text{N} - \text{C} - & \text{O} - \text{R*}
\end{array}
$$

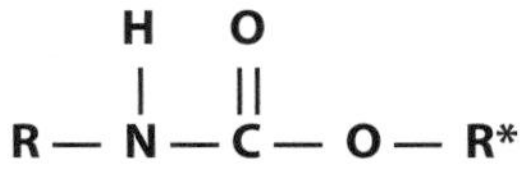

Figure 4.5.10a Structure of the Urethane molecule

Because of its ability to bond with a number of other molecules Polyurethane can behave as a castable thermoplastic elastomer (rubbers), as an injection moulded rigid thermoplastic or as a thermoset.

In the elastomeric form, the molecule is termed a block co-polymer, being made up of two polymers with alternating segments of rigid polyurethane and soft polyester. Cross-linking between the chains occurs between the hard Polyurethane segments to form a three dimensional structure. These materials are used extensively to produce flexible foams that find use in everyday items such as cushions or stretchable material such as Spandex, sold by Dupont as Lycra™.

The harder, more rigid polyurethanes find use as ski boots, foam insulation and structural panels, automobile dashboards, solid tyres, wood replacement, gaskets and abrasion resistant coatings.

In Urea-formaldehyde, (UF), the oxygen atom from the Formaldehyde molecule reacts with a Hydrogen atom from two Urea molecules to form a linear chain, in the process forming a water molecule as a by-product. This type of reaction is known as a condensation reaction. In a similar way Formaldehyde molecules react with neighbouring Urea-formaldehyde chains to form cross-linkages creating the single three-dimensional structure of Urea-formaldehyde.

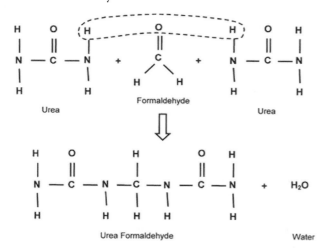

Figure 4.5.10b Condensation reaction of Urea and Formaldehyde molecules

Urea formaldehyde finds use in electrical switches, decorative laminates, toilet seats and construction adhesives.

Plastic in its myriad forms has become one of the most widely used materials today, offering a wide array of properties for most applications, including low unit cost, lightness, corrosion resistance, thermal and electrical insulation, flexibility or rigidity and production by way of processes, ranging from blow moulding to machining.

Apart from structural uses of plastics in applications such as piping and plumbing fittings, structural panels and electrical wire insulation, plastics are used extensively for consumer products such containers for cleaning products, toiletries and food stuffs. It is from the consumer goods part of the market that large amounts of refuse is created such as empty containers and packaging. This domestic waste material is collected and, if not separated for recycling, often finds its way into landfills. Because plastic does not readily undergo the normal processes of biodegradation, plastic in landfills can take up a large volume reducing the effective life of the landfill.

Large amounts of plastic consumer waste is however, also discarded along roadways, in bushland or waterways where it is not only unsightly, but can pose a danger to wildlife that may swallow the material.

In order to reduce the impact on landfills, wildlife and the environment in general, recycling of plastic is increasingly being encouraged. One problem with such programs in the past has been the wide variety of plastics in use and the difficulty of easily and quickly identifying them. To this end, each of the major polymer groups in use have been given a numerical designation from 1 to 6, see Figure 4.5.11 This identification is moulded into the surface of the plastic during manufacture and allows the easy separation of plastic consumer waste into groups for recycling.

Figure 4.5.11 Plastic recycling identification code

Although theoretically recyclable, PVC from domestic sources can pose problem for recyclers due to the large number of fillers that can be used, which may contaminate recycled plastic. Incineration is also of concern due to the potential for the release of toxic byproducts such as Dioxins. Because of these concerns and extra expense incurred by sorting PVC products, many collection agencies continue to send PVC to landfills.

The Homopolymer form of Polypropene contains a carbon 'backbone' in which one of the Carbon atoms is attached to two Hydrogen atoms, while the other Carbon atom has one of the Hydrogen atoms replaced by a Methyl group [CH_3].

Further Reading

Gross, R. A. & Kalra B. (2002). *Biodegradable Polymers for the Environment.* Science. Vol. 297. pp. 806-806.

Kolybaba, M, L. G. Tabil, S. Panigrahi, W. J. Crerar, T. Powell and B. Wang. (2003). *Biodegradable Polymers: Past, Present, and Future.* CSAE Annual Intersectional Meeting, Fargo, North Dakota, USA.

Tuttle, M. E. (2003). *A Brief Introduction to Polymeric Materials.* Dept Mechanical Engineering. University of Washington Seattle.

4.6 CERAMICS

4.6.1 Describe the composition of glass.

© IBO 2007

Glass represents a group of non-crystalline (amorphous) ceramics, in which the constituent atoms are stacked in an irregular, random pattern i.e. there is no long-range order.

There are many different types of glass with different chemical and physical properties. Each can be made by a suitable adjustment to chemical compositions, but the main types of glass are:

- glass fibre
- lead glass
- commercial glass also known as soda-lime glass
- borosilicate glass (low coefficient of thermal expansion - e.g. Pyrex®)

Glasses may be devised to meet almost any imaginable requirement. For many specialised applications in chemistry, pharmacy, the electrical and electronics industries, optics, the construction and lighting industries, glass, or the comparatively new family of materials known as glass ceramics, may be the only practical material for the engineer to use. Like other ceramics, glasses are brittle.

The majority of the glass we see around us in our everyday lives is in the form of bottles, jars and flat glass for windows. This type of glass is known as commercial or soda-lime glass, as soda ash (sodium carbonate Na_2CO_3) is used in its manufacture.

Most commercial glasses have roughly similar chemical compositions of:

70% - 74% SiO_2 (silica)
12% - 16% Na_2O (sodium oxide)
5% - 11% CaO (calcium oxide)
1% - 3% MgO (magnesium oxide)
1% - 3% Al_2O_3 (aluminium oxide)

Commercial glass is normally perceived as colourless, allowing it to freely transmit light although in thicker sections a green colouration can be noticed due to contamination by a small amount of iron oxide. It is their ability to transmit a variety of wavelengths of light (visible, ultraviolet and infra red), chemical inertness and insulating properties that make glasses so versatile.

The presence of impurities in glass produce various colours, as indicated below in Figure 4.6.1.

Metal Oxide	Colour
Cobalt (II) Oxide	Violet blue
Chromium (III) Oxide	Green
Copper (II) Oxide	Turquoise
Iron (II) Oxide	Turquoise
Iron (III) Oxide	Pale yellow green
Manganese (II) Oxide	Colourless
Manganese (III) Oxide	Purple
Antimony Oxide	White
Vanadium Oxide	Yellow green
Titanium Oxide	Violet
Selenium Oxide	Ruby red
Uranium	Fluorescent yellow green

Figure 4.6.1 Colours of soda lime silicate glass

4.6.2 Explain that glass is produced from sand, limestone and sodium carbonate, and requires large quantities of energy for its manufacture.

© IBO 2007

The main constituent of commercial glass is silica sand (SiO_2), and sand by itself can be fused to produce glass, although temperatures of the order of 1700°C are required. In order to reduce the energy requirements, other materials are added to sand to reduce the temperature of fusion. The addition of soda ash reduces the temperature of fusion to about 800 to 1000°C. However, a glass of this composition is relatively soft and water-soluble and is known as water glass. In order to give the glass stability and hardness, other materials such as limestone ($CaCO_3$) and Dolomite ($MgCO_3$) are added. In addition, scrap glass is added to make the process more economical.

Figure 4.6.2 Traditional hand-blowing of glass

4.6.3 Describe the characteristics of glass.

© IBO 2007

Glass has a wide range of characteristics that have seen it used extensively in everyday life. These include:

Transparency: One of the unique characteristics of glass is its ability to allow light to be transmitted with minimal scattering allowing a clear view through it, or to be patterned or frosted in such a way that light can enter a room but a clear view is masked. This feature of variable opacity/transparency leads to a wide variety of uses both functional and aesthetic.

Chemically inert: the lack of reactivity with most chemicals makes glass an ideal material for storage (Figure 4.6.3).

Non-toxic: the lack of reactivity shown by glass and the absence of toxic breakdown products has lead to the extensive use for food storage.

Biocompatibility: relates to the compatibility of a material for the continued health of a biological environment with which it comes into contact.

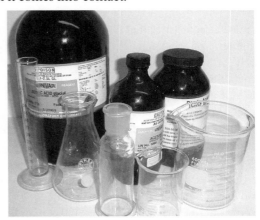

Figure 4.6.3 Inert laboratory glass

Hardness: Glass resists scratching under normal conditions of handling and cleaning leading to long service, with minimal degradation.

Brittle: The main drawback with glass is that it can be brittle and inflexible. On fracture annealed glass may break into numerous sharp shards that can pose a danger. Developments such as laminated glass and toughened glass reduce this risk.

Aesthetic appeal: When molten, glass is extremely plastic, allowing it to be formed, drawn, blown and joined into any imaginable shape. Added to its ability to be coloured, glass has always found favour as a material for artistic expression, in addition to its functional use.

Electrical insulator: Glass is an excellent electrical insulator (or dielectric material) and because of this has found extensive use as an insulator on high voltage overhead electrical transmission lines.

Cheap: The high volume production, abundant raw materials and ability to recycle glass (known as cullet), makes glass a relatively cheap material to produce.

The main drawback with glass is that it can be brittle and inflexible and, on fracture, may break into numerous sharp shards that can pose a danger. Developments such as laminated glass and toughened glass have improved these physical properties.

> 4.6.4 Explain that the desired characteristics of glass can be accurately determined by altering its composition.
>
> © IBO 2007

Changes to the composition of glass can result in significant changes in its characteristics.

One of the characteristics that is modified by composition is coefficient of thermal expansion. As mentioned previously ordinary soda glass is very brittle. This glass has a coefficient of thermal expansion of approximately $9 \times 10^{-6} K^{-1}$. If exposed to a sudden temperature change, as may occur if boiling water were introduced into a cold glass bowl, the sudden thermal expansion can be sufficient to result in fracture.

If some boron oxide B_2O_3 is added to the composition, a glass known as Borosilicate Glass is produced. This glass has a coefficient of thermal expansion of less than half that of silica glass, at approximately $4 \times 10^{-6} K^{-1}$. The Borosilicate Glass produced by Corning and known commercially as Pyrex®, contains approximately 12.6% B_2O_3. Because of its low coefficient of thermal expansion, high thermal shock resistance and chemical resistance, Borosilicate Glass has found use in applications as diverse as home cookware, laboratory equipment and the mirrors of large telescopes.

Lead glass also known as lead crystal contains between 24% and 30% Lead Oxide (PbO), while glass with additions of PbO below 18% is known simply as crystal glass. The lead addition imparts a high refractive index giving a sparkling, bright, relatively soft surface that can be further enhanced by faceting and has lead to great popularity in decorative glassware. Lead glass also finds extensive use in electrical equipment due to excellent insulating properties. The lead

glasses will not, however, withstand high temperatures or sudden changes in temperature, (Figure 4.6.4).

Figure 4.6.4 Polished lead crystal glass

Lead glass with PbO additions above 65%, are used as radiation shielding because lead absorbs gamma rays. Shielding glass is sold in terms of lead equivalent thickness, that is, 12mm of lead shielding glass may have a lead equivalent thickness of 2mm. Possibly the widest use of the glass has been in the funnel of CRT-TV screens to block X-rays.

Alkali-barium Silicate Glass (CRT Glass) contains small amounts of Barium Oxide. This glass was used for the front screen of Cathode Ray Tube televisions to absorb X-rays produced by the CRT.

> 4.6.5 Outline the differences between toughened and laminated glass.
>
> © IBO 2007

One of the main disadvantages of ordinary annealed glass is that when it fractures numerous loose shards are created that can represent a hazard, as do the sharp edges of the broken glass that remain in place (see unit 4.6.3). The typical fracture pattern for a pane of annealed glass is shown in Figure 4.6.5a.

Figure 4.6.5a Typical fracture pattern for annealed glass

Laminated glass (also known as Safety Glass) was developed to avoid the ejection of dangerous shards of glass on fracture by holding them together. This is typically achieved by bonding two sheets of annealed glass together (although toughened glass has also been used) with a polymer interlayer of Polyvinyl butyral (PVB), as illustrated in Figure 4.6.5b. This laminate is formed under heat and pressure in a furnace called an autoclave. If manufactured using annealed glass, laminated glass can be cut to size. When broken, the PVB interlayer holds the pieces of glass together.

Figure 4.6.5b Construction of laminated glass, showing a PVB layer sandwiched between two layers of glass

The fracture of laminated glass produces a characteristic pattern of radial and concentric cracks often described as a spider-web pattern, represented in Figure 4.6.5c.

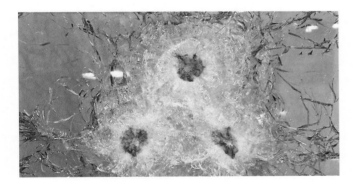

Figure 4.6.5c Typical fracture pattern for laminated glass

Laminated glass will flex before shattering and is strong but not as strong as toughened glass.

Toughened glass, also known as tempered glass is produced by heat treatment, during which the glass is heated to a temperature of appropriately 650°C, and then subjected to an air quench to rapidly cool the surface. As the surface cools and contracts, it is placed under compression relative to the interior, as illustrated in Figure 4.6.5d.

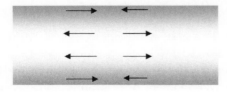

Figure 4.6.5d Stress distribution in toughened glass

Cooling must be controlled to ensure the stress distribution is symmetrical through the mid plane as illustrated in Figure 4.6.5e.

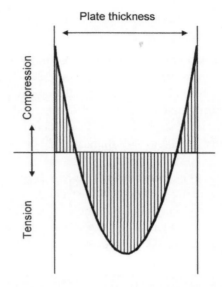

Figure 4.6.5e Profile of the residual stress pattern through a pane of toughened (or tempered) glass

Glass in this form is considered to be in the tempered condition and exhibits two to three times the breaking strength and impact resistance of ordinary annealed glass. However, because toughened glass relies on the integrity of the surface compression zone it cannot be cut. All forming, shaping and cutting operations must be performed before the tempering operation is performed.

Breaching of the compressive layer results in fracture. In this instance fracture results in the formation of numerous small and relatively uniform rounded particles (dice), greatly reducing the potential for injury, as illustrated in Figure 4.6.5f. For this reason, tempered glass is also often referred to as safety glass. The primary disadvantage of this fracture pattern is that vision can be obscured, making it unsuitable for windscreens.

Figure 4.6.5f Typical fracture pattern for toughened glass.

4.6.6 Explain why glass is increasingly used as a structural material.

© IBO 2007

Glass is increasingly being used as a structural material where glass bricks are used in the construction of walls in place of traditional materials and glass plates are being used as flooring materials. The fact that treated glass can have high tensile strength and resist high compressive forces make it ideal for these applications.

Additionally, the transparent nature of glass allows improved aesthetic benefits in construction, e.g. greater amounts of natural light can enter buildings, it can be used to create a more interesting interior by visually linking areas through the use of features such as glass bricks (see Figure 4.6.6).

Figure 4.6.6 Glass bricks

Image by Cate Scott

The Grand Canyon Skywalk in Arizona uses a cantilevered U-shaped glass walkway that protrudes 18.9m out from the canyon wall extending over a 1200m drop to allow visitors a unique experience. The glass walkway is composed of forty six panes, each of which consists of five layers of glass bonded together.

Further Reading

Stienstra, D. Ph.D. *Introduction to Design of Structural Ceramics*. David Rose-Hulman Institute of Technology.

4.7 COMPOSITES

4.7.1 Describe composites.

© IBO 2007

A composite represents a class of material whose properties derive from the combination of two or more materials that are bonded together such that each of the constituent materials contributes to an improvement in mechanical, physical, chemical or electrical properties.

Bone and wood represent examples of composites in nature. Bone is a composite of the ceramic Hydroxyapatite (calcium phosphate) and the natural polymer collagen, contained within a gel like matrix of protein. In bone, the collagen is present as long fibres, which provide a strong flexible structure in much the same way that individual fibres can be formed into a rope. Small crystals of Hydroxyapatite attached to the surface of the collagen fibres provide stiffness. In addition, the collagen fibres are arranged in concentric layers around a central blood vessel, with each layer of collagen contra laid, that is, arranged in opposite directions, as illustrated in Figure 4.7.1a. The structure formed has many similarities with that found in wood. Bone consequently exhibits the characteristics of strength and stiffness while retaining some flexibility.

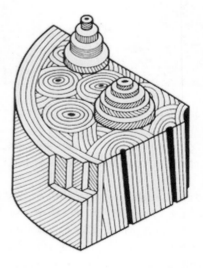

Figure 4.7.1a Schematic representation of the composite structure of bone.

One of the earliest man-made composite materials was straw reinforced bricks. At a much later time, cement, gravel, and steel bars were combined to form reinforced concrete. Development of thin fibres and thermosetting polymers led to the creation of fibre-reinforced materials such as glass reinforced polymers (GRP). Much more recent examples are carbon-polymer and metal matrix composites.

Increasingly, composites are being employed to provide improved properties, increase efficiency, reduce costs and provide additional functionality.

Sporting equipment manufacturers have employed modern composite materials for some time for their improved strength-to-weight ratio and stiffness compared to conventional materials. Typical applications include bicycle frames, golf clubs, tennis racquets, (Figure 4.7.1b), rowing skulls, etc.

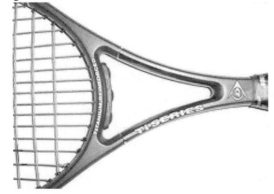

Figure 4.7.1b Composites in sporting equipment

Image by Tamara Bell

Similarly, aerospace industries have invested heavily in composites to reduce weight while maintaining or improving material performance. The Boeing 787 Dreamliner for example, contains over 50% composite material (80% by volume), and for the first time uses a carbon fibre composite to form the fuselage of a commercial jet. The fuselage is constructed from carbon fibre composite barrels, approximately 6m in length. An indication of the extent of composites within the Boeing 787 is provided in Figure 4.7.1c.

■ Carbon laminate
■ Carbon sandwich
■ Other composites
■ Aluminum
■ Titanium

Figure 4.7.1c Composites in the Boeing 787 Dreamliner

The incorporation of the materials into a composite can occur in a number of ways but, generally speaking, there are three basic categories of composite:

- laminar
- fibre-reinforced
- particle reinforced.

Particle reinforced composites consist of a relatively soft matrix in which hard particles of roughly uniform dimensions are embedded. As illustrated in Figure 4.7.1d, these particles may be symmetrical or asymmetrical in shape. The particle reinforced composites generally exhibit isotropic properties, that is, their physical and mechanical properties such as stiffness, strength, conductivity etc., are the same in all directions.

Figure 4.7.1d Particle reinforced composites

Composites within this group include:
- concrete in which aggregate is mixed in a cement matrix composed of sand, water and cement (Figure 4.7.1e)
- cemented carbide in which a ceramic such as tungsten carbide (WC) is contained within a Cobalt matrix (Figure 4.7.1f)
- spheroidal Graphite (S.G.) cast iron (Figure 4.7.1g).

Figure 4.7.1e Concrete in which aggregate is mixed in a cement matrix of sand water and cement

Image courtesy Tamara Bell

Figure 4.7.1f A photomicrograph of a tungsten carbide (WC) cutting tip showing its composite nature in which of Tungsten carbide particles (light grey irregular shapes) are embedded in a cobalt matrix (dark grey).

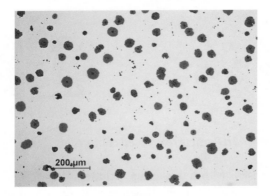

Figure 4.7.1g Spheroidal Graphite Cast iron (also known as ductile iron) consisting of spherical particles of graphite in an iron matrix

Image courtesy Phillip Metcalfe

This group can be further subdivided based on the size of the particulate involved into dispersion-strengthened materials in which powders are mixed and formed to near net shape using powder metallurgy techniques under conditions of high temperature and pressure. An example of this would be TD-Nickel a superalloy that incorporates Thorium particles dispersed in a Nickel matrix.

Fibre-reinforced composites contain a reinforcing material that is in the form of a fibre. These fibres may be relatively short or of a continuous nature, and may be aligned in specific directions throughout the matrix or be randomly oriented, as indicated in Figure 4.7.1h. In contrast to the particle reinforced composites, the fibre reinforced composite may be anisotropic, that is, exhibit directionality in terms of their physical and mechanical properties, depending on the presence of any directionality of the fibres. Carbon fibre and glass fibre reinforced composites belong to this group.

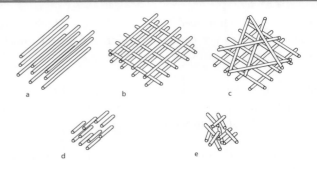

Figure 4.7.1h Schematic representation of different fibre arrangements within the matrix. a) continuous, unidirectional; b) continuous, orthogonal layers; c) continuous, multiple fibres; d) discontinuous, unidirectional, e) discontinuous, random orientation

Reinforced concrete represents a commonly utilised composite material of the continuous fibre, orthogonal orientation type, where steel rods are embedded into a matrix of concrete, as shown in Figure 4.7.1i. The composite formed results in a material that has both the compressive strength of concrete, with improved tensile strength due to the presence of the steel reinforcing.

Figure 4.7.1i Concrete reinforcing rods

Concrete composites have also been produced using short discrete fibres and are known as fibre reinforced concretes (FRC). These composites incorporate the fibres randomly throughout the concrete to increases its structural integrity. The fibre used can vary from steel to glass, depending on the properties desired.

Figure 4.7.1j An example of Fibre Reinforced Concrete (FRC) using sisal fibre as the reinforcement.

Other composites within the fibre reinforced group include free machining steels, in which high additions of sulphur are made in order to promote the formation of a large number of Manganese Sulphide (MnS) inclusions during solidification. During the rolling process these inclusions are deformed into fibres (known as stringers) aligned with the rolling direction, as shown in Figure 4.7.1k. During machining operations these fibres act as positions of weakness that allow the swarf created during machining to break into small pieces keeping the cutting tool free of tangled swarf.

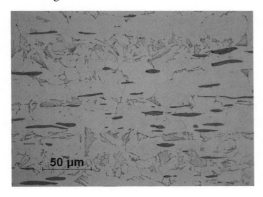

Figure 4.7.1k Free machining steel represent a composite containing discrete unidirectional fibres (inclusions) of Manganese sulphide within a matrix of ferrite and pearlite

Another material containing numerous discrete aligned fibres is the largely obsolete material wrought iron, in which slag from the manufacturing process remained within the iron matrix, as can be seen in the photomicrograph presented in Figure 4.7.1l.

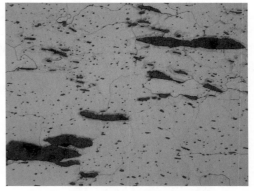

Figure 4.7.1l Photomicrograph of Wrought Iron, showing the elongated slag inclusions (dark) in an iron matrix.

Image by Phillip Metcalfe

Traditionally, engine blocks have been made from flake graphite, grey cast iron castings. However, the relatively high weight of cast iron has led to the increasing use of lighter weight materials such as cast aluminium, often with cast iron inserts as cylinder liners to accommodate the extra wear requirements of this region and to reduce friction. Figure 4.7.1m shows a typical microstructure consisting of randomly oriented flakes of graphite in an iron matrix.

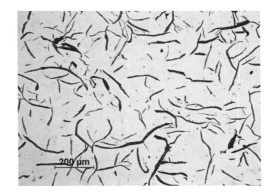

Figure 4.7.1m Flake (Grey) Cast Iron

Image by Phillip Metcalfe

Laminar composites, as the name suggests, consist of materials constructed in layers. The materials of this group are particularly diverse and include natural materials such as teeth and bone, along with man made products such as pencils, plywood and laminated glass, operations such as plating and coating, and surface chemistry processes such as carburising and nitriding.

Carburising involves the high temperature diffusion of carbon, from a carbon rich atmosphere into the surface of a low carbon steel. The depth and amount of carbon introduced is controlled by the furnace atmosphere, temperature and time for diffusion. Through carburisation, a hard, high strength, wear resistant surface is produced on a lower strength but generally tougher base. The difference in carbon content is revealed following polishing and etching of the surface, as shown in Figure 4.7.1o.

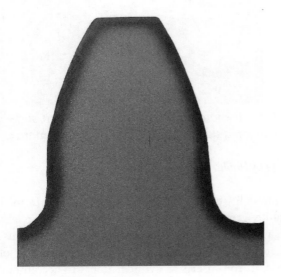

Figure 4.7.1o Carburised gear tooth

Image by Mitchell Metcalfe

Plain bearings are used to provide a low friction surface for crankshaft journals and consist of a number of layers comprising of a low carbon steel backing layer for strength and a facing layer of Babbitt metal, typically a Pb-Sn-Sb alloy. Intermediate layers are often also present as indicated in Figure 4.7.1p.

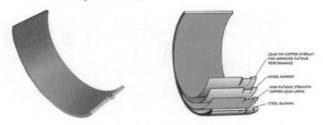

Figure 4.7.1p Schematic representation of a plain bearing of the 'Trimetal' type showing the various layers of metal in its construction

GLARE is a five-layer laminar composite developed by Alcoa and is an acronym for GLAss REinforced Fibre Metallic Laminate (FML). Illustrated in Figure 4.7.1q, it consists of a five-layer composite of aluminium alloy sheets, approximately 0.4mm thick and sheets of fibre/epoxy prepreg, approximately 0.125mm thick.

GLARE was used to form parts of the Airbus A380 upper outer hull. Although more expensive to produce than the aluminium it replaces, Glare is said to offer significant weight savings and improved mechanical properties.

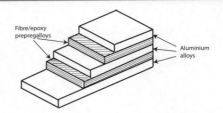

Figure 4.7.1q Schematic representation of GLARE

Smart glass or Switchable Glass is a composite that consists of a thin central laminate of fluid containing a randomly oriented suspension of rod-like particles. This laminate is sandwiched between two layers of glass. When no voltage is present the random orientation of the suspended particles prevents the transmission of light so that the panel looks dark. When a voltage is applied, however, alignment of the particles occurs, allowing the transmission of light and a switch to transparency, see Figure 4.7.1r.

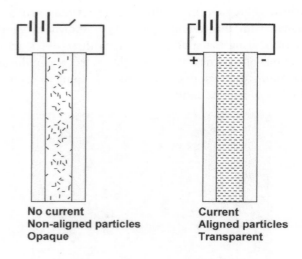

Figure 4.7.1r Smart or Switchable Glass

4.7.2 Define fibre.

A fibre (also spelled fiber) is a continuous filament or discrete length of material possessing a large aspect ratio, that is, a large dimensional difference between its length and cross section.

4.7.3 Describe the matrix composition of composites.

The matrix of a material is generally defined as the principal continuous constituent present, into which other constituents are bound or embedded.

4.7.4 Explain that new materials can be designed by enhancing the properties of traditional materials to develop new properties in the composite material.

© IBO 2007

By combining materials with different properties into a composite, a new material is created that can be designed to fulfil specific requirements.

4.7.5 Describe a smart material.

4.7.6 Identify a range of smart materials.

© IBO 2007

Smart materials have one or more properties that can be dramatically altered, for example, transparency, viscosity, volume, conductivity. The property that can be altered influences the application of the smart material.

Smart materials include piezoelectric materials, magneto-rheostatic materials, electro-rheostatic materials and shape memory alloys. Some everyday items are already incorporating smart materials (coffee pots, cars, eye-glasses, tennis racquets), and the number of applications for them is growing steadily.

4.7.7 Describe a piezoelectric material.

© IBO 2007

A piezoelectric material is a material that responds to the application of an applied stress by producing a small electrical discharge. Similarly when an electric current is passed through a piezoelectric material a shape change occurs in response. By reversing the polarity of the electrical signal the shape again changes. An AC current can therefore produce a shape change about the rest state of the material. Piezoelectric materials are widely used as sensors in different environments. Quartz (SiO_2) is a commonly used piezoelectric material, and has been extensively used in watches. A number of ceramics are also used such as barium titanate ($BaTiO_3$) and lead zirconate titanate ($Pb[Zr_xTi_{1-x}]O_3$), known as PZT.

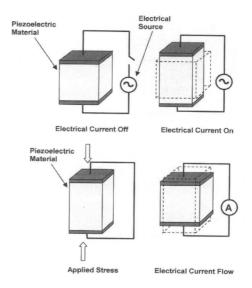

Figure 4.7.7a Illustrations of a piezoelectric material responding to an electric potential by changing shape (top), and producing a current as a response to an applied stress (bottom)

4.7.8 Outline one application of piezoelectric materials.

© IBO 2007

Piezoelectric materials are widely used for the thickness testing of pipes and vessels and the detection of internal flaws by ultrasonic testing.

In ultrasonic testing, an alternating voltage is supplied to a probe containing a piezoelectric crystal. The voltage stimulates the crystal to change dimensions (vibrate), producing sound waves of a defined frequency. When the probe is placed on the test surface the sound waves travel into the material and are reflected back from the other side of the test piece and from any internal discontinuities.

When these returning sound waves reach the probe surface, the vibrations stress the piezoelectric crystal sufficiently to produce an electrical voltage in response. The initial sound pulse and the returning signal are recorded on an oscillograph screen allowing visual interpretation by a technician.

Figure 4 .7.8 shows a typical ultrasonic test unit along with an assortment of probes. Depending on the material and construction under test, one or two probes may be used, as illustrated.

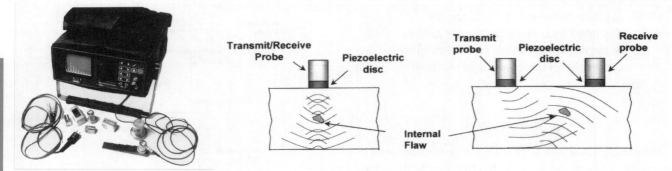

Figure 4.7.8 Ultrasonic test device and schematic representation of testing procedures

4.7.9 Describe electro-rheostatic and magneto-rheostatic materials.

© IBO 2007

Electro-rheostatic (ER) and magneto-rheostatic (MR) materials are fluids that can undergo changes in their viscosity, becoming semi-solid when exposed to an electric or magnetic field respectively. When the applied field is removed, the materials return to their original fluid state.

These materials are most commonly colloidal suspensions within oil. Because of this, one of many considerations in their use is the length of time the particles remain in suspension. As a general rule, as the particle size decreases, time in suspension increases.

The shear yield strength of an ER fluid is determined by the strength of the applied electric field, such that varying the field strength can control the viscosity. Similar to electro-rheostatic fluids, the shear yield strength of magneto-rheostatic (MR) fluids is determined by the strength of the applied magnetic field, such that varying the field strength can control the viscosity.

The ER and MR fluid must satisfy a number of criteria:

- low toxicity
- non-abrasive
- non-corrosive
- long storage life
- long working life
- high boiling point
- low freezing point
- particles must remain as a colloidal suspension and not settle out.

An example of an ER fluid is one containing Lithium Polymethacrylate particles in paraffin or silicon oil, while small ferromagnetic particle such as particles of Carbonyl Iron have been used in MR fluids.

The major advantage of MR fluids is that they can resist large forces, while ER fluids have the advantage that relatively small actuating elements can be developed.

4.7.10 Outline one application of electro-rheostatic materials and one application of magneto-rheostatic materials.

© IBO 2007

The control over viscosity has allowed the ER and MR fluids to find uses in clutches, hydraulic valves and shock absorbers. The 2002 Cadillac Seville STS and second generation Audi TT automobiles have used MR fluids in the suspension system, while the National Museum of Emerging Science in Tokyo, Japan has installed MR fluid devices throughout the building to reduce shock loading from high winds and seismic activity (see Terry Stephens (2003). *Special dampers may shake up engineering field.* http://djc.com/news/ae/11151055.html).

Potential uses include suggestions for medical devices to prevent sleep apnea, in which the wind-pipe closes during sleep, and devices to deliver cardiac massage. Haptic applications such as a Braille Tablet and gloves providing tactile stimulus to accompany computer generated scenarios (see Jennifer Ouellette (2004). Smart fluids move into the marketplace: Magneto- and electro-rheological fluids find new uses. http://www.aip.org/tip/INPHFA/vol-9/iss-6/p14.html).

4.7.11 Describe shape memory alloys (SMAs).

© IBO 2007

SMAs are metals that exhibit pseudo-elasticity and shape memory effect due to rearrangement of the atomic lattice. Discovered in the 1930s, the shape memory alloys represent a group of materials that are capable of changing shape or size in a predetermined manner by undergoing a solid-state phase change at a defined temperature. Despite creating a great deal of interest, these alloys remained largely a laboratory curiosity until the 1960s, when the NiTi alloy Nitinol (an acronym of the Nickel and Titanium Naval Ordinance Laboratory) was produced. Due to its excellent mechanical properties and biocompatibility, Nitinol has since become one of the most widely used shape memory alloys. Nitinol is nonmagnetic and consist of almost equal amounts of Ni and Ti in a simple cubic lattice arrangement.

One of the defining characteristics of the shape memory alloys is pseudo elasticity.

If a shape memory alloy is in the stable lattice arrangement of the austenite phase, and is exposed to a mechanical stress, slip can occur leading to distortion of the lattice and the formation of martensite. Normally a reduction in temperature would be required to achieve this change, but under the influence of an applied stress, martensite formation can occur without the involvement of a temperature change and is referred to as deformation martensite. This change in structure is accompanied by an apparent non-linear deformation, typically associated with plastic deformation.

When the applied stress is removed, however, the atomic lattice returns to the austenite phase and the material returns to its original shape. Figure 4.7.11a illustrates this phenomenon, in which an applied stress essentially increases the temperature at which martensite will form and shows the reversible change back to austenite on the removal of the applied stress.

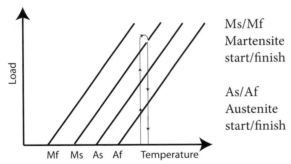

Figure 4.7.11a Load diagram of the pseudo-elastic effect. [Shape memory alloys. http://www.cs.ualberta. ca/~database/MEMS/sma mems/sma.html]

Pseudo elasticity can be expressed symbolically as:

Austenitic Structure + force (stimulus)
leads to
Martensitic Structure - force (stimulus)
leads back to
Austenitic Structure

Shape memory alloys (SMA) also exhibit pseudo-elasticity by way of a reversible martensite transformation. In this case, however, removal of the applied stress does not result in the material returning to the austenite phase and its original shape. This change requires moderate heating up to approximately 100 °C.

At elevated temperatures these alloys have an austenitic structure that is relatively strong. On cooling these alloys undergo a phase transformation to martensite, which is relatively soft. The unique character of these alloys is seen when the alloy is formed to shape in the austenitic condition and then cooled to martensite. If another forming operation is then performed while it is in the martensitic condition, changing the shape of the material, it will maintain that shape until reheated to austenite at which time the alloy reverts to its previous shape.

Some alloys even have the ability to change back when the temperature has again been reduced resulting in a two-way memory effect. These alloys can therefore cycle between shapes with changes in temperature.

A number of shape memory alloys have been developed, which operate at a variety of different temperatures, as indicated below in Figure 4.7.11b. Precise control of the material composition is required to ensure the reliable reproduction of the transformation temperatures.

Alloy	Transformation Range °C	Transformation Hysteresis °C
Ag-Cd	-190 to -50	~15
Cu-Al-Ni	-140 to -100	~35
Cu-Zn	-180 to -10	~10
Ni-Al	-180 to 100	~10
Ni-Ti	-50 to 110	~30
FeMnS	-200 to 150	~100

Figure 4.7.11b Transformation temperature ranges for a selection of SMA's, ASM Handbook

The shape memory effect can be illustrated as shown in Figure 4.7.11c in which the phase changes have been represented at each stage, along with the changes that would be seen with an arterial stent made from the shape memory alloy Nitinol. Nitinol being a non-ferrous alloy of an almost equal mixture of nickel and titanium and deriving its name as an acronym of the Nickel and Titanium Naval Ordinance Laboratory, where it was developed in the 1960s. Nitinol is non-magnetic and exhibits excellent mechanical properties and biocompatibility. It is used increasingly in products such as stents, medical staples, guide-wires, orthodontic arch-wires and components of eyeglass frames.

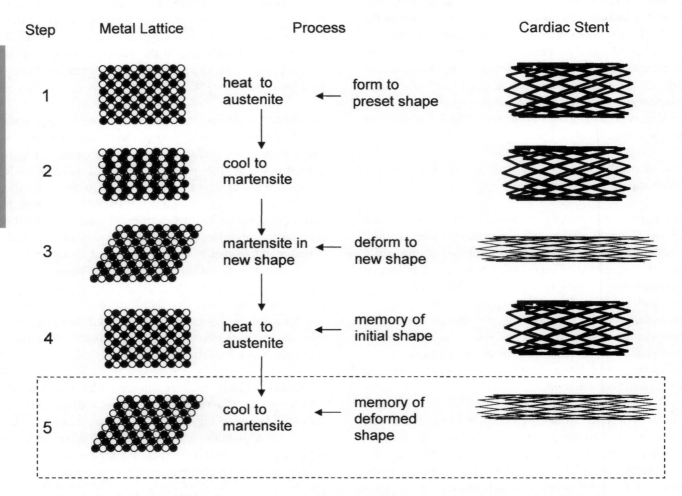

Step	Metal Lattice	Process		Cardiac Stent
1		heat to austenite	← form to preset shape	
2		cool to martensite		
3		martensite in new shape	← deform to new shape	
4		heat to austenite	← memory of initial shape	
5		cool to martensite	← memory of deformed shape	

Figure 4.7.11e Illustration of the stages of transformation in an SMA. Stages 1 to 4 represent a one-way shape memory, while the addition of stage 5 represents a two-way shape memory

4.7.12 Identify applications of SMAs.

© IBO 2007

SMAs are considered to be passive response type devices, as they do not require separate sensors to operate, but rather react directly in response to the external stimulus, as opposed to the ER and MR fluids and piezoelectric materials that can be considered active response devices.

In this capacity of passive response, the pseudo-elastic materials have found use as eyeglass frames and antennas for mobile phones.

Shape memory alloys have been used in products such as electrical connectors, safety taps to prevent hot water scalding children, vascular stents to repair blocked arteries, airflow controls, orthodontic arch wires and components of eyeglass frames.

The excellent biocompatibility of Nitinol combined with its non-magnetic nature and excellent mechanical properties have resulted in its extensive use in biomedical applications such as coronary stents.

Some use of SMAs has been made in passive dampening systems to mitigate earthquake damage. The roof of the St Francis Basilica in Assisi has been joined to the wall with Nitinol anchors consisting of wire bundles that stretch in response to vibrations, dissipating the seismic loads.

Further Reading

Ouellette, J. (2004). *Smart fluids move into the marketplace: Magneto- and electro-rheological fluids find new uses.* http://www.aip.org/tip/INPHFA/vol-9/iss-6/p14.html

Stephens, T. (2003). *Special dampers may shake up engineering field.* http://djc.com/news/ae/11151055.html

Exercises

1. Glasses are called amorphous because they:
    A.   are transparent
    B.   are highly structured
    C.   have no crystalline structure
    D.   have low coefficients of expansion.

2. Fluids that can undergo changes in their viscosity, becoming semi-solid when exposed to an electric field respectively are known as:

    A.   piezoelectric
    B.   electro-magnetic
    C.   electro-rheostatic
    D.   magneto-rheostatic.

3. Thermosetting polymers are difficult to recycle because of their:

    A.   strength
    B.   3D bonding
    C.   linear chains
    D.   insulative properties.

4. A material's ability to resist cracking is called:

    A.   strength
    B.   ductility
    C.   toughness
    D.   malleability.

5. Explain how alloying may increase the strength of a material.

6. List reasons why carburising may be chosen over other hardening processes.

7. Discuss why laminated glass is preferred for car windscreens over tempered glass.

8. Outline why superalloys find application in diverse fields such as aeronautics and petrochemical industries.

9. Discuss the use of thermosoftening polymers from environmental and manufacturing perspectives.

10. Describe why man-made LVL is a popular choice over natural timber in construction.

PRODUCT DEVELOPMENT

CONTENTS

Prior to the Industrial Revolution manufacturing was carried out by hand. Craftsmen were held in the highest esteem, their pursuits and products seen as a gift from God. They were often portrayed as 'master craftsmen' (see title image).

The Industrial Revolution saw a period of societal and technological upheaval. Not all of the changes were welcomed as cottage workers saw their livelihoods disappear and populations moved from dispersed agrarian lifestyles to crowded polluted cities with little or no infrastructure. Resistance to 'progress' appeared in the form of the group known as 'Luddites' who attempted to sabotage factories and halt production.

Since the Industrial Revolution, mechanization, automation and, more recently, digital technologies, have revolutionized manufacturing and the workplace.

Figure Intro 1 Boston Manufacturing Company 1813

5.1 MANUFACTURING TECHNIQUES

5.1.1	Define manufacturing technique.

The term manufacturing comes from the Latin manu factura, or 'making by hand' and is the organised use of tools and labour to create new products. More commonly, manufacturing is known as the range of industrial and craft processes used to fabricate products.

5.1.2	Outline the techniques of moulding, casting, weaving, fusing, stitching, cutting, machining, abrading, using adhesives and using fasteners.
5.1.3	Describe how the techniques in 5.1.2 relate to different materials.

Moulding is the process of manufacturing by shaping pliable raw materials using a rigid shape, called a pattern. The material to be moulded may be naturally pliable, a liquid suspension or made flexible upon the addition of heat, in some cases to the point of melting. Moulding covers such technologies as injection moulding, hand forming, thermoforming, vacuum forming, blow moulding and extrusion moulding. Food, metals, polymers, ceramics and non-metals etc. may all be moulded.

Casting involves transforming materials into a liquid form before pouring (casting) them into a mould or pre-prepared cavity for solidification or setting. Metals, food (jelly, chocolate), plastics (resins), composites (metal matrix composites) and ceramics (glass and concrete) are all suitable materials to cast. Neither timber nor textiles lend themselves to this approach.

Figure 5.1.2a Metal casting

Weaving is the process of passing fibres or threads of material under and over each other, (most often at right angles, called warp and weft) in an interlacing fashion. Textiles (cotton, linen, wool), metals (woven wire jewellery, fence panels), ceramics (fibreglass mat), plastics (outdoor furniture, mats), composites (woven fabrics within resin matrices) and timber (cane, rataan, veneers, wicker weave) all respond to weaving. Food may be plaited as seen in pastries. Weaving appears in Egyptian writings and biblical references and it is thought that forms of weaving existed in the Palaeolithic era.

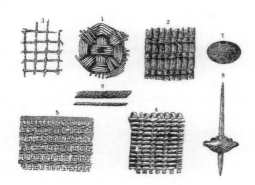

Figure 5.1.2b Prehistoric weaving samples

Fusing or fusion involves the joining of materials through the process of melting, mixing and solidification. The base materials alone may be locally fused, or an additional filler material may be added to the site to provide bulk and reinforcement. Fusion techniques include but are not limited to manual metal arc, metal inert gas, tungsten

inert gas, friction, laser, electron beam, electro-resistance, plastic and spot welding. The technique chosen for fusing materials is dependent on materials to be joined, their thickness and the load specifications of the design. The process may or may not involve the addition of pressure. Fusing may be used in the textiles, polymer, food and metal fabrication industries.

Figure 5.1.2c Fusion welding of metal

Stitching or lacing involves the joining together of materials through the use of fastening threads or loops. Textiles lend themselves to stitching, but their constituent materials may be sourced from natural, synthetic plastic (Kevlar) or ceramic fibres (fibreglass). Many threads and yarns are also based on polymeric materials. Stitched fabrics may then also be incorporated into the fabrication of composite materials.

Metals may be 'stitched' using a process also known as metalocking. It refers to a technique developed to secure cracked metals together that would otherwise be difficult to repair by welding. The use of 'plugs' or 'stitching pins' inserted into pre-drilled holes lock the sections together.

Food and timber do not readily lend themselves to stitching as a manufacturing process.

Cutting is the act of separating or severing materials most often using a shearing process. Laser or plasma cutters however work on melting or vapourising of the parent materials, while water cutting jets use an abrasive action.

Machining is a subtractive process covering a variety of power-driven methods for removing materials. Processes include turning, routing, milling, drilling, boring and countersinking etc. Timber, metal, plastics, composites and ceramics all respond to machining.

In metal machining the process of cutting involves plastic deformation where the metal is softer than the cutting tool and the chip rides up and over the tool as it is removed. If the same tooling were used for carbon fibre reinforced plastics (CFRP), such as those used to produce modern aircraft, the material would shatter. CFRPs have a range of specific requirements including; diamond or carbide-based tooling, specific tool geometry and material support jigs to minimize vibration and delamination.

Machining may be controlled manually or using a computer through the use of CNC (Computer Numerical Control) systems. Computer-aided ultrasonic milling is an example of such a process now used for advanced materials including carbides, glasses and ceramics.

Abrading involves the physical wearing away of surfaces by means of rubbing, friction or erosion. The harder the material the more resistant it is to abrasion. Processes employed depend on the material to be abraded. Abrasives may be bonded into:

- rigid tools such as abrasive wheels
- directed by fluid jets including sand blasting
- suspended in a liquid e.g. water jet cutting of ceramics (concrete) and polymer matrix composites.

Adhesives are materials that act as bonding agents between surfaces to meet the technical definition it must flow at the time of application. Mechanisms for adhesion include: absorption, electrostatic attraction and diffusion; most adhesives exhibit a combination of these.

Fastening or joining materials mechanically through the use of techniques such as screws, rivets, bolts, pins, clips, nails, press-studs and snaps has been in common use for hundreds of years. Archimedes is credited with the invention of the screw thread in the 3rd Century BC, but it was not until 1841 that Sir Joseph Whitworth, proposed the introduction of standard fastener sizes to the Institution of Civil Engineers. The major advantages associated with the use of fasteners is that they are quick and easy to use, dissimilar materials may be joined and they allow for quick and easy assembly or disassembly of product components. However, most require a hole to be drilled into the materials to be joined. This requires additional design considerations including materials selection, weakening or stress raising, disruption to an otherwise smooth surface.

| 5.1.4 | Discuss advantages and disadvantages of using the techniques to manufacture products. |

© IBO 2007

Moulding covers a huge array of technologies. Depending on the technology employed, material appropriateness varies as do the final properties of the moulded object. Some of the more popular processes include:

- compression moulding - for plastics and rubber. The forcing of uncured rubber into a preformed mould while applying heat, cures and shapes the product
- injection moulding - for mass produced articles of a good quality finish. Polymers and metals are injection moulded by forcing them into a metal die
- blow moulding - often used for hollow plastic or glass mass produced containers, however, wall thickness can, on occasions, be difficult to control.

Casting is a very economical process for mass production. Objects may be produced quickly to high tolerances using a wide range of materials. It is less economical for one off production. Sand cast objects require post-machining and cast objects, although good in compression, are often quite weak in tension. Defects such as porosity and inclusions also require careful monitoring

Weaving offers the advantages of simple cottage industry production technologies through to highly sophisticated computer operated looms. Materials vary from natural organic fibres to high-tech polymers. Fibre choice, weave pattern and manufacturing technologies all affect the properties of the final product, but also range from stiff rigid structures to flexible, stretchy fabrics.

Fusing or welding is a permanent process. Disassembly of welded items requires breaking the join and most probably the product itself. Manufacturers require specialized equipment, skilled tradesmen and specially prepared environments for welding.

Stitching is a reversible process. In most situations, seams and joins can be unstitched for repairs or alterations. Manufacturers may employ unskilled labour or mechanize the process. Some materials, however, can be damaged by the stitching process and may require replacement if stitching has to be undone.

Cutting technologies are heavily reliant on the technique used and which material is to be cut. The essential issues relate to wastage of material, quality of finish and any heat generated that may distort or damage surfaces.

Machining is a subtraction process. Pieces machined may be produced to very fine tolerances. Skilled workers are required to operate machines, or technicians to monitor automated processes. In both cases, expensive capital equipment is required.

Abrading may be used to remove material, shape an article, smooth or add texture to a surface. Materials suitable for abrasion include: ceramics, concrete, glass, polymers, metals and composites.

Adhesives, depending on their bonding action, may allow for the separation of parts with little or no damage to the original surfaces. They are commonly used to join thin or dissimilar materials and don't employ heat which may cause distortion or damage. Some adhesives, composed of metallic flakes, are even electrically conductive, cure at room temperature and cause no damage to heat sensitive componentry.

Further reading

Hollaway, L. C. (2005). *Advances in adhesive joining of dissimilar materials.*

Eagar, T. W. (1990). *Challenges in Joining Emerging Materials.* Pergamon Press. Montreal. Canada.

5.2 CRAFT PRODUCTION

> 5.2.1 Define craft production and one-off production.
>
> © IBO 2007

Craft manufacturing or one-off production involves the production of single unique individual products.

> 5.2.2 Describe why most products were manufactured by craft techniques prior to the Industrial Revolution.
>
> © IBO 2007

Before the Industrial Revolution, manufacturing, known as craft production, was centred around local craftsmen in medieval villages. Young apprentices, often serving as long as seven years, supported small, sometimes home-based, workshops driven by skilled artisans. Much of the machinery in use had changed little since the Middle Ages. The machines that were used were small and generally either hand, animal powered or powered by wind or running water. At this point, there was little need to generate a surplus other than insurance against crop failure, or inclement weather. Neighbouring villages often produced the same crops so trade, while local, was still minimal. The town's craftsmen included bakers, blacksmiths and carpenters. The village, to a large degree, was self-sufficient with products made from local materials, manufactured on site and repaired within the village. Energy was generated either by hand or animal

power. In some instances earlier Roman-design water wheels were employed.

As transport routes were developed and improved, village craftsmen such as weavers started to buy additional raw materials to be spun into thread or woven into cloth and be sold to the emerging local merchants. Cottage labourers selling their work to merchants in an organised fashion has been termed 'proto-industrialization'. Craft products soon became tradeable commodities, and cottage workers who owned their own equipment either dealt directly with the local market, or used merchants to trade farther afield.

The opportunities of increased trade promised by improved transport contributed to the need for changes in the means of production. The main change involved the mechanization of processing and the centralization of production in large factories located in the cities. Many smaller, more diversified operations, (cottage industries), were no longer able to compete and closed. These changes led to large population shifts from the country to the cities.

> 5.2.3 Explain the advantages and disadvantages of craft production.
>
> 5.2.4 Discuss the importance of craft production for developed and developing countries.
>
> © IBO 2007

Craft production generally involves manual skills, where the skill of the artisan determines the quality of one off unique pieces. While often slow, this method was often locally based and allowed clients to converse directly with the manufacturer to produce customized items. Because craftsmen manufacture a project from start to finish they may be required to have a variety of skills. One off production is often used for prototype development and testing, before moving to larger scales of production. Today, master craftsmen produce individually designed pieces tailored to clients' requests These pieces exhibit both high quality and cost. Examples of this approach include: haute couture fashion, jewellery and customized furniture.

In developing countries one off production is still viable due to the low cost of labour and lack of distribution infrastructure. Locally based artisans met the needs of local clients with appropriate technologies and available materials.

Further Reading
Crafts, N. (2002). *Productivity and Growth in the Industrial Revolution.* London.

5.3 MECHANIZATION

5.3.1 Define mechanization.

Mechanization involves the introduction of machinery into a process with the intent of automating the process to some degree. In its simplest form, it replaces hand-crafting operations with machine based tooling.

5.3.2 Describe how the availability of new sources of power in the Industrial Revolution led to the introduction of mechanization.

The centrepiece of the industrial Revolution was the availability of new sources of power and the accompanying mechanization. Before the Industrial Revolution, humans or animals supplied power. James Watt's improved Newcomen engine proved to be an effective and reliable source of power. Steam engines soon found applications in fields other than mining and boosted productivity in the booming textiles industry. While waterpower was still used as a source of power, steam engines provided more flexibility and allowed industry to spread across the countryside, away from sources of running water.

See Option D.3, Evolution of textile processing for specific reference to textiles, automation and the Industrial Revolution.

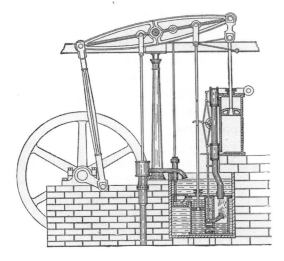

Figure 5.3.2 Watt condensing steam engine

5.3.3 Define assembly-line production.

5.3.4 Explain the relevance of assembly-line production to mechanization.

Assembly-line production is an industrial process used in mass production. It involves the movement of the product to be manufactured from station to station, often using conveyor belts or other transportation systems. The product moves past workers, tooling and machinery stations until the product is complete.

Often referred to as 'reductionism', assembly line workers were typically involved in work reduced to simple, repetitive tasks that had no association with the production of a final product. People worked to a 'rhythm' but were involved in tasks devoid of any interest, thought or problem solving. With production methods and operations standardized workers were often deskilled compared to the craftsmen of previous times. As mechanization increased, many of the tasks simply became machine tending.

While Henry Ford was not the first to use the assembly line, he is credited with refining the controlled movement of standardized parts and revolutionizing mass production. Labeled as 'Fordism', this allowed the mass production of vehicles of a consistent quality. Consumers at this point, however, had their purchase options limited as defined by Ford's legendary quote, "My customers can also get any color, as long as it's black." Figure 5.3.3 shows workers on a Ford assembly line in 1930

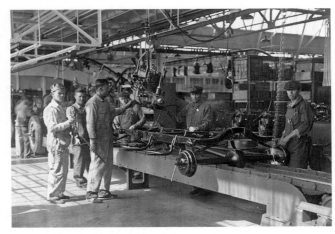

Figure 5.3.3 Ford assembly line (1930)

5.3.5 Outline two advantages and two disadvantages of mechanizing a production process.

© IBO 2007

As a general rule, mechanization has allowed for the production of cheaper products, faster, and of an improved quality. Mechanized assembly lines also removed much of the physical burden placed on workers. However, mechanization tends to introduce tedious, repetitive work that in some instances becomes little more than machine tending. In many situations workers are deskilled. Mechanization of any process tends also to reduce the workforce required.

5.3.6 Define batch production and mass production.

5.3.7 Compare batch production and mass production in a mechanized production system.

© IBO 2007

Batch production fits between craft production and mass production. In batch production, a limited quantity of the product or 'batch' is produced. Many batches may be produced in succession, but flexibility exists in between batches to make modifications to the product or change the product batch completely. An example of batch production occurs in bakeries. In simple terms, mass production involves the production of high product volumes through the use of machinery.

Batch production is often a technique used by smaller enterprises that do not have the resources to proceed to full-scale mass production, or need the cash flow to maintain viability. Batch production can allow quicker responses to individual clients and the marketplace. Mass production lines tend to be less flexible. Their efficiencies come from large volume productions runs with little or no variation. The high capital investment makes changing product an expensive exercise.

Further reading

Barlow, J. (1999). *From Craft Production to Mass Customisation? Customer-focused approaches to house building.*

5.4 AUTOMATION

5.4.1 Define automation.

© IBO 2007

Automation involves the replacement of human labour with mechanical, electronic or computer controlled machinery processes and systems that operate automatically or independently.

5.4.2 Describe how the development of computer and information technology in the 'technological revolution' led to the introduction of automation.

© IBO 2007

First mechanization, then automation, continued the evolution of factories. Productivity, quality control and costs per unit part all continued to improve. Coincidental with this came reductions in the workforce and human physical labour. Employment patterns changed from large numbers of unskilled workers to lesser numbers of machine tenders. Machine, process and system control also evolved from mechanical to electromechanical. Reliable electrical power now becomes an imperative to smooth operation of equipment.

The advent of the technological age, computers and numerical devices heralded new are more sophisticated control of machinery and processes. Robotic arms replaced human operators for movement of parts. They also completed complex and sometimes dangerous tasks with their ability to act in environments potentially hazardous to human health.

The introduction of computer aided design and manufacturing generated finer tolerances, more complex operations, faster production rates and the ability to work in dirty and dangerous environments. Computer control also removed the labour force from dirty, dull and dangerous operations.

5.4.3 Define computer-aided manufacture (CAM) and computer numerical control (CNC).

© IBO 2007

CAM is an acronym for computer aided, (assisted), manufacture. Referring to a range of computer based technologies that assisting designers, engineers and manufacturers. These technologies are applied not only to assist with product design, but with manufacturing, stocktaking and life cycle assessment etc.

CNC stands for computer numerical control. CNC systems employ machine tools that read computer code to control their operations. CNC machines offer increased productivity and flexibility. See Option C Cad/CAM for more details.

> ### 5.4.4 Explain how CAD, CAM and CNC contribute to an automated production system.

The emergence of CAD/CAM has had a major impact on manufacturing, by automating many processes and procedures. Although capital investments may be high, it has significantly reduced costs and improved both productivity and quality. Some typical applications where CAD/CAM may enhance automation include:

- quality control and inspection
- process planning, efficient workflow and effective scheduling
- design of complex dies and moulds for casting, with preprogrammed shrinkage allowances
- programming for NC, CNC, and industrial robots for automating processes, holding or transporting components.

> ### 5.4.5 Define just-in-time (JIT) and just-in-case (JIC).
>
> ### 5.4.6 Explain the advantages of JIT and JIC to manufacturing.

Just-in-time management systems aim to eliminate or at least reduce all forms of waste caused as a by-product of manufacturing, while simultaneously improving product quality and productivity. All stages of production from procuring of raw materials to product inventory and distribution is managed on a needs or just-in-time basis. To be successful, JIT requires careful predictions of need throughout the production chain. This can only be maintained through smooth, effective and efficient quality assurance at each stage of production. Also called lean manufacturing, JIT has been commonly adopted by carmakers and budget computer manufacturers. The advantages of JIT manufacturing include the prevention of waste and overproduction. Overheads are reduced as

are warehousing space and inventory held. Improved production management and quality control systems, all lead to an improved return on investment. Carefully timed and linked transport networks also improve product distribution.

Just-in-case can be considered to be the opposite of just-in-time. Large inventories are held ready to be used 'if or when' they may be required. Just-in-case is more of a traditional approach to manufacturing. This excess capacity to manufacture, not only includes materials and components but extends to the workforce and manufacturing capacity. The advantages of JIC manufacturing include its ability to respond better to unpredictable spikes in demand.

> ### 5.4.7 Define mass customization.

Mass customization employs flexible manufacturing systems, (often computer driven), to bring the efficiencies of mass production to short job runs even down to single orders. The advantages include low costs and fast production times. In some ways it is considered to be the opposite of mass production where large numbers of identical products are produced.

> ### 5.4.8 Outline how mass customization is changing the relationship between the manufacturer and the consumer.

Mass customization places the individual consumer in control. Rather than companies responding to market expectations, individuals tender their requests direct to the manufacturer. Coupled with online technologies, manufacturers can meet consumer demands from computers in their homes, where they can review products that are modified at the click of a mouse.

A clear example of mass customization coupled with online communication is Nike's ID program. Consumers can logon to the Nike website and customize the style, colour and any text additives of footwear while reviewing these changes on screen. The completed design can be purchased online and despatched to the consumer directly from the factory.

5.4.9 Discuss the impact of automation on working conditions.

Automation introduces significant advantages to the workforce but it also has its drawbacks. Machines should take over complex, repetitive operations in dangerous or dirty environments. In this manner they may relieve some tedium, but also reduce the need for physical strength from workers. Workers also have higher-level skills and training.

Along with these advantages appear of series of disadvantages including, reductions in the workforce, higher levels of stress as the complexity of work increases and production rates rise. Over-reliance on technology and an accompanying loss of physical craft skills can also be of concern for future generations. The workplace can also be void of social interaction as workers concentrate on tending equipment. With more input from machinery and technology, workers have less of a tendency to identify with a product or take pride in the quality of their work. This is particularly the case in piece-work, where the worker does not see the product through to completion.

5.4.10 Outline how automation has improved the type and range of products available to consumers.

Automation brings with it faster production times, reduced costs, finer tolerances, automated mass customization and near-perfect repeatability. Faster production rates also gives manufacturers the opportunity to change production runs more often, allowing for a diversity of product types.

Further Reading

Just-In-Time Manufacturing. (2006), AIDT

Lai, K. H. &. Cheng T. C. E. (2009). *Just-in-Time Logistics.* Gower Publishing. Aldershot England.

5.5 ECONOMIC CONSIDERATIONS

5.5.1 List the costs that contribute to the final cost of a product.

Costs that contribute to final product vary both in their type and relative value. The range of these costs includes but may not be limited to:

- marketing
- distribution
- transportation
- government taxes
- energy consumption
- overhead expenditures
- research and development
- capital costs (plant and machinery)
- warehousing and inventory storage
- profit margins value and price of raw materials
- time manufacturing (hourly rates for employees).

5.5.2 Define fixed costs and variable costs.

5.5.3 Identify the factors in 5.5.1 as fixed costs or variable costs.

Fixed costs do not vary with sales, i.e. expenses that must be paid no matter how many goods or services are sold. Examples of the fixed costs include all start-up costs, rent, building maintenance, capital equipment (machinery/computers) etc. Fixed costs are often quoted in annual amounts. Variable costs vary with output. They generally increase at a constant rate relative to production which, in turn, is designed to meet sales predictions or market orders. These costs include: wages, utilities (water, electricity), materials and components used in production, raw materials, inventory warehousing, transportation.

5.5.4 Explain how the costs in 5.5.1 relate to craft production, mechanization and automation. Outline how automation has improved the type and range of products available to consumers.

Fixed costs for manual or craft production are generally low but considerably higher for mechanization and automation due to the purchase of capital equipment.

Variable costs for automation are lower than craft production due to cost of wages.

Clearly from this relationship, the scale of production would most likely determine the method of production chosen. Low volume work, would most likely be produced by craftsmen, whereas, high volume work would be more suited to mechanized and/or automated processes. Materials selection also has a part to play in production method choices. Some materials and production methods are only suited to mechanization/automation.

> **5.5.5** Explain the concept of 'break-even point' in relation to fixed and variable costs.

'Break even' occurs where neither profit is made nor losses incurred. Graphically it can be represented as the intersection of the two lines – sales income and costs, (a combination of fixed and variable costs). Figure 5.5.5 indicates fixed costs, variable costs and the breakeven point.

Mathematically, the breakeven point may be calculated as:

$$\text{Breakeven point} = \frac{\text{Fixed Costs}}{(\text{Unit Selling Price - Variable Costs})}$$

After the breakeven point profit can be made.

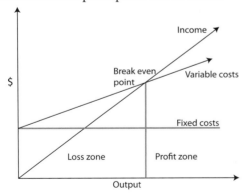

Figure 5.5.5 Profit/loss graph

5.6 CLEAN MANUFACTURING

> **5.6.1** Explain why the introduction of mass production increased damage to the natural environment.

At the time of the Industrial Revolution there were no models of environmental practice to follow and governments were encouraging industries to grow, tackling demand from both local and export markets. Damage to the environment increased at alarming rates and continued unchecked for many decades. The Industrial Revolution not only translated into air, soil and water pollution, but also poor working conditions for individuals and a decline in the health of the general population. Hair analysis in 1979, from samples identified as belonging to noted historical figure Isaac Newton, (1642–1727), showed traces of the toxic heavy metals antimony, mercury, lead and arsenic. These metals are not naturally present in human hair and are assumed to have been absorbed from the environment of the time. Other hair samples from individuals living elsewhere in Europe at the same time have also been tested with similar results.

The mass production of goods led to massive consumption of raw materials and requirements for very large amounts of energy. Until recently there has been little to safeguard the environment from the depletion of natural resources used for both fuel and raw materials. Additional to this has been the limited control of emissions and waste produced by industry over time. Mass production has led to mass consumption and the appearance of the 'disposable society'.

> **5.6.2** Outline the reasons for cleaning up manufacturing.

Until recently, most modern cultures have seen themselves as separate from nature and that through technology they have been liberated from such primitive concerns. With the onset of the Industrial Revolution this mastery over nature was becoming more evident. At the same time, a small number of people also began to express disquiet at both the rate of change of society and the local environment. Authors such as the Englishman Thomas Malthus, (1766–1834), warned that population growth, if unchecked would exceed the capacity of the earth to provide food, a position again proposed by Paul Ehrlich in his 1968 publication, 'The Population Bomb'. Larger populations, from the 1700s onwards were coincidental with the Industrial Revolution, mass production and mass consumption. These circumstances placed pressure not only on food production, but also finite resources and the ability of the environment to cope with the ensuing rise in pollution.

Up until the last half of the twentieth century, unfettered industrial development was often seen as a sign of progress. Much of this development was fed by increasingly efficient means of manufacturing with often little regard for the environment. With the growth of the environmental movement, however, concerns about ecological degradation and concepts of sustainable development have changed the attitudes of many to pollution.

> **5.6.3** Outline that an initial response to reducing emission of pollutants is adding clean-up technologies to the end of the manufacturing process.
>
> © IBO 2007

Most often, the approach to reducing emissions and pollutants from manufacturing cycles is attempted at the end of the production process. This technique is known as the 'end of pipe' approach. While there are multiple mechanical, biological and chemical approaches that may be adopted, a more realistic and effective response would be to minimize the waste steam and pollutants before they are generated. Through measures aimed at reducing pollutants before they occur, intervention measures are also less dramatic and smaller in scale. Reduced emissions and waste can also save resources in terms of raw materials and energy requirements. Cleaner manufacturing or production technologies also reduce the need for managing pollutants.

Beverley Thorpe, (2009), of Greenpeace writes, "Clean production is any practice which eliminates at source the use or formation of hazardous substances through the use of non hazardous chemicals in production processes, or through product or process redesign, and thereby prevents releases of hazardous substances into the environment by all routes, directly or indirectly".

In economic terms, it is cheaper to prevent any potential environmental damage and deal with these issues at the source, rather than try to mitigate their effects after the offending emissions, wastes or inefficiencies have already occurred.

The development of clean technologies not only benefits the environment, but will improve a company's position

not only as a supplier of product, but as a potential provider of high-value clean manufacturing technologies and processes, thus boosting the domestic economy and providing long term jobs growth.

> **5.6.4** Explain how legislation provides an impetus to manufacturers to clean up manufacturing processes.
>
> © IBO 2007

Legislation, both supportive and punitive, is enacted by governments to coerce manufacturers to conform to environmental standards.

Supportive legislation includes such strategies as:

- removal of state taxes and duties on clean technology infrastructure including photovoltaic cells and wind turbines
- grants and stimulus packages provided for research and development
- general tax benefits accrued based on a company's product or process that is environmentally beneficial.

Punitive legislation may take the form of:

- carbon taxes that may be levied on companies that use fossil fuels and release greenhouse gases through their burning
- fines for breaches of environmental regulations
- general environmental taxes levied on a company's product or process that is harmful to the environment
- non-granting of export/import licenses for non-compliant manufacturers.

> **5.6.5** State that the legislation can be policed by monitoring through the collection of quantitative data.
>
> © IBO 2007

One method employed by governments is to introduce legislation requiring the mandatory reporting of greenhouse gas emissions towards the achievement of predetermined targets. These targets, often referred to as environmental quality criteria, (EQC), provide numerical values or benchmarks for environmental outcomes.

> **5.6.6** Explain that strategies for cleaning up manufacturing are mainly reactive, and that more radical approaches require a rethink of the whole system and may result in significant product and/or process modification or radically new technologies.
>
> © IBO 2007

Companies may employ simple action cycle models to gather, analyze, review and implement changes based on the assessment of quantitative data in a reactionary fashion, in response to existing problems.

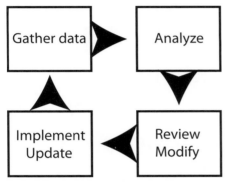

Figure 5.6.6 Action cycle for improvement

What is required is a more proactive innovative approach employing an holistic, long term vision for innovation in new materials, manufacturing and management. This vision must encompass efficient use and conservation of natural resources and the reduction waste in all its forms.

> **5.6.7** Explain that targets for reducing pollution and waste from industry are agreed internationally, but not all industrial nations agree to the targets.
>
> © IBO 2007

While international agreements are hard-fought gains in the battle against pollution on a global scale, this show of unity is not necessarily reflected in the various member countries at a political, business or social level. Governments within individual countries are answerable to their own populations and national debates are subject to the views of the entire population, including special interest groups. Company Boards of Directors need to meet the expectations of shareholders while attempting competitiveness in a global economy. Local jobs, wages, costs and taxes, as well as environmental issues, regularly dominate discussions. Even today, countries trying to reel in the production of greenhouse gases through the introduction of carbon taxes meet stiff resistance from industry and manufacturers. Governments are labeled as 'anti- manufacturing' or as 'economic vandals' as the debate rages.

Further Reading

Thorpe, B., (2009). *Clean Production Action. Clean Production Strategies: What is Clean Production?* Greenpeace International

Dougherty, P. J. (2010). *Advanced Materials & Manufacturing for The Clean Energy Future.* Strategic Marketing Innovations.

State Monitoring and Evaluation Framework Discussion Paper. (2003). EPA. Western Australia.

1. Metal machining involves:

    A.   additive processes
    B.   plastic deformation
    C.   elastic deformation
    D.   working with molten materials.

2. End of pipe pollution control is:

    A.   the most effective method available
    B.   the cheapest approach to pollution control
    C.   most effective because it deals with all the known by-products
    D.   less effective because it allows unnecessary pollution to occur.

3. Craft production is suited to:

    A.   only small enterprises
    B.   only large enterprises
    C.   large scale mass production
    D.   manufacturing of one off unique pieces.

4. Just-in-time management involves:

    A.   large inventories ready for emergencies
    B.   rapid response to spikes in unpredictable demand
    C.   involves rigorous quality control testing at the end of production
    D.   involves rigorous quality control testing at every stage of production.

5. Discuss the advantages and disadvantages of casting as a production method.

6. Discuss the advantages and disadvantages associated with the use of fasteners as a method of joining.

7. Explain the relationship between the different types of costs manufacturers face and the setting of product pricing.

8. Explain why automation of an industry may not always be a good thing.

9. Outline the role governments can play in encouraging the development of cleaner technologies?

10. Discuss strategies governments may use to encourage manufacturers to reach environmental protection targets.

PRODUCT DESIGN

CONTENTS

The application of ergonomic principles continues to be a challenge for designers, manufacturers and consumers. Early evidence of the practice of ergonomics appears in the writings of 5th Century Greeks. Hippocrates, (the Ancient Greek physician), describes how a surgeon's tools should be designed, and then arranged in the most propitious fashion. One of the most famous archaeological collections of surgical instruments are those found in the ruins of a house in the Roman city of Pompeii, buried in 97 AD as a result of the eruption of Mt Vesuvius. A selection of these instruments is shown below. Remarkable features of these designs include how well they are made and the addition of decorations that also served to improve the surgeon's grip in what must have been wet and slippery environments.

Historic anthropometric data is still available to researchers today. The graph below shows the range of height measurements of Union soldiers in 1864. The average height in this instance was 5 foot 8 ¼ inches. While no soldier may of been of this exact height, all of the information contained in the graph may have been useful for producing a suitable range of sizes in clothing or weaponry.

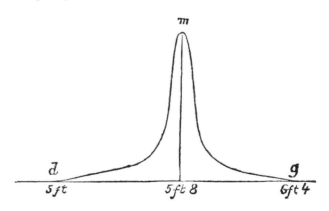

Range of Union Soldier heights 1864

More recently ergonomists use data obtained from measuring the human body to collect sufficient information to allow devices and products to be manufactured in a way that facilitates their ease of use

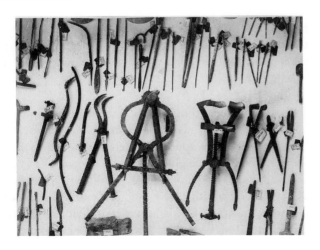

Early Roman surgical instruments

6.1 ERGONOMICS

6.1.1 Define ergonomics, anthropometrics and percentile range.

© IBO 2007

- Static or stationary physical measurements – weight, height, ear size etc.
- Dynamic or moving measurements – reach envelope, force of grip, reaction speed to external stimuli etc.

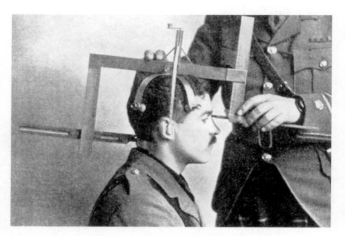

Figure 6.1.1b A 'head-measurer' tool designed for anthropological research in the early 1910s

Ergonomics is derived from the Greek words: ergon, (work), and nomos, (natural laws). Together, the formation of the word ergonomics refers to the science of people and their relationship with work. Therefore, ergonomics is broadly the study of people's efficiency in their working environment. In the field of design, ergonomics involves creating products that allow users to perform tasks comfortable, effectively and efficiently.

Figure 6.1.1a shows a diagram plotting the symmetrical actionable envelope created by a seated individual. Awareness of this space would then allow designers to consider issues associated with reach, posture, comfort, accessibility etc.

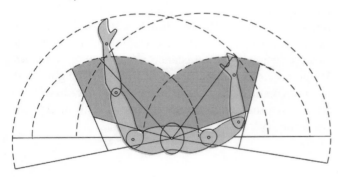

Figure 6.1.1a Symmetrical operating areas of the stationary human body

Image by Bolumena Creative Commons Attribution-Share Alike 3.0 Unported

Anthropometrics is the scientific study of human body measurements. This field involves measurement of the human body. Early in 20th Century, anthropometry was used in an attempt to classify differences between races. It was often employed as 'proof' that some races were inferior to others. Anthropometrics further developed alongside ergonomics during WWII through the design of controls for military equipment.

Today, anthropometric data gathered in the form of tables, or available online, saves designers considerable research time. The data provides information about the size and capabilities of individuals as part of a larger population. The information may be gathered in one of two ways:

A common use of anthropometric studies is to determine the range and quantity of clothing sizes required. Today, anthropometric measurements are taken using 3D scanners rather than primitive tools such as the one shown in Figure 6.1.1b.

Percentiles refer to 100 equal groups into which a sample population can be divided according to the distribution of values of a particular variable. As an example an individual in the 70th percentile has scored as well, or better than, 70% of those in the total sample population.

Percentile ranges are used to measure dispersion within a sample population. A spread between the 95th and 5th percentiles would be expressed as: P95 - P5.

Percentiles shown in anthropometry tables determine whether the measurement given relates to the 'average' person, or someone who is above or below average in a certain criteria.

If the heights of a group of adults are sampled, many will have data recorded showing them be around the same height. Some will be appreciably taller while others may be shorter. The 'same height' group will be near the average or 'mean' and will be displayed in anthropometry tables as the 50th percentile. The 50th percentile in this case, identifies the most likely height of an individual within the group. In a design context, determining which percentile value or range may be critical to success depends on what is being designed and for whom the design needs to cater. Age, gender and even cultural background can affect ergonomic design.

6.1.2 State that ergonomics is multidisciplinary, encompassing anthropometrics, psychological factors and physiological factors.

Ergonomics draws on many disciplines in its study of humans and their environments. It includes, but is not limited to anthropometrics, biomechanics, materials science, engineering, physiology and psychology. Due to the multi-disciplinary nature of the field, ergonomists may care to specialize in particular sectors such as:

- physical – movement and physical performance
- psychological – information processing, perception, memory retention and mental stress, environment
- sociological – effects of policies and procedures, meeting human needs.

6.1.3 Describe a design context where the 5th–95th percentile range has been used.

The commonly chosen design range of 5th—95th percentile of a population is a trade-off that allows for the inclusion of almost everyone in a design context and only excluding the extremes.

The practice of catering for a larger percentile range is often called 'design for more types'. Traditionally, using a range from the 5th to the 95th percentile, it is deemed to provide the best coverage without being skewed by extremes, i.e. the greatest 5% and the least 5% in the data range. Consumers outside this range often have to seek customized solutions to meet their needs. Products designed to meet these requirements would include chairs, one size fits all, (free size), clothing and motor vehicles.

An example of a product using only the 95th percentile would be the standard architectural doorway. The tallest people should then be able to negotiate the opening. The 5th or 50th percentile people being smaller in stature would naturally be catered for in this design as well.

Conversely 5th percentile data only may be used in such instances as vehicle controls, where ease of reach would be the determining constraint. Here data as low as the 5th percentile may be required to gather in a sample population, including those with the shortest of reaches.

6.1.4 Describe a design context where the 50th percentile has been used.

6.1.5 Explain the limitations of using the 50th percentile as a means of designing for the 'average' person.

In anthropometrics there is no such thing as a 50th percentile person. The perfect average simply does not exist. Statistics and reality separate at this point. The 50th percentile, or average individual, could not possibly fit all of the criteria that may be applied. Thus, while an individual may be of average height, they will probably not meet the average criteria for weight, reach or hand span etc.

Even though designing for the mean seems to make sense, the majority of people are actually excluded, i.e. outside the range of this group. Designing for the average user can also be difficult if the range of users cross age and/or gender boundaries.

A design context where 50th percentile data has been used relates to the development of crash test dummies. In 1971 General Motors created Hybrid I, a crash test dummy modelled on the 50th percentile male, i.e. it was developed from data recording average male height, mass, and proportion. Hybrid I was a redesign of 'Sierra Sam', (Figure 6.1.4a), a 95th percentile male dummy (heavier and taller than 95% of human males) used by the aviation industry to test emergency situations involving: ejection seats, aviation helmets and pilot restraints.

Figure 6.1.4a Early crash test dummy 'Sierra Sam'

Due to the lack of data available for other occupants in vehicles, crash test dummies have now been developed for women and children.

The crash test dummy family, Hybrid III, shown in Figure 6.1.4b now consists of a male, a smaller female and three children based on data replicating a 6-year-old, a 3-year-old, and a 12-month-old infant. The use of these models generates very different data than that gathered from the earlier testing of male models.

Figure 6.1.4b Hybrid III crash test dummy family

6.1.6 Identify specific design contexts where the designer would use percentile ranges for particular user groups.

© IBO 2007

The development of crash test dummies to now incorporate percentile range models across strategically selected age groups, is a good example of where particular user groups are identified within a very specific design context.

Many products developed for children will also require careful consideration of anthropometric data and ergonomic design. Specifically, the designing of computer furniture, (seating and tables), for primary school age students is a complex issue requiring consideration of a large percentile range, 5th–95th, across genders and encompassing significant age variation. Appropriate design would encourage correct posture, reduce fatigue, facilitate ease of use and avert long-term health problems.

6.1.7 Outline the significance of psychological factors (smell, light, sound, taste, texture and temperature) to ergonomics.

© IBO 2007

The effectiveness of a product or environment can be affected by an individual's reaction to external sensory stimuli. Design should take into account these factors to improve an operator's efficiency and/or comfort. A range of influencing factors is included in the table shown as Figure 6.1.7.

Stimulus	Factors affecting
Sight	ease of visibility, readability computer screens
Hearing	pitch, frequency, volume mobile phones
Touch	texture, grip, friction, temperature keyboards, dentistry tools
Taste	ingestion of toxins children's toys
Smell	aroma, perfume, odour workspaces

Figure 6.1.7 Physiological factors affecting design

6.1.8 Outline physiological factors that affect ergonomics.

© IBO 2007

Ergonomic design may involve the analysis of physiological responses in situations where a complex interplay of variables such as: heat, noise, available space, illumination etc. all combine to affect a user's experience with a product, system or environment.

Physiological factors would be of critical concern to the ergonomic design of the workspace for pilots in long haul aircraft. Performing multiple tasks requiring high levels of concentration for long periods of time, pilots achieve this in a small space seated in a chair. Surrounded by instrumentation they are required to visually monitor a range of systems and physically manipulate controls. Factors such as comfort, fatigue, attention spans, temperature and humidity must all be considered.

6.1.9 Discuss the influence of perception when collecting data relating to psychological factors.

Individuals perceive the world in different ways. This may be a factor of their upbringing, experience, culture etc. Qualitative data is gathered in this context to better elicit meaningful responses from individuals and groups. Examples of the type of information required and why the responses are so varied includes:

Temperature - Individuals experience temperature in different ways. A range of comfort zones will exist based on body mass, manner of dress or even physiological changes that can be developed from exposure to a particular temperature or environment over time.

Space - Space is another part of the environment perceived by individuals differently. Comfort zones or personal space vary from culture to culture.

Taste - Responses to taste are also a factor of culture and experience.

Value - may be perceived as a function of cost, features, prestige, rarity etc., or a combination of these factors.

Further reading

Blanchonette, P. J. (2010). *Human Modelling Tool: A Review,* Air Operations Division DSTO Defence Science and Technology Organisation. Victoria. Australia.

Licht, D.M., Polzella, D.J., & Boff, K.R. (1998). *Human Factors, Ergonomics, and Human Factors Engineering: An Analysis of Definitions.*

Nickpour, F. & Dong, H. (2009). *Anthropometrics Without Numbers! An Investigation of Designers' Use and Preference of People Data.* London.

Talbot, J. (2005). *New interactions? The role of 'Affective Human Factors' in design.* Ergonomics Australia. Vol. 19,. Number 1.

Ergonomic Principles in the Design of Healthcare Environments. (2003). Herman Miller for Healthcare, Michigan.

6.2 THE DESIGNER AND SOCIETY

6.2.1 Discuss moral and social responsibilities of designers in relation to green design issues.

Social and moral issues exist for designers and not just in terms of green design. Within the product design community, ethical debate has always been around whether it is the designers and manufacturers who should consider all of the moral and ethical issues associated with product use and abuse, or whether the choice should be left with the consumer to decide to purchase and then make their own decisions about how the product should be used.

This debate is rooted in history. Galileo, (1564—1642), championed the pursuit of science regardless of the social or religious upheaval caused by its advancement. After WWII the blame for the catastrophic destruction caused by the development and dropping of the atomic bomb was clearly laid at the feet of the users of the product, in this case the politicians who chose to deploy the weapon, rather than the developers.

Alternatively, Archimedes, (287—212 BC), the Greek mathematician and inventor, took the opposite position to Galileo when he refused to record some of his engineering discoveries, fearing their use.

Appearing alongside other ecological social movements of the 1960s, the socially responsible design movement, challenged the nature of excessive or 'consumer-led' design. Fuelled by the oil crisis, the movement drew attention to pollution, long term ecological damage and the rapid depletion of finite natural resources. Designers and manufacturers were tasked with developing products that focused on functionality, durability and eco-friendliness rather than fashion trends and aesthetics.

The original proponents of socially responsible design were: Nigel Whiteley, Victor Papanek, and Ernst Schumacher. They defended criticism of their approach, countering that socially responsible design should be functional but did not have to be unattractive. As consumers became more environmentally aware, designers were pressured to consider green design issues as part of successful marketing plans. Designers were forced to address issues such as responsible use of resources, materials selection, manufacturing processes, durability and energy efficiency.

The pressure to maintain an ethical approach to design and the environment continues today in the form of sustainable design. In sustainable design, product responsibility extends beyond the life of a product through life cycle analysis and 'cradle to cradle' philosophies.

6.2.2 Define planned obsolescence.

Also known as 'built-in obsolescence', planned obsolescence is a deliberate tactic employed by manufacturers to create products with a limited lifespan. It is designed to force consumers to purchase a product repeatedly. Planned obsolescence exists in such diverse product areas as computer software, mobile phones and automobiles.

Companies often used planned obsolescence to control costs, but other effects can include significant environmental impacts through consumers continuously replacing, rather than repairing, products. This generates more waste, pollution, energy consumption and consumption of resources.

6.2.3 Outline how planned obsolescence influences the design specification of a product.

Planned obsolescence is not a new phenomenon and is documented as early as the 1930s, when General Electric improved the efficiency of flashlight lamps through a corresponding decrease in their lifespan. Engineers at this time were encouraged to build items with a limited lifespan to increase sales and boost the economy. The proposition was received with mixed responses but proponents accepted this new ethical paradigm with almost patriotic vigour.

Adopting a philosophy of planned obsolescence allows designers to create a desire for product replacement, or update, rather than repair. Design features of planned obsolescence may include:

- low durability
- style obsolescence
- not easily or cheaply repaired
- difficult to disassemble thus restricting maintenance
- regular introduction of newer technologies or 'improved' models.

The features listed allow manufacturers to cut costs and boost sales. This approach by manufacturers is known as 'value engineering', however, as markets develop and competition increases, pressure is brought about to increase product life spans as consumers migrate to companies producing reliable, more durable products.

6.2.4 Describe the advantages and disadvantages of planned obsolescence to the designer, manufacturer and consumer.

Advantages for consumers include opportunities to upgrade products as new technologies become available and to access the latest in fashionable design. Manufacturers are constantly making replacement products and generate higher profits based on volume sales and lower costs, as quality and durability costs are reduced. Strength in the consumer market has general flow-on effects to national economies and job prospects for the local population.

Disadvantages are essentially around the constant need for replacement and associated inconvenience. Lack of repairability may mean consumers have to purchase a product before they may be ready, or replace a model whose features they are entirely happy with. New models and new technologies often bring new ways of operating and this can also be disconcerting for some consumers. Increased consumerism through less durable goods wastes both energy and raw materials, while at the same time increasing pollution and the production of greenhouse gases.

6.2.5 Define fashion.

Fashion is a general term for a currently popular style or practice. Fashion trends may extend to include design features such as: shape, form, colour, style, materials, finish etc. Fashion trends appear in a diverse range of fields including, but not limited to: vehicles, architecture, food, clothing, jewellery, footwear etc.

6.2.6 Compare the influence of fashion and planned obsolescence on the product cycle.

Planned obsolescence, as the name suggests is predetermined by the manufacturer and can be an inbuilt component of product design. Fashion trends can be unpredictable. However, planned obsolescence may be timed to meet changing fashion cycles.

Perceived value and cost are vastly different and measured using entirely different criteria. Value for money is associated with cost, while perceived value, also incorporating cost may also include prestige, rarity and other social implications within a consumer's assessment. While planned obsolescence often uses lesser quality materials and production values to cut costs, the prestige of owning a similar item, branded differently but priced at a premium, may still draw customers. Labeled the 'Veblem effect' after Thorstein Bunde Veblen, (1857—1929) this theory describes counter-intuitive consumer behaviour. Reasons for this behaviour include the thought that pricing is an indication of quality and conspicuous consumption of expensive items provides a form of social prestige for the consumer.

Researchers commenting on product aesthetics have established a response from product users called, 'the theory of aesthetic pleasure'. This theory identifies a link between users and the entire range of effects generated by the product experience. This set of effects includes the degree to which our senses are satisfied, including visual gratification, feelings, emotions etc.

The original design for the Coca Cola Bottle is one of the most often quoted in this field. Designers describe the organic-shaped, twin-sphered body and the way it fits neatly into the hand, with its smooth, ribbed grip on a cold and wet glass bottle as conveying both comfort and confidence.

Figure 6.2.8a shows an image of Earl R. Dean's 1915 glass, contour, Coca-Cola prototype bottle. It is claimed there remains only two of these bottles in existence.

Figure 6.2.8a Coca Cola glass bottle prototype

Image by Gavinmacqueen (Own work) [CC-BY-SA-3.0] via Wikimedia Commons

Another more recent example, where aesthetics have influenced consumer behaviour and generated market success, appears in the watch industry. In the 1980s, the Swiss watch making industry was under pressure from cheap digital watches produced in Asia. Swiss watches were seen as reliable, but expensive and boring. Swatch came up with a budget watch designed to be fun, fashionable and colourful. The watches were cheap enough to be discarded as fashion trends changed, yet also encouraged consumers to own multiple watches where previously one had been sufficient. Today, the Swatch group is not only a successful manufacturer of fun budget watches, but owns many leading watch companies across a range of market sectors, including: Longines, Rado, Tissot, ck Calvin Klein, Certina, Mido and Flik Flak etc.

Figure 6.2.8b Swatch watch

Image by Cormullion Creative Commons Attribution 2.5 Generic

6.2.9 Discuss the conflict that a designer faces when attempting to balance form with function in the design of products.

© IBO 2007

Designers are faced with the challenge of developing aesthetically pleasing, functional products for an identified market. If the functional nature of the brief is a given, then other variables such as: time, materials selection, fashion trends and cost ceilings all come into play. In many cases, the final appearance of a design can be either constrained, or enhanced by, the combination of all of these factors. In simple terms, design geometries can vary dependent on production processes. The addition of materials choices adds another dimension, and so on, until the complex interplay of all the aforementioned variables affects the final form of the design.

Well-developed testing and evaluation tools are used to evaluate the functional features of a product. Aesthetic preferences are another matter entirely and can prove to be elusive with constantly changing fashion trends.

The Bauhaus School of Design (1919—1933), based its work on the premise that function should be the driving influence behind an object's design. Bauhaus furniture design was often simple and light. Proponents of this style believed purity of function would create simplistic, elegant design without elaborate decoration, following only the needs of the consumer.

Figure 6.2.9a Bauhaus design, Breuer club-chair, 1925 - 1926

In the post-modern era, the product aesthetic became the driving force. Objects took on creative or arbitrary forms. Functionality took a back seat to appearance. The products were often marketed as unique or collectable. The most publicized example of this style is the 1980s Philippe Starck designed lemon squeezer, or 'Juicy Salif', (see Topic

1). Barely performing its espoused function, this product soon became an iconic, albeit expensive 'must have'.

Today, good design is not just restricted to high quality expensive products. In a consumer driven, global market, form has become function. Good ergonomic design is as much a feature of the appearance of a product as is its form and functionality. Well-designed products, from razor blades to mobile phones, intertwine good ergonomic design with functionality and pleasing forms.

This steel bodied safety razor, typical of the 1960s, featured a twist-to-open head to allow blades to be replaced. A moveable ring below the head also allowed the blade to be adjusted.

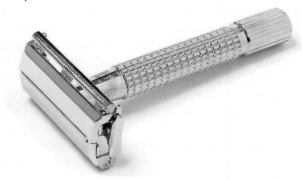

Figure 6.2.9b Safety razor design circa 1960

Introduced in 1998, this 3-blade model also featured an ergonomic plastic body, flexible head and lubrication strip that faded over time to encourage users to replace the device.

Figure 6.2.9c Mach 3 razor design

Further Reading

Beder, S. (1998). *Is Planned Obsolescence Socially Responsible?* Engineers Australia. p. 52.

Bhamra, T. & Lofthouse, V. (2004). *Design for Sustainability - A Practical Approach.* Gower Publishing.

Davey, C. Et Al. (2005). *Design for the Surreal World? A New Model of Socially Responsible Design.* Germany.

Hekkert, P. (2006). *Design Aesthetics: Principles of Pleasure in Design,* Psychology Science. Volume 48. p. 157–172.

Exercises

1. Physiological factors include:

    A. the five senses
    B. emotional responses
    C. the range of all human physical activity
    D. all of the above.

2. Anthropometrics:

    A. is a relatively new practice
    B. requires creation of statistics
    C. involves measuring the human body
    D. includes the designing effective work spaces.

3. Design for more types includes:

    A. children and adults
    B. both males and females
    C. 100% of a sample population
    D. 5th to the 95th percentile range.

4. Ergonomics:

    A. is a new practice
    B. was developed after WWII
    C. includes the field of anthropology
    D. has elements rooted in ancient cultures.

5. Explain why the use of ergonomic design expanded rapidly during WWII?

    A. large sums of money were made available
    B. wartime conditions required effective design
    C. pressures of war made successful design solutions an imperative
    D. all of the above.

6. Discuss the nature of moral and ethical design and where responsibilities lay.

7. Explain the difference between ergonomics and anthropometrics.

8. Explain how planned obsolescence affects: designers, manufacturers and consumers.

9. Identify issues that can make fashion a transient and changing feature of design.

10. Explain the theory of 'aesthetic pleasure' and how it affects consumer purchasing patterns.

CORE

EVALUATION

CONTENTS

7

An evaluation is an assessment of something with respect to defined criteria. It is a process in which information is obtained that allows decisions to be made regarding such disparate criteria as progress, performance, value and appearance. As such, evaluations are constantly being made, either in a formal or informal manner, by large corporations and individuals.

The criteria used in an evaluation will often change depending on the stage of development at which the evaluation in undertaken. The aim of evaluation in many instances can be distilled into the requirement of usability. As defined by the International Standard ISO9241-11, usability is:

"The extent to which a product can be used by specified users to achieve specified goals with effectiveness, efficiency, and satisfaction in a specified context of use."

7.1 EVALUATION AND DESIGNING

7.1.1	Outline the general criteria used to evaluate products.

©ISO 2007

A wide variety of criteria can be used to evaluate products depending on the stage within the production cycle the evaluation is performed. Primary among the criteria are those listed below.

Safety: Safety is a very broad criterion and includes direct toxicological considerations for products that are intended to be ingested or placed in contact with the skin, such as food additives, pharmaceuticals and cosmetics.

Safety considerations also need to be taken into account, for the unintended, more indirect situations encountered with products such as paints, chemical treatments and plastics that may be absorbed as fumes in the event of fire or inadvertently ingested by a child during play.

Issues of 'fitness for purpose' are typically involved in evaluations of product safety. Such assessments are used to set criteria with regard to material properties, the presence of acceptable material flaws, product performance, maintenance and operating limits, electrical isolation and insulation, flammability, swallowing hazards, etc. These criteria are then used to establish factors of safety within a design, assuming the product is used in its intended manner.

Environmental impact: Evaluation of environmental impact extends from the raw materials and processes used in manufacture through maintenance and to end-of-life issues such as recyclability.

Performance: The evaluation of performance can include a wide range of measures such as those indicated in Figure 7.1.1a. These factors revolve around the ability of the product to perform the tasks for which it was designed.

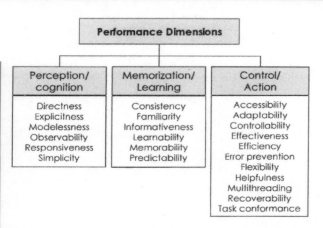

Figure 7.1.1a Performance dimensions

Han, S.H. et al. (2000). Evaluation of product usability: development and usability validation of usability dimensions and design elements based on empirical models. Int. J. Ind. Erg. 26, 477-488.

Aesthetics: Evaluation of aesthetics can be one of the more difficult dimensions to measure, as it is subject to fashion and individual taste. Some of the factors involved are indicated in Figure 7.1.1b.

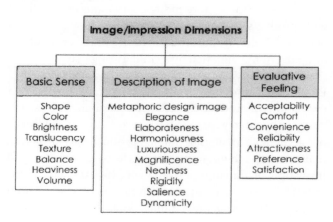

Figure 7.1.1b Image/Impression dimensions

Han, S.H. et al. (2000). Evaluation of product usability: development and usability validation of usability dimensions and design elements based on empirical models. Int. J. Ind. Erg. 26, 477-488.

Cost: When evaluating any product, questions of cost and value for money invariably arise. Consumers will decide what they are prepared to pay for the product on offer based on their individual circumstances and judgements. They will also make decisions about the various degrees to which the other defining characteristics meet their needs or desires.

7.1.2 Explain how the criteria used to evaluate products will vary depending on the purpose of the evaluation.

© IBO 2007

As indicated previously, the criteria used in an evaluation depend on the product concerned and the purpose of the evaluation. Some of the purposes for an evaluation are indicated below:

a. To determine if the product complies with relevant national or international standards:

While many standards are issued as guidelines to good practice they are often not mandatory. However, compliance with such standards is often a requirement specified by a purchaser, and testing is performed to confirm compliance before acceptance. These standards allow some confidence that products purchased from anywhere in the world will meet performance expectations. Products are often therefore affixed with a mark indicating compliance to an assessment standard.

Figure 7.1.2 Selection of logos found on products to indicate compliance with a standard

Some standards are mandatory and are typically regulated by governments to ensure consumer safety, others are voluntarily adopted by manufacturers as indicators of good practice and reliability.

Many countries maintain authorities charged with the responsibility of enforcing mandatory product safety and information standards, such as:

- The Australian Competition & Consumer Commission (ACCC)
- The United States Consumer Product Safety Commission (CPSC)
- The Product Safety Enforcement Forum of Europe (PROSAFE).

b. To determine competitiveness against an existing product:

The practice of 'benchmarking' could be included within this category and is the process of evaluating the best practices in existence, against which the design/system/process/product/service will be compared.

c. To investigate the cause of product failure and determine issues related to design/use/misuse:

Product failure can range from relatively benign issues that cause customer annoyance or dissatisfaction, to issues of safety associated with fracture or failure to operate. All failures, however, have the potential to impact adversely on the reputation of the product and the manufacturer. Product failures therefore need to be investigated thoroughly to identify the root cause, and to allow timely correction. The examination of failures allows a review of assumptions made during design and manufacture about the robustness and fitness-for-purpose of the product when exposed to use by consumers.

d. To compare the features of competing products in order to guide purchasing decisions.

Every day, consumers make decisions regarding the purchase of similar items from different suppliers, whether these are daily essentials such as foodstuffs or discretionary purchase items such as electronics or automobiles. Information used to make such decisions comes from numerous sources, such as product claims on packaging and in brochures, cost, independent reviews, family and friends etc.

> ### 7.1.3 Apply the general criteria to evaluate products.
>
> © IBO 2007

An example of using the general criteria for the evaluation of a product is outlined below, in which four variations on an instrument for the removal of corks from bottles are shown in Figure 7.1.3a. This device is generically referred to as a 'Waiters Friend' and contains a corkscrew, a lever arm with a bottle top opener and a foil cutting device (usually consisting of a short knife blade), all arranged in a folding pocket knife type body. There are a large number of designs available for the 'Waiters Friend' type device alone. The selection offered here are all basically similar in operation.

Operation involves screwing the corkscrew into the cork and then positioning the end of the lever arm onto the lip of the bottle, creating a second order lever (see Topic 10). By lifting the body of the device, the cork is pulled from the bottle. Each of the four options shown in Figure 7.1.3a can fulfil the operational requirements of removing a cork.

Figure 7.1.3a Product evaluation

A summary of the features of each option is provided in Figure 7.1.3b.

Option	Design	Corkscrew length	Mechanism	Foil-Cutter
A	Straight-sided body design. Plain carbon steel body and mechanism.	45mm	Firm	40mm long straight folding knife with a flat cutting edge
B	Straight-sided body design. White plastic body with plain carbon steel mechanism	30mm	Corkscrew wobbles at attachment	35mm long curved folding knife with a flat cutting edge
C	Crescent shaped body design. Stainless steel body with light-coloured wood inlay. Stainless steel mechanism	50mm	Firm	35mm long curved folding knife with serrated cutting edge
D	Curved back body design. Polymer 'non-slip grip' body. Stainless steel mechanism.	45mm	Firm	Cutting disc recessed into body

Figure 7.1.3b Features of the four 'Waiters Friend' options

An evaluation of the various options based on the general criteria is summarised in Figure 7.1.3c.

Option	Safety	Environmental Impact	Performance	Aesthetics	Cost
A	Satisfactory	Easily recycled	Satisfactory	Functional Plain carbon steel body can rust	$4.50
B	Corkscrew and knife too easy to open	Easily recycled mechanism. Plastic body	Satisfactory although corkscrew wobbled in mechanism	Decorative colours possible. Plain carbon steel body can rust	$2.90
C	Satisfactory	Easily recycled	Improved fit to hand	Appealing shape and inlay	$6.95
D	Improved by providing an alternative to a knife blade	Easily recycled mechanism. Polymer body	Improved fit to hand along with non-slip grip	Appealing shape and feel	$11.99

Figure 7.1.3c Summary of the features of each option based on the general criteria

Safety: This device is intended for use by adults, but may be found in a kitchen draw or picnic basket, accessible by children. All four options contained a corkscrew with the sharp point nested against the body when closed, preventing accidental contact. The mechanism to open the corkscrew and foil cutting knife was firm for options A and C but required only light effort to open in option

B. Option D provided a firm corkscrew mechanism and a safer alternative to the foil-cutting knife.

Environmental impact: The steel components of all four options can be recycled. The plastic components of B and D involve some additional environmental impact associated with their manufacture and disposal.

Performance: All performed their intended function satisfactorily. Options C and D, however, provided a more comfortable fit in the hand. Option D was particularly effective in this respect because of the 'non-slip grip' body. Option D is also rated as dishwasher safe.

Aesthetics: Options A and B were a conventional straight sided design. The plastic body of option B can be obtained in different colours. The use of plain carbon steel, however, means that A and B are subject to corrosion, which will reduce their appearance and functionality with time. The crescent shape of option C is stylish as is the wood inlay and would make it suitable as a gift. Option D is also stylish and would compliment other kitchen utensils exhibiting similar 'non-slip grip' style handles.

Cost: All four options are less than twelve dollars so may be considered relatively inexpensive but a decision about value for money will depend on such factors as, how many are to be purchased, how often and where it will be used, and durability or life expectancy.

Conclusion: Infrequent use and storage in a kitchen draw or picnic basket may lead to a decision based primarily on price leading to selection of Option B or A. Similarly, if a large number were to be purchased for the staff of a restaurant, option A might be chosen. Regular use or selection as a gift may result in the purchase of options C or D.

> **7.1.4** Explain the use of qualitative and/ or quantitative tests, models and experiments used to evaluate ideas at the design development stage (developing chosen solution) of the design cycle.
>
> © IBO 2007

The type of information obtained from an assessment can be divided into two broad groups; quantitative and qualitative.

Qualitative assessments are those that obtain information about some quality aspect of the subject being analysed. These include preferences or feelings about the product. Such assessments are often determined using instruments such as:

- interviews
- observation
- focus groups
- questionnaires
- telephone surveys.

These instruments aim to determine what the surveyed population feel about an idea/product/service – their level of satisfaction.

Quantitative assessments are those that obtain some form of numerical data, and as such, determine a quantity. Such assessments are often determined using instruments such as:

- data logging
- scale models
- full-scale tests
- questionnaires
- computer simulations
- controlled experiments.

A quantitative assessment of attitude towards an idea/product/service can be obtained by attempting to determine the level or intensity of feeling. This is done by using questionnaires that ask for a rating scale usually organised from 'strongly dislike' through to 'strongly like' or 'strongly disapprove' through to 'strongly approve' etc. Such a scale can have a numerical value assigned to each choice for later analysis. Such a scale is known as a Lickert Scale.

In these questionnaires, a final summation and averaging of the responses provides an overall determination of the participant's evaluation. The evaluation of this participant can then be analysed along with responses from other participants using statistical methods for factors such as age, gender, etc.

The System Usability Scale (SUS), developed by John Brook in 1986, represents a widely used example of a Lickert Scale for product usability. While a Lickert Scale questionnaire is a widely used instrument for obtaining a quantitative measure of participant reactions. Such instruments can take considerable time to construct and validate, since the aim of being able to determine a final overall number requires that the questions be of equal value.

Scale models may be used as part of an evaluation strategy to assess shape and form. They may also be employed to obtain quantitative data on issues of strength, fluid flow, etc. using techniques of similitude. Similitude techniques allow models to be tested at less extreme temperatures and pressures to those required of the full size component.

	Strongly disagree				Strongly agree
1. I think that I would like to use this system frequently	1	2	3	4	5
2. I found the system unnecessarily complex	1	2	3	4	5

Figure 7.1.4 Sample of two questions from the ten question System Usability Scale (SUS), ©Digital Equipment Corporation, 1986. [www.usabilitynet.org/trump/documents/Suschapt.doc]

In the same manner, experimental protocols may be established to test the viability of; materials, components, assemblies and impacts of design alternatives.

7.1.5 Define literature search.

The starting point for any research project is the collection and evaluation of prior learning relevant to the topic. This is the aim of a literature search. The literature search therefore involves the systematic search for published material in order to establish the current levels of knowledge and criticism related to the topic of interest and to inform future research directions.

This search is usually performed using sources of information recognised as being authoritative, such as; peer reviewed academic journals, books and published theses, but may also include information published by consumer magazines, government agencies and industry.

7.1.6 Describe one advantage and one disadvantage of literature search for data collection.

A properly conducted literature search will uncover the state of knowledge about a topic, preventing unnecessary duplication of effort, while highlighting areas of potentially fruitful study.

A problem with literature searches, particularly in the current age of electronic information retrieval, is the sheer amount of information that can be retrieved and must be sorted through for relevance to the specific project being undertaken.

7.1.7 Evaluate the importance of ICT in aiding literature searching.

The search for published resources was traditionally begun by consulting volumes containing a collection of abstracts from papers published, within the targeted field of study, such as Engineering Abstracts, Metallurgical Abstracts, etc. Every article published in any particular year was listed in the annual volume of abstracts. Entries were also arranged in alphabetical order by subject and author. These compendiums were, however, generally available only at major institutions, such as Universities and Colleges, so that access to such resources for research had some geographical limitations.

While each article found would generally contain a list of references for further examination, a researcher would usually have been required to examine a significant number of annuals in order to ensure coverage of the field.

As prospective papers were found, the researcher would commonly create an index card onto which the details of the abstract and reference would be entered for later consultation. In this way a reference index of articles relevant to the specific research topic was created. The manual nature of the process was however relatively laborious and time consuming.

The introduction of ICT (Information & Communications Technology) has revolutionized the whole process of searching abstracts and the development and management of resources. Today, abstracts are stored on searchable databases and are available to anyone with access to the internet. Searches on key words in tools such as Google Scholar, for example, can uncover numerous articles, some of which can even be downloaded free of charge, while other articles are available for download from the publisher as pdf files for a small fee.

127

Similarly, the management of personal reference/ bibliographic databases has immensely benefited from ICT, with numerous programs available to record, organize and search abstracts collected. Programs such as Bibus, EndNote®, RefWorks®, ProCite®, and Reference Manager® along with many others allow the searching of internet databases and the download and storage of abstracts, along with the interfacing with popular word processing programs, to assist in the formatting of references.

7.1.8   Define user trial.

7.1.9   Describe one advantage and one disadvantage of a user trial to collect data.

© IBO 2007

A user trial (also known as task analysis) is a trial in which members of the community for which the product is ultimately intended are observed using the product. The investigator records the participants during the trial for later analysis. These trials are usually undertaken in a laboratory environment as initial observations, in which the participants are asked to perform a number of tasks simulating typical use. The recording of such trials may include the use of hidden cameras and/or data loggers that record participant interaction with the product.

An advantage of a user trial is that, because the participants are not specialists, usability issues can be highlighted. That is, information about how users actually interact with the product is obtained. In addition, a relatively large number of participants can be included at low cost.

A disadvantage of such a trial is that inexperience with the product may result in simple errors-of-use by the trial participants.

7.1.10 Define user research.

7.1.11 Describe one advantage and one disadvantage of user research to collect data.

© IBO 2007

User research involves the questioning of users regarding their experiences and opinions of the product. Methods typically used include: questionnaires, participant diaries and focus groups.

Collection of data is generally easy and relatively cheap, however, the data obtained is generally more qualitative than that obtained by user trials and it may be difficult to keep participants from deviating from issues related to the product.

7.1.12 Compare user research with user trial.

© IBO 2007

User research collects data from participants about their experiences with, and responses to, the product, typically using questionnaires or interview techniques. User trials observe the actual interaction that has taken place as recorded by an investigator or data logging equipment. User research is therefore generally more qualitative in nature compared to the more quantitative nature of user trials.

A graphical representation of the mix of user evaluation techniques is presented in Figure 7.1.12a showing how psychological factors such as consumer attitude (user research) and behaviour (user trial) are incorporated into both qualitative and quantitative forms of investigation.

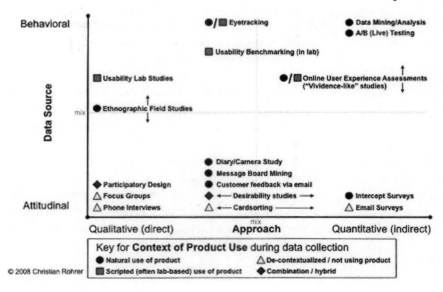

Figure 7.1.12 User evaluation techniques

Christian Rohrer (2008). When to Use Which User Experience Research Methods. [Jacob Nielsen's Alertbox, (October 2008): http://www.useit. com/alertbox/user-research-methods. html]

7.1.13 Define expert appraisal.

7.1.14 Describe one advantage and one disadvantage of using expert appraisal to collect data.

This is a process in which an expert, chosen on the basis of his or her training and knowledge of the area concerned, is asked to give their opinion.

An expert appraisal is generally qualitative in nature and has the advantage that a limited number of participants are required. Because of this, such appraisals are often completed quickly and typically include advice on potential directions for development.

A disadvantage of expert appraisals can be the difficulty of locating someone with the appropriate depth and breadth of knowledge to provide a comprehensive and authoritative opinion free of bias.

Further Reading

Thompson, J. L. (1974). *Product safety: suggestions for better use and purchase behaviour through consumer education and information, in Advances in Consumer Research* Volume 01, eds. Scott Ward and Peter Wright: Association for Consumer Research, Pages: 101-107.

7.2 EVALUATION AND MANUFACTURING

7.2.1 Identify the nature of evaluation at different stages of the product cycle.

The 'product cycle' or more fully the 'product life cycle' represents the stages of development through which a product typically passes and is illustrated in Figure 7.2.1a.

The stages of the product cycle include:

Initial Concept: This stage represents the period from the initial realisation that a new or improved product is needed, to the development of initial designs. Assessments of market segment, manufacturing feasibility and estimated cost typically occur at this stage

Product development: This stage involves the development of the concept into a physical product and involves a large number of decisions such as performance criteria, materials, component supply, tooling and manufacturing.

The decisions made at these two early stages can have a significant impact on future success. Some of these decisions are indicated in Figure 7.2.1b along with their potential cost impact. Cash flow at this stage is usually negative as costs have been incurred but no sales have been made.

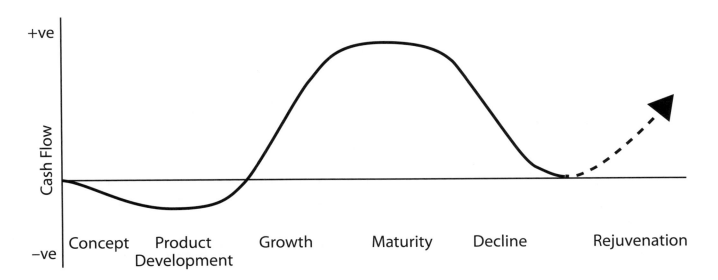

Figure 7.2.1a Graphical representation of the Product Life Cycle

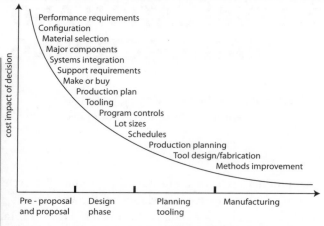

Figure 7.2.1b Cost impact vs decision (Burstein 1988).

Introduction to the Market: This period of the life cycle represents the introduction and sale of the new product into a market in which there are few competitors.

Growth: Rapid growth of product sales and capture of market share. Competitors also begin to enter the market and refinement of the product continues.

Maturity: The product has been in the market for a relatively long period of time and many competitors are present leading to a flattening of sales.

Decline: Many competitors exist and are competing on cost. Sales begin to decline.

Rejuvenation or end of life: Sales continue to fall and costs rise until the product is withdrawn or the product is re-imagined leading to increased sales growth.

Evaluation is a continuous process throughout the product life cycle, from initial concept through to end of life. Each evaluation with have unique features related to the stage concerned, but all will share the common goal of attempting to determine competitiveness in the market place and identifying opportunities for improvement. A summary of the evaluations that may be performed in each of the various stages of the product cycle is presented in Figure 7.2.1c.

Figure 7.2.1c Summary of evaluations

Product development	Phase characteristics	Actions	Assessment methods
Initial concept	Feasibility determination	Definition of problem Initial idea Design concept Manufacturing feasibility Market determination Unit cost estimate	Brainstorming Literature/patent search Data mining Focus groups User workshops Benchmarking
Product development	Costs high, negative cash flow	Detailed drawings Materials selection Quality control Price determination Design review Cost estimate	Prototype Ethnographic studies Computer simulations, FEA Focus groups Expert appraisal Failure analysis
Introduction to market	Sales begin	Advertising Quality control	User trials Questionnaires Customer feedback
Growth	Increased sales, competitors enter market	Increased market share Optimize design Quality control	Focus groups Customer feedback Failure analysis
Maturity	Market saturation many competitors	Advertising Product/brand differentiation Reduce costs	Focus groups Customer feedback Desirability studies
Decline	Sales decline costs increase	Advertising Product/brand differentiation Reduce costs	User workshops Focus groups
Rejuvenation or end-of-life	Sales end or product is re-imagined	Discontinue manufacture or Redesign/reconceptualize Find new niches and market segments	Brainstorming User workshops Focus groups Benchmarking

7.2.2   Define cost-effectiveness.

7.2.3   Explain the importance of cost effectiveness to manufacturers.

© IBO 2007

Cost-effectiveness is the concept that an appropriate return will be obtained from the costs incurred. Costs are typically measured in monetary terms but can include time, stress, environmental change, man-hours etc. Similarly, the benefit is also often measured in monetary terms but can include cultural, heritage, lifestyle and environmental factors.

In terms of design, a decision may need to be made during the design process to accept an achievable compromise solution in order to bring a product to market, as opposed to continue toward a 'perfect' solution that ultimately may be too expensive for the target market. In order to maximize profits or meet a target sales cost, manufacturing methods and materials will be selected during the design and product development stages for efficiency and cost effectiveness.

7.2.4   Define quality control and quality assurance.

© IBO 2007

Quality control represents the creation of a system of process controls that lead to the production of products that meet defined specifications of quality. Quality control aims to reduce variation in manufacture through the statistical analysis of process variables, in order to identify changes in the process and correct them before quality is impacted. Central to the quality control process is the drive for continual improvement embodied in the Shewhart Cycle also known as the PDCA cycle, representing the stages of Plan, Do, Check and Act, illustrated in Figure 7.2.4.

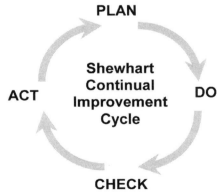

Figure 7.2.4 The Shewhart PDCA cycle

The philosophy of quality control and quality assurance was promoted by a number of consultants after World War II as part of a general movement toward quality management. This process has been largely credited with the rapid reputation for quality gained by products from Japan in the 1950s and 1960s. Notable among those involved in the quality movement were W. Edwards Deming, Joseph M. Juran and Walter A. Shewhart. These men, among others, changed the focus of quality from the removal of non-complying product during final inspection, to one of 'building in' quality at every stage of the process, thus avoiding waste and costly re-work.

Companies operating under quality assurance systems employ a process that details the procedures by which they manage their business at each stage of their operations, in order to identify and eliminate issues that may affect quality. The quality assurances approach aims to eliminate the need for intensive final inspection by ensuring that quality has been assessed progressively throughout production.

The international standard for quality assurance is ISO9001 and a company can undergo an auditing process to assess their systems for certification to this standard.

7.2.5   Compare quality control with quality assurance for manufactured products.

© IBO 2007

Quality control refers to the use of statistical methods of monitoring processes in order to maintain the process within defined limits.   Figure 7.2.5 illustrates two commonly used control charts used to monitor variation of mean and standard deviation. The X-axis may represent sample number or time.

By monitoring operations based on a statistical control of the various parts of a process, trends away from target can be highlighted and adjusted for, in order to maintain conformity and quality of output.

Quality assurance refers to the maintenance of a system that ensures that each stage of the process from design and purchasing through to final packaging and invoicing meets quality requirements, as detailed in a quality assurance standard such as ISO9001. Companies operating under a quality assurance regime must regularly open their systems to external audit to confirm that they are maintaining their systems, in order to retain quality assurance registration.

Control Chart

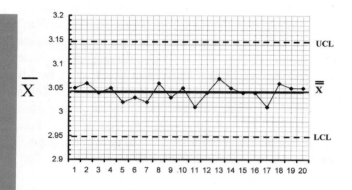

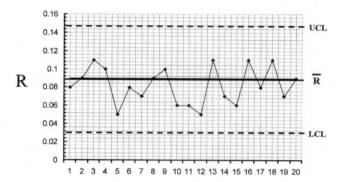

Figure 7.2.5a Process control charts monitoring variation of mean and standard deviation within upper and lower control limits.

7.2.6 Define performance test.

© IBO 2007

The performance test involves an assessment for compliance in relation to defined measures of performance, under conditions representing those expected in service. Such tests include the following:

- driving licence test
- fire protection testing
- safety testing of vehicles e.g. crash testing
- pressure testing of watches after a battery change.

7.2.7 Describe one advantage and one disadvantage of using a performance test to collect data.

© IBO 2007

Performance testing allows the collection of quantitative data on useability that may be difficult or dangerous to obtain using other methodologies.

Performance testing can have the disadvantages of requiring considerable time, effort and cost to perform. Costs associated with performance testing may also be prohibitive. In these circumstances virtual models may be tested, examples include: flow analysis for drag coefficients of vehicles, flight simulation testing of aircraft through finite element analysis, heat induced expansion and flammability tests etc.

7.2.8 Define field trial.

7.2.9 Describe one advantage and one disadvantage of using a field trial to collect data.

© IBO 2007

A field trial (sometimes called a product-in-use trial) takes the concept of a user trial into the general market place to observe how people 'actually' interact with the product. Participants are generally unaware that they are being observed.

This sort of investigation is important because consumer behaviour (what they do) is often different to what they say they would do. This data may not be detected during laboratory based user trials. Analysis of field trial data however, can be time consuming and interpretation sometimes difficult.

Further Reading

Darnell, M. J. *Bad Human Factors Designs* [http://www.baddesigns.com/]

7.3 EVALUATION AND THE CONSUMER

Value for money can be defined as the value gained for cost incurred. Good value for money would therefore indicate that the purchaser has made an assessment that a favourable exchange has been made. Such assessments will vary from purchaser to purchaser, depending on many different criteria of value, some of which are listed below:

- rarity
- quality
- prestige
- antiquity
- aesthetics
- usefulness
- peace of mind.
- heritage or cultural significance.

The price at which a consumer product is offered is extremely important for the success of any product. Manufacturers need to have accurately determined the need within the market for their product so that prices are set, such that consumers feel they are getting value for money. This position establishes the maximum price that can be charged.

Similarly, the manufacturer must make sufficient sales to recoup development and manufacturing costs, and eventually make a profit. The timeframe over which this payback is budgeted for will determine the minimum price charged.

Some manufacturers are able to offer their products at a price premium based on the popularity of branding or benefits accrued to the consumer through functionality, ease of use, reliability, brand loyalty or perceived prestige gained from purchasing and owning a particular product.

Consumers make assessment of value for money over the lifetime of their relationship with any consumer product.

At the pre-purchase stage this evaluation is largely, by necessity, based on reports from various sources such as friends, consumer groups, advertising, manufacturers specifications and reputation for quality and cost. A powerful influence is also prior experience of the consumer with the brand.

Following purchase, the consumer will assess value for money in terms of how well their expectations of the product have been met. At this stage, considerations of functionality, reliability, ease of use, running costs and performance become measurable factors.

Over the long term, the extent to which the product has maintained the characteristics for which it was purchased becomes increasingly important, however, fashion trends and desirability of a product may still be overriding features of a consumer's choice.

When making a decision, not all factors are of equal importance. In order to accommodate these differences in importance and allow an overall numerical value to be determined for the various options under consideration, a weighting is often assigned to the various factors reflecting their relative importance.

In order to assign a weighting, a scale needs to be agreed upon that allows an appropriate reflection of importance, and allows some consistency when applied across the various factors that will be considered. For instance, if a rating scale of 1 to 5 is chosen, the scale criteria may look like that shown in Figure 7.3.4a.

Scale	Criterion
1	Low importance
2	Slightly important
3	Medium importance/desirable
4	Moderately high importance
5	High importance

Figure 7.3.4a Weighting scale

The weighting is then assigned to each criterion, depending on the degree to which each of the competing products satisfies the consumer's requirements creating a decision matrix. When all of the numerical values are totalled for

each product, the product with the highest score should represent the best choice.

Note that, in making the decision matrix shown in Figure 7.3.4b, the desirable end of each factor would attract the maximum rating of 5 so that a high safety rating has attracted a weighting of 5, as has low cost.

Based on the relative importance assigned to each of the criteria, and the extent to which each option satisfied those criteria, the decision matrix shown in Figure 7.3.4b would suggest option 1 most fully meets the requirements of the consumer. Any number of specific criteria could of course be included within the decision matrix.

	Safety Rating Importance 5	Environmental Importance 3	Performance Importance 4	Aesthetics Importance 4	Cost Importance 5	Total
Option 1	$5 \times 5 = 25$	$5 \times 3 = 15$	$3 \times 4 = 12$	$4 \times 4 = 16$	$3 \times 5 = 15$	83
Option 2	$3 \times 5 = 15$	$3 \times 3 = 9$	$3 \times 4 = 12$	$3 \times 4 = 12$	$3 \times 5 = 15$	63
Option 3	$5 \times 5 = 25$	$3 \times 3 = 9$	$4 \times 4 = 16$	$3 \times 4 = 12$	$3 \times 5 = 15$	77
Option 4	$4 \times 5 = 20$	$4 \times 3 = 12$	$3 \times 4 = 12$	$1 \times 4 = 4$	$4 \times 5 = 20$	68
Option 5	$5 \times 5 = 25$	$4 \times 3 = 12$	$2 \times 4 = 8$	$2 \times 4 = 8$	$5 \times 5 = 25$	78

Figure 7.3.4b Decision matrix

7.3.5 Explain the relevance of quality assurance to consumers.

© IBO 2007

The indication that a company complies with a quality assurance standard, such as ISO9001, provides reassurance that the manufacturer has been assessed as maintaining a quality system that produces products to defined standards.

This means that the consumer can rely on the product meeting the standards of quality and useability advertised and that, should the product fail to meet those standards, some redress is available.

7.3.6 Discuss the role of consumer associations for product evaluation.

© IBO 2007

Consumer associations play an important part in informing consumers about the latest products and their relative merits. Through their magazine and website outlets, many of these associations supply independent third party test results to assist consumers in the process

of informed decision-making. A selection of these is listed below:

- Consumer Reports Magazine
online at http://www.consumerreports.org/
- Consumer Magazine
online at http://www.consumer.org.nz/
- Consumer Choice Magazine
online at http://www.consumer-voice.org/
- Choice Magazine
online at http://www.choice.com.au/
- Ethical Consumer Magazine
online at http://www.ethicalconsumer.org/
- Tashikana Me (Critical Eyes)

Within this group could be included the crash testing of cars, that, while undertaken by manufacturers to provide information in the design process, is also undertaken by independent third party organizations to rate impact safety for consumers in systems such as the New Car Assessment Program (NCAP), which gives a safety rating of up to five stars for the safety of new vehicles.

Euro NCAP : European New Car Assessment Program
ANCAP : Australasian New Car Assessment Program

7.3.7 Explain the contribution of the media and education to product evaluation.

© IBO 2007

In addition to the work of consumer associations, many specialist publications are available for the consumer to consult as part of their pre-purchase evaluation of products. These sources of information help educate the purchaser about the various product criteria issues they should consider before making a purchase.

Through the medium of television, a range of strategies may be employed to raise consumer awareness. 'Lifestyle' programs raise issues associated with new product launches, existing product reviews and consumer rights education.

Education curricula around the world incorporate enquiry and evaluative skills into many of their courses. Specific teaching courses are written to provide information about product evaluation techniques (Design and Technology), consumer rights (Business Studies), design and aesthetics (Art) and materials testing/properties (Science).

Further Reading

Berens, G., van Riel, Cees B.M. & van Bruggen, G. H. (2005). *Corporate Associations and Consumer Product Responses: The Moderating Role of Corporate Brand Dominance.* Journal of Marketing. Vol. 69. pp. 35–48.

Laroche, M., Papadopoulos, N., Heslop, L. A., Mourali, M. (2005). *The influence of country image structure on consumer evaluations of foreign products.* International Marketing Review 22 (1), pp. 96–115.

Souiden, N., Kassim, N.M., Hong, H.J. (2006). *The Effect of Corporate Branding Dimensions on Consumers' Product Evaluation - A Cross-cultural Analysis.* European Journal of Marketing. Vol. 40 No. 7/8, pp. 825–845.

Exercises

1. Field trials:
   A.   test products in fields
   B.   test a product's economic survivability
   C.   test product prototypes to determine durability
   D.   test products in environments where they are going to be used.

2. Performance tests may also be known as:
   A.   benchmarking
   B . compliance testing
   C.   quality control testing
   D.   environmental testing.

3. Expert appraisal:
   A.   may be difficult to procure
   B.   produces better results than a user trial
   C.   involves teams of experts consulting users
   D.   produces the most accurate information on a new product design.

4. The concept of value for money:
   A.   is a result of expert opinion
   B.   is determined by consumers
   C.   involves a very precise calculation
   D.   remains a constant once established.

5. Explain how consumer associations assist purchasers.

6. Explain how digital technologies have improved the efficiency of literature searches.

7. Explain how financial cost effectiveness relates to design.

8. Explain the difference between qualitative and quantitative assessment.

9. Discuss the nature of field trials for product evaluation.

10. Explain the differences between quality control and quality assurance.

11. Outline why product evaluation criteria may require different weightings.

12. Discuss how consumer advocate groups can affect product design.

ENERGY

8

CONTENTS

AHL

The word energy comes from the Greek word *energeia*, and appears in the writings of Aristotle as early as the 4th Century BC. Before the Industrial Revolution, societies relied on physical strength and animal power, supplemented by water, fire and wind to assist improving lifestyles. The Industrial Revolution brought enhanced waterpower, steam engines, mechanization and, eventually electricity, which delivered significant benefits to industry, national economies and social structures. Today, the digital revolution has improved automation, refined quality control and assisted industry and consumer access to global markets.

This unit exams global energy demands and the rapid rise of developing economies presenting a new set of challenges, as traditional finite fuel resources continue to be depleted and the earth's environment responds to years of accumulated polluting emissions from industry, power generation and transportation systems.

Bangkok's BRT, rapid transit system

Image by Cate Metcalfe

8.1 HISTORICAL OVERVIEW

8.1.1   Outline two types of energy.

© IBO 2007

There are many forms of energy: heat, chemical, gravitational and electrical to name but a few. Each of the various forms of energy may be classified as either Kinetic or Potential Energy. Both forms of energy are measured in joules and their respective formulae broken down into the units: 1 (kilogram (metre squared)) per (second squared) = 1 joule.

Kinetic Energy is the energy of motion and may be calculated through the formula: $KE = \frac{1}{2}mv^2$, where Kinetic Energy is equal to half the mass (kg) multiplied by its velocity squared (m/s^2).

Kinetic energy exists in objects and materials such as:

- light
- sound
- wind
- electricity
- microwaves
- objects in motion.

Potential Energy is stored energy and may be calculated through the formula: $PE = mgh$, where Potential Energy is equal to an object's mass (kg) multiplied by the force

137

of gravitational attraction (9.8 m/s^2) and its height (m) above the ground. Potential Energy exists in objects and materials such as:

- oil
- batteries
- magnets
- nuclear fuel
- compressed springs
- objects suspended above the ground.

Note, every object, (whose temperature is above absolute zero), possesses thermal energy.

> 8.1.2 Describe how human muscle power was the only source of energy for (craft) production until the Industrial Revolution.
>
> © IBO 2007

While windmills and water-wheels had been around for centuries, energy for craft production was mostly provided by human muscle. Most manufacturing took place in cottages in rural villages. Hand-operated bellows forced air into the blacksmith's forge, hand or foot operated spinning wheels allowed for plant and animal fibres to be spun into thread, while others wove the yarn into cloth. Timber fashioned with basic hand tools. Leather goods, clothing, silverware and food products were all made in a similar fashion. Little changed from one generation to the next as sons adopted the role their fathers had previously occupied.

> 8.1.3 Describe how development of machines based on flowing water led to a revolution in production.
>
> © IBO 2007

With the introduction of automation, new materials (such as wrought iron) and a better understanding of hydraulics, water-wheels found a place as effective and efficient providers of energy. Water-wheels soon found uses driving flourmills, textile equipment and mechanical hammers for forging and tool making. Richard Arkwright provided a breakthrough in cotton thread production with the introduction of his water or spinning frame in 1769. Using the constant speed provided by flowing water, this device combined eight threads at once to produce a coarser, though stronger and tighter twisted yarn than that produced by the spinning jenny. The water frame improved the speed of textile produced and thus reduced costs.

Unfortunately water-wheels could only be placed near reliable, fast flowing rivers. They, of course, were permanent installations, and thus provided little flexibility.

> 8.1.4 Describe how the invention of the steam engine and the use of steam as the basis for the operation of machines led to a large increase in scale of production based on coal.
>
> © IBO 2007

The Industrial Revolution saw the switch from sustainable forms of energy: man, animal and waterpower, to an increasing dependence on steam power, essentially fuelled by coal.

Man, water or beast could not provide the power required for the newly developed machine technologies Steam engines provided this power through the exploitation of Great Britain's large deposits of coal. The Industrial Revolution was dependent on coal, not just for its capacity to drive steam engines, but also in the manufacture of iron.

The coincidental development of steam power and iron making technologies created a symbiosis that was to drive the Industrial Revolution for years. Coal provided the much needed power to drive steam engines that were, in turn, required to assist in the making of iron. The circle closes when the improved quality of iron allows better machinery to further develop tools and machinery that, again, improve the efficiency of steam engines. Better machinery and tools assist with the building of bridge networks across the country and ships that were the great enablers of improved trade.

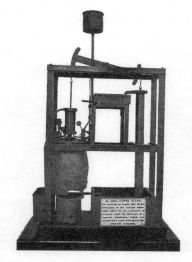

Figure 8.1.4 Newcomen steam engine, improved by James Watt between 1763 and 1775, resulting in the first modern steam engine.

Steam powered mechanization of industries, such as the production of cotton textiles, saw production rates soar and prices plummet. In the first half of the 18th Century cotton prices fell by 90% while production rates multiplied by a factor of 150 in Britain alone. Other industries felt similar benefits. Britain's textile industry grew to rival that of India and China and eventually became the leader in a globally competitive industry.

With a more flexible power source, steam powered textiles factories spread across the British landscape, no longer limited to riverside locations. British industry was thriving, not only on textiles manufacturing, but also on the manufacturing of textiles related machinery. By 1840 the cotton industry had left behind waterpower and embraced steam-powered mechanization. Most other industries were lagging behind. It wasn't until the middle of the 19th Century that mechanization had spread throughout the entire British manufacturing industry. Previously, cotton had been the sustaining force behind the development British engineering.

> 8.1.5 Explain how the development of electricity led to a technological revolution and an increased volume of production.
>
> © IBO 2007

In 1809, the British scientist Humphry Davy invented the first electric light when he connected a battery to a charcoal strip. The charged, glowing, carbon became the first arc lamp.

Humphry Davy's laboratory assistant was Michael Faraday, who in 1821, demonstrated the conversion of electrical energy into mechanical energy. He passed a current through a suspended wire, (dipped in a container of mercury and placed on a permanent magnet). The resulting rotation of the wire around the magnet showed the current giving rise to a circular, magnetic field around the wire.

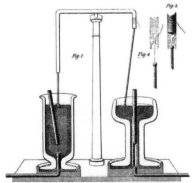

Figure 8.1.5 Drawing of Michael Faraday's experiment demonstrating electromagnetic rotation

Although others, such as Peter Barlow and Ányos Jedlik, further developed these principles. These devices were for demonstration purposes only.

It wasn't until 1832 that British scientist William Sturgeon developed the first commutator-type DC motor with the capability to power machinery. Commercial versions of this development followed when Emily and Thomas Davenport, (1837), patented a 600 rpm motor capable of running machinery and a printing press.

Telecommunications, however, was the first area to benefit significantly from electricity as a series of inventions revolutionized the speed and reliability of long distance communication through innovators such as:

- Joseph Henry (1797–1878) working independently of Faraday, established the principle of the electromagnetic telegraph in the USA
- William Fothergill Cooke (1806–1879) and Charles Wheatstone (1802–1875) demonstrated a five-needle electric telegraph
- Samuel Morse (1791–1872) created the single wire telegraph in 1838 with the help of the engineer Alfred Vail.

With a reliable system of sending messages, the use of the telegraph grew tremendously throughout the world. European countries adopted a modified form of the Morse Code in 1851, which became known as 'continental' or 'international code'. The Society of Telegraph Engineers (later to become the Institute of Electrical Engineers) was founded in 1871 and the growth of telegraphy closely followed the development of rail transportation. This was largely due to the existing clearways as well as the need of the railways themselves for an efficient means to control train movements. Better transport management meant more efficient trade.

Well into the 1800s, apart from lighthouses, electricity for lighting was still uncommon. It wasn't until steady, continuous current was available, without the overheating of generators, that electricity became more affordable and arc lamps were a practical alternative to gaslight.

Through a series of unrelated but important inventions, the cost of electricity dropped and its reliability improved. This led to greater uptake as the use of electricity spread rapidly from the 1870s onwards. By 1900 the cost of an incandescent light bulb was 20% of what it had been only 20 years earlier, its efficiency had also improved 100%.

The combination of electricity and the rearrangement of working styles through such approaches as assembly-line production improved the efficiency of factories. Interchangeable parts, and the continuous flow of product on electrically driven conveyor belts past stationary workers, allowed the chassis line in the Ford motor plant in 1913, to reduce assembly times from 12½ hours to 2 hours 40 minutes within 3 months of being installed. Reductions in production times directly translated to greater production volumes and reduced prices.

> **8.1.6 Identify uses for the electric motor in industrial production.**
>
> © IBO 2007

Like other forms of classification, motors may be categorized in a variety of ways. Essentially, they may be divided into to forms based on their power source i.e. alternating current (AC) or direct current (DC), electrical motors. However other categories include:

- application
- power source
- internal construction
- type of motion provided.

A sample of some of the different types of motors, their features and applications appears below.

AC motors are low cost, low maintenance, reliable motors most often tasked to fixed speed applications in both industrial and household applications. The overwhelming majority are AC induction motors found in: air conditioners, washing machines, clothes dryers, industrial machinery, fans, vacuum cleaners etc.

Brushed DC motors stem from the very earliest designs of electric motors. They are most often used where variable, or speeds, or torque, control is required. Most industrial DC motors can operate over a wide range of speeds and down to as low as 5% of base speed. Heat dissipating properties of DC motors allow these low operating speeds to be achieved.

Servomotors may employ AC or DC power to rotate their shafts. These shafts, while not rotating freely, do move very accurately to predetermined positions, based on angular displacement. They differ from stepper systems in that they employ a continuous position feedback system while the motor is running. Servo motors find application in: vehicle steering boxes, camera auto focusing systems, movement control in robotics and computer hard disk drives.

Stepper Motors are fast spinning motors that can be controlled precisely. They are often used in industrial situations where extreme precision is required, such as multi-axis CNC machinery, pick and place robots, computer printers and plotters.

Figure 8.1.6 Range of motor types and sizes

Image by C J Cowie GNU free documentation license, version 1.2

> **8.1.7 Explain how the production and distribution of electricity led to large-scale energy usage, security of supply and the geographical spread of production away from the source of energy supplies.**
>
> © IBO 2007

Thomas Edison created the world's first large-scale electricity distribution network when he supplied 110 volts of DC to a small number of customers in Lower Manhattan. For years, a significant and acrimonious battle raged between Edison and Tesla over the most suitable style of current to be adopted in a widespread fashion. While AC cannot be stored in a battery for later use, it can be readily transformed to higher or lower voltages. Because of this, very high voltages can be transmitted from power stations and later stepped down by local transformers for domestic use. Similarly, small individual transformers can be used to operate portable low voltage appliances. Unfortunately, DC voltage cannot easily be changed to allow us to reduce transmission losses through a conductor. The result of this is that DC cannot usually be sent efficiently over long distances. This was a major factor in the widespread adoption of AC for electrical power distribution.

In 1888 Alternating Current won the day with Nicola Tesla being generally credited with its establishment as an efficient and safe means of electrical transmission over long distances. However, even at the beginning of the

AHL

20th Century, electricity was still a relatively expensive commodity in comparison with other sources of energy such as gas, which was still well entrenched in the supply of energy for lighting, not to mention heating and cooking. Electricity availability, such as it was, was confined to the provision of lighting and was therefore generated only during the evening.

Once AC power was adopted, economies of scale developed as interconnected generating plants sprung up across the countryside. Demand increased, reliability improved, capital investment requirements reduced and lower costs were offered to consumers. The supply of electricity supported the rapid growth of infrastructure and economic development of industrialized nations. In many situations, the expansion of government built generation plants was boosted by the needs of WWI. These plants were later connected to domestic networks, sometimes requiring long distance transmission.

Today, power stations, such as those shown in Figure 8.1.7, are strategically positioned around the country. They supply electricity grids with three-phase power across large areas to power heavy industry via sub-stations. Alternative voltages are distributed dependent on customer need, load requirements and duration of load.

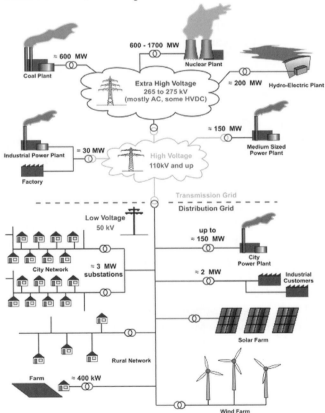

Figure 8.1.7 Electricity grid schematic

Image by MBizon [CC-BY-3.0 (www.creativecommons. org/licenses/by/3.0)], via Wikimedia Commons

8.1.8 Explain how the development of localized, portable sources of electrical energy in the form of batteries changed the nature of energy usage and the development of new types of products.

© IBO 2007

A battery consists of an electrochemical cell converting stored chemical energy into on-demand electrical energy. Allessandro Volta is credited with the development of the first battery or 'voltaic pile'. It was built of many individual cells, each consisting of a disks of copper and zinc or silver, separated by cloth soaked in acid or brine.

Today, batteries come in many sizes, from miniature cells used to power small portable devices to back-up battery systems providing emergency power for industry. They have now become a commonplace technology, powering everything from essential everyday items to industrial machinery.

Figure 8.1.8a Alessandro Volta's voltaic pile, invented in 1800, the first electric battery

Image by Luigi Chiesa (Own work) [GFDL (www.gnu.org/ copyleft/fdl.html) or CC-BY-3.0 (www.creativecommons. org/licenses/by/3.0)], via Wikimedia Commons

The mobile phone industry owes its current success to the development of smaller and less bulky phones. This was brought about by simultaneous innovations in battery technology and more energy-efficient electronic components. Battery technologies have continued to develop alongside the miniaturization of electronic devices and their subsequent computerization. Innovation in this field continues as technology strives to improve battery life and increase power delivery in smaller, lighter and cheaper packages. The range of battery sizes and energy capacities include:

- micro batteries for: watches, calculators, mobile phones, hearing aids etc.
- small batteries for portable equipment including: torches, toys, remote controls, radios, laptops, UPSs etc.
- medium sized batteries for powering automobiles, motorbikes, lawnmowers, forklifts etc.
- large batteries find application in industrial situations as reserve power supplies, powering conventional submarines and storing power from solar cells.

Figure 8.1.8b AA alkaline battery

Further Reading

Clark, G. & Jacks, D. (2007). *Coal and the Industrial Revolution, 1700–1869.* European Review of Economic History, 11, 39–72. Cambridge University Press. United Kingdom.

O'Brien, Patrick, K., Griffiths, Trevor, and Hunt, David (1996). *'Technological Change during the First Industrial Revolution: the Paradigm Case of Textiles,'* in Technological Change: Methods and Themes in the History of Technology, ed. By R. Fox, Amsterdam, Harwood, pp. 155-76.

Sieferle. R. (2001). *The Subterranean Forest: Energy Systems and the Industrial Revolution,* Cambridge.

Temin, Peter (1997). *'Two Views of the British Industrial Revolution,'* Journal of Economic History, Vol. 57, pp. 63-82.

Motors. (1997). *Power Transmission Design* (Excerpted from an article by Siemens in the May 1996 issue of PTD).

8.2 TYPES OF ENERGY: ECONOMIC, ENVIRONMENTAL AND POLITICAL ASPECTS

8.2.1 List the main forms of non-renewable energy sources.

8.2.2 Discuss the efficiency of conversion of fossil fuels into electrical energy.

© IBO 2007

Oil, coal and natural gas are the most commonly used forms of non-renewable energy, but oil shales and tar sands are alternative forms of fossil fuel. While timber can be a renewable resource, as a fuel it cannot be replaced as quickly as it is consumed.

The efficiency of coal and natural gas-powered electricity generation plants vary due to a range of factors, however, statistics produced by the energy industry itself show their relative effectiveness:

- coal fired   37% - 44%
- natural gas   50% – 54%

Data source: The American National Petroleum Council, (2007). Oil is not often used for generation of electricity, (less than 1% in America), but efficiency figures fall somewhere between coal and natural gas.

From the figures above it can be determined, regardless of the fuel used, between 40% and 60% of the energy potential of fossil fuels is lost through cooling towers and smoke stacks, most often in the form of heat.

8.2.3 Outline how modern industrial societies have become dependent on non-renewable fossil fuels as the major sources of energy supply and electricity production.

© IBO 2007

After, and as a consequence of the Industrial Revolution, greenhouse gases have continued to rise. Many scientists believe this a direct consequence of the burning of fossil fuels for power generation, land clearing and changing agricultural practices.

Today, while non-industrialized economies still produce large percentages of their energy requirements from the physical efforts of people and/or animals, cheap, readily available and reliable supplies of electricity continue to meet the needs of more industrialized nations. In the US alone, coal-fired power stations produce the bulk of the electricity consumed. The US Department of Energy, (2005), quotes fossil fuel energy production at 86% of the nation's output. These figures are similar in other industrialized nations. Dependence on oil and, to a lesser degree, natural gas also continues. However, price fluctuations, supply issues and the looming depletion of fossil fuels make the long-term maintenance of this situation unsustainable.

> **8.2.4** Outline the main pollutants produced from the large-scale burning of fossil fuels worldwide.
>
> © IBO 2007

Combustion of coal and oil produces both significant amounts of nitrogen oxides, sulphur dioxide, carbon dioxide and mercury compounds.

Nitrogen oxides and sulphur dioxide, contribute to the formation of acid rain. This in turn has led to the acidification of soils and waterways as well as the corrosion of buildings and civil structures. Sulphur dioxide is also associated with respiratory disease and the aggravation of existing cardio-vascular problems. While carbon dioxide is a good transmitter of light, its resistance to the free passage of infrared radiation passing from the earth contributes to global warming and all of its associated issues. The burning of coal and fuel oil also releases particulate matter into the atmosphere. Mixing with sulphurous impurities and water vapour, this mixture creates a chemical fog, or smog, that covers many industrialized cities. Toxic ash is an after-product of the burning of coal and is most often simply disposed of in landfill.

Natural gas is the cleanest of all the fossil fuels to burn, producing lesser amounts of carbon dioxide and carbon monoxide than oil and coal. Water vapour is a harmless by-product of combustion, but small amounts of sulphur dioxide and oxides of nitrogen and particulate matter are generated.

> **8.2.5** Describe the main effect of carbon dioxide emissions from the large-scale burning of fossil fuels.
>
> © IBO 2007

Carbon dioxide is not technically classified as an atmospheric pollutant because it naturally occurs in the atmosphere and is a requirement to enable natural processes, such as photosynthesis in plants. The burning of fossil fuels releases carbon dioxide that has been stored for millions of years. Scientists and climatologists cite the accumulation of carbon dioxide and other greenhouse gases as contributors to trends in global warming. While there is some debate over the causes of the increased levels of greenhouse gases, as a reality, global warming has particular climatic, ecological, political, economic and social implications.

Professor Ove Hoegh-Guldberg, Director, Centre for Marine Studies, The University of Queensland, (2007), states, "There is no longer any serious doubt that the earth has warmed by 0.6—0.8 degrees Celsius since 1880 and will warm a further 2—6 degrees Celsius by 2100, almost exclusively due to human activity. Atmospheric concentrations of carbon dioxide are now 100 parts per million above those seen over the past 650,000 years, and rates of increase are 2—3 orders of magnitude above most of those periods in which the temperature of the planet changed."

The effects of global warming include:

- transmission of disease through warmer temperatures and standing water
- destruction of ecosystems, habitat and biodiversity as climate patterns change
- more intense droughts and heat waves increases causing food security problems
- rising sea level caused the melting of polar ice and glaciers increasing the amount of water in seas and oceans
- economic discontinuities brought about by damage to land, infrastructure and crops caused by intense storms and flooding.
- overall increase in worldwide precipitation, giving rise to flooding and storms; warmer ocean waters increase severe storm activity.

> **8.2.6** Discuss the use of technologies to make energy conversion from fossil fuels more efficient and cleaner.
>
> © IBO 2007

Clean coal technologies are aimed at improving the environmental impact of coal fired power plants at every stage of the energy production life cycle. Examples of this 'clean' technology in action include:

- capturing carbon dioxide and sequestering it permanently underground
- removing of impurities from coal before burning to improve combustion and reduce emissions
- capturing the greenhouse gas methane during mining operations to be used as an additional source of energy
- adopting more stringent pollution control measures designed to capture greater amounts of atmospheric pollutants generated when coal is burned
- employing new, more effective combustion processes such as gasification technologies to convert coal directly to hydrogen gas - to extract the maximum amount of energy from the coal.

8.2.7 Discuss two approaches to reducing the enhanced greenhouse effect based on international agreements to reduce emissions of CO_2 and the promotion of clean technologies.

© IBO 2007

The Kyoto Protocol was adopted in Kyoto, Japan, in December 1997. It is an international agreement of 37 countries linked to the United Nations Framework Convention on Climate Change and establishing legally binding targets created to reduce greenhouse gas emissions. The protocol identifies the need to cut worldwide carbon dioxide emissions by 5% from levels measured in 1990. The Kyoto Protocol encourages the meeting of targets through a range of economic or market-based processes. These approaches were designed to provide a framework to encourage green investment and include:

- emissions trading
- joint implementation
- clean development mechanisms.

The Asia-Pacific Partnership on Clean Development and Climate (APPCDC) was created to assist with the development and deployment of clean energy technologies. It is sometimes seen as an alternative to the Kyoto protocol particularly by nations who have not agreed to ratify the agreement. The model uses a unique combination of government and private industry representatives to achieve goals aimed at reducing pollution and greenhouse gases, addressing the affects of global warming, improving

national energy security and promoting sustainable economic growth and poverty reduction throughout its member nations. The significance of the group's seven member countries: Australia, Canada, China, India, Japan, Republic of Korea and the United States lies in the fact that, combined, they encompass more than 50% of the world's economy, population and energy use.

The vision statement from the Inaugural Ministerial, held in Sydney, Australia in 2006 stated, "we will work together, in accordance with our respective national circumstances, to create a new partnership to develop, deploy and transfer cleaner, more efficient technologies and to meet national pollution reduction, energy security and climate change concerns, consistent with the principles of the U.N. Framework Convention on Climate Change (UNFCCC)". Specifically the APPCDC has approved the formation of task forces to investigate technological solutions surrounding:

- steel
- cement
- aluminium
- coal mining
- cleaner fossil energy
- buildings and appliances
- power generation and transmission
- renewable energy and distributed generation.

8.2.8 List the main forms of renewable energy sources.

8.2.9 Explain why there is increasing pressure to use renewable energy sources.

© IBO 2007

Renewable energy technologies include: solar, wind, biomass, geothermal, wave or tidal and hydroelectricity. Increasing pressure to use these renewable energy sources comes from a number of considerations:

- fossil fuel prices continue to rise
- burning fossil fuels generates greenhouse gases
- alternative energy sources are free after infrastructure costs
- alternative energy sources generate no pollution from their production
- fossil fuels are a finite resource yet alternative fuel sources are sustainable
- pollution from burning fossil fuels is hazardous to the environment and human health
- supplies and costs of fossil fuels are not always reliable due to areas of political instability.

8.2.10 Discuss the limitations of the use of renewable energy resources as alternatives for fossil fuels.

Each of these systems has a range of advantages and disadvantages associated with their use. At this point because of the high capital investment in infrastructure large scale applications come at a premium. Figure 8.2.10b evaluates each of the technologies independently. Solar and wind technologies are reviewed in detail in section 8.3.

Figure 8.2.10a A small segment of the San Gorgonio Pass Wind Farm White Water California

By Khashmi316 at en.wikipedia [GFDL (www.gnu.org/copyleft/fdl.html) or CC-BY-SA-3.0 (www.creativecommons.org/ licenses/by-sa/3.0/)], from Wikimedia Commons

Energy type	Advantages	Disadvantages
biomass	plants and trees can be re-grown quickly for reuse assists in the management of solid waste prevent atmospheric venting of methane	extraction/refining of biomass energy can be expensive carbon based and thus causes air pollution similar to fossil fuels competition for arable land and food crops
geothermal	power plants take little room potential to supply base-load energy low running costs	suitable locations difficult to find often remote locations harmful gases may be released as part of the drilling process sites may inexplicably lose their ability to produce steam
wave / tidal	potential for base-load energy no fuel and no waste inexpensive to operate and maintain costs are projected to be reasonable	can be costly to develop remote location for plant environmental impact
hydroelectricity	well developed proven technology long life plant inexpensive to operate easily stopped and started	limited potential locations large areas may be flooded and dammed adverse environmental impact

Figure 8.2.10b Evaluation of a range of alternative energy technologies

8.2.12 Discuss the role of energy conservation in energy policy.

As a direct consequence of the oil crises of 1970s, oil importing nations became concerned about both the price and volatility of energy supplies. National energy policies started to consider not only energy conservation but also sustainable, renewable alternatives to fossil fuels, in particular oil. The burning of coal for energy has also come more into focus not only from a supply perspective, but more in terms of greenhouse gas generation. Developments in renewable energy policy, energy efficiency and conservation are complementary. Through government policy and legislation they combine to meet the following goals:

- reducing dependence on a single fuel types
- mandating energy performance and resource usage criteria
- replacing imported energy with a sustainable domestic supply
- adoption of energy conservation legislation and education programs
- increasing research and development into new and renewable forms of energy
- substituting fossil fuel-based energy with alternative, renewable energy types across a range of fields including: building, manufacturing and transport.

8.2.13 Outline new sources of energy.

© IBO 2007

Biofuels such as biodiesel and ethanol may provide sustainable alternatives to traditional fossil fuels. They do however come with their own unique set of problems and, as outlined below are not panaceas for the current problems surrounding non-renewable fuel resources.

Biodiesel is a sustainable fuel produced from a variety of natural sources including vegetable oils and animal fats and is a cleaner burning alternative to petroleum-based diesel. Biodiesel has experienced some success at using both small and large-scale production methodologies. There is a large range of source materials from which to create the fuel including but not limited to: rapeseed, cottonseed, soybean, flax, sunflower, peanut, canola, safflower, palm oil, hemp, corn, waste vegetable oils, fats and tallows.

Ethanol can be manufactured from the conversion of renewable plant materials such as: sugar cane, sugar beets, sorghum, switch grass, corn, wheat and barley. It may be combined with gasoline to act as a conventional fuel extender. While ethanol burns cleaner and generates fewer toxic emissions than gasoline, not all vehicles can use 100% ethanol, many however, can cope with ethanol/gasoline blends.

While biofuels may be better for the environment, growing crops for fuel places a strain on food supply chains and may increase food costs. As a side issue, until distribution infrastructure improves, biofuels will not a viable alternative.

New sources of biofuel continue to be uncovered and tested. In 2007, Sony announced research into a Biofuel Cell using sugar in the form of glucose. American scientists have also recently tested a biodiesel created from chicken feather meal. The 237th National Meeting of the American Chemical Society also reviewed a study outlining the environmentally friendly process of converting algae into biodiesel.

8.2.14 Discuss the contribution of biomass as a renewable energy resource.

© IBO 2007

Biomass is a renewable source of energy derived from plants and animals. There are a variety of ways of extracting the solar energy stored in these organic, carbon-based materials including:

- direct thermal conversion or burning to produce heat or steam for generating electricity
- biochemical fermentation involving the extraction of ethanol or biodiesel from plant material such as corn, for use as vehicular fuel alternative or supplement to gasoline
- bacterial decay of dead plants and animals to produce combustible gaseous fuels such as methane. Some landfills are currently used as recovery sites for methane gas.

Biomass fuels currently provide around 4% of the energy used in the United States.

Further Reading

Baliunas, S. (2002). *The Kyoto Protocol and Global Warming*. The Lavoisier Group Inc. Australia.

Matysek, A., Ford, M., Jakeman, G., Gurney, A. & Fisher, B. S. (2006). *Technology its Role in Economic Development and Climate Change*. Abare Research Report. 06.6.

Nordhaus, N. (2010). *Economic Aspects of Global Warming in a Post-Copenhagen Environment*. Department of Economics. Yale University. New Haven. USA.

Rockwell, R. C. (1998). *From A Carbon Economy To A Mixed Economy: A Global Opportunity*. Consequences. Vol. 4, No. 1.

Risten, R.A. & Kraushaar, J. P. (2005). *Energy and the Environment*. Wiley. 2nd Edition.

8.3 CASE STUDIES

Solar power

> 8.3.1 Describe how solar power can be harnessed for use in domestic products.
>
> © IBO 2007

Active solar energy may be harnessed in one of two ways for use in domestic products. Solar energy may be collected as thermal energy or gathered and converted into electricity via a photovoltaic cell.

Thermal energy collected by solar panels may be used for heating:

- water
- interior spaces
- swimming pools.

Photovoltaic panels use sunlight to produce electricity. While power may only be generated during daylight hours these panels can not only supply power to a household but may sell excess power back to the grid. Modular by nature, solar panels may be assembled to create units of varying size and generating capacity Off-grid solar arrays require battery back up to store energy for use when panels are unable to generate a current. Photovoltaic cells may be employed to generate electricity for:

- portable equipment
- general urban domestic use
- commercial building applications
- equipment or households in remote situations.

> 8.3.2 Identify the advantages and disadvantages of solar power.
>
> © IBO 2007

Advantages	Disadvantages
Small units available for domestic use	Costly initial capital outlay
Can be employed in remote locations	Cannot provide continuous base load supply
Solar cells make no noise and generate no pollution in their use	Night time, rain and cloud affect performance
	Battery back up or hot fluid storage required
Ease of installation and maintenance	Panels can be energy intensive to manufacture

> 8.3.3 Describe the design of a solar cooker.
>
> 8.3.4 Discuss the importance of solar cooking in sustainable development.
>
> © IBO 2007

Solar cookers are used for a variety of purposes including cooking food, boiling or purifying water and, sterilizing instruments and grains.

They take a variety of design forms including box and parabolic. However, all effective solar cooker designs must consider the following three principles:

- heat gain – solar cookers are designed to accept direct and indirect forms of sunlight. They often use shiny reflective surfaces to concentrate sunlight onto darker areas (such as cooking pots) that more readily absorb the heat energy. As a rule, the more direct sunlight collected, the greater the energy absorption.
- heat loss – to maintain cooking temperatures solar cookers must trap incoming energy and minimize heat losses that may occur through the mechanisms of conduction, radiation, and convection. Sealing air gaps and adding insulation may reduce heat loss.
- heat storage – once trapped heat may be stored in thermal mass inside the cooker or in the cooking pot itself.

The importance of solar cooking and its social impact on communities in developing economies is examined in Sustainable Development, Topic 12.1.3.

Energy and transport

> 8.3.5 Compare individual and mass transport systems for sustainable development.
>
> 8.3.6 Discuss the barriers to transition from individual cars to mass public transport systems.
>
> © IBO 2007

Sustainable transportation systems are designed to limit damage to the environment. They do this through reduced emissions, reduced dependence on fossil fuels and recovery of landuse from transport infrastructure towards re-establishing natural habitats and ecosystems.

AHL

The European Council of Ministers of Transport (ECMT, 2004), endorsed the following three criteria meeting the definition of sustainable transport:

- Allows the basic access and development needs of individuals, companies and society to be met safely and in a manner consistent with human and ecosystem health, and promotes equity within and between successive generations.
- Is affordable, operates fairly and efficiently, offers a choice of transport mode and supports a competitive economy, as well as balanced regional development.
- Limits emissions and waste within the planet's ability to absorb them, uses renewable resources at or below their rates of generation, and uses non-renewable resources at or below the rates of development of renewable substitutes, while minimizing the impact on the use of land and the generation of noise.

There exists a range of transport systems and approaches available, each of which have their advantages, disadvantages and varying degrees of sustainability. Major types include:

Heavy Rail - this mode of transport may have high impacts on land use through track deployment and station space required. Its major advantages stem from carrying capacity, speed and accessibility. Heavy rail may also appear in a subway configuration.

Commuter Rail – uses existing rail lines and services outlying areas from major development centres. This option potentially removes thousands of cars from inner city roads, reduces congestion and subsequent pollution. Larger distances are involved than heavy rail and lesser stations located further apart.

Light Rail – improving in popularity, this form of transit system comprises of smaller networks offering residents local transportation in densely populated urban locations, often over walkable distances.

Each of the rail alternatives heavy: commuter and light rail are costly and tied to fixed routes. Careful planning is required to ensure future needs and potential changes to population needs do not make the chosen solution inappropriate.

Streetcar or tram – these systems run on overhead power lines connected via a pantograph. Networks are quickly established and inexpensive compared to rail alternatives. Networks are also easily extended if required. Streetcars run in conjunction with other road users including trucks,

buses, cars, and cyclists. Individual cars hold between 45 to 100 passengers. Replica and vintage streetcars often evoke a sense of nostalgia and are popular as tourist attractions where they have been resurrected with some success.

Figure 8.3.5a Streetcar Nagasaki Japan

Buses are a lower-cost solution to mass transit. As a means of public transport buses can be effective and affordable. Taking little more road space than a few vehicles, buses can carry many more passengers. Modern bus systems are quieter, less polluting and more comfortable than their older counterparts. Buses are an important alternative in developing nations as passengers move from being pedestrians or cyclists to passengers.

In highly congested CBDs, public transport systems are seen as time efficient modes of transport particularly when dedicated tracks or lanes are provided to cut through traffic congestion.

Individual vehicles - In industrialized nations car use dominates public transport, cities are planned around their use, yet congestion, pollution and space required for infrastructure (roads, parking etc.) has not stalled its progress. Car use is still the preferred mode of travel for individuals and families. Car ownership translated directly in the vehicle being the major form of transport used. Some attempts have been made in urbanized centres to reduce car use through strategies such as: car pooling, higher parking fees, provision of better public transport networks, adding dedicated cycle ways and pedestrian walkways.

Motorcycles – While motorcycles are smaller than cars and offer a great deal of flexibility and freedom to riders, there is some debate over their contribution to pollution. Some researchers report motorcycles as being more polluting than automobiles. In developing nations, the transition towards industrialization also raises worker's standards of living and their desire for better forms of personal transport. The motorcycle is often used as a transition vehicle between the bicycle and the automobile. In developing economies such as Viet Nam the number of motorcycles continues to increase. The Viet Nam National Environmental Performance Assessment Report, (2001), noted, *'the number of motorcycles in Viet Nam has been increasing rapidly. In 2000 alone, an increase of 14.2% was observed, and the numbers are expected to continue to grow. Associated with this rapid increase in vehicles has been poor air quality in urban areas.'*

Figure 8.3.5b Motorcycle congestion HCMC Viet Nam

Walking and cycling are sustainable transportation modes but they are often only regarded as recreational activities. The aim of governments is to translate this interest into a serious transportation alternative. Through the development of dedicated cycle ways and pedestrian only networks, local governments can reduce traffic congestion and greenhouse emissions while improving community health and fitness.

> 8.3.6   Discuss the barriers to transition from individual cars to mass public transport systems.
>
> © IBO 2007

City planners can incorporate improvements in public mass transport systems that assist with congestion, pollution and meeting consumers needs to travel to popular destinations, but successful sustainable transport requires a shift in demand from the populous. Issues surrounding; personal freedom, accessibility, flexibility, security and safety all play a role in the decision making process. Any shift in demand must be supported and encouraged by governments through the provision of better-integrated, economical and efficient public transport networks. Technological improvements and the provision of better infrastructure however are not the entire solution to the problem of non-sustainable transport. Successful changes towards sustainable modes of transport will require

both technological and social elements. OECD research, into environmentally sustainable transport also found, *'that one-third of the effort necessary to meet the criteria expressed in the definition will come from technology and two-thirds from demand-side management'*. (Information on the program of research projects on environmentally sustainable transport, 1999).

Wind energy

> 8.3.7   Identify the advantages and disadvantages of small-scale and large-scale wind energy generating plants.
>
> 8.3.8   Discuss the issues associated with the siting of large wind farms.
>
> © IBO 2007

Wind turbines produce clean, emission-free energy through the harnessing of naturally occurring moving air. Most systems (regardless of size) consist of three blades connected directly to a turbine and a tail used to direct the blades into the most efficient orientation. Tail vanes may be programmed to automatically redirect blades away from high wind conditions that may damage the turbine. Larger installations may also be fitted with variable pitch control to maximize the turbines' performance, but also protect the turbine in the aforementioned situation of damaging winds.

Small wind turbines can be used to power a home, farm, school, or small business. Some models vary from the traditional propeller blade style and use a vertical corkscrew configuration. Like photovoltaic cells, wind turbines may be connected to the electricity grid to supplement supply or allow for power to be sold back into the grid when power excess to requirements is generated. Applications for small power generating turbines, (50 - 150 Watts), include power for: lighting, general power, battery charging, water pumping, telecommunications etc.

Hybrid systems using a combination of two or more energy sources may be employed to guarantee security of supply. While capital costs for such systems are higher, in remote communities the fossil fuel alternatives such as diesel are more expensive and damaging to the environment.

Disadvantages around wind turbine power relates to the unpredictable nature of winds. Areas that do provide suitable average wind speeds are not always located close enough to energy demand to be convenient. Noise pollution caused by the movement of blades through the air, aesthetic impacts to the environment and potential for bird strike must also be considered when locating

AHL

not just single but larger, multiple turbine or wind farm installations.

Technology continues to develop making turbines quieter, more efficient and better able to blend into the environment. The advantages and disadvantages of wind turbine power are summarized in the below.

Advantages

- wind turbines occupy a small footprint
- range of sizes and generation capacities
- may be deployed in remote locations or areas of high wind
- may be combined with other forms of eco-friendly power generation to create a more reliable source of energy.

Disadvantages

- expensive capital outlay
- generation is difficult to predict
- negative aesthetic changes to countryside
- Intermittent generation, impacting on transmission
- wind turbines, generators and gearboxes, produce significant noise pollution
- groups of turbines or wind farms are needed to where large amounts of power are required
- electromagnetic interference - some television frequency bands are susceptible to interference from wind generators.

Unlike the trend toward large-scale grid connected wind turbines in developed economies, developing nations are opting for smaller turbines in the 5–100 kW range. Connected to individual households or small collectives, these turbines are often supplemented by a range of alternative systems grouped together. These hybrid systems may include technologies such as, wind, solar and diesel generating capacities.

Further Reading

Boschmann, E, & Kwan M. (2008). *Toward Socially Sustainable Urban Transportation: Progress and Potentials.* International Journal of Sustainable Transportation. Volume 2, Issue 3, pp. 138 – 157.

Harper, D., Denruyter, J. & Oglethorpe, J. (2009). *Sun, Wind, Water and More - Renewable Energy in WWF Field Projects.* WWF. United States.

Macintosh, A. & Downie C. (2006). *Wind Farms: The facts and the fallacies.* The Australia Institute. Discussion Paper Number 91.

1. Magnetic induction was discovered by:

   A. Thomas Edison
   B. Michael Faraday
   C. Ernst Rutherford
   D. Sir Humphry Davy.

2. To have kinetic energy an object must be:

   A. in motion
   B. accelerating
   C. at an elevated position
   D. travelling at constant velocity.

3. Which of the following are sustainable alternatives:

   A. oil, coal, biomass
   B. solar, wind, nuclear
   C. geothermal, wave, LNG
   D. biodiesel, ethanol, hydroelectricity.

4. AC was chosen over DC as a supply for electricity grids due to its ability to be:

   A. stored in batteries
   B. transmitted in large voltages
   C. cheaper
   D. easily stepped up or down via a transformer

5. Explain why waterpower played a key role in the Industrial Revolution when it had been known about for hundreds of years.

6. Discuss: If fossil fuels hold large amounts of energy, and since energy is conserved, why is the use of fossil fuels so inefficient? Where has all the energy gone and, where did it come from originally?

7. Outline the reasons why cleaner, alternative forms of energy have not replaced more polluting fossil fuel generated energy.

8. Explain why agreements like the Kyoto Protocol do not receive universal support.

9. Outline the relationship between Kinetic Energy and Potential Energy in terms of energy conservation.

10. Discuss the advantages and disadvantages of the use of fossil fuels.

STRUCTURES

CONTENTS

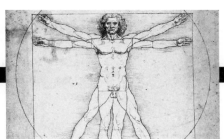

AHL

All engineered structures are designed and built with consideration of resisting the same fundamental forces of tension, compression, shear, bending and torsion. Structural design is a balance of these internal and external forces. At the same time, materials selection, component specification, joining techniques, individual member design and assembly must be also considered.

Historically, designs for structures have developed on a trial-and-error basis, until a basic understanding of material properties and 'rule-of-thumb' or empirical guidelines provided greater success. As new materials and technologies became available design options also expanded. Over time, these guidelines have been supplanted or validated by engineering calculations based on theories of material properties and design that allow 'proof of concept' while projects are still on the drawing board. Standardization of material tests, processing, design and drawing terminology etc., allow successful techniques to be conveyed unambiguously throughout the design community.

Knowledge of the mechanical properties of materials and how they perform is a must for designers, engineers and architects. It is this knowledge of a material's performance relative to standardized tests and benchmarks that gives designers greater certainty in the structural integrity of their designs.

9.1 YOUNG'S MODULUS – STRESS AND STRAIN

> **9.1.1 Define Young's modulus.**
>
> © IBO 2007

Young's modulus is the ratio of stress to strain within the elastic region of the stress strain curve (prior to the yield point). It is a measure of the stiffness of a material and is also known as the modulus of elasticity.

> **9.1.2 State that the stress (load) is force per unit area acting on a body or system.**
>
> © IBO 2007

Stress is the relationship between an applied load and a material's cross-sectional area measured in Mega Pascals (MPa).

Where: $\text{Stress} = \dfrac{\text{Load}}{\text{Area}} \quad \text{or} \quad \sigma = \dfrac{L}{A}$

In this situation Load is quoted in Newtons and the area is measured in mm^2.

9.1.3 State that strain is the ratio of a change in dimension to the original value of that dimension.

Strain is an engineering quantity that measures the change in length of a body relative to its original length when subjected to a load. Strain is a dimensionless quantity.

Where: Strain = $\dfrac{\text{extension}}{\text{original length}}$ or $\varepsilon = \dfrac{x}{l_o}$

Extension and original length are both measured in millimeters.

9.1.4 Draw and describe a stress/strain graph and identify the elastic region, plastic flow region, yield stress and ultimate tensile stress.

Testing of sample pieces to destruction in either tension or compression will produce data that can be plotted to produce a curve better known as a load-extension diagram. A tensometer (Figure 9.1.4a) is used to produce this information. Data gathered from this test may later be translated into a stress-strain diagram.

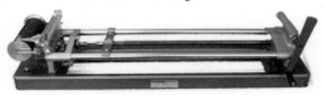

Figure 9.1.4a   Tensometer

Image by Cate Scott

Ductile materials often 'neck' (reduce in cross sectional area) while continuing to elongate before fracture (Figure 9.1.4b). Both elongation and reduction of area are measures of ductility.

Temperature also affects tensile properties. As environmental temperatures increase, tensile values decrease.

Stress-strain diagrams such as Figure 9.1.4c can be generated for axial tension, compression, and shear loading conditions.

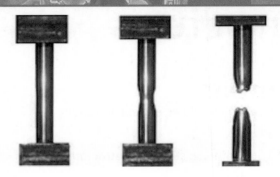

Figure 9.1.4b Progressive tensile test samples showing necking and failure

Image by Nicholas John

Almost all of the mechanical properties of a material can be obtained from its stress-strain diagram curve and includes information such as:

- ductility
- resilience
- toughness
- elongation
- brittleness
- elastic limit
- yield stress
- ultimate stress
- breaking stress
- Young's modulus.

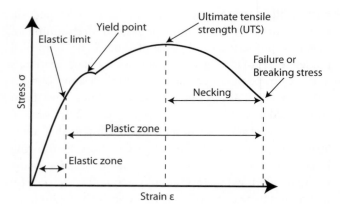

Figure 9.1.4c Stress strain curve

Robert Hooke was a 17th Century scientist principally remembered for his work on the elastic nature of materials. Hooke's Law describes the amount of elastic deformation that a material can sustain in tension or compression before it undergoes permanent plastic deformation. Hooke's law states: 'stress is directly proportional to strain within the proportional limit.'

From this, the mathematical relationship can be expressed as:

$$\text{Stress} = k \times \text{Strain or}$$

$$k = \text{Stress/Strain}$$

Where: k is a constant of proportionality. This constant is known as Young's modulus (E) and has the units of GPa (10^3 MPa).

The elastic limit is the maximum load that can be sustained before plastic deformation will occur. Before the elastic limit any extension (or reduction) that takes place in a material is reversed once the load is removed, i.e. the material returns to its original length. Elasticity is directly related to the bonding between atoms and their respective energies. This is most easily demonstrated by the relationship between melting points and elasticity of various materials. The higher the melting point, i.e. the energy required to disrupt atom-to-atom bonding, the higher the modulus of elasticity. Similarly, for a given material, as the test temperature increases the Young's modulus decreases.

Figure 9.1.4d shows a range of stress strain curves. The shape and gradients of stress-strain curves give an indication of a material's properties. A brittle material displays linear elastic behaviour and fails with little strain e.g. ceramics and glasses (1). A soft and tough material, on the other hand, exhibits a very small initial slope, but strain hardens and withstands larger strains before failure e.g. low carbon steel (2). Materials such as aluminium show no definite yield point (3). Elastomeric materials display non-linear elasticity e.g. natural and synthetic rubbers (4).

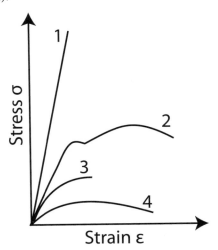

Figure 9.1.4d Stress strain curves

A material's stress-strain curve also indicates the overall toughness of the material. The area under the curve is a measure of a material's toughness. The greater the area,

the tougher the material, and the greater the amount of energy required to break it. Temperature also affects tensile properties – as environmental temperature increases, tensile values decrease. Figure 9.1.4e shows examples of typical curves showing distinct properties;

a)   elastic material obeying Hooke's law

b)   ductile material displaying plastic deformation

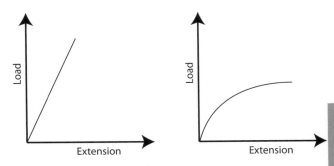

Figure 9.1.4e Examples of stress strain curves

'Engineering stress' is calculated using the ratio of the applied load to the non-deformed (original) cross-sectional area. This method ceases to be an accurate measure when large amounts of deformation take place.

'True stress' is defined as the ratio of the applied load (L) to the instantaneous cross-sectional area (A). True stress and strain are practically indistinguishable from engineering stress and strain at small deformations, yet as shown in Figure 9.1.4f, it can be seen that as the strain becomes large and the cross-sectional area of the specimen decreases, the true stress becomes much larger than the engineering stress.

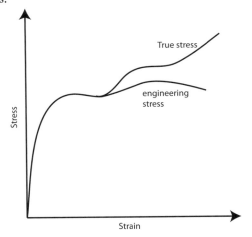

Figure 9.1.4f Engineering stress-strain curve vs. true stress

153

9.1.5 Outline the importance of yield stress in materials.

Yield stress occurs on a stress-strain diagram where the test specimen continues to stretch (strain) without an increase in load (stress). Some materials, notably low carbon steels, exhibit two such points that are identified as the upper and lower yield points.

For structural applications, the yield stress is usually a more important property than the tensile strength, since once the yield point is passed, the structure has deformed beyond acceptable limits. Beyond the yield point permanent or plastic deformation occurs.

The yield strength of most materials is determined by their grain size, such that as the grain size reduces, yield strength increases as illustrated in Figure 9.1.5a. The Hall-Petch equation presented below describes this relationship.

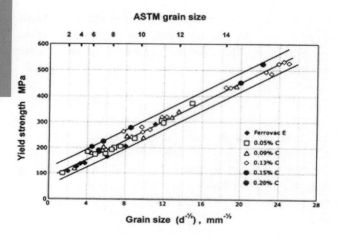

Figure 9.1.5a Plot of yield strength against grain size

Image adapted from Morrison, W.B. & Leslie, W.C. (1973). Metallurgical Transactions. Vol 4, pp 379-381.

Proof stress

Many alloys do not show either a definite elastic limit or yield point. Because of the importance of the yield point to designers, calculations have been developed to produce an artificial approximation. This approximation is known as 'proof stress' and relates to a pre-determined amount of permanent deformation measured against the strain axis. A line parallel to the initial gradient of the stress strain diagram is drawn. Where the drawn line and the curve intersect is the proof stress (Figure 9.1.5b). Proof stress is most often calculated around the values of 0.1% and 0.2% of the gauge length. The diagram below shows the method for finding 0.1% proof stress.

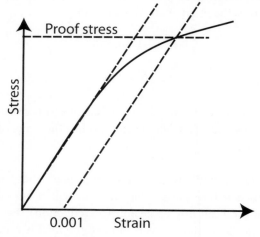

Figure 9.1.5b 0.1% Proof stress

9.1.6 Explain the difference between plastic and elastic strains.

On a stress-strain diagram, the elastic limit denotes the point where the maximum load that can be sustained before plastic deformation will occur. Up until the elastic limit the removal of any applied load will see the material return to its original length. This is known as elastic strain or elastic deformation. When stress passes the limit of a material's elasticity it continues into the plastic zone. Within the plastic zone all deformation is permanent.

9.1.7 Calculate Young's modulus of a range of materials.

Calculate the Young's modulus (E) for an 18 mm square section of steel 3 m long given it is stressed to 21.6 MPa and exhibits an extension of 0.2 mm.

Stress (σ) $= 21.6$ MPa

Strain (ε) $=$ extension / original length
$= 0.2 / 3 \times 10^3$

E $= 21.6 / 6.66 \times 10^{-5}$
$= 324$ GPa

Figure 9.1.7a shows a range of materials and their typical Young's modulus values. Note: The values are approximations for these materials as consistencies and compositions vary.

Material	E (GPa)
Pine (along the grain)	10
Aluminium	70
Glass	50—90
Brass	110
Stainless Steel	190—200
Titanium (unalloyed)	105—110
Gold	10.8
Cortical bone	15—30

Figure 9.1.7a Young's modulus for a range of materials

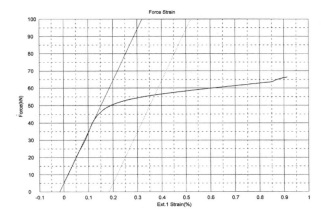

Figure 9.1.7b Ductile Iron force-strain plot

> 9.1.8   Explain how the knowledge of the Young's modulus of a material affects the selection of materials for particular design contexts.
>
> © IBO 2007

The modulus of elasticity provides an indication of the stiffness of a material. The gradient of the straight-line section (elastic region) of the stress-strain curve indicates the relative stiffness of the material, i.e. the steeper the gradient the stiffer the material.

The stiffness of a material is important to the specification of individual parts based on the physical requirements of the design in question. Specifying materials with limited amounts of deflection or distortion are critical to the design of towers, bicycles, ships etc.

If the Young's modulus of a material is known, then it is possible to calculate the deflection or movement that would occur in a product, component or structure for a range of loads. This can then be employed to calculate the maximum compressive load that would cause a concrete column to fail, or the amount of force that may cause a bicycle brake cable to extend beyond its elastic limit.

In most cases, the Young's modulus of a material in tension is no different from that in compression. However, the strength of the material can be significantly different in compression and in tension. This is, in fact, the reason for creating steel reinforced concrete beams. In this situation concrete, (good in compression), is combined with steel, (good in tension). While ever within its limits (UCS) the beam would maintain its structural integrity due to concrete's high compressive strength. However, to improve unmodified concrete's tensile strength, it may be reinforced with steel rods, secured in place during casting.

9.2 FORCES

> 9.2.1   Describe what is meant by an external load acting on a structure.
>
> © IBO 2007

External or applied loads involve some form of physical contact. Loads from vehicular and pedestrian traffic, vehicle braking, expansion and contraction, wind, water from stream flow, ground movements etc. Whether dynamic or static, all of these forces cause shock, impact or vibration loads. These loads may be periodic, random or transient.

> 9.2.2   Describe what is meant by body load.
>
> © IBO 2007

The mass of a structure itself generates a body load that must be taken into consideration in the design phase. Static by nature, this load is due to weight of the structure. Alternatively known as the dead load, it remains constant and because it is caused by gravity, it always acts vertically.

> 9.2.3   Describe the difference between weight and mass.
>
> © IBO 2007

The mass of an object is a measure of the amount of matter that an object contains. Mass is therefore an intrinsic property of an object and does not vary.

While mass is a property inherent to an object, weight is not. Weight is a force and represents the mass of an object under the influence of acceleration due to gravity. Because of this, weight can vary depending on the amount to which gravity varies.

The force of gravity accelerates all matter. On earth, the acceleration due to gravity (g) varies slightly from place to place but is approximately 9.8 m/s². This means that if an object is dropped from rest, at the end of one second it will have travelled 9.8 m. That is, it will have reached a velocity of 9.8 m/s. At the end of the next second, it will have increased its velocity by another 9.8 m/s to a value of 19.6 m/s. Acceleration has therefore been 9.8 metres per second per second.

For the purposes of simple calculation, 10 m/s² is often accepted as an approximate value for acceleration due to gravity on earth. As mentioned previously, weight is a force and represents the mass of an object accelerated under the influence of gravity.

An object of 5 kg mass sitting on a table and assuming acceleration due to gravity is 10 m/s², has a weight of 50 N. If the mass is not moving down through the table, the table is said to be exerting a matching reactive force against the object as shown in Figure 9.2.3.

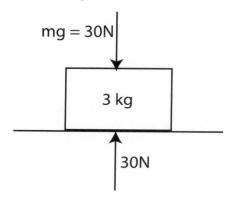

Figure 9.2.3 Reactive forces

The net force on the object is zero, it does not move and is therefore in a state of equilibrium. Many forces of various magnitude and direction can act upon an object of course, but it is only the net force, that is of interest in determining the movement of an object.

9.2.4   State the units of weight and mass.

Sir Isaac Newton found that a relationship existed between the forces acting on an object and its acceleration. This has come to be known as Newton's Second Law of Motion. The net force acting on an object is directly proportional to, and in the same direction as, the acceleration of the object.

F_{net} is constantly proportional to a

The constant of proportionality was subsequently defined as the mass of the object, thus,

$$F_{net} = m\,a$$

The units of force are kg m/s² since acceleration is measured in metres per second per second (m/s²). In honour of Newton's achievements, the units of force were named after him as the Newton and are abbreviated as a capital N.

The unit of mass within the SI system is the kilogram (kg). As with all measures, the kilogram is an arbitrarily derived quantity that must be capable of accurate determination in disparate locations. In the 18th century when its standardization was initially undertaken, the kilogram was defined as one litre of water at 4°C. Problems with adjustments for the mass of any container and difficulties in the measurement of the volume of water, led to the adoption of a platinum-iridium (Pt-Ir) alloy cylinder as the reference standard. The international prototype kilogram is held at the International Bureau of Weights and Measures in Sevres, France. The appropriate authority in each country holds replicas of this standard, known as Secondary standards. From this standard a set of auxiliary standards are produced for use by laboratories and industry.

9.2.5   Explain the relationship of external loads to internal forces and the concept of the balance of equilibrium of forces within a structure.

Structures such as bridges and towers are designed to follow Newton's First Law where a body in equilibrium is at rest or in uniform motion. These structures are of course static by nature and therefore do not move. External loads applied to structures generate opposing internal loads within the structures members. The nature of balancing these forces, equal in size and opposite in sense, means the structure must satisfy the following three rules:

The sum of the vertical forces must be equal
$$\Sigma\, FV\uparrow = \Sigma\, FV\downarrow$$

The sum of the horizontal forces must be equal
$$\Sigma\, FH\rightarrow = \Sigma\, FH\leftarrow$$

The sum of the moments must be equal
$$\Sigma\, M\,\circlearrowleft = \Sigma\, M\,\circlearrowright$$

Like all matter, particles of material within structural members are bonded together at an atomic level (see 3.4.3). The magnitude of these bonds determines the strength of materials and thus individual structural members.

Loads applied to structures are transmitted to individual members that, in turn, generate internal balancing forces (Figure 9.2.6a). While the internal forces are less than the bond strength of the member, the particles will return to their original positions when the load is removed. Once the internal forces exceed the bond strength of the particles, permanent deformation (buckling) and, eventually, failure will occur.

9.2.6a Balancing forces within individual members

While external forces within structures must balance, so too the external forces must balance to maintain equilibrium. Figure 9.2.6b shows the balancing external forces occurring in a simply supported beam.

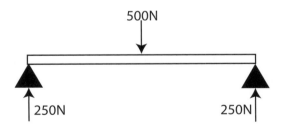

Figure 9.2.6b Simply supported beam in equilibrium

Under load, beams will bend slightly. When bending (as shown in Figure 9.2.6c), the lower surface has a tendency to increase in length while the upper surface wants to contract. These tensile and compressive stresses vary across the beam with the maximum values occurring at the outside surfaces. There also lies a region in the centre (the neutral axis) where the forces are balanced but where shear is at its greatest. In a symmetrical beam the neutral axis will be at the geometric centre. This is where beam design compensates for the mechanical performance of the beam material.

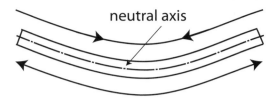

Figure 9.2.6c Stress variation in simply supported beams

In a simple truss structure the distribution of internal forces allows for the total structure to be in equilibrium. A typical internal and external force distribution for a simply loaded truss would appear as shown in Figure 9.2.6d. Reactive external forces would also occur at the two support points. Both of these forces would be directed vertically upwards.

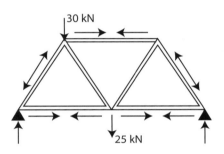

Figure 9.2.6d External loads and balancing internal forces

Applied loads form stresses within a material that are typically identified as tensile, compressive or shearing. Tensile forces are those trying to pull apart or lengthen a material. Compressive forces however try to compress or reduce the length of a material. Shear forces attempt to slide one part of the material over the other. Shear forces may be single, double or punching. To maintain the equilibrium of a structure the forces within the system must balance. Figure 9.1.7 displays the three fundamental types of stress.

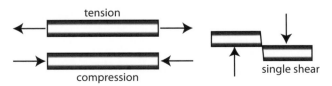

Figure 9.2.7 Types of stress

9.2.8 Calculate a tensile or compressive stress, given values of force and area.

© IBO 2007

Tensile stress sample calculation.

Calculate the stress (σ) created in a 10 mm diameter rod if it is subjected to a tensile load of 1.1 kN.

Data
Load $= 1.1 \times 103$ N
Diameter $= 10$ mm
Area $= \pi\, 102\, /4$
            $= 78.54$ mm^2
Calculation
σ_t $=$ Load / area
            $= 1.1 \times 103 \div 78.54$
            $= 14$ N/mm2
            $= 14$ MPa

Compressive stress sample calculation.

Calculate the compressive stress in a 2cm diameter punch if a force of 12 kN is applied and used to create holes in a 8 mm thick steel plate.

Data
Load $= 12 \times 103$ N
Diameter $= 20$ mm
Area $= \pi\, 202\, /4$
            $= 314.2857$ mm^2
Calculation
σ_C $=$ Load / area
            $= 12 \times 103 \div 314.2857$
            $= 38.18$ N/mm^2 or 38.18MPa

9.2.9 Calculate a tensile or compressive strain, given values of the original dimension and the change in dimension.

© IBO 2007

Tensile strain sample calculation

Calculate the tensile strain present in a 2 m long, 10 mm diameter steel rod if it extends 1.5 mm when loaded.

Data
Length $= 2 \times 103$ mm
Extension $= 1.5$ mm
Calculation
ε_t $=$ extension / original length
                 $= 1.5 \div 2.0 \times 10^3$
                 $= 0.00075 \qquad = 75 \times 10^{-3}$

Compressive strain sample calculation

Calculate the compressive strain present in a 4.55 m long aluminium bar if it undergoes compressive forces causing a reduction in length of 2.5 mm.

Data
Length $= 4.5 \times 10^3$ mm
Extension $= 2.5$ mm

Calculation
ε_t $=$ extension / original length
                 $= 2.5 \div 4.55 \times 10^3$
                 $= 5.49 \times 10^{-4}$

Note: As long as the units used are consistent there is no need to convert millimeters into meters. Compressive strain causes a reduction in length rather than the increase associate with tensile strain. There is, however, no need to use a negative sign.

9.2.10 Evaluate the importance of forces in a design context.

© IBO 2007

Materials selection, component design, joining techniques, configuration and adherence to local building codes all play their part in the design process, but the goal of designing structures is essentially an exercise in balancing forces thus creating a structure that will carry loads in a safe and functional fashion. Loads take many forms, including static and dynamic. It is these forces and the resultant deflections that must be kept within reasonable limits. These deflections allow structures to move, such as the expansion of bridge decks due to heat or the sway in skyscrapers due to wind loads.

The forces of tension, compression, shear and torsion affect all structures. It is the designer's responsibility not only to accommodate these forces, but also to generate a solution that will determine how frequently they occur and where they are distributed throughout the structure.

Careful planning, analysis and testing in the design phase will take the variety of forces experienced in the service life of a structure into account. Failure to accurately allow for loading conditions can cause: cracking, excessive movement, misalignment of components, permanent deformation of members and even structural failure.

9.3 STRENGTH AND STIFFNESS OF STRUCTURES

9.3.1 Explain the relationship between deflection and stiffness in structures.

© IBO 2007

Forces acting on the beams or structures cause bending, thereby creating deformation in the shape of a curve. The deflection generated at any point is found by measuring the displacement from the original unloaded datum. The amount of deflection is relative to the force applied and the stiffness of the structure or beam. Generally speaking, lateral deflections are very small when compared to axial displacement.

Stiffness is often measured as the load that will produce a predetermined amount of deflection. A stiff structure or structural member is one that can withstand a large load and will deflect only to a small degree. The gradient of a curve plotted using load vs. deflection will give a visual interpretation of stiffness. Similar to a stress-strain diagram the steeper the curve, the stiffer the material or structure under examination.

Young's modulus is an intrinsic property of a material and indicates the elasticity of a material, regardless of its design. The stiffness of a beam however is a mechanical property that can be affected by: material selection, length and the cross-sectional design of the member in question.

9.3.2 Calculate the stiffness of a structure.

© IBO 2007

Simple calculations for relative stiffness may be determined using the generic formula:

Stiffness = load/deflection or: $k = P / \Delta x$

Where: k = the constant of stiffness for the beam
P = load and Δx is the change in deflection.

For a concrete beam that deflects 0.28 mm under a load of 914 kg, the stiffness calculation would appear as:

k $= P / \Delta x$
        $= 914 / 0.28$
        $= 3\ 264$ kg/mm

9.3.3 Outline what is meant by bending moment in relation to structures.

© IBO 2007

Bending moments are the internal turning forces that a beam has to resist, acting at any given point on an individual member. They may be calculated mathematically or graphically.

Internal forces within a beam vary along its length. Shear force and bending moment diagrams are graphical representations illustrating the magnitude of these varying forces at any given point a long a beam. To find the internal forces acting in the beam as shown in Figure 9.3.3a a series of points are examined along its length and calculations made to determine the shear force acting at that point. Once the shear force is known the bending moment may in turn be calculated.

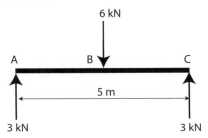

Figure 9.3.3a Loaded beam force diagram

To determine the shear force at point A, only consider the forces acting on the beam up to this point.

The shear force acting on the beam equals 3 kN↑ therefore for equilibrium 3 kN↓ is acting internally within the beam. To determine the bending moment at point A the length of the beam up to this point must be considered. To maintain equilibrium the bending moment at A must be 0 kNm because the force on the beam acts through the fulcrum as shown in Figure 9.3.3b.

Figure 9.3.3b Zero bending moment

The section to be examined next is the beam up to point B. The shear force acting on the beam here is:

3 kN – 6 kN – SF = 0

Therefore   SF = – 3 kN

To determine the bending moment at B, the length of the beam up to this point (zero) must be considered as shown in Figure 9.3.3c.

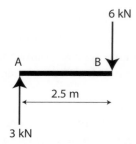

Figure 9.3.3c Calculating bending moments at B

The bending moments around B are:

$$3 \times 2.5 = BM$$

Therefore, BM at B $= 7.5$ kNm

The last point on the beam to be examined is point C. To determine the shear force at point C only consider the forces acting here. Shear force acting on the beam $= 3$ kN$\downarrow$ therefore to create equilibrium 3 kN$\uparrow$ is acting internally within the beam.

To determine the bending moment at point C the length of the beam (zero) is used as the moment arm. The bending moment at C can only be 0 kNm for the same reasons explained for point A on the beam.

Figure 9.3.3d Zero bending moment

Values calculated for shear force and bending moments may be plotted graphically to show the changing values over the beam as shown in Figure 9.3.3e. The shear force diagram is constructed by simply treating the forces on the force diagram as either up or down. Each force is then plotted on an axis and after all forces considered, the points are joined up. Notice that the maximum bending moment occurs where the shear force diagram cuts the axis.

Analytically bending moments can be calculated as the area under the shear force diagram and the relevant value plotted on the bending moment diagram.

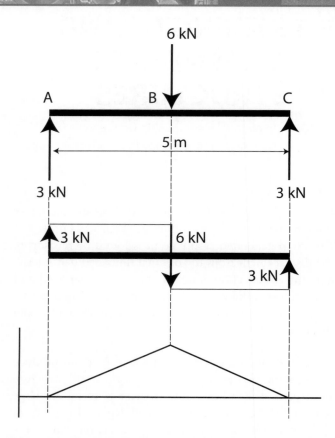

Figure 9.3.3e Force shear force and bending moment diagrams

9.3.4   Outline what is meant by moment arm.

If a force is applied to a body fixed in space, this force tends to create a rotating effect on the body. An example of moments created by a force includes the use of a spanner to loosen or tighten a nut.

The perpendicular distance between the force causing the moment and the turning point known as the pivot or the fulcrum is called the moment arm. The magnitude of a moment is calculated by multiplying the perpendicular distance in meters between the applied force and the pivot by the force itself. Moments are vector quantities and are measured in Newton meters (Nm).

The following formula applies:

moment = force × perpendicular distance

Note: a force applied to or through the fulcrum will have no turning effect on the body.

When attempting to create equilibrium in a system, the mathematical formula stating the sum of the clockwise moments equals the sum of the anticlockwise moments is appropriate or mathematically:

$$\Sigma\, M\circlearrowleft = \Sigma\, M\circlearrowright.$$

The SI units for a moment or a couple are Newton meters, (Nm). In engineering the moment of a force is known as torque. A belt turning a pulley exerts a torque on the pulley.

9.3.5 Explain the need for a factor of safety in structural design.

Factor of safety is a complex concept having a number of means of calculation but in its simplest form could be defined as the extent to which the design strength exceeds expected service loads. Designers often use a factor of safety calculation to determine the maximum allowable stress for a structure.

Factors of safety permit structures to accept working loads well within their theoretical limits and allow for uncertainties in both the design process and working life of the structure. These uncertainties include:

- size and type of applied loads
- assembly operations welding, bolt tightening etc.
- effects of ageing on strength due to fatigue, corrosion etc.
- precision of information about mechanical properties of materials
- variations or defects in members from machining/ manufacturing processes.

9.3.6 Calculate the factor of safety for a structure.

The simply supported rectangular steel beam shown in Figure 9.3.6 shows a beam having a UTS of 1.18 GPa. Calculate the factor of safety if the beam has a cross sectional area of 125 mm^2 and is centrally loaded with a force of 15 kN.

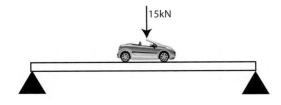

Figure 9.3.6 Factor of safety

Data

$$FOS = UTS\ /\ \text{stress in beam}$$

$$\sigma_{UTS} = 1.18\ \text{GPa or}\ 1\,180\ \text{MPa}$$

$$\begin{aligned}\sigma_B &= L/A\\ &= 15 \times 10^3\ /\ 125\\ &= 120\ \text{MPa}\end{aligned}$$

$$\begin{aligned}FOS &= 1.18 \times 10^3\ /\ 120\\ &= 9.8\end{aligned}$$

There are many applications where chain, rope, cable or wire is used for pulling, hauling, lifting or hoisting objects.

9.3.7 Apply the concept of factor of safety to other areas of design.

In addition, wire and crimped connectors are used in multiple quality-critical or safety-critical scenarios requiring tensile tests to be performed to judge or validate system performance and reliability.

Testing to destruction using random samples is also routinely performed to confirm factor of safety calculations. Cyclic loading tests may also be carried out to simulate working conditions and fatigue effects that would be expected over many years of service. Examples of areas of design where factor of safety can be critical include the design of: airframes, car bodies, engine crankshafts etc.

As a guide, Wayne Hale, (NASA engineer, 1978–2010), states, 'the standard factor of safety for the cables in elevators is 11. So you could, if space allowed, pack eleven times as many people into an elevator as the placard says and possibly survive the ride. For many applications, 4 is considered to be a good number. In the shuttle program the standard factor of safety for all the ground equipment and tools is 4.'

9.3.8 Evaluate the importance of strength and stiffness in a design context.

Strength and stiffness are mechanical properties of materials that allow structures to maintain their shape and integrity when loaded. Appropriate levels of stiffness are required to limit deflection, bending and damaging vibrations leading to instability. Columns that flex inappropriately under compressive loads, effectively shorten their length and can then increase shear and torsional forces in surrounding structural members potentially leading to failure.

9.4 BEAMS

9.4.1 Describe a beam.

Beams are rigid structural members that support and transmit loads acting at 90° to their longitudinal axis. They may be made from masonry, wood, metal or composite materials. When loaded shear stresses and bending moments cause beams to flex or deflect.

Beams are usually classified based on the mechanism used to support them. Types of beams include:

- cantilever
- overhanging
- simply supported.

Figure 9.4.1a shows a simply supported beam deflecting under load. A fallen log spanning a creek would be an example of a simply supported beam.

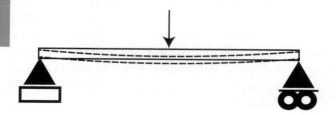

Figure 9.4.1a Simply supported beam

In engineering applications it is usual for one end of the beam to have a fixed hinged or pinned support and the other a roller or rocker. Configurations such as this allow the beam to be supported, while at the same time allowing for movements due to vibration, thermal expansion and dynamic service loads. Figure 9.4.1b shows the line of force reaction at roller supports is always directed perpendicular to the line joining the centres of the rollers.

Figure 9.4.1b Roller support reactions

The reaction at the pinned support can be at any direction. This yet to be determined direction is often shown by a wriggly line (Figure 9.4.1c) and is governed by the need to maintain equilibrium.

Figure 9.4.1c Fixed or pinned support reaction

Figure 9.4.1d shows a cantilever beam deflecting under load. A cantilever beam is fixed at one end and free at the other. A diver's springboard would be an example of a cantilever beam.

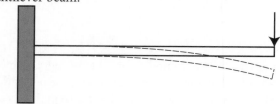

Figure 9.4.1d Simply supported beam

Figure 9.4.1e shows an overhanging beam. The section of the beam between the two supports behaves like a simply supported beam while the overhanging section acts like a cantilever beam.

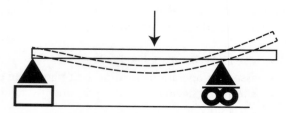

Figure 9.4.1e Overhanging beam

The shelter shown in Figure 9.4.1f is constructed from a series of rectangular wooden beams, steel 'I' beams and reinforced concrete slabs. The beams demonstrate a combination of simply supported and overhanging structures. Note also that the vertical beams would all be in compression.

Figure 9.4.1f Beam structure – Shanghai sculpture park

The loads shown in the above examples represent those applied over a very small area or concentrated to act at a point. If the load is uniformly distributed over an area (UDL) it may be expressed as force per unit length. Figure 9.4.1g shows a block 2m long with a mass of 2kg a load of approximately 1kg/m. This block would therefore exert a force of approximately 20N uniformly over its length.

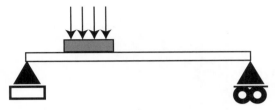

Figure 9.4.1g Uniformly distributed load (UDL)

9.4.2 Describe how beams are designed to transfer forces and distribute loads through the beams.

As described in 9.4.1 loads on beams can cause them to bend or flex. These forces need to be considered when designing beams for specific purposes.

Beam design involves the specific placement of mass to cope with anticipated loads. Composite beams may involve the placement of reinforcing materials to take advantage of their inherent properties. A clear example is the placement of steel reinforcing in the lower half of concrete beams to take advantage of steel's greater tensile strength. In this situation, the top half of the concrete beam performs well due to concrete's excellent compressive strength. The tensile strength of steel improves the strength of the beam's lower half where the tensile forces are greatest and thus improves the beam's overall load carrying capacity. The movement of mass towards the outer extremes (see 9.4.5) of a beam to increase its stiffness is also another example of judicious material placement. Within structures it not just beam design, but beam placement, that is crucial. External loads need to be distributed throughout a structure to avoid concentrating loads.

Figure 9.4.2 Structural design showing load distribution

9.4.3 Describe the historical development of the materials used to manufacture beams.

Masonry and stone materials have long been used for construction and are some of the oldest building materials. Abundance of supply and suitable forming tools allowed the Romans and stonemasons of the Middle Ages (since about 1100 AD) to build structures such as bridges, aqueducts (Figure 9.4.3a) and cathedrals from masonry. Masonry arches achieve stability due to the massive nature of the structure itself. Properties such as high strength in compression compared to a relatively low tensile strength enabled structures made of hard stone and built on stable ground to survive thousands of years. In an effort to improve the tensile strength of masonry, reinforcing in a variety of forms has been used. The use of reinforcing greatly extends the structural uses of masonry materials.

Figure 9.4.3a Roman masonry aqueduct Malta

Unfortunately, stone has become very expensive, if considered solely from the point of view of construction costs. Stone is nowadays usually confined to decorative surfaces, the stones being preset or fixed as facing for abutments, piers or arches. Of course, sound weather-resisting stone such as granite, gneiss and porphyry must be chosen.

Timber has favourable qualities of strength for resisting compression, tension and bending. Rough tree trunks or sawn timber beams have been used since primitive times for constructing beams. The introduction of trussed frames and arches soon allowed longer spans. In earlier times, wood was also abundant and cheap. Good hardwood made an excellent material of construction. Wood, therefore, was the material most often used, even for major structures. Unfortunately, when wooden structures are exposed to the elements they are quickly attacked by decay (unless protected), especially at the critical connections

AHL

between members. These locations allow the retention of moisture leading to rotting of the timber or corrosion of metal pins, bolts, rivets and/or fixtures. Many bridges built in the 18th century were often provided with a roof and sheathing to protect them from the elements. The result was the 'covered bridge' (particularly popular in the USA).

Fire and decay are enemies of all wooden structures, and one or the other generally ended the life of most wooden constructions. Wood has one outstanding advantage. It complains audibly before failing, giving a warning that something is amiss. Recently, timber beams have been given a new impetus by glue technology that allows larger laminated cross-sections and longer joined lengths to be manufactured than can be cut from naturally grown stock. New gluing and laminating techniques can now produce timber products to a wide range of structural forms with improved mechanical properties. Moreover, timber can now be better protected against weather and insect attack. Timber needs to be regularly treated with chemicals to resist rot and insect attack. Chemically treated wood can require special handling and disposal, and chemicals can also leach into the environment either while in service or if the wood is not disposed of properly. Untreated wooden structures have to be maintained periodically by coating with preservatives.

Figure 9.4.3b Timber truss bridge New York River 1917

The first iron bridge was constructed in 1779 at Coalbrookdale in England over the Severn River (Figure 9.4.3c). The design was an arched bridge and made good use of the compressive strength of cast iron.

Individual members were crafted in wood and used as templates from which sand moulds were made. Cast iron was then poured into the moulds to produce each member. Even though structural members were made from cast iron, it was assembled using the methods common for timber construction of the time. The members were connected with traditional woodworking joints such as dovetails, rather than bolts or rivets. The Ironbridge was able to take advantage of the large-scale production methods of Abraham Darby, who developed a method of using coke instead of the rapidly diminishing supply of

charcoal for iron smelting. Coupled with the blast furnace, this technique provided a more effective way of removing impurities than manual blacksmithing.

Figure 9.4.3c The world's first metal bridge, Ironbridge at Coalbrookdale, Shropshire

A major disadvantage of cast iron is that it is brittle and relatively weak in tension, as opposed to wrought or malleable iron, and steel, which are ductile materials. It is because of this inability of cast iron to yield that the Ironbridge today has a number of members which have fractured, and the bridge has been closed to vehicular traffic, although it still has sufficient strength to carry pedestrians. At the time, however, the Ironbridge was seen as a great step forward and the use of cast iron as a structural material increased rapidly.

Cast iron increasingly became the material of choice until the failure of Robert Stephenson's Dee Bridge in 1847. This railway bridge was a trussed girder design that failed under lateral torsion loads. From that time onwards, sturdier truss designs were developed and cast iron was only used for compressive members. Increasingly engineers also turned to wrought iron as a tougher, more reliable material for the carrying of tensile loads.

Wrought iron was first employed in trusses during the 1840s, and by the mid-19th century, rolling mills were using this material to generate a wide variety of structural shapes, such as 'I' beams, angles, plates and other members. Wrought-iron link chains were also used at this time to support suspension bridge decks.

Even with the benefits of wrought iron, which allowed the increasing loads demanded by the developing railway system, bridges began to fail by a new mechanism, which came to be known as 'fatigue'.

By the 1890s, steel had replaced wrought iron as the universal material for trusses. Amongst bridge materials, steel has the highest and most favourable strength qualities and is therefore suitable for the most daring bridges with the longest spans. Typically, steel has compressive and tensile strengths of 370 MPa (N/mm^2), about ten times the compressive strength of a medium concrete and a hundred times the tensile strength. A special advantage of steel is its ductility: it deforms considerably before it breaks because it begins to yield above a certain stress level. This yield strength is used as the first consideration in standard quality terms. For bridges, high strength steel (HSS) is often preferred. The higher the strength, the smaller the proportional difference between the yield strength and the tensile strength, and this means that high strength steels are not as ductile as those with normal strengths. The high strengths of steel allow small cross-sections of beams or girders and therefore a lower dead load of the superstructure. Steel must be protected, (often with a protective coat of paint), against corrosion.

Increasingly, concrete is being used to form structural members of bridges. Possessing inherently high compressive strength, the low tensile strength of concrete is overcome by the incorporation of steel. The final product created depends on the mode in which steel is incorporated into the concrete, i.e. reinforced, pre-stressed or post-stressed concrete depending on the requirements of the structural member concerned.

Because tensile stresses occur in abutments and piers due to ground movements, wind and internal temperature gradients, reinforced concrete is used in these situations. Reinforced concrete is usually cast in-situ. Structural members which must resist relatively high tensile stresses are manufactured from pre-stressed concrete. Pre-stressed concrete has revolutionized the design and construction of bridges. With pre-stressed concrete, beams can be made more slender and span considerably greater distances than with reinforced concrete.

Pre-stressed members can also be manufactured in a modular fashion far from the construction site and brought to site only as required. Pre-stressed concrete, if correctly designed, also has high fatigue strength under the heaviest traffic loads. Pre-stressed concrete bridges in many instances have become much cheaper than steel bridges, and generally have greatly reduced maintenance requirements.

All types of structures can be built with reinforced, pre-stressed or post-stressed concrete: columns, piers, walls, slabs, beams, arches, frames, and even suspended structures. In bridge building today, concrete beams and arches predominate. Particular care however is required to ensure that the reinforcing steelwork is adequately protected against corrosion.

9.4.4 Identify a variety of shapes for sectional members of a structure.

While many beam bridges originally consisted of solid wooden beams, the two most common beam designs today are box and 'I' beams (Figure 9.4.4a). Manufactured from steel, the 'I' beam has the cross sectional shape of a capital I and is made up of a central vertical web and two horizontal plates know as flanges. For beam designs of similar cross sectional area the 'I' beam has the greatest strength because it places the largest amount of material as far away from the neutral axis of the beam as possible. 'I' beams are also easily manufactured by hot rolling processes at steel mills.

A box beam typically has two webs and two flanges. The webs in this design give the box beam greater resistance to twisting or torsional forces and is most often used in preference to an 'I' beam in curved structures where torsional forces play a greater part. The box section has reduced weight due to its hollow section and an efficient profile in loading both horizontally and vertically, however, it has a lower value for second moment of area so is less stiff.

Figure 9.4.4a Box angle rectangular and 'I' beam designs

Castellated beams have allowed designers to develop lighter, stronger, easy to assemble and cost effective designs since the 1950s. Their perforated webs allow for the easy installation of electrical work and cabling. A major advantage of this design is the increased depth without any subsequent increase in weight. This modification has the affect of improving axial strength, stiffness and raising the second moment of inertia (see 9.4.5). While advantages outweigh disadvantages there are increased manufacturing costs in fabricating castellated beams through the process of cutting and re-welding traditional 'I' beam sections.

Cellular beams, (Figure 9.4.4b), produce an even more effective solution through their inherent flexibility. Castellated beams are based on a fixed geometry where cellular beams can have their proportions modified to suit engineering requirements. The result is an even stronger lighter beam.

Figure 9.4.4b Cellular beam

9.4.5 Describe how the shape of sectional members of a structure makes the most effective and economic use of materials.

© IBO 2007

The location of the neutral axis is important in calculating bending stress but so too is the cross-sectional shape of the beam and how the mass is distributed around the neutral axis. Beams of equal mass per unit length will not necessarily deflect in the same fashion. Applying the same load to the beams (of equal cross-sectional area) shown in Figure 9.4.5a will obviously cause differing bending stress results.

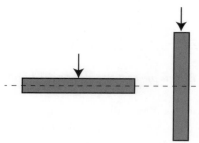

Figure 9.4.5 Bending stress relative to the neutral axis

The deflection of a beam under load depends not only on the load, but also on the geometry of the beam's cross-section. The second moment of area or moment of inertia (I_{xx}) is a property of beams generated from their cross sectional shape relative to their neutral axis. When considering beam shapes, the larger the second moment of area the greater a beam's resistance to bending or deflection. The second moment of area provides a means for calculating the relationship between the neutral axis, the cross-sectional shape of the beam and the distribution of the mass. Compared with simple square or round beams, 'I' beams (of the same cross sectional area), are the strongest of the three sectional types. This strength is obtained from the placement of large amounts of the beam's mass away from the neutral axis.

9.4.6 Explain that sectional members of a structure may be manufactured in sheet material.

© IBO 2007

Sheet materials such as LVL (Laminated Veneer Lumber) may be suitable for high strength structural applications. Manufactured from thin veneers of timber that are rotary peeled from logs these large sheets of may be cut, dried, glued and assembled under heat and pressure.

Because the veneers are rotary peeled, long continuous lengths are available to be manufactured into boards of very large dimensions. Unlike plywood the grain on each LVL veneer is most often laid in the same orientation as the length of the product. Once the individual sheets are manufactured they may then be cut and reassembled into a variety of cross-sections such as 'I', 'H' or box profiles.

9.4.7 Outline the benefits of using LVL beams in the construction industry.

© IBO 2007

LVL provides a number of benefits when used in the construction industry:

- varying sectional profiles may be constructed to order
- high dimensional stability and little tendency to warp, bow or twist
- beams exhibit improved strength and stiffness compared to solid timber
- sheets may be manufactured to specific sizes and available in dimensions larger than those traditionally available from milled timber
- knots and defects have little impact on the performance of LVL sections as they are randomly distributed in very thin sections over the material.

In most cases LVL is employed for its structural properties. However, it has a low quality finish and often requires surface treatment, such as fine, before painting to produce a suitable finish.

9.4.8 Explain the importance of factor of safety in the design of beams.

© IBO 2007

When considering factors of safety the approach most often used in designing engineering beams and ultimately structures is to examine the relationship between the ultimate tensile stress (UTS) of the beam and its working stress (σ). The Factor of Safety is mathematically defined as:

$$FS = UTS/σ$$

From this relationship it can be seen the factor of safety should always be greater than one. The size of the safety factor employed is determined by a number of considerations:

- certainty of loads
- design life of structure
- quality of manufacture
- consequences of failure
- environmental influences
- criticality of the component
- ease of repair or maintenance
- certainty of material properties
- statutory and code requirements.

Factors of safety generated from reliable strength values of materials give designers greater flexibility when specifying both materials and sectional sizes. When these figures are employed, costs may be effectively reduced through the economic choice and use of materials while still conforming to required safety margins. It is important that the allowable stress is below the elastic limit to guarantee no permanent deformation takes place under loading.

Sample calculation

Calculate the minimum diameter of a round steel beam carrying a tensile load of 30kN. Use a factor of safety of 4 and a UTS of 590 MPa for the steel beam.

$$
\begin{aligned}
FOS &= UTS/σ \\
σ &= UTS/FOS \\
&= 590/4 \\
&= 147.5 \text{ MPa} \\
σ &= Load/Area \\
A &= L/σ \\
&= 30 \times 10^3/147.5 \\
&= 203 \text{ mm}^2 \\
\text{But } A &= π\, d^2/4 \\
d^2 &= 203 \times 4/π \\
d &= 16 \text{ mm}
\end{aligned}
$$

Therefore the minimum beam diameter is 16mm.

Further reading

The 'Smart Solution', Billy Milligan, P.E., Modern Steel Construction, May 2001

Exercises

1. Ductile materials:
   A. are brittle
   B. 'neck' before failure
   C. show crystalline fracture surfaces
   D. all of the above.

2. A force described as a moment is:
   A. a tensile force
   B. a turning force
   C. a shearing force
   D. happening at that time

3. Hooke's law states:
   A. stress equals strain
   B. stress is always greater than strain
   C. stress is directly proportional to strain within the plastic limit.
   D. stress is directly proportional to strain within the elastic limit.

4. When designing, factor of safety considerations are based around a material's:
   A. toughness
   B. failure values
   C. yield strength
   D. ultimate tensile strength

5. 'I' beams demonstrate superior strength due to their:
   A. web thickness
   B. materials selection
   C. low second moments of inertia
   D. greater mass from the neutral axis

6. Using the force-strain plot obtained for the Ductile Iron sample shown in Figure 9.1.7b calculate the Young's modulus.

7. Explain why strain is a dimensionless quality.

8. Explain why steel is a suitable material for inclusion in pre-stressed concrete beams.

9. Identify the factors that LVL a suitable alternative to solid timber

10. Explain the difference between true stress and engineering stress.

11. Discuss the issues surrounding treating structural timber with preservatives.

12. Explain how structures balance forces 'on' and 'within' individual members.

MECHANICAL DESIGN

CONTENTS

Machinery in all of its numerous forms makes possible much of what we take for granted in our modern world, from the clothes we wear and food we eat to modern communication systems, mechanisms and machinery have been an integral part of the process chain.

Since before recorded history, machinery played an important part in human progress. Machinery has improved the lot of mankind through its ability to reduce physical burden on both men and animals. While the efficiency, capacity and capability of modern machinery has increased dramatically from that of antiquity, the same basic elements we call the 'simple machines' remain.

All of today's complicated machines are based on six simple machines. These six machines are the:

- lever
- screw
- wheel
- pulley
- wedge
- inclined plane.

The value of simple machines comes in the mechanical advantage (MA) they provide. In simple terms this means simple machines help us to do work with less effort.

10.1 GENERAL CONCEPTS

10.1.1 Define mechanical advantage, velocity ratio and efficiency.

© IBO 2007

Mechanical advantage (MA) is the actual benefit obtained using simple machines such as levers and is directly calculated using the relationship between the load (resistance) and the effort, i.e. it represents the amount to which the machine amplifies effort

For example, if by using a simple machine a 500N object can be moved by applying an effort of only 10N, a mechanical advantage of 50 was obtained.

Since both the load and effort are measured in Newtons they cancel each other out so that MA is a dimensionless number.

$$MA = \frac{Load}{Effort}$$

The velocity ratio (VR) is the ratio of the distance moved by the effort compared with the distance moved by the load.

$$VR = \frac{distance\ moved\ by\ effort}{distance\ moved\ by\ load}$$

Values of VR greater than 1 indicate there is a magnification of effort operating, while values less than 1 indicate that a

AHL

diminution of effort exists. Again, since both the figures in this equation have common units they cancel out to produce a dimensionless result.

Efficiency (η) is a measure of the effectiveness, expressed as a percentage, with which the effort supplied is translated by the machine into work, or a measure of the output compared with the input.

$$\eta = \frac{\text{Work output}}{\text{Work Input}} \times 100$$

Since Work = Force × distance

$$= \frac{\text{load} \times \text{distance moved by load arm}}{\text{effort} \times \text{distance moved by efort arm}} \times 100$$

$$= \frac{MA}{VR}$$

For an ideal machine, where no energy losses occur due to friction or gravity, the efficiency is 100%.

> 10.1.2 Calculate mechanical advantage (MA), velocity ratio (VR) and efficiency for simple mechanical systems.
>
> © IBO 2007

Levers

The lever consists of a beam that by rotating about a fixed point, known as the fulcrum, can be used to move a load. Depending on the class of lever considered, and the location of the load and effort relative to the fulcrum, the distance and rate at which the load and effort move can vary considerably.

Consider the three arrangements for a first class lever, in which the fulcrum is placed between the load and effort, shown in Figure 10.1.2a. The dotted line in this figure represents the new position of the beam, following the application of sufficient effort to move the load.

As can be see in the examples of Figure 10.1.2a, the distance moved by the effort and load can vary considerably, resulting in a significant change in the velocity ratio and the mechanical advantage.

Most first and second class levers would be expected to provide a VR > 1, although, as can be seen from the left most illustration in Figure 10.1.2a, a VR < 1 for a first class lever is possible. In this arrangement, a diminution of effort results in a magnification of movement and since the load is made to move a greater distance than the effort in the same time, a greater velocity is achieved.

This arrangement was the basis of the Trebuchet, (illustrated in Figure 10.1.2b), a medieval war machine used to hurl missiles. When a weighted basket was allowed to fall under gravity the beam rotated about the fulcrum accelerating the load (missile), which was projected towards the opposition.

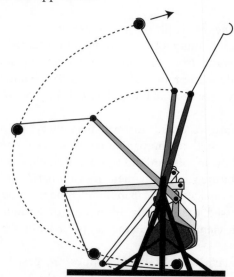

Figure 10.1.2b Representation of trebuchet in action

Image by Onno (Own work)[GNU Free Documentation License, Version 1.2], via Wikimedia Commons

Many first class levers evident in the human body are not magnifiers of effort, but are magnifiers of motion and have a VR < 1. Third class levers always have a VR< 1.

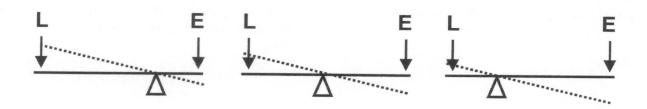

Figure 10.1.2a Three arrangements of Load and Effort relative to the Fulcrum for a first class lever

Wheel and Axle

The wheel and axle consists of a wheel through the centre of which passes an axle, that is fixed in place such that both the axle and wheel turn together. Therefore, if a turning force is applied to either the wheel or the axle the other component of the pair will also turn.

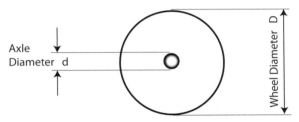

Figure 10.1.2c Wheel and axle

The mechanical advantage obtained arises from the difference in the diameter of the wheel and axle, or more accurately from the difference in their radii, since the arrangement can be thought of as either a second or third order lever system with the fulcrum at the centre. Figure 10.1.2d illustrates a second order lever arrangement, in which the effort applied to the turning of the wheel turns the axle and a MA >1 results. If the positions of the load and effort are swapped such that an effort is applied to the axle in order to rotate the wheel, a third order lever arrangement results for an MA<1, although a faster rotational speed will be produced in the wheel compared with that of the axle.

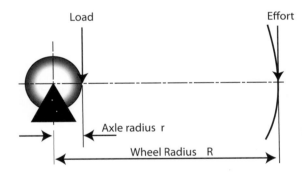

Figure 10.1.2d Second order lever

The velocity ratio calculated based on one revolution for Figure 10.1.1d is:

$$VR = \frac{\text{load} \times \text{distance moved by load arm}}{\text{effort} \times \text{distance moved by effort arm}} \times 100$$

$$= \frac{\Pi D}{\Pi d} \qquad = \frac{D}{d}$$

Pulleys

Pulleys are an adaptation of the wheel and consist of a grooved wheel into which a belt or cable is positioned. The pulley is used to transmit power, change the direction of a force and provide assistance through mechanical advantage. There are two basic classifications of pulley systems: fixed and moveable.

A fixed pulley system has the pulley anchored in a frame known as a block, which is in turn fixed to an elevated position.

A simple, single fixed pulley system is shown in Figure 10.1.2e. In this arrangement, the effort is equivalent to the load force (assuming 100% efficiency). The pulley simply changes the direction of the force but there is no mechanical advantage (MA), that is, MA = 1. Similarly, the distances moved by the load and effort are the same so VR=1.

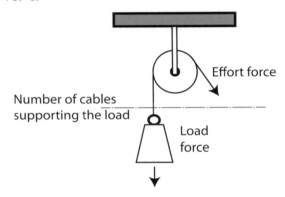

Figure 10.1.2e Single pulley system

Single pulleys alone offer no mechanical advantage but do change the direction of the effort relative to the load, i.e. a downward force translated through a single pulley causes upward movement.

In all pulley systems the MA and VR are dependent on the number of cables present within the system, the number of cable supporting the loads and the overall efficiency of the system, (mostly determined by friction).

In the two-pulley system shown in Figure 10.1.2f. the lower pulley is attached directly to the upper pulley which is, in turn, attached to the fixture. The MA of this system (assuming 100% efficiency) is 2, as two cables are said to be supporting the load force. The combination of fixed pulleys and moveable pulleys in a system is known as a 'block and tackle'.

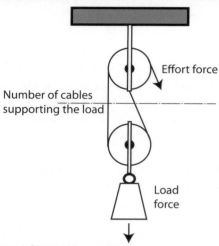

Figure 10.1.2f Fixed two pulley system

In the moveable pulley system shown in Figure 10.1.2g, even though there is only one pulley, the mechanical advantage gained is 2 due to the fact that two cables are supporting the load.

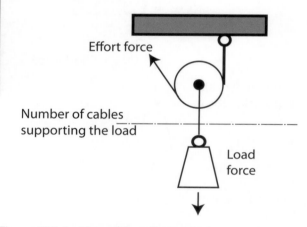

Figure 10.1.2g Moveable pulley system

Similarly, using the two-pulley system in a moveable configuration shown in Figure 10.1.2h three ropes are said to be supporting the load therefore the velocity ratio is three. Note that in a moveable system the bottom pulley is not attached directly to the upper pulley. The upper pulley is attached to the fixture.

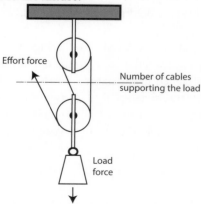

Figure 10.1.2h Moveable two pulley block and tackle

Inclined Plane

The inclined plane consists of a slope angled to the horizontal and by which a load can be raised vertically with less effort than might be otherwise required, as illustrated in Figure 10.1.2i.

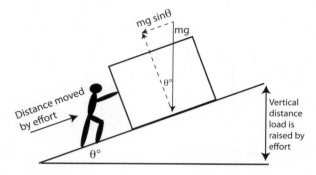

Figure 10.1.2i Forces acting on an inclined plane

The effort force required to push the Load up the incline depends on the height to which the load is being raised which in turn depends on the angle of the incline. The load force is represented by a mass (m) measured in kilograms acted on by gravity, that is $L = m \times g$.

Therefore assuming an ideal case with no frictional forces opposing movement, the effort required to move the load up the incline is $mg \sin\theta$;

$$MA = \frac{Load}{Effort}$$

$$= \frac{mg}{mg \times \sin\theta}$$

$$= \frac{1}{\sin\theta}$$

Similarly,

$$\sin\theta = \frac{\text{Vertical distance moved by load}}{\text{Distance moved by effort along incline}}$$

or

Vertical distance moved by load = Distance moved by the effort along the incline $\times \sin\theta$. Thus the Velocity Ratio of an inclined plane can be expressed as:

$$VR = \frac{\text{distance moved by effort}}{\text{distance moved by load} \times \sin\theta}$$

Wedge

The Wedge is similar to the inclined plane, although here the effort is not applied to move the load up an incline, it is applied in a direction to reach a maximum depth of penetration, as illustrated in Figure 10.1.2j. A wedge may be used as a device for holding, as in the case of a door stop, or for separating as in the case of a wood splitting wedge, axe or chisel.

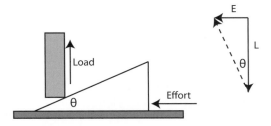

Figure 10.1.2j Wedge

The MA of a wedge is the depth of penetration attained for the amount of separation achieved

$$\text{Tan}\theta \quad = \quad \frac{\text{Effort}}{\text{Load}}$$

$$\text{Effort} \quad = \quad \text{Tan}\theta \times \text{Load}$$

$$\text{MA} \quad = \quad \frac{\text{Load}}{\text{Effort}} \quad = \quad \frac{1}{\text{Tan}\theta}$$

Similarly,

$$\text{VR} \quad = \quad \frac{\text{movement along horizontal}}{\text{movement along horizontal} \times \text{Tan}\theta}$$

$$= \quad \frac{1}{\text{Tan}\theta}$$

Screw

Screws represent an application of the inclined plane in which the incline has been cut into a spiral path around the circumference of a rod, as the rod turns it advances along the incline relative to a mating thread, as illustrated in Figure 10.1.2k.

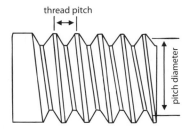

Figure 10.1.2k Screw thread as an inclined plane

For each complete turn, the screw advances the distance represented by the distance between adjacent threads, as measured at the thread crown. This distance is the thread pitch (p). In moving any load the distance of one thread pitch, the Effort must move the distance represented by a circle. The theoretical velocity ratio of the screw can be obtained by assuming the diameter traced by the effort is represented by the thread Pitch diameter (Dp). In practice, a larger diameter is usually employed as represented by the diameter of a screwdriver handle or the diameter of the circle described by a capstan handle.

The velocity ratio for a thread can therefore be represented as shown below:

$$\text{VR} \quad = \quad \frac{\Pi \, D}{p}$$

Since the screw is an application of the incline the mechanical advantage is the same as the velocity ratio.

> 10.1.3 Describe first-, second- and third-class levers.

The mechanical advantage obtained by a lever depends on the relative positions of the fulcrum, load and effort. There are three basic categories of levers based on the arrangement of these elements. A lever is therefore variously described as a first, second or third order (or class) lever.

The easiest way of remembering the designation of levers into the three classes is to remember the element in the centre by the anagram FLE.

E F L 1st Class

F L E 2nd Class

F E L 3rd Class

Although levers have been in use since before recorded history, the name of one person is most associated with the lever - the Greek engineer and mathematician, Archimedes. It was Archimedes, who gave a mathematical description to the lever. He is recorded as saying in 230BC, "Give me a lever long enough and a place to stand and I will move the World". Archimedes showed that the distance the effort and load were situated from the fulcrum was important and affected the effort required to move or balance a load. The distance from the fulcrum for any force on a lever is called the lever arm. More specifically, when considering the distance of the effort from the fulcrum the distance is known as the 'effort arm' and, similarly, the distance of the load from the fulcrum is known as the 'load arm'. The load and effort each represent forces moving the lever around the fulcrum, this turning action is known as a moment or the torque (l). The lever arm is therefore sometimes described as the moment arm or torque arm.

> **10.1.4** Discuss the relevant efficiencies of the three classes of lever.
>
> © IBO 2007

Due to the magnifying effect effort moment arms generate, no matter which system is employed it will always is easier to move a load the closer it is to the fulcrum.

> **10.1.5** Explain that, when a lever is in equilibrium, the net moment is zero.
>
> © IBO 2007

Archimedes found that for equilibrium to be obtained, the moments about the fulcrum must be zero, (i.e. clockwise turning forces equal anticlockwise turning forces). These turning forces are found using the product of the distance from the fulcrum and the acting force.

Mathematically it may be expressed as:

$$\Sigma(\text{effort} \times \text{effort arm}) = \Sigma(\text{load} \times \text{load arm})$$

$$\Sigma(\text{effort} \times \text{effort arm}) - \Sigma(\text{load} \times \text{load arm}) = 0$$

$$\text{or } \Sigma\text{Moments} = 0$$

In the example of a first class lever represented by a seesaw shown in Figure 10.1.5a, two children of equal weight sit on opposite sides and at the same distance from the fulcrum. This situation is also represented in Figure 10.1.5a as a force diagram. Because the children are of equal weight and distance from the fulcrum the moments about the fulcrum cancel each other and the system is balanced or is said to be in equilibrium.

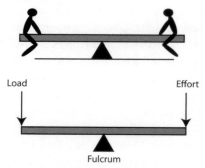

Figure 10.1.5a Representation of a first class lever - a seesaw, in equilibrium, with associated force diagram

Sample calculation

Use the information supplied in Figure 10.5.1a plus the following data. The child on the left of the see saw weighs 40kg and sits 3m from the fulcrum while the adult on the right weighs 90kg. Calculate how far the person on the right must sit from the fulcrum to achieve equilibrium.

In the first part of the solution the weight of the seesaw occupants must be converted into a force acting on the lever. This is accomplished by simply multiplying the respective masses by acceleration due to gravity, where (g) is approximated as: 10 m/s^2.

The child's weight therefore becomes;
$40 \text{ kg} \times 10 \text{ m/s}^2 = 400 \text{ kgm/s}^2$ or 400 N

Similarly, the adult's weight becomes;
$90 \text{ kg} \times 10 \text{m/s}^2 = 900 \text{ kgm/s}^2$ or 900 N

For equilibrium $\Sigma\text{Moments} = 0$
$(\text{effort} \times \text{effort arm}) - (\text{load} \times \text{load arm}) = 0$
$(900 \times d_E) - (400 \times 3) = 0$
$900\, d_E = 1200 \qquad \text{thus } d_E = 1.33 \text{ m}$

Therefore, in order to balance the child, the adult would need to move to within 1.33 m of the fulcrum.

The law of levers can therefore be simply stated as follows: In a simple lever, effort applied at right angles to the lever, multiplied by the effort arm equals the load times the load arm.

> **10.1.6** Calculate mechanical advantage and effort for first-, second- and third class levers.
>
> © IBO 2007

The mechanical advantage (MA) will vary for each class of lever depending on the relative position of the load, effort and fulcrum. Assuming the load in each of the cases presented below, the effort required to maintain equilibrium can be calculated and subsequently the MA.

Figure 10.1.6a shows the MA advantage of a first-class lever can vary from force multiplier to force reducer.

Figure 10.1.6b demonstrates second-class levers as force multipliers because the load is always between the fulcrum and the effort.

From Figure 10.1.6c it is clear that third-class levers are always force reducers because the effort is always between the fulcrum and the load.

First Class Lever

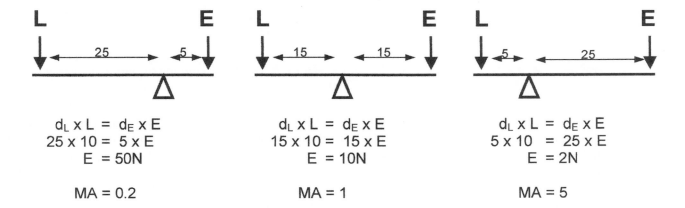

$d_L \times L = d_E \times E$
$25 \times 10 = 5 \times E$
$E = 50N$

MA = 0.2

$d_L \times L = d_E \times E$
$15 \times 10 = 15 \times E$
$E = 10N$

MA = 1

$d_L \times L = d_E \times E$
$5 \times 10 = 25 \times E$
$E = 2N$

MA = 5

Figure 10.1.6a First class lever

Second Class Lever

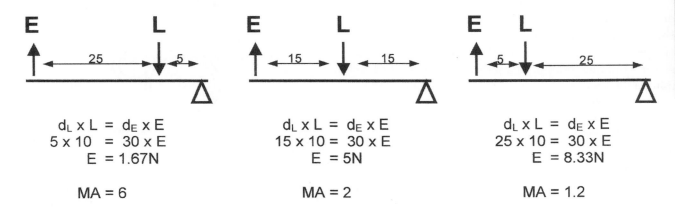

$d_L \times L = d_E \times E$
$5 \times 10 = 30 \times E$
$E = 1.67N$

MA = 6

$d_L \times L = d_E \times E$
$15 \times 10 = 30 \times E$
$E = 5N$

MA = 2

$d_L \times L = d_E \times E$
$25 \times 10 = 30 \times E$
$E = 8.33N$

MA = 1.2

Figure 10.1.6b Second class lever

Third Class Lever

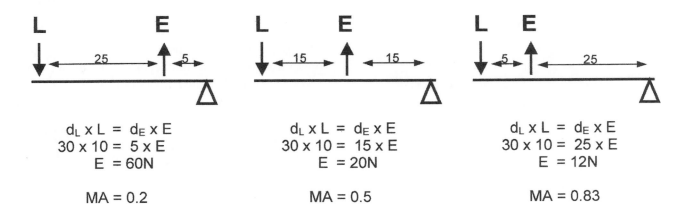

$d_L \times L = d_E \times E$
$30 \times 10 = 5 \times E$
$E = 60N$

MA = 0.2

$d_L \times L = d_E \times E$
$30 \times 10 = 15 \times E$
$E = 20N$

MA = 0.5

$d_L \times L = d_E \times E$
$30 \times 10 = 25 \times E$
$E = 12N$

MA = 0.83

Figure 10.1.6c Second class lever

Gears

10.1.7 Describe gear systems.

© IBO 2007

Gears have existed since 2600 BCE and the invention of rotating machinery, in which they provided a means of controlling the speed of rotation. Early gears were made from wood, with cylindrical pegs for cogs, lubricated with animal fat. Today, gears are rarely made from wood, but are manufactured from a wide variety of alternate materials including steel, aluminium, brass, plastic and composites, depending on the application. The motive force to drive gears has also varied from human and animal to wind, water, steam, diesel and electricity.

In essence, gears consist of cantilevered protrusions (teeth) arranged in equal spacing around the edge of a disc connected to a central shaft. Through their positive engagement by the meshing of teeth on the surface of one gear with the teeth on another, the transmission of power from one location to another is accomplished by transferring rotary motion from one shaft to another (Figure 10.1.7a). For this transfer to be accomplished efficiently, lubrication is necessary between the meshing surfaces of the gear to reduce frictional forces that would oppose motion.

Gear systems typically contain both a gear transmitting power (the drive gear) and a gear that is receiving the transmitted power (driven gear or idler gear). Depending on the combination and type of gears used, the speed, torque and direction of rotation can be affected. When two gears mesh together, the smaller of the two is called the 'gear pinion', while the larger is called the 'gear'.

Figure 10.1.7a Multiple gears transferring rotary motion

Rather than drawing complex gears (including individual teeth), gears are often represented by circles or concentric circles of various sizes (Figure 10.1.7b).

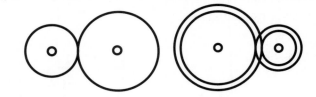

Figure 10.1.7b Representation of gears and gear systems

Gears are not only able to increase speed and change the direction of motion, but may also be configured to increase torque or turning forces. When two gears are meshed, as in Figure 10.1.7c, they act in the same way as levers. Each gear tooth acts like a lever, with the fulcrum at the centre of the gear. The longer the lever is, the greater the force that is applied to the shaft of the follower. The simple gear train shown in Figure 10.1.7c shows two meshed gears of differing size. The result of gear A making one revolution (clockwise) will be gear B making 4 revolutions (anticlockwise). This occurs due to the fact that it takes gear B four revolutions to match the travel of the 60 teeth moved through one revolution of gear A. An increase in output speed is therefore obtained although a decrease in torque occurs.

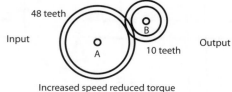

Figure 10.1.7c Meshing gears

When a smaller gear drives a larger gear (Figure 10.1.7d) there is a reduction in output speed and an increase in torque.

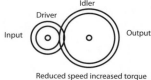

Figure 10.1.7d Relationship between gear sizes, torque and power

Most gears (with the exception of the worm gear) transmit power from one gear to another by rolling contact between mating teeth as illustrated in Figure 10.1.7e.

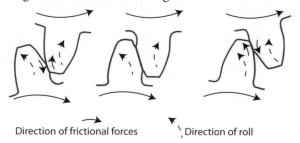

Figure 10.1.7e Rolling contact between gear teeth

10.1.8 Calculate velocity ratio for gear systems.

The velocity ratio for a gear system (or simply the gear ratio) is a measure of the amount to which a gear train increases or decreases the speed of the drive gear (sometimes called the input gear).

If, for example, the drive gear has 60 teeth and the driven gear has only 15 teeth the velocity ratio of gears can be calculated by applying the following formulae. One is based on the number of gear teeth while the other is based on gear wheel speeds.

$$VR = \frac{\text{number of teeth on the driven gear}}{\text{number of teeth on the driving gear}}$$

$$VR = \frac{15}{60} = 0.25$$

$$VR = \frac{\text{speed of driving gear}}{\text{speed of driven gear}}$$

$$VR = \frac{1 \text{ revolution}}{4 \text{ revolutions}} = 0.25$$

In these circumstances the gearing configuration is designed to increase speed. If the system were reconfigured with the 15 tooth gear as the driver, the effect would be one of reducing speed but providing a velocity ratio of 4 (and a mechanical advantage up to 4, depending on the efficiency of the system).

Figure 10.1.8 shows a gear box for a hand drill. The handle turns a helical wheel that has 37 teeth. This gear is in mesh with another, smaller, helical gear of 16 teeth, which turns a 34 tooth crown gear on the same shaft. The crown gear is in mesh with another, smaller, bevel gear of 15 teeth.

Figure 10.1.8 Hand drill gear configuration

The gear arrangement shown transfers motion from a vertical plane to a horizontal plane, however, while the style and number of intermediate gears will determine operations in terms of direction and plane of movement, they do not influence the gear ratio. The gear ratio is only determined by the ratio of the number of teeth on the drive gear (in this instance 37) to the output gear (in this instance 15). The calculation for the Velocity Ratio of this system would be as follows:

$$VR = \frac{\text{number of teeth on the output gear}}{\text{number of teeth on the drive gear}}$$

$$= \frac{15}{37}$$

This means that for every 15 turns of the handle, the drill bit will turn 37 times. This gear arrangement is therefore a multiplier of speed.

These formulae hold for each of the different types gear systems. The worm drive gear, however, is considered to consist of only one tooth.

10.1.9 Describe the function of different types of gears in a range of objects.

Gears can be divided into a number of categories, such as spur, helical, bevel, hypoid, and worm. Each of these categories has unique features that are utilized to perform specific tasks.

A Spur gear consists of teeth arranged transversely across the gear edge as shown in Figure 10.1.9a. Line of contact is parallel to the axis of rotation. Typically used when power is to be transferred between parallel shafts. Many spur shafts can be used together in a gear train to create large gear reductions.

Figure 10.1.9a Spur gear

Spur gears are easy to design and manufacture. They produce no axial thrust and are generally used when both speed and loads are low. They may be used in high speed and high load applications, where noise is not a consideration.

Spur gears find a wide range of applications most often appearing in automotive transmissions.

In helical gears, the line of contact is diagonal across the face of the tooth, that is, the teeth are inclined to the axis or rotation, as shown in Figure 10.1.9b. This results in a gradual engagement of each tooth leading to a smoother transfer of load than found in spur gears, and hence results in quieter operation and the transfer of heavy loads at higher speeds. As with Spur gears, Helical gears can be used to transmit power between two parallel shafts, they can however, also be used a crossed orientation allowing right angle drive.

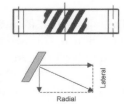

Figure 10.1.9b Helical gears

Because of the diagonal nature of tooth loading, helical gears are subject to both radial and thrust loads. Thrust loads are out-of-plane or axial loads. These thrust load may need to be balanced by other gears or bearings.

A common solution to counteract thrust loading is to use a double helical gear arrangement known as a herringbone gear, in which two helical gear patterns are cut back-to-back as shown in Figure 10.1.9.c

Figure 10.1.9.c Herringbone gear configuration

Herringbone gears have their teeth inclined to the axis and operate more quietly than spur gears. For the same width, teeth are longer than those of spur gears and have higher load carrying capacity.

Cutting of these gears is more costly than spur gears and axial loading is imposed on the shaft (due to the helix angle). Shaft support bearings have to be designed to take the axial load and the longer surface of contact between

teeth reduces the efficiency of a helical gear relative to a spur gear.

Helical gears find application in constant mesh gearboxes of automobiles and planetary gears.

Bevel gears consist of a conical surface into which the teeth have been cut. Teeth can be cut in straight, spiral or hypoid patterns, with the teeth tapering in both thickness and height along the taper. Bevel gears are used for transmitting power between two non-parallel shafts usually at 90° to each other, i.e. intersecting shafts.

An example of a straight bevel gear is presented in Figure 10.1.9d. Use is generally limited to low speed applications where noise is not an issue.

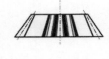

Figure 10.1.9d Straight bevel gear

Straight bevel gears are used for right-angle or any angular drive where 1:1 and higher velocity ratios are required. They are generally used when speeds and loads are low, <5m/s, but may be used in high speed and high load applications, where noise is not a consideration. Additional to being noisy, these gears can be of low efficiency. They find uses as differential side gears

An example of a spiral bevel gear is presented in Figure 10.1.9e, and consists of a bevel pinion gear in mesh with a crown wheel gear, such that the axes intersect at 90° to each other. The crown gear is one of the oldest gear styles and is considered to be a special form of a bevel gear since it can only mesh accurately with another bevel gear. The teeth of a crown gear are arranged at right angles to the plane of the wheel as in a crown and may be found on both sides of the wheel. The teeth of crown gears can be cut in straight or spiral forms.

Figure 10.1.9e Spiral bevel gear

Spiral bevel gears have more teeth in contact at the same time compared with straight cut teeth since the next pair of teeth begins engagement before the currently enmeshed teeth disengage. This sharing of loads over several teeth also results in a reduced pressure on the teeth, leading to a higher load capacity of spiral bevel gears. The curved nature of the teeth also results in a larger contact area, further reducing contact pressure. Because contact occurs over several teeth, a smoother, quieter operation results.

Spiral bevel gears replaced straight cut bevel gears in automotive rear axles due to quieter operation and have since been replaced by hypoid bevel gears, although they are still found in front wheel drive and rear engine vehicles.

Hypoid bevel gears are a modification of spiral bevel gears in which the shaft axes, while still at 90° to each other, do not intersect.

The main disadvantage of this gear type appears through the increase in sliding action between teeth resulting in increased sensitivity to correct lubrication. Extreme pressure (EP) lubrication is required in order to maintain an oil film between teeth.

Widely used in automobile driveline power transmission, they are also used for right angle drives. They have largely replaced spiral bevel gears in automotive rear axles of front wheel drive vehicles as the offset axis of the bevel pinion gear allows a lowering of the drive shaft and largely eliminates the hump in the vehicle floor.

Worm gears, or worm drives, consist of a continuous spiral tooth cut around a cylindrical surface that engages with a worm wheel containing individual teeth arranged around the edge of a wheel, similar to a spur gear. Figure 10.1.9f. shows a typical configuration. As the worm drive turns, its tooth engages a tooth on the worm wheel and transports it along the spiral, through sideways sliding contact, from one end of the worm to the other. Before this worm wheel tooth has reached the end of the worm drive the next tooth begins engagement with the worm. The result is a smooth, controlled movement of the worm wheel. Worm gears are used when large gear reductions are required.

Figure 10.1.9f Worm gear

Due to shallow angle on the worm gear, the worm can easily turn the meshing gear wheel, but the gear wheel cannot be used to turn the worm gear due to friction. Worm gears also lock if power to the worm drive is lost. A major advantage is the ability to obtain high reduction ratios in a compact space, with reductions of 20:1 or greater being common.

Unfortunately, the sliding, rather than rolling action of the tooth contact can produce tooth wear and considerable frictional heat requiring good lubrication for heat dissipation and to improve efficiency.

Worm gears are often used for transmitting power between two non-parallel shafts usually at 90° to each other, i.e. intersecting shafts. They also appear in materials handling and transportation machinery, machine tools and automobiles. In elevators, their self-locking nature, in the event of a power failure, is an added safety feature.

A rack and pinion system consists of a circular pinion gear in mesh with teeth machined into a flat bar known as the rack, which can be considered to be a gear of infinitely large diameter, see Figure 10.1.9g. A rack and pinion system is used to convert rotational motion into linear motion.

Figure 10.1.9g Rack and pinion gear system

Rack and pinion gear systems convert rotational motion into linear motion. They are used where high loads and high velocity ratios are required. As a variation, straight cut teeth may be machined in a helical pattern.

Rack and pinion systems are regularly used for automobile steering mechanisms. They also find application where fine linear adjustments are required, such as microscope stages or drill press machine tables.

| 10.1.10 | Explain a design context in which a compound rather than a simple gear train would be appropriate. |

A compound gear train is a gear system in which two or more component gears of differing diameter and tooth counts, are fixed together on a common shaft and rotate

AHL

together. The rear hub gearing on a bicycle is a common example of a compound gear. Compound gears are used extensively where changes in speed or torque are required. The gearing system of a metal cutting lathe is another common application of compound gears. An example of a lathe thread cutting gear train is shown after removal of protective covers in Figure 10.1.10a. These gears are found at the headstock end of the lathe.

1   Pulley connected to drive motor
2   Pulley driving gear box and chuck
3   Gear driven from gearbox - connected to chuck (30 teeth)
4   Compound (or pick-off) gears, (120 and 127 teeth)
5   Gear driving lead screw for screw cutting (60 teeth)
6   Adjusting bolt to adjust gear mesh of lead screw

Figure 10.1.10a Compound gear train

As may be seen in Figure10.1.10a, power is provided to the lathe by an electric motor, which is connected to a pulley wheel (1). The shaft connected to the driven pulley wheel (2) transmits motion to a gearbox that, in turn, drives the lathe headstock. The gearbox allows a number of headstock speeds to be selected. A shaft connected to the headstock passes from the gearbox to the rear of the machine and is connected to a small drive gear (3). This gear meshes with the compound gear (4), which can be seen more clearly in Figure 10.1.10b.

In this instance, changing from one of the gears in the compound set to the other is achieved by manually changing them, leading them to sometimes be known as 'pick-off' gears. By providing two gears, a different set of gear ratios can be accessed, such as might be required for metric or imperial threads.

Figure 10.1.10b Compound gear train meshing

When the lead screw gear (5) is brought into mesh with the compound gear (4) the rotation of the lead screw, and therefore the tool carriage that it drives, are moving in relation to the headstock. In other words, because the gearing from the head stock (3) is connected to lead screw gear (5) via the compound gears (4) for every turn of the head stock the lead screw will turn an amount determined by the gear ratio. As the lead screw rotates the tool carriage advances and a thread of desired pitch can be cut in the work piece. Many lathes also employ a 'quick-change' gearbox to increase the ability to change the gear ratio and increase the number of thread pitches that can be cut. This gearbox is located at the front of the lathe and often uses a set of compound gears that can be selected via a lever to change the rate of rotation of the lead screw. A simplified schematic illustration of the gear system is presented in Figure 10.1.10c.

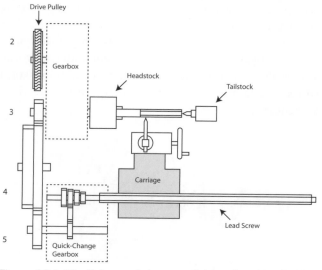

Figure 10.1.10c Schematic layout of thread cutting lathe

10.1.11 Discuss the function of different types of gears in a range of objects.

© IBO 2007

Shifting Spanner - worm gear

An invaluable member of any toolbox, the shifting spanner can accommodate a wide range of sizes by using a fixed and an adjustable jaw. By turning a worm wheel that is in mesh with a gear rack, the adjustable jaw can be moved in or out to the desired opening, see Figure 10.1.11. The linear motion of the adjustable jaw occurs in a direction parallel with the worm wheel axis of rotation.

Figure 10.1.11 Adjustable or shifting spanner

10.1.12 Describe a belt or chain drive system.

© IBO 2007

Belt and chain drive systems, at their simplest, are modified pulley systems consisting of two wheels connected by a flexible, continuous intermediary, as illustrated in Figure 10.1.12a. This intermediary may be made from any number of materials, such as leather, plastic, rubber, steel etc., depending on the capacity requirements of the system.

Belt systems rely on maintaining sufficient frictional contact between the wheel and the belt so that slippage does not occur and rotational motion of one wheel is transmitted with minimal loss to the other wheel. The cross-sectional shape of the belt can also vary from flat, square, round and vee shaped to match a complimentary shape in the wheel periphery in order to provide adequate surface area for friction. In contrast, chain drive systems use wheels with teeth around the periphery known as sprocket wheels or sprocket gears, which mesh with the spaces in a chain in order to transport the chain around the sprockets. Because friction is not required to maintain contact, chain drives can generally accommodate greater loads, in fact lubrication is required to reduce energy loss and wear through the frictional contact between the sprocket teeth and chain.

A simple belt or chain drive is an example of a flexible drive system in which rotational motion is transferred from one pulley to another by way of continuous flexible belt or chain. One pulley of the pair is the drive pulley, while the other pulley is the follower or driven pulley.

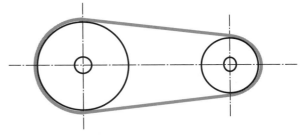

Figure 10.1.12a Simple belt or chain drive

Typically, the two pulleys are of differing diameter. The stepped cone pulley system (such as the one shown in Figure 10.1.12b), is often used to control spindle speeds for spindles in a drill press.

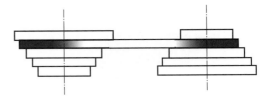

Figure 10.1.12b Stepped cone pulley

Belt drives are able to transmit power over large distances while absorbing a certain amount of shock and vibration, along with some degree of misalignment between the driven and drive ends. For these reasons they find extensive use in bulk goods conveyer systems.

10.1.13 Calculate velocity ratio for belt or chain drive systems.

© IBO 2007

The velocity ratio of a belt drive is the ratio of the driver to the follower. The length of the belt that will pass over either wheel in a defined period of time is $L_1 = \pi d_1 N_1$ and $L_2 = \pi d_2 N_2$, where L_1 and L_2 are the length of belt passing over the driver and the driven wheels respectively, and where d represents the diameter of the wheel and N is its rotational speed. Since the same amount of the belt (L) will pass over both wheels within any period of time.

$$L_1 = L_2$$

$$\pi d_1 N_1 = \pi d_2 N_2$$

The velocity ratio of a belt drive is therefore:

$$\frac{N_2}{N_1} = \frac{d_1}{d_2}$$

If the thickness of the belt is taken into account the relationship becomes:

$$\frac{N_2}{N_1} = \frac{d_1 + t}{d_2 + t}$$

10.1.14   Compare belt or chain drives and gear systems.

© IBO 2007

The sprocket and chain in concept lies between the pulley and gear systems and consists of two sprocket gears joined by a continuous chain. The chain typically consists of repeated, interlocking units comprised of two side plates joined at either end by a pin and separated by a bush. The pin and bush connection between the chain links allows them to articulate freely, producing a strong, flexible unit.

Figure 10.1.14a Continuous, flexible interlocking chain

Similar to gear systems in which power is transmitted by the meshing of the gear teeth, in a sprocket and chain system, power is transmitted by the meshing of the chain with the sprocket teeth. Effectively, the chain can be thought of as an interconnecting gear

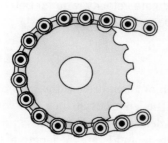

Figure 10.1.14b Chain and sprocket assembly

10.1.15   Design a system to provide belt torsion to a belt-and-pulley system.

© IBO 2007

Several methods of providing belt torsion are illustrated in the following diagrams.

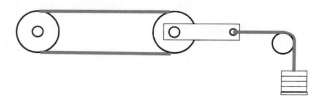

Figure 10.1.15a Belt torsion provided by weights attached to one moveable pulley

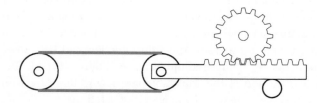

Figure 10.1.15b Belt torsion provided by rack and pinion type arrangement attached to one moveable pulley

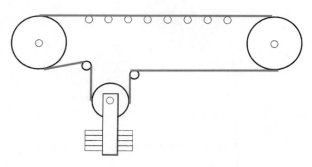

Figure 10.1.15c Variation on the weighted system shown in Figure 10.1.15a and typically found in coal conveyor systems. Weights attached to a moveable pulley arrangement between two fixed pulleys.

10.1.16   Describe a pulley system.

© IBO 2007

Pulleys are an adaptation of the wheel. They are used to transmit power, change the direction of a force and provide assistance through mechanical advantage.

In the simple single pulley system shown in Figure 10.1.16a, the effort is equivalent to the load force, (assuming 100% efficiency). The pulley simply changes the direction of the force.

The ability of a pulley to make work or effort easier can be measured in several ways. One of the most common means of expressing the advantage that such a device provides is the measure known as Mechanical Advantage (MA).

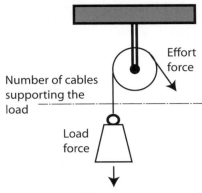

Figure 10.1.16a Single pulley system

In Figure 10.1.16a, because the load is equal to the effort there is no mechanical advantage (MA). The MA is 1. Note also that mechanical advantage is a dimensionless measure, since the same units are used in the numerator and denominator (N) and thus cancel each other. Mathematically this relationship is expressed as:

$$MA = \frac{\text{load force}}{\text{effort}} \quad \text{or} \quad MA = \frac{L}{E}$$

Another measure of assistance is the velocity ratio (VR), which actually represents the relative distances moved by the effort (d_E) and the load (d_L):

$$VR = \frac{d_E}{d_L}$$

Velocity ratio can be determined solely on the basis of the number of strings or cables involved in supporting the load, as can MA, when conditions of 100% efficiency are assumed.

When considering calculations involving pulleys, the following assumptions apply:

- all ropes are considered to be massless and inelastic (i.e. they do not stretch). They support loads in tension only and the force is always through the axis of the cable or rope
- all pulleys are considered to be massless and to have frictionless bearings. The magnitude of the tensile force remains constant around the pulley and there is no slipping between the pulley and the rope or cable
- single pulleys alone offer no mechanical advantage but do change the direction of the effort relative to the load, i.e. a downward force translated through a single pulley causes upward movement. The combination of fixed pulleys and moveable pulleys in a system is known as a block and tackle.

A fixed two-pulley system is shown in Figure 10.1.16b. Note that in a fixed pulley system the lower pulley(s) are attached directly to the upper pulley(s), which are themselves attached to the fixture. The MA of this system (assuming 100% efficiency) is 2, as two cables are said to be supporting the load force.

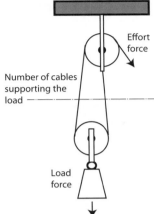

Figure 10.1.16b Fixed two pulley system

Using the block and tackle arrangement in Figure 10.1.16c, if the load is raised 250 mm the load-supporting ropes (4) will each shorten by 250 mm, therefore the effort will need to travel through 4 × 250 = 1000 mm. Mathematically this translates as:

$$VR = d_E \div d_L$$
$$VR = 1000 \div 250$$
$$VR = 4$$

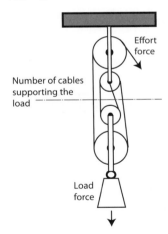

Figure 10.1.16c Block and tackle pulley system

For any simple machine the velocity ratio, once established, is a constant. The mechanical advantage however changes with the overall efficiency of the system. The greatest reductions in efficiency are generally caused by friction. When considering any simple machine:

$$MA = VR \text{ while ever the efficiency is 100\%.}$$

To calculate the MA when efficiency is less than 100% the following formula is applied:

$$\text{Efficiency } (\eta) = MA / VR$$

Efficiency (η) is a dimensionless value and may be expressed as a decimal or percentage value, e.g. 0.8 or 80%.

In the moveable pulley system shown in Figure 10.1.16d, even though there is only one pulley, the mechanical advantage gained is 2, due to the fact that two cables are supporting the load.

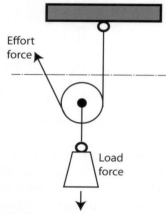

Figure 10.1.16d Moveable pulley system

Similarly, using the two-pulley system in a moveable configuration shown in Figure 10.1.16e, three ropes are said to be supporting the load, therefore the velocity ratio is three.

Note that in a moveable system the bottom pulley is not attached directly to the upper pulley. The upper pulley is attached to the fixture.

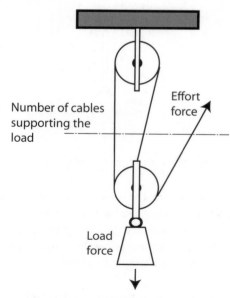

Figure 10.1.16e Moveable two pulley Block and tackle system VR = 3

Using the pulley system shown in Figure 10.1.16f, calculate the load able to be lifted, given the system has an efficiency of 76%. An effort of 750 N is again applied.

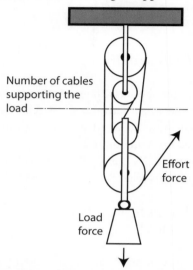

Figure 10.1.16f Moveable four pulley Block and tackle system

VR = 5 number of ropes supporting lower block

Efficiency η	$= 76\%$ or 0.76
0.76	$= MA \div VR$
0.76	$= MA \div 5$
MA	$= 0.76 \times 5$
MA	$= 3.80$

Since
MA	$= L \div E$
3.80	$= L \div 750$
L	$= 3.80 \times 750$
L	$= 2850$ N or 285 kg.

A simple rope and pulley system has a VR of 5. Find the effort required if the efficiency of the system is 45% and the load to be lifted is 2kN.

Efficiency	$= MA / VR$
0.45	$= MA \div 5$
MA	$= 2.25$
MA	$= L \div E$
2.25	$= 2000 \div L$
L	$= 2000 \div 2.25$
L	$= 888.9$ N.

Using Figure 10.1.16c, calculate the load able to be lifted given the system has an efficiency of 76%. An effort of 750 N is applied.

$$\eta = MA \div VR$$
$$0.76 = MA \div 4$$
$$MA = 0.76 \times 4$$
$$MA = 3.04$$
$$MA = L \div E$$
$$3.04 = L \div 750$$
$$L = 3.04 \times 750$$
$$L = 2280 \text{ N or } 228 \text{ kg.}$$

10.1.18   Describe an inclined plane.

An inclined plane is simply a flat surface inclined to the horizontal along which an object may travel, and by which an object can be raised in height. The simplest example of an inclined plane is perhaps a ramp that connects two positions of different height.

10.1.19   Explain the advantage of an inclined plane.

The inclined plane allows objects to be raised with less effort than required to raise the same object with a direct vertical movement. Note that the same amount of work is done whether using a larger force to lift the load vertically over a small distance, such as a step, or using a lesser force to raise the load gradually by travelling a longer path.

The screw thread can be considered a generic term for an inclined plane following a helical path along a curved symmetrical surface. What we commonly refer to as a screw has the inclined path located around the circumference of a conical surface. A bolt, on the other hand, has the inclined path located around the circumference of a cylindrical surface. In these manifestations, the incline represented by the helical path of the thread allows precise control of movement in metering devices e.g. micrometer screw gauge or screw feed system. The screw advances only the distance represented by the distance between adjacent threads, i.e. the thread pitch, for each complete turn, as shown previously in Figure 10.1.2k.

10.2 MECHANICAL MOTION

10.2.1   Describe linear, rotary, intermittent, oscillating, reciprocating and irregular motion.

Linear motion: motion in a straight line. This motion is typically achieved using a guide system of some form such as a shaft, screw thread, rollers, slides, rail or channel. Typically, measured in terms of velocity (distance per second).

Rotary motion: movement in a circular pattern about a central axis. Most gear and pulley systems exhibit rotary motion. Typically measured in terms of number of revolutions completed within a set time e.g. rpm (revolutions per minute).

Intermittent motion: motion that starts and stops regularly and is often provided with the aid of a ratchet and pawl assembly.

Oscillating motion: Back and forth motion about a pivotal point. Oscillatory motion is measured in terms of the angle of throw (angle formed by extreme positions of a cycle), period (time required to complete a cycle), and frequency (number of cycles completed in a given period). The pendulum and metronome are typical examples of this motion.

Reciprocating motion: Back and forth motion in a straight line. Reciprocating motion is measured in terms of throw (distance between extremes) and period.

Irregular motion: motion with no obvious pattern.

10.2.2   Explain how linkages can be used to change the direction of motion of components.

Linkages consist of mechanical components such as rods and levers, which connect one component to another allowing the transfer of motion. In the example of a linkage shown in Figure 10.2.2a, three bars are joined by pins, acting as pivots. The central bar is further secured to a fixed pivot position. Movement imposed on one of the outer bars will be transmitted to the other outer bar through the linkage.

AHL

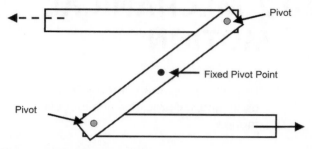

Figure 10.2.2a Simple linkage

Figure 10.2.2b shows how a linkage may be employed to change direction of motion and apply mechanical advantage. The device shown allows hand pressure to shear steel bolts.

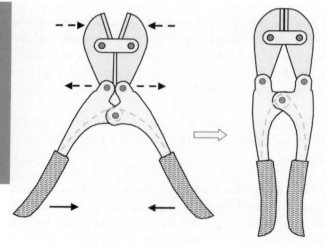

Figure 10.2.2b Diagram of bolt cutter linkage

The photograph in Figure 10.2.2c shows locking vice grips and the mechanical linkage that allows them to open and close.

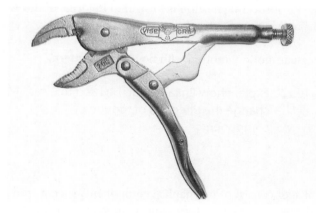

Figure 10.2.2c Vise grips or locking pliers

10.2.3 Discuss mechanical motion in a range of contexts.

The bicycle (Figure 10.2.3a) uses a sprocket and chain system to translate the reciprocating motion of the rider's legs on the bicycle pedals into rotational motion of the wheels, to produce forward linear motion of the bicycle.

Figure 10.2.3a Bicycle

The car jack, such as the Scissor jack shown in Figure 10.2.3b uses the mechanical advantage obtained with threads to raise a vehicle.

The Scissor jack uses linked folding support members that are gradually drawn together by the jackscrew, as the handle is turned. As the support members come together a lifting action occurs. Rotary motion of the turning handle is therefore translated into both horizontal and vertical linear motion.

Figure 10.2.3b Scissor jack

The egg beater uses a gear system that translates rotary motion in one direction (vertical) to rotary motion in another direction (horizontal).

In the example shown in Figure 10.2.3c, turning the handle rotates a large central double crown gear. Two beaters with a spur gear at their top mesh with either side of the crown gear. Because there are more teeth on the crown gear than on the spur gears, for a relatively slow turning of the handle (low effort), rapid rotation of the beaters is obtained.

Figure 10.2.3c Egg beater

10.2.4 Define torque.

© IBO 2007

The term torque has a number of meanings, but is generally defined as a rotational force. In physics, any force that results in rotation about a point is called 'torque' and is represented by the Greek symbol tau (τ). In mechanical engineering the force that results in rotation about a point as represented by a lateral force on a beam, is known as the moment and the term torque is restricted to the specific condition of axial rotation down a shaft.

10.2.5 Discuss the design features of a ratchet and pawl system.

© IBO 2007

The ratchet and pawl systems are used to break up continuous motion into regular intermittent motion and to allow that motion to occur in only one direction. The ratchet and pawl utilises a ratchet consisting of a wheel with saw-tooth shaped teeth around the perimeter and a pawl that consists of a mechanism (often a lever) that engages with a tooth.

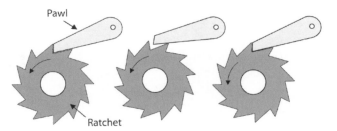

Pawl

Ratchet

Figure 10.2.5a Illustration on the stages of rotation of a ratchet and pawl system (moving left to right) in which anticlockwise motion of the ratchet wheel is allowed while the pawl prevents clockwise motion.

Ratchet and pawl systems are typically used to regulate rotational motion as illustrated in Figure 10.2.5a. As the ratchet wheel turns in the anticlockwise direction, the pawl lever moves about its pivot point as it is pushed upward by the next tooth. As the tip of the tooth passes the end of the pawl, the familiar 'click' is heard as the pawl falls, or is forced by a spring, back into mesh.

Ratchet and pawl systems are found in such diverse applications as the escapement mechanism of a clock (Figure 10.2.5b) and tie down strap buckles (Figure 10.2.5c).

AHL

Figure 10.2.5b Clock escapement mechanism

The ratchet and pawl system shown in Figure 10.2.5b gathers the mechanical advantage of the lever and applies it to the strap to force it to tighten. The ratchet and pawl allows for the tightened strap not to loosen and only be undone when 'released'.

Figure 10.2.5c Tie down strap ratchet and pawl

10.2.6 Describe simple cam shapes and their advantages.

10.2.8 Explain the use of a series of cam and follower mechanisms to achieve a set purpose.

© IBO 2007

10.2.7 Identify cam followers and state their use.

© IBO 2007

A cam forms part of a mechanical linkage and is typically used to transform rotational motion into linear motion, while controlling changes in acceleration, deceleration and rest. This control is obtained by machining a specific profile into the surface of the cam. When another linkage, known as the follower, is positioned against the cam, the follower is moved in or out as determined by the cam profile and through other linkages transmits the movement on to other parts of the machine. As might be imagined, a wide variety of cam designs have been developed.

Typical shapes are: cylindrical, drop and pear (tear drop).

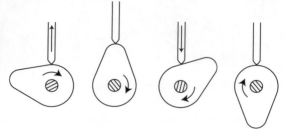

Figure 10.2.6a Pear shaped cam

Pear shaped cams are often used to control valves in engines. For about half of their rotation they remain in one position, then rise before falling back to the original height.

Drop cams are shaped like a snail shell.

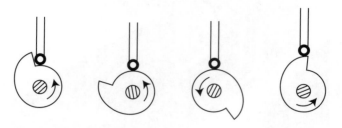

Figure 10.2.6b Drop cam

Cam followers track the movement of a cam and transfer this movement from the rotating cam to other machinery components. Pressure is often applied to the cam follower to maintain contact with the rotating cam, creating a repeating pattern of movement in the follower.

Wear and friction are both considerations in cam follower design. Cam followers with sharper or more pointed profiles may wear quicker and require more frequent adjustment or even replacement. However, broader or more heavier designed followers may trace the cams movement less accurately.

As the complexity of the cam design increases, so too does the complexity of the motion required to be transferred by the follower.

Cam follower types include:

- roller
- flat-faced
- knife-edge
- spherical-faced
- oblique flat-faced.

Cam and follower systems appear in, motor vehicles, animated toys.

Figure 10.2.7 Cam and follower

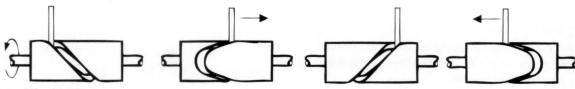

Figure 10.2.6c Cylindrical cam

AHL

10.3 CONVERSION OF MOTION

10.3.1 Identify how mechanisms allow conversion of one form of motion to another.

Linear motion: motion in a straight line. This motion is typically achieved using a guide system of some form such as a shaft, screw thread, rollers, slides, rail or channel. Typically, measured in terms of velocity (distance per second).

Rotary motion: movement in a circular pattern about a central axis. Most gear and pulley systems exhibit rotary motion. Typically measured in terms of number of revolutions completed within a set time e.g. rpm (revolutions per minute).

Intermittent motion: motion that starts and stops regularly and is often provided with the aid of a ratchet and pawl assembly.

Oscillating motion: Back and forth motion about a pivotal point. Oscillatory motion is measured in terms of the angle of throw (angle formed by extreme positions of a cycle), period (time required to complete a cycle), and frequency (number of cycles completed in a given period). The pendulum and metronome are typical examples of this motion.

Reciprocating motion: Back and forth motion in a straight line or an arc. Reciprocating motion is measured in terms of throw (distance between extremes) and period. Cranks are used in internal combustion engines to convert rotary motion into the reciprocating motion of the pistons.

Figure 10.3.1 Rotary to reciprocating motion

Irregular motion: Motion with no obvious pattern. Linkages consist of mechanical components such as rods and levers, which connect one component to another allowing the transfer of motion. In the example of a linkage shown in Figure 10.2.2a, three bars are joined by pins, acting as pivots. The central bar is further secured to a fixed pivot position. Movement imposed on one of the outer bars will be transmitted to the other outer bar.

10.3.2 Identify the mechanisms in a bicycle.

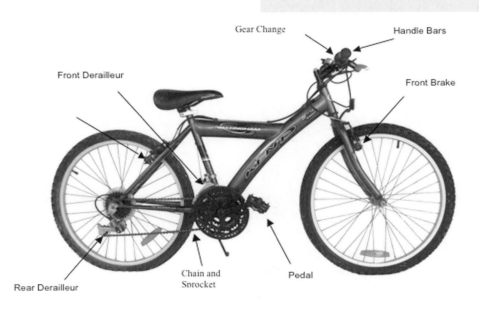

Figure 10.3.2a Bicycle mechanisms

The simple mechanisms in Figure 10.3.2a include:

- chain drive with velocity ratio varied through front derailleur and rear gear clusterbars
- pedal crank arms and handlebars using simple levers
- front and rear brakes applied by lever pressure transmitted via cable to another simple lever.

Figure 10.3.2b Close-up of brake caliper

10.3.3 Design combinations of mechanisms to achieve specific tasks.

The following tasks may be achieved in a variety of ways through the application of single mechanisms or combination of mechanisms used in concert.

Alter the axis of rotation - bevel gears may be employed to change an axis of rotation by 90°.

Figure 10.3.3a Bevel gears

Image by Cate Metcalfe

Change the type of movement - cams may be used to turn rotational movement into a series of patterned, cyclic linear movements. The two rotating cams shown in Figure 10.3.3b both change linear motion into repeating linear motion through a cam follower pressed against the rotating perimeter of the cam. Figure 10.3.1 also shows a compound gear train and slide to turn rotary motion into a reciprocating action.

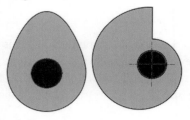

Figure 10.3.3b Cam movements

Increase force and decrease speed. The block and tackle illustrated in Figure 10.1.16c uses a four pulley system to increase force and decrease speed. A similar action may be introduced through a simple connection of two gears where the smaller of the two is the driving gear.

Figure 10.3.3c Speed reduction gear

Pulleys may be used in a similar fashion to the gear system shown above. Levers, and linkages may also be used to increase power. Figures 10.3.4b and 10.2.2b show such systems respectively.

A decrease of force and increase in speed may be achieved by reversing the action of the gear system shown in Figure 10.3.3b, i.e. the larger gear becomes the driving gear and the smaller follower thus moves faster. Figure 10.3.3c shows how a third order lever reduces the force applied to the load.

Figure 10.3.3d Tweezers

Image by Richard Wheeler Creative Commons Attribution-Share Alike 3.0 Unported

10.3.4 Discuss how designers make use of simple mechanisms in the home.

© IBO 2007

The can opener shown in Figure 10.3.4a demonstrates a first order lever and a traction gear driven by a force couple.

Figure 10.3.4a Can opener

The pizza cutter illustrated in Figure 10.3.4b uses a simple lever combined with a wheel and axle to deliver force at the perimeter of the cutting disc.

Figure 10.3.4b Pizza cutter

The nutcracker shown in Figure 10.3.3c uses the force multiplying effect of a second order lever to crack nuts.

Figure 10.3.4c Nutcracker

Further Reading

Pace, S. (1999). *Teaching Mechanical Design Principles on Engineering Foundation Courses,* International Journal of Mechanical Engineering Education. Vol. 28, No. 1.

Exercises

1. Screw threads are similar to:
    A. levers
    B. chain drives
    C. pulley systems
    D. an inclined plane.

2. Mechanical advantage is always:
    A. equal to efficiency
    B. equal to velocity ratio
    C. greater than velocity ratio
    D. less than or equal to velocity ratio.

3. Worm gears are used where:
    A. noise is an issue
    B. faster speeds are required
    C. intermittent motion is required
    A. large gear reductions are required.

4. When making calculations for pulleys:
    A. ropes are always elastic
    B. pulleys remain massless
    C. some ropes may be in compression
    D. pulleys are allocated a standard mass.

5. Using the system shown in Figure 10.1.16g calculate the maximum load that can be lifted if the effort employed is 85 N and the overall efficiency is 75%.

6. A wheelbarrow, acting as a second class lever, holds a load of 60 kg at the centre of gravity, 200 mm from the wheel hub, (the fulcrum). Calculate the effort required if the handle has a length of 1.5 m? Assume all forces are acting normal to the lever.

7. Explain why different designs in cam followers may be specified.

8. Identify the multiple functions that gears may perform.

9. Discuss the relative merits of chain and pulley drives.

10. Explain with diagrams how a ratchet and pawl system may be used to constrain motion.

11. A third class lever, represented by a pair of tweezers is shown in Figure 10.1.5d. What effort is required to exert a force of 12 N at the tip if the tweezers are 150 mm long and the effort is applied in the mid-body position?

AHL

ADVANCED MANUFACTURING

11

CONTENTS

11.1 Joining

11.2 Moulding

11.3 Casting

11.4 Forming

Throughout history, the development of new materials have required the exploration of new methods of manufacture and construction. The manufacturing techniques presented in this chapter represent some of the advances in processing that have occurred over the last century in response to changing materials, equipment and design.

Some of these changes represent extensions of processes used for centuries, but applied now to new materials, while others represent processes only possible with the assistance of modern machinery and computer control.

In the last 50 years, industry has had the opportunity to test materials and manufacturing processes in environments beyond the Earth. The ubiquitous cutting tool, used in a multitude of manufacturing situations is benefiting from space-age research through the application of a new process called defect trapping. Space offers a unique environment in which to examine the solidification of metals and evaluate defects. In conjunction with techniques such as liquid phase sintering, researchers are examining ways to eliminate defects from products made on Earth.

Figure 11. Intro Liquid phase sintering

11.1 JOINING

AHL

11.1.1 Describe friction welding.

© IBO 2007

Friction welding is a solid-phase welding process in which the parts to be joined are brought into contact under pressure. During solid phase welding processes no part of the joint is molten, although heating to a semi-molten state may occur. Critical to the operation is the presence of an oxide free interface that might prevent the formation of a metallurgical bond.

A variation of this process is friction stir welding where an external tool, rotating at high speed provides both friction and pressure to seams to join them in the same fashion as occurs in standard friction welding.

Figure 11.1.1 Friction stir welding as used on the bulkhead and nose-cone of the Orion spacecraft

11.1.2 Explain how two metal parts are welded using friction.

© IBO 2007

Friction welding, also known as inertia welding, involves the joining of two materials using the heat of frictional contact created by rotating one half against the other non-rotating half. When sufficient heat has been produced that the interface is in a semi molten state, the rotation is stopped and the two halves are forced together and held in position until the part has cooled.

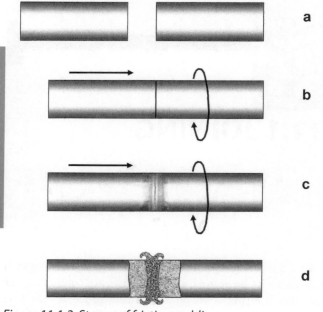

Figure 11.1.2 Stages of friction welding

As the parts are brought together, lateral flow of the semi-molten material at the interface occurs, ejecting any impurities, such as surface oxides, from the interface.

Advantages: Lower energy necessary compared to other welding processes, dissimilar metals can be joined, no fumes or scale formed, narrow heat affected zone.

Disadvantages: parts to be joined must be symmetrical.

11.1.3 Describe plastic welding.

© IBO 2007

Plastic welding is the process of joining plastic parts through the softening of the interface sufficiently to allow bonds to be formed. As will be appreciated from this description, only thermoplastic materials can undergo such treatment. A wide range of techniques are available under the banner of plastic welding, some of which are described below in section 11.1.4.

Hot air welding is one of the most common forms of plastic welding employed and is similar in many respects to oxy-fuel welding of metals. In the hot air welding processes a special gun is used to produce a jet of hot air in order to soften the region to be joined, while additional filler material is introduced into the weld region. The filler material used must match the type of plastic being welded. The basic stages of creating a hot air weld are shown in Figures 11.1.4a to 11.1.4d

The parts to be joined need to be clean and the joint line prepared sufficiently to allow the filler material to enter the joint. A vee type preparation is therefore typically created with a burr.

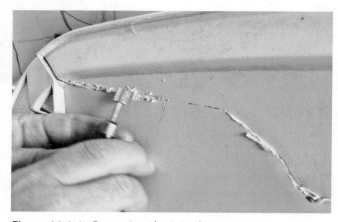

Figure 11.1.4a Preparing the joint line

Tacking of the interface is then performed by carefully passing the heat gun along the groove to ensure that a sufficient bond is created that the joint surfaces will not move. The filler cord is then introduced into the weld groove and the heat gun used to melt the base material and filler. The heat gun is gradually moved back along the groove maintaining a distance of approximately 10mm as the filler cord is progressively melted and pressed into the groove.

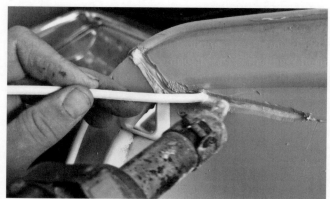

Figure 11.1.4b Repairing the crack line

Sufficient weld runs are performed to fill the groove. Gouging of the weld root from the opposite side of the weld may also be performed to ensure a full section weld, as is common in oxy-fuel welding.

Figure 11.1.4c Grinding the welded surface

On completion of the weld runs, the weld surface is ground flush. In many instances filler metals of the same colour as the part to be welded are available making further work unnecessary. In instances where this is not the case, and a repair line might be considered unsightly, painting may follow.

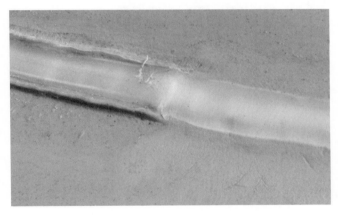

Figure 11.1.4d Adjacent welded and finished surfaces

Images by Farmer Bros - Bumper & Automotive supplies

Typical applications include the repair of automotive bumpers and headlight housings, motorbike fairings, water tanks, pump housings, medical containers, golf buggy roofs etc.

Materials include: ABS, Acrylic, Nylon, Polycarbonate, Polyethylene (HDPE and LDPE) and Polypropylene.

A section through a hot air weld in polypropylene is presented in Figure 11.1.4b. In this repair, the weld runs have been performed using different colour polypropylene fillers to highlight each run.

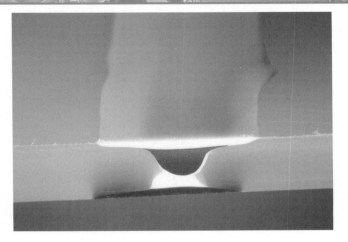

Figure 11.1.4e Section through a hot air weld in polypropylene. Different colour polypropylene fillers used to highlight weld runs

Solvent welding involves the use of a chemical solvent that will dissolve the plastic surface sufficiently that the polymer chains of the two surfaces so treated will mix and entangle when pressed together, forming a bond, as shown in Figure 11.1.4f. As the solvent dissipates the plastic within the weld region regains its strength. This process has the advantage that it is performed at room temperature, although the solvents used need to be handle with care. It finds applications joining materials such as: ABS, Nylon, Polycarbonate, Polystyrene and PVC.

Figure 11.1.4f Magnified view of the joint interface formed in nylon by solvent welding

Ultrasonic welding uses high frequency sound energy in the 15kHz to 40kHz region focused at a joint line between plastic parts to create vibrations. These vibrations result in frictional heating at the interface and softening of the plastic, allowing a bond to be formed.

11.1.5 Define permanent joining techniques.

11.1.6 List a range of permanent joining techniques.

© IBO 2007

Permanent joining techniques are those that once formed cannot easily be separated without damage.

Hot riveting is now largely consigned to history. Traditionally, it was the primary method of joining iron and steel structural plates used in the construction of buildings, ships, bridges and pressure vessels for over a century, before being superseded in the 1950s by welding and structural bolts.

The rivet consisted of a pin or shank, with a head at one end and was originally made from wrought iron and later from low carbon steel. These materials are relatively soft with good ductility and did not require tempering after cooling.

While riveting was an efficient operation it was labour intensive, typically requiring a skilled team of four workers. Operations required the rivets to be heated in a small furnace close to the installation site, usually with the pin, shank down, in order to keep the head cooler and retain some strength during installation. When an appropriate temperature was reached the rivet would be removed from the heat with tongs by one member of the team, and thrown a short distance to be caught by another team member with a funnel, who would position the rivet in the hole prepared in the plates to be joined, before getting ready to catch the next rivet. A third team member would force the rivet head against the plate surface while a partner on the other side deformed the end with a pneumatic hammer. As the rivet cooled and contracted a strong, permanent, watertight joint was formed.

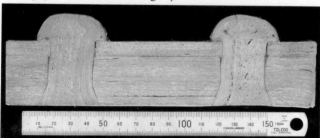

Figure 11.1.6a Section through a wrought iron countersunk head rivet from the Morpeth Bridge NSW, built in 1898.

Image by Glen Barry - Bureau Veritas

A cross section through two wrought iron rivets from a bridge built in 1898 is shown in Figure 11.1.6a. A wide range of different factory head styles was used, depending on the application. In the example provided, rivets with a countersunk factory head were used, while a tool with a concave end was used to produce a rounded shop head. The slag stringers of the wrought iron allow the flow lines to be seen in the rivets. Note the tight joint formed by the rivets between the two wrought iron plates.

The riveted joint was a physical connection with no melting or metallurgical bond being formed between any of the components. While providing some strength in tension, the riveted joint was strongest in shear, arising from both the rivets themselves and the frictional contact that was achieved between the plates joined. Rivets were typically installed in groups, with each rivet separated from its neighbour by a distance of 3-5 shank diameters. An example of steel rivets in a bridge structure is presented in Figure 11.1.6b.

Figure 11.1.6b Steel rivets present in a bridge

Image by Michael O'Brien – Bureau Veritas

Advantages
- variety of heads styles available
- may be used to join dissimilar metals
- can join metals of different thickness
- strong, stable, watertight joint can be formed
- no adverse microstructural changes in the materials joined.

Disadvantages
- access to both sides usually required
- skilled team required, compared to a single worker needed to install bolts
- must be drilled out to remove compared to bolts, which are easily removed
- not strong under tensile loading or cyclic stresses that could lead to fatigue.

Blind rivets (also known as breakstem rivets and Pop-rivets) are typically used for the joining of sheet metal and consist of a solid stem or mandrel terminating in a button-like head. A short tubular body or shaft with a flanged end is positioned on the stem just below the head, as may be seen in Figure 11.1.6c.

This joining method is not intended for structural applications.

Figure 11.1.6c Pop-rivets of various size

Installation is achieved by inserting the shaft into a prepared hole in the sheet metal being joined so that the head of the mandrel protrudes from the other side. A setting tool is then positioned over the mandrel stem such that the flanged head of the shaft is held against the sheet metal surface. With the aid of the setting tool, the mandrel is pulled back through the tubular shaft. As this takes place, the button head of the mandrel compresses and deforms the end of the shaft between itself and the sheet metal surface. Compression continues until the tensile strength of the mandrel is exceeded and it fractures, leaving behind a completed joint. An example of a blind rivet installation is presented in Figure 11.1.6d where blind rivets have been used to secure a cabinet hinge.

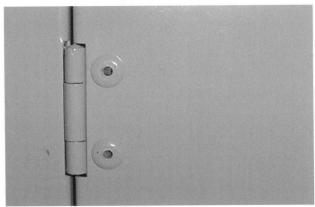

Figure 11.1.6d Pop-rivets securing a hinge in a sheet metal cabinet

Advantages
- heat not involved
- single operator installation
- can be installed from one side
- installation does not require high level of skill

Disadvantages
- surfaces have to perforated with a drill
- can only be used on relatively thin material

Soldering and brazing are similar operations and involve the joining of two or more parts by melting a filler metal with a heat source. The molten filler metal flows into the joint and on solidifying, holds the parts together. The heat source for soldering is usually a hot 'iron' while brazing is accomplished with the aid of an oxyacetylene torch or as a bulk process in a furnace.

The primary difference between the processes is the temperature at which the filler metal solidifies. The dividing line between the processes is somewhat confused however, as some definitions quote a liquidus temperature of approximately 450°C, while other a solidus of 500°C. Perhaps because of this, terminology is sometimes confusing, as with the process of 'silver soldering', which uses an silver alloy filler metal with a liquidus of about 450°C and which is considered to be a brazing operation.

Regardless of the exact division, soldering, shown in Figure 11.1.6e, uses low temperature filler metal alloys (e.g. Pb, Sn, Sb etc.) while brazing uses higher temperature alloys (e.g. Ag, Cu, Ni, Al, etc.). A section through a brazed joint between a copper tube and copper expansion bellows performed by silver soldering is shown in Figure 11.1.6f.

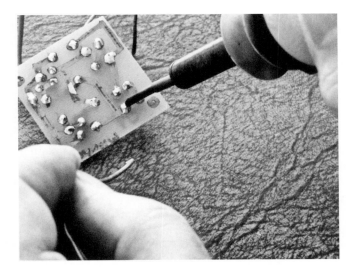

Figure 11.1.6e Soldering of an electronics circuit board

Both processes require the surfaces that are to be joined are free of oxides, so that the filler metal can 'wet' the surface. Fluxes designed to remove oxides from the surface are used to provide a clean joint, while some diffusion occurs across the boundary between the filler metal and parent metal.

In both cases the filler metal is drawn into the joint by capillary action. While both processes are performed below the solidus of the materials to be joined, joint strength relies on more than a mechanical attachment. In both processes small amounts of the parent metal interface dissolves to form inter-metallic compounds with the filler metal, producing a metallurgical bond.

Figure 11.1.6f Section through a brazed 'silver solder' joint in copper tubing.

Fusion welding involves the heating of the surfaces to be joined until melting and intermixing at the joint occurs to form a 'metallurgical' bond. This heat may be provided by a variety of methods including gas, friction, electric-resistance or electrode arc. Additional metal may be introduced to the joint using either a consumable electrode, as in manual metal arc welding (MMAW), or by a separate filler wire that is fed into the heat source, as in gas welding or tungsten inert gas (TIG) welding.

Other heat sources for specialized applications include laser and electron beam welding. In order to maintain a clean surface and reduce the chances of oxides forming during fusion welding, a protective slag or inert gas shield is generally provided. The joint formed is usually as strong as the parent material and is probably the most widely used method of fabrication in use today.

A macro-etched cross section through a butt weld joining two plates is shown in Figure 11.1.6g. The weld has been polished and etched to show the weld metal, heat affected zones (HAZ's) and parent metal. This weld was performed from one side with the aid of a 'backing bar' at root.

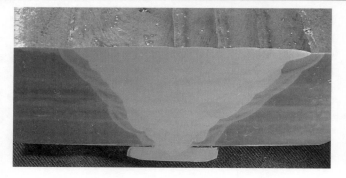

Figure 11.1.6g Section through a butt weld joining two plates, formed by multiple weld runs.

Adhesive bonding involves the introduction of a thin layer of liquid polymer between the surfaces to be joined. The adhesive undergoes polymerisation in-situ. Adhesion to surfaces is generally considered to be through the interaction of van der Waals forces or polar forces.

11.1.7 Discuss how permanent joining techniques lead to planned obsolescence and environmental issues.

© IBO 2007

Because articles joined with permanent joining techniques cannot be easily separated without damage, such items are not easily repaired or modified, tending instead to be discarded in favour of a new item exhibiting the functions and capacities desired.

11.1.8 Define adhesive.

11.1.9 Identify a range of adhesives suitable for joining metals, woods and plastics.

© IBO 2007

An adhesive is a substance in a liquid or semi-liquid state that, when applied to the surface, can be used to bond or adhere one object to another.

Polyvinyl Acetate (PVA) – A water-based adhesive suitable for bonding porous materials such as wood, paper or cloth.

Epoxy Resin – Can be used to join most materials and is available in one or two-part systems consisting of a resin and hardener.

Contact Adhesive – Applied to both surfaces to be bonded to form a strong bond. Commonly consists of polychloroprene (Neoprene).

Cascamite – A powdered adhesive based on urea-formaldehyde that is mixed with water before use. Forms a strong waterproof joint when cured.

Tensol Cement - Used for bonding a wide range of thermoplastics such as Perspex.

Cyanoacrylate (Superglue) – Represents a special type of acrylic resin. Fast curing through a reaction with moisture. Joints must be close fitting.

Polyurethane Glue - Available in one or two-part systems. Fast curing. Often used with primers. Forms a flexible bond.

Anaerobic Acrylic – Cure when air is excluded often and are used as thread locking compounds.

Toughened Acrylic - Fast curing high strength adhesive, usually as a two-part system.

Adhesive	Metal	Wood	Plastic			
			Polycarbonates	Nylons	PVC	Polyurethane
Poly Vinyl Acetate						
Epoxy Resin						
Contact Adhesive						
Cascamite						
Tensol Cement						
Cyanoacrylate (Superglue)						
Polyurethane Glue						
Anaerobic Acrylic						
Toughened Acrylic						

Figure 11.1 .9 Table of adhesives and materials

11.1.10   Discuss the advantages and disadvantages of using adhesive bonding in products.

© IBO 2007

In order to achieve a secure bond, the surfaces being joined generally need to be held in intimate contact for the period required for curing of the adhesive. Curing time varies considerably among adhesives, from several seconds to over 48hrs, depending both on the adhesive and temperature of the environment. In order to ensure that the joint is not disturbed during this period, it is generally clamped in a jig, especially for curing times of more than a few minutes. Surfaces also need to be prepared such that they are clean, dry and free of contaminates such as oil, grease and dust to produce a reliable bond.

Where a physical bond is created rather than a chemical one, the surface may need to be scored or etched in order to provide a surface into which the adhesive can create a mechanical key into the surface. This can be particularly important when adhesively bonding metal, as the bond formed is primarily a physical one. The bonding of slippery surfaces such as nylon also benefit from surface roughening.

Most of the adhesives used to join wood, plastic and metal are hazardous to health. Exposure to the skin or the breathing of vapours needs to be guarded against. Typical precautions include working in a well-ventilated area and the wearing of personal protective equipment such as long sleeved shirts, closed footwear, safety glasses and gloves.

Further Reading

Adhesives Toolkit – *The adhesives selection module* http://www.adhesivestoolkit.com/Toolkits/ AdhesiveSelector/Introduction.xtp

11.2 MOULDING

Sprue is the channel in a mould down which molten metal is poured when casting.

Flash is a narrow sheet of molten metal that penetrates between the joint line of a mould during casting and subsequently solidifies in place. The flash is removed later during the clean-up procedure known as fettling, during which all extraneous parts of the casting process are removed, such as runners and risers.

Parison, from the French paraison, from parer to prepare. It is the name given to both the unshaped mass of glass before it is moulded into its final form, and the plastic tubular preform used in blow-moulding of bottles. Figure 11.2.1a shows a plastic parison in position in a bottle that has been blow moulded from a similar parison. As can be seen from Figure 11.2.1a, the parison already incorporates the threaded portion that will become the bottle top.

Figure 11.2.1a Stretch Blow moulded bottle with the plastic preform (parison), to create the bottle, in place

Image by AG Krones

Dies are permanent moulds used in the die casting or injection moulding processes, consisting of at least two metal platens into the surface of which is machined a shape to be cast. When the die is closed, the cavity enclosed forms the mould into which material is injected.

The dies are typically machined from hardened tool steel to provide wear resistant surfaces.

Figure 11.2.1b Permanent metal dies

The **draft angle** is the angle or taper of the mould wall, perpendicular to the mould parting line, that allows the casting to be easily removed from the mould.

Injection moulding involves the injection under pressure of molten thermoplastic into a closed die mould. When cooled sufficiently, the die is opened and the part formed is ejected before the die is closed in readiness for the next injection cycle. Parts from small to moderate size (up to ~16kg) can be produced. Intricate parts with fine detail and thin walls can be produced, although hollow objects cannot be produced, unless assembled into such items as illustrated by the model aeroplane, produced by injection moulding, shown in Figure A.2.11c.

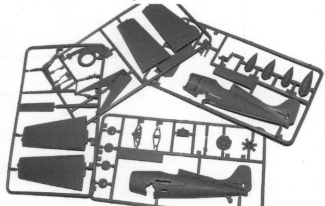

Figure 11.2.1c Model Aeroplane manufactured by injection moulding

The injection moulding process uses a mechanism composed of two basic parts, consisting of the injection unit and the clamping unit as shown in Figure 11.2.2. The injection unit consists of the polymer processing section where polymer granules are heated to a molten state ready for injection, while the clamping unit comprises a permanent mould consisting of two platens, one of which is fixed and the other moveable.

AHL

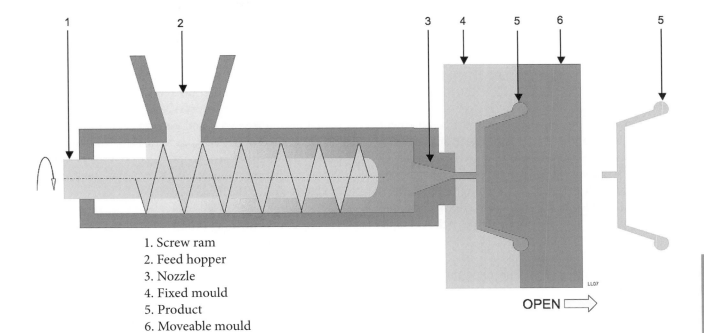

1. Screw ram
2. Feed hopper
3. Nozzle
4. Fixed mould
5. Product
6. Moveable mould

OPEN ⇨

Figure 11.2.2 Permanent metal dies

Products are produced one after another in an automated cycle in which polymer granules loaded into the feed hopper are fed under gravity into the barrel containing a screw system. Heaters on the outer surface of the barrel melt the polymer as it is carried by the screw towards the end, where a non-return valve allows molten material to build-up increasing hydraulic back-pressure against the screw. Sensors monitor this pressure and when sufficient molten material has accumulated, rotation of the screw is stopped and the hydraulic cylinder and ram move the screw forward. Then the accumulated molten polymer is pushed through the nozzle and into the sprue, injecting the polymer into the die. The molten polymer passes along a runner system machined into the platen surface before passing into the product. The runner system is therefore located at the die parting line.

The mould remains closed until the polymer has cooled sufficiently, following which the moveable platen is retracted, and the part formed is ejected.

11.2.3 Outline the advantages of injection moulding.

Although the initial capital cost of machinery and dies is high - surface finishes are excellent, intricate detail can be achieved and large production runs lower costs per unit.

11.2.4 Discuss how standardized bottle caps have constrained bottle design, but have cut costs for manufacturers.

Bottle caps have become a standardized item. Preforms or parisons are created by injection moulding with the bottle screw top as part of a blind tube in preparation for blow moulding to form a bottle. Figure 11.2.4 shows a number of bottle preforms. Because of this standardization, preforms can be purchased ready for blow moulding.

Standardization of screw cap threads may place design constraints particularly at the mouth of the bottle, however, individual manufacturers can quote to supply a variety of different companies giving a benefit from improved economies of scale thus reducing unit costs.

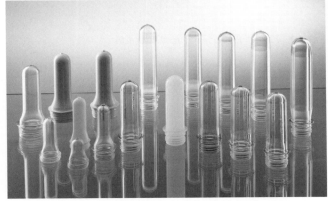

Figure 11.2.4 Bottle preforms produced by injection moulding

Image by AG Krones

AHL

11.2.5 Describe how a blow-moulded product is made.

© IBO 2007

Blow moulding is used where a large hollow object such as a bottle is required. The process involves the confinement of a semi-molten hollow plastic tube (parison) within a mould such that one end of the tube is closed and the other open. While the plastic tube is still at a temperature above its glass transition temperature, (softening temperature), compressed air is blown into the open end of the tube, expanding it until it conforms to the shape of the mould.

Three variants of blow moulding are used known as: extrusion blow moulding, injection blow moulding and stretch blow moulding.

Extrusion blow moulding is illustrated in Figure 11.2.5a, and involves the extrusion of molten plastic through a die to form a tube of plastic. The extruded tube passes between the two halves of an open blow mould in an inverted orientation. The mould is closed pinching off the tube at the mould base to create the parison. Compressed air is then force through the bottle top, expanding the plastic against the mould wall. When the plastic has cooled sufficiently, the mould is opened and the bottle removed.

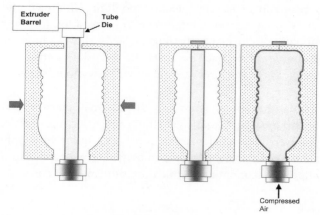

Figure 11.2.5a Extrusion blow moulding

Advantages:
- low capital costs
- low tooling costs
- high production rate
- small production runs possible.

Disadvantages:
- high scrap rate
- poor surface finish
- limited wall thickness control
- scrap needs to be trimmed from container.

Injection blow moulding is a two stage process and is illustrated in Figure 11.2.5b. The first process stage involves the initial injection of molten plastic into a mould containing a parison core. When solidified, the mould is opened and the core with the surrounding parison attached is transferred to the blow mould while still hot, ready for the second process stage. The blow mould is closed around the core and parison and compressed air blown into the core. The core then acts as a blowing rod, forcing the plastic parison out against the mould wall. When cooled the blow mould opens and the product is ejected ready for the next cycle.

The injection moulding process is also known as transfer blow moulding and is the slowest of the blow moulding processes but can be used to produce complex shapes and is often used in the production of small plastic medicine bottles.

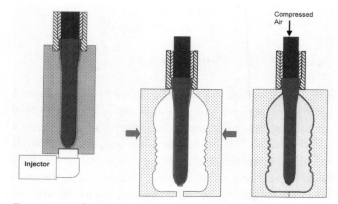

Figure 11.2.5b Injection blow moulding

Advantages:
- high production rate
- no scrap to be trimmed
- superior transparency compared to extrusion blow moulding
- injection moulding of the parison allows control of its shape and size.

Disadvantages:
- two moulds needed
- high initial capital cost.

Stretch blow moulding is illustrated in Figure 11.2.5c and involves the positioning of a parison body into a mould where the parison body is heated to the glass transition temperature. Once this temperature is reached, a blowing rod is inserted through the top and compressed air is blow through the end of the rod, stretching the parison longitudinally while air is also ejected from the surface of the blowing tube, pushing the parison radially toward the sides of the water-cooled mould, where it cools.

The stretching operation aligns the molecular chains, increasing the strength of the walls while also improving solvent resistance and transparency.

Widely used for PET, PE and PVC bottles. The high wall-strength produced allows the containment of pressures associated with carbonated drinks.

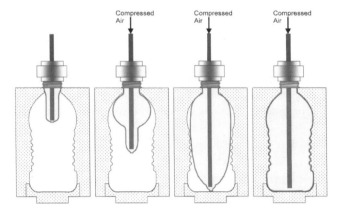

Figure 11.2.5c Stretch blow moulding

Advantages:
- low scrap
- low labour costs
- good surface finish
- high production rates
- variety of parisons available 'off-the-shelf.'

Disadvantages:
- because of the thin wall, the process needs to be tightly controlled to avoid scrap.

The mould chamber for stretch blow moulding is shown in Figure 11.2.5d.

Figure 11.2.5d Stretch blow moulding chamber

Image by AG Krones

Rotational moulding also known as rotomoulding is used to produce hollow plastic products and involves the rotation or spinning of the mould in two axes to allow centrifugal forces to force the molten plastic against the inner surface of the mould. The process involves four basic stages:

- fill mould chamber with the required amount of the thermoplastic plastic powder
- heat mould chamber until the plastic is molten
- spin the mould chamber to evenly distribute the molten plastic within the mould
- cool the chamber to solidify the plastic.

The mould rotation is then stopped, the product removed and the process repeated. Typically, this process is employed in the manufacture of seamless water tanks.

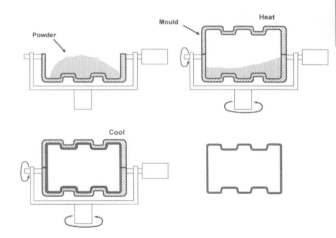

Figure 11.2.6 Rotational moulding of thermoplastic

Compression moulding represents a generic term for a number of processes that rely of the application of pressure, often in concert with elevated temperature, to distribute polymer over a mould to form a product. One example of compression is shown in Figure 11.2.7 and is known as matched die compression moulding. In this process two metal platens, one fixed and the other moveable, are used to form the mould. These platens can generally be internally heated and/or cooled. When the

203

die is closed, a fixed gap exists between the platens in the shape of the product to be formed. A polymer, in sheet or granular form, is placed in the open mould and the moveable platen or plug positioned on top. The mould is then heated while the top plug applies pressure. The polymer is heated to above its glass transition temperature where it softens and flows to fill the mould cavity. Heat and pressure are maintained until the polymer has cured, at which time heating is stopped and the mould cooled, before the pressure is released and the plug remove to allow removal of the product.

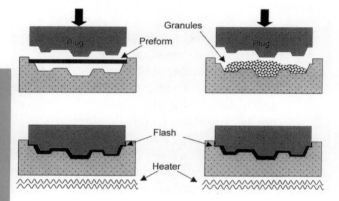

Figure 11.2.7 Matched die compression moulding

Advantages:

- high volume output
- excellent surface possible.

Disadvantages:

- high capital cost
- when using preformed sheets, mismatches in thickness between the sheet and die cavity can lead to non-uniformity of pressure, resulting in a variation in consolidation.

11.2.8 Discuss why some products have to be made using compression moulding.

Compression moulding can be used on both thermoplastics and thermosets. The thermosets can only be manufactured using a compression moulding technique because they will not readily flow unless subjected to constant temperature and pressure conditions. Cooling to solidification must occur while pressure is maintained for a satisfactory product density to be achieved.

11.2.9 Describe how a vacuum-formed product is made.

Vacuum forming is typically used to form thermoplastic sheets into simple shapes. The process involves the clamping of a heated thermoset sheet over a mould in order to create a sealed, airtight region within the mould. Evacuation of air from the mould pulls the sheet down into conformance with the mould surface under the influence of atmospheric pressure present above the mould. Once the plastic has cooled below the glass transition temperature, the formed product has sufficient strength to be removed.

A similar process, in which gas is introduced into the region above the mould, in order to increase the pressure above atmospheric pressure, is known as pressure or autoclave forming since the process is performed in a sealed pressure vessel known as an autoclave.

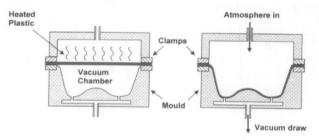

Figure 11.2.9 Vacuum forming process

Advantages:

- low forming pressure
- low cost tooling can be used
- high production rates possible.

Disadvantages:

- dimensional accuracy poor
- holes and threads cannot be formed.

11.2.10 Identify manufacturing methods suitable for thermoplastics and thermosets.

Methods suitable for forming thermoplastics include: injection moulding, transfer moulding, vacuum forming, blow moulding and rotational moulding.

Methods suitable for forming thermosetting plastics include: injection moulding, transfer moulding and compression moulding.

11.3 CASTING

11.3.1 Describe lost wax casting.

© IBO 2007

Lost wax casting, also known as investment casting and precision casting, is a foundry process in which high precision items are produced. While the process is one of the oldest known to man, it is used today as then for its dimensional accuracy and fine surface finish, along with its ability to create castings of great complexity.

11.3.2 Describe how lost wax cast products are made.

© IBO 2007

In the lost wax casting process, a permanent mould or die often made of metal is used to produce an expendable wax pattern. The pattern may then be incorporated into an assembly with similar patterns, and attached to a wax feeding system. The whole assembly is subsequently dipped into a ceramic slurry to build up a coating. Fine sand is then added to form a strong shell and the assembly allowed to dry. The dry assembly is then placed in a mould flask and surrounded by a coarser sand/slurry mixture and dried. This courser sand/slurry backing is technically known as the 'investment'. After setting, the mould is gently heated to melt the wax pattern leaving a smooth mould cavity behind. In the final stage of production metal is cast into the mould to form the part.

Controlled breakdown of the sand/binder mixture from exposure to the temperature of the solidifying metal allows the solidified casting to be easily removed from the mould for fettling. During the fettling operation the casting is separated from the metal feeder system of sprue, runners and in-gates.

Advantages:

- near net shape
- freedom of design
- no joint lines present
- allowance for pattern removal not required
- production of thin sections and sharp detail
- high dimensional tolerances and surface finish possible
- no limit to cast metal composition, subject to restrictions of melting fluidity and soundness.

Disadvantages:

- labour intensive
- casting size limited
- high initial die costs
- thick sections not generally cast
- die design changes may be costly.

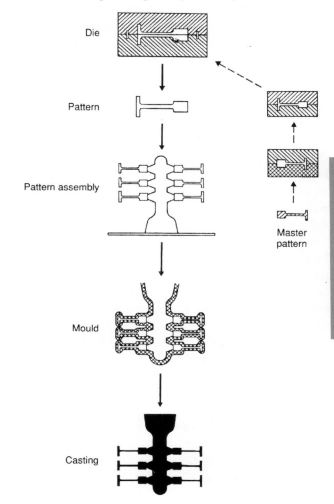

Figure 11.3.2 Lost Wax Process

Image by Beeley, P.R. & Smart, R.F. (1995) Investment Casting

11.3.3 Explain how a range of products are made using lost wax casting.

© IBO 2007

Lost wax casting, represents a sub-set of sand casting and is a somewhat ironic inclusion into the category of an advanced manufacturing technique. We would generally assume such a description applies to a modern development in manufacture. This is however far from the case for the lost wax casting process.

AHL

It is sobering to think that a process often used today for specialized components has its origins, based on archaeological evidence, in Mesopotamia around 3000-4000BCE and that the process was in use in most civilizations around the ancient world, mostly for artistic purposes, from jewellery to statuary, both large and small. The bronze statue of Perseus holding the head of Medusa produced by Benvenuto Cellini in 1554, and the aluminium statue of Eros in London's Piccadilly Circus cast by Alfred Gilbert in 1893, are famous examples of the process.

While the lost wax process continued to be used in artistic circles because of the intricate detail, excellent surface finish and near net shape characteristics it offered, the mainstream engineering use of the process did not begin until the Second World War. At that time, capacity restraints in machining led to the use of the lost wax process because of its ability to produce components that did not require machining.

Following the war, the development of the jet engine created an increasing demand for the process in the production of high precision castings of refractory metals used for components such as gas turbine blades.

Today, the lost wax process also finds use in the production of hip and knee prosthetics, dental implants, valves and auto parts, along with traditional roles in the production of items such as jewellery, and instrument keys.

Figure 11.3.3 Statue - Eros in Piccadilly Circus London, made in 1893 and one of the first statues to be cast in aluminium

11.3.4 Describe high-pressure casting.

Two forms of die-casting are performed and are named after the method by which molten metal enters the die: gravity die-casting and pressure die-casting. Both forms of die-casting use a permanent mould consisting of two platens, with the product shape and runner system machined into the surface. The die-casting mould is typically machined from tool steel for wear resistance and strength. Metals suited for die-casting are those with good fluidity and low melting points such as lead, tin, magnesium, zinc, aluminium and their alloys.

In gravity die-casting, metal is poured from a ladle into the sprue and the molten metal fills the mould under gravity. Because of the relative simplicity of the process after the cost of the die have been taken into account, gravity die-casting is relatively inexpensive. Automation can, of course, be included for high volume production if required. The casting of lead sinkers, once performed by many anglers at home, is an example of gravity die-casting. Figure 11.3.4a shows 'Tin' soldiers, approx. 65 mm high, being cast in antique moulds from the early 20th Century. The two mould halves are clamped together, and the molten metal alloy of tin and lead, (approx. 300°C) is poured by hand from a ladle into the mould. Once the metal has solidified the, the mould is opened. Sprues, (pouring channels), and extraneous flash seen in the bottom image are eventually removed during the fettling process.

Pressure die-casting involves machinery consisting of a fixed die platen and a hydraulically activated moveable platen as shown in Figure 11.3.4b. A modern die casting machine is shown in Figure 11.3.4c in which molten metal from a melting furnace is sucked under vacuum into an injection chamber before being injected at high velocity under pressure into a water-cooled die. Pressure is maintained until the casting has solidified and cooled sufficiently that the mould can be opened and the cast part ejected using injection pins. The die is then closed ready for the next cycle. High production rates are possible with this process, producing parts of near net shape and excellent surface finish. As molten metal enters the die any air trapped within the cavity will be entrained in the molten metal and result in the formation of compressed bubbles within the casting. If such bubbles are present, heat treatment is not recommended as expansion of the entrapped air can lead to cracking. In those instances where heat treatment is desired, special provisions must be included to remove the air.

Figure 11.3.4a Gravity casting

Image by Janke [CC-BY-SA-2.5 (www.creativecommons. org/licenses/by-sa/2.5)], via Wikimedia Commons

Two techniques for air removal involve either the use of a vacuum to evacuate air prior to metal injection, or the provision of several small channels leading from the die cavity to the outside known as vents. The vents allow the displacement of air from the die as metal enters.

Unlike other casting processes die-casting does not incorporate a metal reservoir such as a riser to feed the cooling and contracting metal. Metal shrinkage is controlled by the injection pressure and appropriate design of the metal flow.

Figure 11.3.4b Die casting machine and dies

Image by Swoolverton (Own work) [CC-BY-3.0 (www. creativecommons.org/licenses/by/3.0)], via Wikimedia

Figure 11.3.4c Die casting machine and operator

Image by METT Pty Ltd

Advantages:
- low unit costs
- good surface finish
- high volume production.

Disadvantages:
- tooling costs high
- not all alloys can be die-cast
- parting line restrictions limit shapes possible.

11.3.5 Describe how high-pressure die-cast products are made.

© IBO 2007

In high-pressure die-casting metal is melted in a furnace and held at the appropriate casting temperature. A cylinder is introduced into the molten metal allowing a measured amount of metal to enter. A plunger is then pushed into the cylinder forcing molten metal up a curved spout, known as a gooseneck, and through a nozzle into the die under pressure

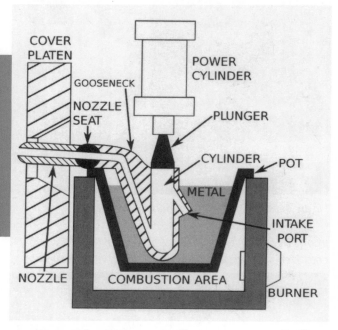

Figure 11.3.5 Hot chamber die casting

11.3.6 Explain how a range of products are made using high-pressure die-casting.

© IBO 2007

High-pressure die-casting is particularly suited to high volume production and is used extensively for products such as automotive trim, handles, iron sole plates, disc drive chassis, musical instruments, rotors for electrical motors, kitchen faucet and steering wheels.

11.3.7 Outline two advantages and two disadvantages of high-pressure die-casting.

© IBO 2007

Advantages:
- low unit cost
- rapid production rate
- thin walls possible typically less than 1mm.
- excellent surface finish (typically 1 - 2.5Ra)
- high dimensional accuracy typically within 0.1mm.

Disadvantages:
- size limitation
- changes to die difficult
- limited number of metals can be used
- high capital cost of equipment and dies.

Further Reading

Beeley, P.R and Smart, R.F. (1995). *Investment Casting.* The Institute of Materials, London: UK.

Lost-wax casting
http://en.wikipedia.org/wiki/Lost-wax_casting

Investment casting
http://www.efunda.com/processes/metal_processing/invest_casting.cfm

Precision Castings
http://www.astmsrl.com/Precision%20Castings.pdf

Investment casting
http://www.fortus.com/uploadedFiles/North_America/Downloads/Application_Guides_(All)/AG-InvestmentCasting-0109.pdf

Die-Casting
http://en.wikipedia.org/wiki/Die_casting

About Die-Casting - FAQ
http://www.diecasting.org/faq/

11.4 FORMING

11.4.1 Describe the process of spray-up.

The spray-up process involves the use of a spray gun to spray a mixture of chopped glass fibres, (typically 10-40mm in length), and resin, simultaneously onto the surface of an open mould, forming a layer of fibreglass over the surface. Prior to spraying, the mould surface is coated with a gelcoat release agent. This coating ensures that the article manufactured will be easily removed from the mould, allowing its reuse.

The chopped fibres for the spray-up process can be supplied to the gun pre-cut or as a strand of glass fibre, known as roving, that is chopped as it enters the gun. Once the glass fibre/resin composite mixture has been deposited onto the mould surface, it is compacted by workers using rollers to spread the composite evenly over the surface and remove air bubbles.

Laminates may be created if desired by placing wood, foam or other core materials onto the surface of the first layer before spraying another fibreglass layer.

The process has the advantages of allowing the production of parts varying in size from small to large, relatively quickly and at low cost.

Because of the skilled nature of the work and batch type nature of the process, dimensional tolerances and fibre volume fraction can vary, limiting application of the process to products where such consideration are not critical.

Advantages:
- high output
- small and large parts possible.

Disadvantages:
- operator dependent.

11.4.2 Identify products that could be made using spray-up processes.

The spray-up process can be performed on both convex and concave surfaces and finds applications in the forming of swimming pools, pleasure boats, storage tanks, caravan bodies, shower cubicles and bathtubs.

11.4.3 Describe the process of hand lay-up.

In contrast to spray lay-up where the fibre and resin are sprayed simultaneously over the surface, hand lay-up involves the manual laying of fibre, either in the form of woven mats or chopped strand, over the mould surface, followed by the application of a catalysed resin by brushes and rollers. After the layer has cured another layer can be applied and the process continued to build up to the required thickness.

Hand lay-up has better control of thickness than spray-up process but lower fibre wetting and more voids than achieved by spray-up. Hand lay-up also has a lower production rate compared to spray-up.

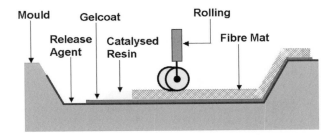

Figure 11.4.3 Hand Lay-up process

Advantages:
- low capital investment
- small and large parts possible
- better thickness control than spray lay-up.

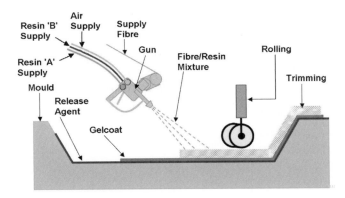

Figure 11.4.1 Spray-up process [http://nl.wikipedia.org/wiki/Bestand:Spray_lay-up_process.png]

AHL

Disadvantages:
- labour intensive
- operator dependent
- lower production rate than spray lay-up.

11.4.4 Identify products that could be made using hand lay-up processes.

© IBO 2007

Products can be quickly manufactured without the use of specialised equipment. Products of small to moderate size can be produced of a similar nature to that produced by spray lay-up, such as boat hulls and water tanks.

11.4.5 Describe the process of filament winding.

© IBO 2007

Filament winding involves the winding of a continuous length of fibre around a shaped mandrel to produce hollow cored components. Shapes are typically oval or circular in section. The filament can be wound onto the mandrel in an almost circular pattern (or hoop pattern), or in a helical criss-cross pattern. The operation is repeated until the required number of layers has been deposited over the surface.

The filament process, shown in Figure 11.4.5, represents the 'wet' winding variant and shows the fibre filaments (Tows) passing through a resin bath before being wound onto the mandrel. Once cured, the mandrel is deflated and the component removed.

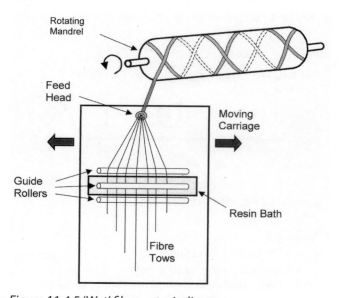

Figure 11.4.5 'Wet' filament winding process

A 'dry' winding process is also used where filaments are supplied pre-impregnated with resin in the partially cured condition. A 'post-impregnation' process is also used where filaments are first wound onto a mandrel and then brushed with resin.

Advantages:
- high output
- reproducibility
- high-strength parts

Disadvantages:
- high capital cost
- limited to symmetrical shapes

11.4.6 Identify products that could be made using filament winding processes.

© IBO 2007

A variety of products across a diverse range of applications may employ filament winding process, including:

- pipes
- golf clubs
- fishing rods
- sail boat masts
- transmission poles
- gas and water tanks
- lightweight components.

11.4.7 Describe the process of vacuum bagging.

© IBO 2007

The vacuum bagging process is a variant of the hand lay-up process in which pressure is applied to the laminates to ensure a bond. Vacuum bagging uses atmospheric pressure to help compress composite layers that have been layed-up in a mould or over a former. Once the laminate is in position, the whole assembly is enclosed in a vacuum bag. Once sealed, the air is evacuated by vacuum pump from the bag to create a vacuum.

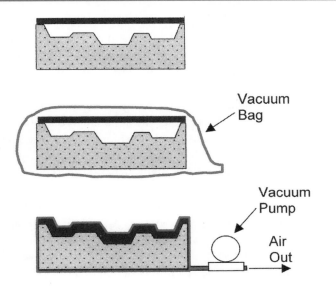

Figure 11.4.7 Vacuum bagging process

11.4.8 Outline the benefits of using vacuum bagging when using composite lay-up techniques.

The advantages of vacuum bagging as part of composite lay-up techniques include:

- good surface finish
- low moulding costs
- large products are possible
- production of a superior bond compared to other processes
- simple lightweight mould design due to air pressure being evenly distributed around the mould
- elimination of clamps and staples to hold laminates in position and results in improved distribution of pressure or a good uniformity of lay-up.

11.4.9 Identify products that can be made using vacuum bagging processes.

The vacuum bagging processes can be used on laminates constructed from wood or synthetic materials. Products made using this process include:

- furniture
- boat hulls
- wind turbine blades
- racing-car components
- laminated curved furniture
- structural panels or decorative skins.

11.4.10 Explain how a curved shape is produced in timber using lamination.

Laminating a number of thinner layers together is typically used to produce curved shapes. A thin layer of plywood is laid over a curved former and secured in place before a thin coating of adhesive is spread over the top surface. Another layer of plywood is then laid over the first layer, clamped into position and held until dry. In some instances, the assembly is transferred into a vacuum bag and atmospheric pressure used to force the plywood layers into intimate contact. When dry, air is allowed back into the bag and the assembly removed ready for a repeat of the cycle to build up the laminate thickness.

Larger thickness of plywood can be steamed to in order to assist in the positioning over a curved former.

11.4.11 Discuss how lamination can be used to strengthen material.

Timber is an orthotropic material, meaning that properties vary depending on the directions of; length, width and thickness. In addition to this variation, because it is a natural product, size limitations exist and imperfections can be present such as knotholes, cracks and borer damage that can affect properties.

Engineered timbers such as laminated veneer lumber (LVL) and plywood overcome these disadvantages by constructing a product from veneers glued together. By arranging the various laminates such that the grain of alternate layers are at right angles to each other, (in the case of plywood), and flaws in any one layer do not correspond with flaws in the other layers, a stronger material is produced.

AHL

11.4.12   Describe how LVL differs from plywood.

Laminated veneer lumber (LVL) is a structural laminate composed of a number of layers of timber veneer (each typically 3.2mm thick) glued together such they all share a common grain direction, aligned with the member length. This arrangement takes advantage of timber's strength and stiffness associated with the longitudinal direction (parallel with the grain). The product is typically a beam or billet form having a high aspect ratio, in that the length is significantly longer than the width and thickness. LVL lengths are commercially available up to 12m, although this presents concerns, primarily associated with transportation of longer lengths. Plywood by contrast is manufactured in a panel-like form in which length and width are significant dimensions with a relatively low aspect ration compared to thickness.

	Advantages	Uses
LVL	Uniform properties Good longitudinal strength Less likely to warp compared to solid timber	Scaffold planks, structural beams, rafters and columns
Ply	Low Cost Resistance to splitting Good impact resistance High shear strength Good dimensional stability	Flooring, furniture, wall cladding, bracing

Figure 11.4.12 LVL/plywood comparison

11.4.13   Discuss how forming techniques have enabled designers to be more flexible in the way they approach the design process.

With the wide range of materials and forming operations available today, many different solutions to a design problem are often available and compete for selection, based on the relative fit they provide for considerations such as cost, reliability, repair, strength, durability, toughness, sustainability, and aesthetics.

At the beginning of the Industrial Revolution, for example, the increased availability of cheap cast iron and the rise of steam power created the need for bridges that could carry the new locomotives. Difficulties in obtaining sufficient wood, led to cast iron being used as a structural material in 1779 with the construction of Ironbridge at Coalbrookdale in England. Joining techniques, however, were borrowed from those familiar to carpenters and employed dovetail and mortice type joints. Cast iron provided strength in compression but was poor in tension and was brittle. Designs with this material were therefore limited, as subsequent failures of other bridge designs made from cast iron were to later attest. The apparent success of the Ironbridge, however, led to the introduction of cast iron as a structural material and saw its inclusion, along with wrought iron and wood in many structural designs, with each contributing their unique properties. The Great Exhibition Hall of 1851, also known as The Crystal Palace due to the large amount of glass used, is perhaps the best example. This building introduced the concept of prefabricated space frame construction, innovative for the time, but contained a number of potentially disastrous flaws related to the joining of the cast iron columns and resistance to transverse loads, along with accommodation of thermal expansion.

The structural design limitations of cast iron eventually led to the development of wrought iron girders, which were used in the Eiffel Tower built in Paris in 1889. The Eiffel Tower demonstrated the flexibility of design possible with such material, along with the ease of construction using rivets to join the members. The development of steel, with its greater uniformity of properties, however, quickly replaced wrought iron as a construction material and further freed designers. So too the development of each new material (e.g. aluminium, plastics, composites) and manufacturing process has allowed designers an increased number of options and alternatives in the solution of engineering problems.

Further Reading

MacGregor, J. (Editor) (2007). *Structural Plywood & LVL Design Manual,* Engineered Wood Products Association of Australasia. [http://www.timber.org.au/resources/Structural%20Plywood%20&%20LVL%20Design%20Manual%20V1%5B1%5D.pdf]

Peters, T.F. *The apparent setback to the iron skeleton system of construction after the experience with The Crystal Palace of 1815*
http://www.international.icomos.org/publications/19eisen36.pdf

Petroski, H. (1985). *To engineer is human.* Macmillan London Ltd.

Petroski, H. (1996). *Invention by design: How engineers get from thought to thing.* Harvard University Press.

1. Which casting method uses a wax pattern?

   A.   sand casting
   B.   investment casting
   C.   continuous casting
   D.   pressure die casting

2. A taper, designed into a mould pattern, making a casting easier to remove from the mould is called a:

   A.   draft allowance
   C.   distortion allowance
   B.   machining allowance
   D.   gas discharge allowance.

3. Permanent metal dies are dies typically machined from tool steel due to their:

   A.   ductility
   B.   hardness
   C.   castability
   D.   machinability.

4. Laminating thin veneers of timber is done to produce:

   A.   curved shapes
   B.   orthotropic properties
   C.   heavier structural members
   D.   a product with uniform grain properties throughout.

5. Vacuum bagging is used to:

   A.   reduce exposure to oxygen
   B.   form thermoplastic materials
   C.   reduce the overall size of a material
   D.   assist in moulding some composite materials.

6. Explain the different joining mechanisms found within: soldering, brazing and welding.

7. Identify the reasons for choosing either gravity or high-pressure die-casting.

8. Explain how friction welding differs from the fusion welding process.

9. Compare two types of riveting systems, describing advantages, disadvantages and applications.

10. Discuss the advantages and disadvantages associated with permanent and temporary joining methods.

AHL

SUSTAINABLE DEVELOPMENT

12

CONTENTS

12.1   Appropriate technology and sustainable development

12.2   Sustainable building design

Interest in sustainable development first appeared in the 1980s. Researchers were responding to political debate and increasing public awareness of the ecological consequences related to the patterns, pace and style of human development. This research was a direct consequence of the environmental movements of the 1960s and 1970s.

At governmental levels, the framing of sustainable development as a structure with guidelines and goals was originally developed in the groundbreaking, 'Brundtland Report, Our Common Future', presented at the UN World Commission on Environment in 1987. In essence, the report called for the world to adopt sustainable development practices that could satisfy current needs and demands without compromising similar opportunities for generations to come.

12.1 APPROPRIATE TECHNOLOGY AND SUSTAINABLE DEVELOPMENT

12.1.1 Define appropriate technology, sustainable development and triple bottom line sustainability.

© IBO 2007

Appropriate technology has been around for centuries.

It has only been in the last few decades that it has been categorized and attempted to be deliberately replicated and transplanted as a concept for development. Many researchers refer to Gandhi as the 'father' of appropriate technology for his work championing the cause of villagers and village technologies. His most often quoted statement in this field, "…not mass production but production by the masses", defined his approach.

The term 'intermediate technology' was originally coined by E. F. Schumacher. Schumacher saw intermediate technology as a transitive, interim step between indigenous technologies and highly expensive, capital intensive technologies of industrialized nations. The term 'appropriate technology' replaced Schumacher's intermediate technology as it was seen as more inclusive of social and political factors. Schumacher, however, has been credited with the widespread adoption and use of this term.

Of the multiple and complex definitions available for appropriate technology the simplest comes from the English journalist Paul Harrison, who in 1980, referred to appropriate technology as any technology making the best use of a country's natural resources, financial capital, labour and skills, while at the same time furthering local, national and social aims.

Sustainable development is a term used only recently. Its origin is attributed is to the report, 'Our Common Future', (1987), by the World Commission on Environment and commonly known as the 'Brundtland Report', so named after the Chair of the Commission, Gro Brundtland. Delivered in Geneva, Switzerland in June 1987, the report offered the following definition; 'Sustainable development is development that meets the needs of the present without compromising the ability of future generations to meet their own needs.'

The term 'triple bottom line' (TBL) is attributed to John Elkington, (1995), and refers to financial, environmental and social sustainability. The TBL approach forces organizations to deal with environmental and societal issues and not just the economics of profit making. It has been popularized through a variety of catch phrases such as, 'economy, environment, equity' or 'planet, people, profit'.

At its best TBL encompasses all the values, attitudes, performances and process that a company implements to maximize financial, social and environmental benefits. Cynics claim TBL is little more than an opportunity for corporations to pay lip service to the environment through the application of a framework for reporting purposes.

> **12.1.2 List four characteristics of an appropriate technology.**
>
> © IBO 2007

Ernst Schumacher, the German economist and conservationist, proposed four characteristics of appropriate technology in his book, Small is Beautiful: Economics as if People Mattered, (1973). In keeping with Harrison's definition, quoted in 12.1.1, Schumacher determined appropriate technology should:

- involve decentralised production
- promote multiple production sites
- incorporate little technical or specialized knowledge
- manufacture products using locally sourced materials
- remain cheap to allow maximum involvement of the population.

These four precepts again reinforce Ghandi's, "..not mass production but production by the masses", approach.

> **12.1.3 Describe one example of an appropriate technology.**
>
> © IBO 2007

One of the earliest examples of appropriate technology, from the very roots of its beginnings comes from Gandhi's India. The spinning wheel was Gandhi's ideal target for developing appropriate technology in India. Gandhi saw

the ubiquitous spinning wheel as a liberating symbol of independence, available to the masses with levels of technology familiar to the populace.

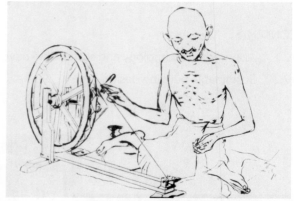

Figure 12.1.3a Gandhi at the spinning wheel

Image by Unknown author [Public domain], via Wikimedia Commons

Another example of appropriate technology is the solar cooker. Requiring no fuel, producing no emissions and using simple technology, solar cookers in many ways provide an exemplary example of appropriate technology at work.

Using the power of the sun instead of (most often), timber-based fuels, solar cookers preserve the natural habitat, reduce soil erosion and eliminate the work associated with the gathering of fuel. Additionally, solar power is free and requires no transportation.

Solar cookers have multiple and widely varied applications from slow cooking of food (without a naked flame and the associated fire risks), to killing insects in dry grains, dyeing fabrics and sterilizing medical instruments. Viewed from a social standpoint, solar cookers generate local work as part of their production, move cooking activities outside thus reducing heat build up inside homes and make available more space inside the dwelling. Figure 1.2.3b shows a simple solar cooker in use in Nepal.

There are however disadvantages associated with this form of technology including the fact that it can only be used on a sunny day. Lifestyle changes may also be required in that cooking must now be done outside, it takes longer than traditional forms and meal times may need changing.

Figure 12.1.3b Solar Cooker

Image by Practical Action: The Schumacher Centre for Technology and Development Warwickshire

12.1.4 Identify the three key dimensions of triple bottom line sustainability

The interlinked relationship between financial sustainability, social responsibility and environmental sustainability is shown graphically in Figure 12.1.4. The overlapping sustainable portion of the diagram represents the concept of triple bottom line sustainability. Each of the components as described below.

Environmental sustainability – involves maintaining the integrity of an ecosystem by assessing and working within its capacity while at the same time recognizing and respecting biodiversity.

Social sustainability – includes empowering the local population through maintenance of cultural identities, implementation of equitable principles and practices, creating a stable environment.

Financial sustainability – incorporates the principles of economic development through responsible growth while improving productivity and efficiency.

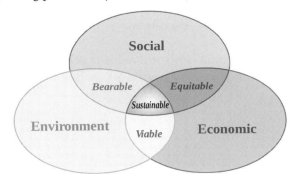

Figure 12.1.4 Triple bottom line diagram

Image by Johann Dréo [Creative Commons Attribution-Share Alike 2.0 Generic] via Wiki Commons

12.1.5 Explain how global conferences (for example, Rio de Janeiro, Johannesburg) provide a platform for the development of global strategies for sustainable development.

The 1987 Brundtland Report provided the impetus for the Earth Summit in Rio de Janeiro in 1992. The staging of the conference coincided with the 20th anniversary of the UN Conference on the Human Environment (Stockholm, 1972). In Rio, the UN aimed to bring together as many participants as possible to reach consensus on ways governments around the world could work in unison to stop the continued use and depletion of finite resources, at the same time reducing emissions and pollution of the environment.

Global conferences focusing on the environment provide the opportunity to bring together a wide variety of people, views and perspectives in an effort to develop goals, pathways and strategies towards sustainable development. The statistics shown below speak for themselves in demonstrating the sheer volume, importance and diversity of the group assembled for the Earth Summit in Rio.

- 178 countries represented including more than 100 Heads of State
- 2,400 representatives of non-governmental organizations (NGOs)
- 17,000 people attended the parallel NGO Forum
- 10,000 on-site journalists broadcast the summit's message around the world.

With so many conference delegates from around the world working towards developing a consensus-based approach on sustainable development, the summit was bound to encounter difficulties, yet, it was still able to reach agreement on number of issues. Key developments of the summit included the:
- Agenda 21
- Principles of Forest Management
- Convention on Biological Diversity
- Framework Convention on Climate Change
- Rio Declaration on Environment and Development
- Creation of the UN Commission on Sustainable Development.

In 2002 the World Summit on Sustainable Development held in Johannesburg led to more governmental commitments and helped extend the sustainability concepts into the areas of business, local government and civil society.

AHL

12.1.6 Explain the ongoing challenges facing the achievement of a consensus on a strategy for sustainable development.

It has proven difficult in the past to achieve consensus between the rich and affluent countries with consumer-based economies opposed to the developing nations with large populations, lower standards of living and widespread poverty.

Developed countries with consumer-based economies have found difficulties on economic grounds when increasing costs based around implementing new technologies, materials and processes. Any increased costs were seen to make their goods uncompetitive against developing countries with larger populations and lower labour costs.

Developing countries on the other hand saw affluent nations reaping the benefits of the Industrial Revolution that had already contributed to greenhouse gas emissions. Developing nations continued to ask for the same opportunities affluent nations had already exploited. Developing nations still require more technology and infrastructural development. Many of these high-technology fixes for environmental controls are often produced by developed nations and this in turn exacerbates the problem.

The originally proposed Agenda 21 was weakened by compromise and negotiation, yet it was still seen as a comprehensive and potentially effective international program requiring signatories to commit to developing a nationwide approach to sustainable development.

12.1.7 Outline the Bellagio principles.

The Bellagio principles include 10 guidelines produced to assess progress towards sustainable development.

As early as 1987, the Brundtland Commission Report called for the creation of ways to evaluate progress towards sustainable development. This call was repeated in Agenda 21, developed at the 1992 Rio Earth Summit. As a direct result of these conferences, a gathering of researchers met in Bellagio, Italy in 1996 to analyze progress towards sustainable development and develop a set of guidelines to assist others with the assessment process.

The 10 guidelines agreed upon, now known as the 'Bellagio Principles', follow a similar pattern to any assessment program in that they contain the following groupings of elements:

- review processes allowing for continued cycling of assessment procedures
- establishment of clearly identified aims, well defined goals and definitions
- communication components dealing with transparency, accessibility and participation
- structural elements of the assessment including; timing, scope, social, ecological and standards frameworks.

12.1.8 Explain how progress towards sustainable development might be assessed using the Bellagio principles.

The Bellagio principles serve as practical guidelines for the complete assessment process from system design to identification of evaluation tools. They offer a framework that is able to link the evaluation process to the key characteristics of sustainable development. As such they should be applied as a complete set. These links to the evaluation process appear in four stages:

- establishment of clear goals for SD that provide a practical definition in terms that are meaningful for the decision-making process
- assessment content must combine current priority issues with a practical focus of the overall investigation
- transparent assessment processes, open for public participation and able to communicate results to a wide audience
- ongoing evaluation processes requiring a continuing capacity for evaluation and related institutional arrangements.

12.1.9 Explain why sustainable development requires systems-level changes in industry and society.

Sustainable development requires an holistic, systems-level approach because of the complex connections between legislative, technological, social, environmental and economic factors. This complex interplay of forces, if not fully understood, can lead well-intentioned technologically advanced companies down the wrong path when attempting to develop sustainable systems, processes, technologies and products. As an example, in an effort to improve the environmental impact of its paint-line, one well-intentioned manufacturer found environmental costs had simply been transferred from paint emissions into energy consumption.

A number of systems-level approaches that companies can adopt are shown below. They are further detailed in Topic 3, Green Design, but may include strategies such as:

- life cycle assessment
- design for environment
- product recycling or 'take-back' programs.

Difficulties occur for companies when integrating sustainable development practices into a successful business plan. Technologically there are many solutions to the problems associated with product design, use of toxic materials, emissions, waste by-products, energy consumption and recycling. The focus however, of all these issues must be the intended market, with variables including the consumer's: age, values, needs and aspirations.

Successful development of sustainable products and services can only be achieved if there is a measure of public support from consumers. Governments and manufacturers must cooperate by educating and encouraging consumers to participate in programs involving: recycling waste, returning merchandise as part of take back programs or supporting companies with verified green credentials.

> **12.1.10** Explain how sustainable development requires close cooperation between manufacturers and government.
>
> © IBO 2007

Critical to the success of sustainable development is the role governments play in establishing legislative frameworks, enabling manufacturers to continue to profit, albeit in an environmentally responsible fashion. These frameworks must be implemented through a negotiated process that brings manufacturers and governments together, in a partnership of shared and common goals.

Sustainable development requires legislation sympathetic to its principles, while simultaneously encouraging and supporting manufacturers towards adopting sustainable production methods and products. Without enforceable legislation, manufacturers are able to choose which practices they will implement.

Governments must offer incentives for business to make the transition to sustainable practices and not just rely on fines, or the threat of punitive litigation to enforce adherence. Clear legislative rules provided by governments not only encourage manufacturers to comply, but they promote equity, maintain a competitive marketplace, give consumers confidence and yet may still be used to penalize non-conforming companies. Governments must also issue clear information on standards and accreditation to avoid confusion for consumers when making choices based on a manufacturer's sustainability claims.

> **12.1.11** Explain how a close relationship between manufacturers and government can be difficult to achieve because the two parties may have very different perspectives on sustainability and timescales.
>
> © IBO 2007

Manufacturers and governments have difficulty in achieving close relationships due to differing understandings of the concept of sustainability and the timescales necessary for its achievement and maintenance.

Sustainability is also a widely contested concept that, in its broadest application, implies any development is controlled by the limits imposed by the ecosystem's ability to preserve its diversity and the timeframes required to repair and replenish resource depletion. Alternative, more specific definitions however, endorsed by a variety of groups, place hierarchical emphasis on one or more elements of sustainability in a variety of timeframes or, for example, maintaining economic, social or ecological values now or in the future.

Governments as representatives of current and future citizens are challenged to cater to a wide variety of interests, even as groups or individuals call for their concerns to be of primary importance. For example, manufacturers can validly argue government support financially, or legislatively, can increase productivity which can, in turn, build a healthy economy and provide a means to increase social sustainability for the current generation. However, a holistic approach requires balanced emphasis on all elements of sustainability, including the needs of generations to follow. Therefore as opposed to operating in conflict with governments who must represent varied community interests, close collaborative relationships between manufacturers and governments need to be developed in order for sustainable development to occur for current and future generations.

> **12.1.12** Outline three reasons why it is difficult for governments to introduce legislation to cover all aspects of sustainability.
>
> © IBO 2007

All governments face challenges when seeking to introduce legislation to cover the complex aspects of sustainability. Three reasons for these challenges include:

A global economy with competing states whereby each has different criteria for the advancement of their own interests makes consensus difficult. Here, the notion of good governance is challenged by agreements that benefit particular groups, such as corporate profit over wider human or ecological concerns.

Judicial systems are often powerless to impose the penalties that are sufficient to enforce sustainable practices on non-conforming companies. This is particularly relevant when companies locate their core business outside the jurisdiction of the host nation's borders.

A lack of consensus by the scientific community, and thus scientific understanding on the effects of human action on biophysical interactions, promotes misunderstanding and conflicting notions of how to achieve sustainability.

Under these circumstances, governments are reluctant to be deterministic for, when confusion and conflict become embedded in legislation and policy documents, 'loopholes' are created undermining the purpose of their construction and the governments integrity.

Further Reading

Akubue, A. (2000). *Appropriate Technology for Socioeconomic Development in Third World Countries*, Journal of Technological Studies, Volume XXVI, No. 1.

Anonymous. (2005). *Solar Cooking, , Appropriate Technology*, Hemel Hempstead: Vol. 32. Iss. 1; p. 38.

Anonymous. (2009). *Cardboard box cooker wins prize, Appropriate Technology*. Hemel Hempstead: Jun Vol. 36. Iss. 2; p. 20.

12.2 SUSTAINABLE BUILDING DESIGN

> **12.2.1** Define intelligent building, living building, grey water, black water, building envelope, U value, passive solar design, day lighting and active solar collection.
>
> © IBO 2007

Intelligent buildings may be simple or complex but are essentially buildings that function in an effective and efficient manner, while at the same time responding to the changing needs of the inhabitants and dynamic environmental conditions.

Living buildings are designed and built to have a positive effect on the local environment. They are structures that; use locally sourced building materials, generate all their own power needs and capture and treat their own water.

Grey water (also known as wash water) is domestic or household wastewater (excluding sewage) from hand basins, showers, dishwashing and laundry processes.

Black water (brown water, foul water, or sewage) is wastewater containing biological materials such as feces or grease. Pathogen-contaminated water such as this is dangerous and must be treated before it can be released into the environment or reused.

A building envelope is the structure or shell that protects and shelters us from the elements. It marks the division between interior and exterior environments providing the inhabitants with a measure of environmental control. Typically, building envelopes consist of roof, wall and floor elements. The successful performance of the building envelope is rated in terms of: structural integrity, movement and control of moisture and water vapour, temperature and air pressure control.

U values are used to measure the relative heat conducting properties of materials, i.e. they indicate the rate at which heat can pass through a material. Lower U values indicate a lesser amount of heat transfer through a material. The units used to record U values are measured in terms of watts per square metre per degree Kelvin ($W/m^2.k$). Some countries (USA, Australia) use an R value to measure insulation. R values are the inverse of U values such that as U values decrease, R values increase and measure the resistance of a material to heat flow.

Material	Thermal conductivity *
Window (single glass metal frame)	4.8
Door (external solid timber)	2.4
Wall (outer 225mm solid brick)	2.2
Floor (solid concrete)	0.8
Floor (suspended timber)	0.7

Figure 12.2.1 Common U values

*Thermal conductivity (W/m$^{2\cdot}$K)

Passive solar design is exactly as the name implies. No additional resources are required to take advantage of naturally provided heat and light from the sun. Passive solar design relies on building placement materials choice and feature locations to both heat and cool building interiors.

Day lighting is an application of passive solar techniques designed to manage the controlled admission of sunlight to illuminate building interiors and manage heat loss/gain, thus reducing the building's energy requirements.

Active solar systems collect energy from sunlight through the use of active mechanical or electronic systems. Using a series of fixed or moveable collecting plates, auto-focusing reflective surfaces, and pumps, active solar systems convert solar energy into heat that can be used for space heating or to heat household water supplies.

12.2.2 List five objectives for sustainable buildings.

Sustainable design seeks to minimize environmental impacts, reduce emissions and minimize dependence on non-renewable forms of energy during materials sourcing, construction, occupancy and demolition stages.

Objectives for sustainable buildings include:

- sourcing local, recycled or recyclable materials
- pollution prevention (including indoor air quality and noise abatement)
- energy efficiency – reducing or eliminating consumption of non-renewables
- harmonization with the environment (including environmental assessment)
- resource efficiency – reducing initial project and ongoing maintenance costs
- integrated and systemic approaches (including environmental management systems).

12.2.3 Explain the benefits of intelligent buildings to sustainable building design.

Intelligent buildings employ energy management systems and building controls to evaluate, and optimize services within a structure, be it commercial or domestic. The scope of these 'services' ranges from basic lighting, heating and cooling to security, maintenance scheduling and even staff movement. As systems develop and more holistic approaches are adopted, intelligent buildings are developing the ability to record energy consumption data, post process this data to optimize system performance and even auto-pay suppliers. These processes are applicable to all utilities including water, gas and electricity.

Intelligent building systems offer benefits in relation to:

- energy savings
- operational costs
- lifestyle and security
- scheduled maintenance
- improved indoor environments.

Intelligent buildings are possible only through the convergence of market pressures, new technologies and supporting legislation.

12.2.4 Outline the key features of living buildings.

The philosophy behind living building design is the notion of creating a balance between the natural and built environments, where structures are designed considering the entire ecosystem and not just building inhabitants. Whether it is the passive solar use of sunshine and shade on a specific building site, or using a building envelope that works with local climate living buildings are designed for their local area. They work with local water flow regimes and create habitats that echo what exists in the local environment.

Traditional building design and construction is based on the premise that buildings are made for people. Living buildings are built considering their impact and contribution to all life. Whether it is by adding new habitats for animals or by effectively filtering stormwater and grey water, living buildings enhance and restore local ecosystems.

AHL

All living buildings:

- filter and purify wastewater for reuse
- adapt to changing weather conditions
- operate emission free and generate no harmful wastes
- enhance and restore the health of the local environment
- maintain closed loop water systems that harvest sufficient water resources for use
- use materials that are safe and renewable and have no adverse affect on human or ecosystem health
- integrate control and management systems that automatically maintain efficiencies and assist in promoting the health and comfort of all inhabitants
- provide 100% of their own energy needs and operate in an emissions free manner, i.e. all of the building's energy requirements are generated on-site from renewable sources.

Cherokee mixed-use lofts in Los Angeles is an urban building project designed to exceed local standard building codes. In response to the 'Living Building Challenge', this project employs guidelines for reconciling the built environment with the natural environment through sustainable design and construction principles. The building has features beyond common green design including:

- construction materials carefully selected for their recycled content including: carpets, plasterboard, concrete incorporating fly ash and formaldehyde-free building insulation made from recycled glass cullet
- surface treatments and finishes that minimize using exposed concrete slabs
- an exterior stucco finish applied with an integrated pigment
- roof areas planted with natural drought-resistant grasses acting as catchment areas for stormwater and providing additional insulation
- perforated, anodized aluminium facades covering the front and rear of the structure, providing sound mitigation, shade and requiring no painting. The facade is completely permeable allowing for generous cross-ventilation cutting down the energy demands of air conditioning
- active systems such as a high-tech heat pumps reducing heating and cooling demands by as much as 50% and photovoltaic panels providing in excess of 10% of total energy needs
- energy efficient, compact fluorescent lights and appliances such as refrigerators and dishwashers supplied as standard.

Figure 12.2.4 Living building - Cherokee mixed-use lofts

Image by Calderoliver [CC-BY-SA-3.0], from Wikimedia Commons

12.2.5 Identify ways in which water consumption in buildings can be optimized through reduction of water consumption and recycling.

Water-responsible building design can reduce water usage and contamination through the specification of water gathering, storage and water efficient devices that either reduce water consumption or make it available for reuse.

Reduction in water demand can be achieved through a variety of mechanisms. The result being, less water consumption, decreased waste water volumes and reduced CO_2 emissions. These results can be achieved by:

- repairing leaking taps and pipes
- installing taps appropriate to the situation, i.e. mixer taps in showers to avoid scolding
- specifying water efficient appliances when supplying; shower heads, dishwashers, washing machines and dual flush toilets etc.

Collecting rainwater and diverting it into storage tanks reduces stormwater run off and may also provide water suitable for toilet flushing, laundries, watering gardens and filling swimming pools. Stormwater applies to rainwater plus anything the flowing rainwater gathers. Use of this resource also reduces pollution of waterways, lakes and oceans.

AHL

Wastewater or grey water generated from showers, washing machines, basins and taps may be reused to flush toilets and water gardens.

Outdoor water use can consume up to 60% of household water. This figure can be dramatically reduced during site design and ongoing maintenance activities. Lawns should be replaced with drought tolerant groundcover species, thus preventing runoff and reducing evaporation. The addition of organic matter to soils will also improve quality, permeability and water retention.

Low impact toilets use limited amounts of water. They require no connection to infrastructure developed to deal with blackwater treatment. They also avoid transferring pollutants to the wider environment.

> 12.2.6 Identify ways in which material use can be optimized through the life cycle of a building.
>
> © IBO 2007

Buildings are complex combinations of many materials and processes, each of which contributes to the embodied energy of the structure. Embodied energy is the energy consumed by all of the processes associated with the production of building materials. This includes mining, processing, manufacturing, transport and product delivery. As a rule, more highly processed materials produce higher embodied energy products. Embodied energy does not include the operation and disposal of the building material.

Factors aiding the optimizing of building materials include:

- creating flexible designs that are adaptable to changing needs, facilitate renovation and ease of disassembly. Buildings that are designed to be easily modified or renovated and easy to dismantle require less energy over their lifetime.
- specifying local materials, with low maintenance and high durability. The longer a building lasts, the more efficiently it uses its embodied energy, i.e. (its embodied energy divided by the number of years it exists or is used). Transport costs also add to a material's embodied energy and should be kept to a minimum where possible.
- incorporating recyclable or reusable materials can save as much as 95% of embodied energy. Savings vary due to reprocessing costs, but recycled aluminium contains only approximately 10% of

the embodied energy of the virgin material, while embodied energy savings of 20% can be achieved with recycled glass.

Through the reuse of materials or specifying recyclable materials, more than one building can make use of the embodied energy already invested. Recovery and reuse of assemblies, components and materials allow new buildings to avoid the larger embodied energy costs of virgin materials.

Embodied energy data may be useful for the purposes of comparing materials. Figure 12.2.6 shows embodied energy data for a range commonly used building materials. Care however must be taken when using tables such as the one below. Data shown has been generated using transport information based around delivery to a particular site. As the delivery site varies, so does the embodied energy.

Material	Embodied energy*
Acrylic paint	61.5
Aluminium (virgin)	170
Clay bricks	2.5
Concrete blocks	1.5
Copper	100
Galvanised steel	38
Glass	12.7
Insitu concrete	1.9
Kiln dried sawn hardwood	2.0
Kiln dried sawn softwood	3.4
Laminated Veneer Lumber	11
MDF	11.3
Particle board	8.0
Plasterboard	4.4
Plywood	10.4
PVC	80

Figure 12.2.6 Building material embodied energy - * MJ/

> 12.2.7 Identify waste management strategies appropriate for sustainable buildings.
>
> © IBO 2007

Sustainability may be improved through the application of the three R's – reduce, re-use and recycle. Significant environmental, financial and community benefits may be accrued by adhering to these principles when designing for the built environment. Waste reduction can easily be achieved through the designing of smaller homes and making more efficient use of available space. This not only conserves resources but also reduces the waste stream.

Off-site manufacturing can also reduce waste, allow for effective sharing of resources between projects and improve separation of waste streams. Specifying standard sizes and the use of modular design also reduces waste.

Re-use of recovered building materials (wall studs), components (switchgear), and assemblies (kitchens), reduce demand for virgin materials, processing and manufacturing, while at the same time lowering waste volumes.

To aid in the processes of reuse and recycling an architectural style has developed around the principles of design for materials recovery.

> 12.2.8 Identify ways in which the indoor environment of buildings can be optimized.
>
> © IBO 2007

The quality of indoor environments may be actively improved during the occupancy and maintenance stage of the building, but many features may also be incorporated into the design and construction phase that continue to optimize the indoor environment. Measures to optimize indoor environments include:

- selecting construction materials and surface finishes with low emissions values. Toxic emissions of formaldehyde and VOC's can have a negative effect on the health of occupants. Use of low emissions materials extend to maintenance and cleaning activities.
- designing and constructing the building envelope with heating, ventilating and air-conditioning (HVAC) systems and keeping in mind prevention of moisture and uncontrolled air movement. User control of systems allows for tailoring of thermal conditions.
- careful placement of windows and openings in the building envelope will assist in controlling ventilation and movement of air in and out of the building.
- employing the principles of daylighting supplemented with high-performance lamps and controls. Lighting may be enhanced through lightly coloured walls.
- assuring comfort can be achieved by isolating noisy equipment or sectors through the use of insulation and sound-absorbing materials in floors, walls and ceilings. In air conditioning systems small cross sectional area ducts with high velocity air flow should be avoided.

> 12.2.9 Explain how the building envelope contributes to the amount of energy a building uses during its operation.
>
> © IBO 2007

Operational energy consumption depends on the number of occupants and their patterns of energy usage. Research conducted in Australia by the Commonwealth Scientific and Industrial Research Organisation, (CSIRO), equates the use of embodied energy in a typical home to about 15 years of operational energy. If the house lasts 100 years the embodied energy is still over 10% of the energy consumed over its lifetime.

Specifying a higher embodied energy level may be justified in some situations where it may contribute to lowering operational energy requirements. For example, heating and cooling costs may be significantly reduced if materials of high thermal mass such as concrete are specified as part of well-designed passive solar systems.

Individual building designs should specify the lowest embodied energy content materials balanced against climatic condition requirements, transport distances and availability. Careful selection of materials may allow for specification of products or assemblies with lower embodied energies without any adverse operational energy costs. The material specification must carefully balance operational costs, functionality, longevity, durability, maintenance and recyclability against the embodied energy costs. This is only possible through application of a LCA.

> 12.2.10 Identify the key considerations to take into account when selecting materials for the building envelope.
>
> © IBO 2007

Energy efficient building envelope design is of major importance in optimizing the requirements of ventilation, daylighting, moisture protection and thermal insulation. These factors determine the energy requirements that result from occupants needs and the prevailing climatic conditions. The most effective way to optimize a building for energy efficiency is to incorporate the features into the architectural design. It is the specification of architectural elements (windows, walls ceilings etc.), and the selection of materials that combine to determine the overall effectiveness of the design. The integration of active management and solar systems to value-add or fine-tune energy consumption may be retrofitted layer.

AHL

Energy efficient building envelopes reduce the load on a building's mechanical heating and cooling systems. The envelope controls the flow of energy between the interior and exterior of the building. When these systems have less variation in temperature to regulate, energy consumption drops, translating directly into lower operational costs.

> **12.2.11** Explain how the selection of different construction materials with different U values can contribute to heat loss or gain from a building.
>
> © IBO 2007

Building materials conduct heat at different rates. Components of the envelope such as concrete slabs, walls, windows ceilings and doors can create pathways for heat loss or gain.

Component design style and material selection combine to vary heat loss or gain from buildings. As an example, windows may be selected to have a specific U value. This value can be produced not just from the size or thickness of glass supplied but may include combinations of multiple layers of glass, between-pane insulation (gas), glass coatings, frame size and materials selection. Additionally awnings, blinds and insulated storm shutters can also affect heat transfer rates.

> **12.2.12** Identify four factors that determine the heat flow through a material.
>
> © IBO 2007

The heat transfer rates of various materials depend on:

- surface area
- material thickness
- thermal conductivity
- temperature differentials between the extremities.

Note: Where composite materials are specified, a total U factor is determined by adding up the individual U-factors of the various component materials. The smaller the U-factor, the better the insulation value of the composite structure.

> **12.2.13** Calculate heat loss or gain through a building envelope comprising different materials
>
> © IBO 2007

If the difference between the inside and the outside temperatures of a building were zero, then there would be a thermal balance and no loss or gain in temperature

transmitted. However, if a differential in temperature exists between the interior and exterior, the temperatures will attempt to balance. These boundaries separating inside from outside are the various components of the building envelope and, as previously discussed, conduct heat at varying rates. The conduction effect, or 'T' heat flow (Q_c), is measured in Watts. The following formula may be applied:

Heat flow = wall area × temperature difference × U value

therefore $Q_c = A \times \Delta T \times U$

Where,

Q_c = the resulting heat flow (Watts)
A = the surface area through which the heat flows (m²)
ΔT = the temperature difference
U = the thermal resistance per unit area of the piece of material (m²K/W).

In the following example a 7m² external full brick wall is subjected to a temperature differential of 15° and has a U value of 2.2. Through simple substitution the calculation would be as follows:

Heat flow = 7 × 15 × 2.2
           = 231 W

> **12.2.14** Explain how passive solar design can contribute to passive solar heating and/or cooling and reduce energy consumption in buildings.
>
> © IBO 2007

Passive solar energy systems collect or disperse energy from the sun without the use of any mechanical systems or technologies. Passive solar designs use the local climatic conditions to maintain or improve building interior comfort levels. These systems may be used to heat or cool the architectural environment. Through the coordination of building location, architectural elements and materials choice, solar radiation's ability to reflect, absorb or transmit impacted sunlight is incorporated into building design. Responses may then be used to control heating, cooling and/or ventilation.

Maximizing the harnessing of the sun's energy is a function of hemispheric location i.e. Northern or Southern Hemisphere. While the Sun always rises in the East and sets in the West, its path through the sky like seasonal variations is determined by the 'tilt' or inclination of the earth's axis. The exact passage of the sun varies uniquely with latitude.

AHL

Because the sun is lower in the sky in Winter than in Summer, passive building design maximizes the capture of heat in Winter and minimizes exposure in the Summer months.

Optimal house orientation aligns a buildings major axis, East-West. In the Northern Hemisphere living areas should face south to harness the Sun's energy while in the Southern Hemisphere building living areas should face North. In both cases, exposure to the hot westerly sun should be minimized.

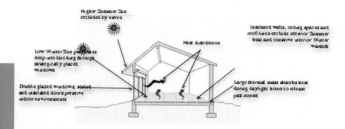

Figure 12.2.14 Passive solar design

12.2.15 Identify three ways in which passive solar design can be achieved.

Passive solar design uses the ability of materials to reflect, absorb or transmit sunlight. Combinations of these elements incorporated in building design can heat or cool spaces, cause the movement of air and assist with ventilation and cooling.

Specific approaches to passive solar design include:

- shading
- daylighting
- building orientation
- provision of thermal mass
- air movement and ventilation.

Appropriate solar orientation of a building is the most important factor when designing to maximize solar heating and cooling affects. East-west axial orientation of a building allows for the placement of windows relative to interior spaces requiring the most light, (living areas, kitchens etc.), to face the sun. Spaces requiring less sunlight, (bedrooms and bathrooms), are then located away from the Sun.

Energy transference through sunlight may be through either direct or indirect gain.

Direct gain is employed where sunlight penetrates a building and directly impacts on surfaces of high thermal

mass. Indirect gain uses natural heat transfer systems of conduction, radiation or convection to transfer energy indoors.

Thermal mass is employed as a heat storage system. Sunlight on tiled or exposed concrete slabs absorbs heat energy throughout the day and re-radiates this heat at night. Thermal mass is particularly effective where there is a large differential between daytime and night-time temperatures. As a general rule, diurnal temperature differences of at least 6°C are required. Water held in tanks, (heated by the sun's rays), may also be fed through pipes or into storage drums for use at night. Properties of materials possessing properties suitable for use as thermal mass include:

- high density
- low values of reflectivity
- moderate heat transference.

Figure 12.2.15a shows typical thermal mass values for common materials.

Material	Thermal mass *
Water	4186
Concrete	2060
Sandstone	1800
Fibro cement sheet	1530
Brick	1360

Figure 12.2.15a Typical thermal mass values $*(KJ/m^3.k)$

Through strategic door and window placement, passive solar design may be optimized. Suitable styles of construction and materials choices improve the efficiency of windows, while sealing and caulking prevents draughts and unwanted heat loss or gain. Appropriate window size and placement not only improves daylighting and directs sunlight towards areas of high thermal mass, but it also allows for cross-ventilation.

Air movement is the single most important factor in passive cooling. Air movement translates directly into temperature reductions. As little as 0.36 km/h can result in a 6°C temperature drop, (at 50% relative humidity). Convective air movement may also be encouraged and allow for hot air inside the building to rise up and pass out through vents or open widows in a higher part of the structure, at the same time drawing in cooler air from shaded external areas.

Shading buildings and outdoor spaces reduces building interior temperatures, improves comfort, saves energy and is cost effective. Effective shading can intercept 90%

of heat producing effects before they enter buildings. Reflective or light-coloured roof surfaces reduce the impact of heat through ceilings, while appropriately fashioned eave overhangs shade windows and walls. Awnings on windows or treatment with shutters and reflective coatings also reduce heat ingress.

Unfortunately, traditional sustainable solutions to ventilation such as the Malqaf (Figure 12.2.15b), have been discarded in favour of modernity and technology, such as air conditioning.

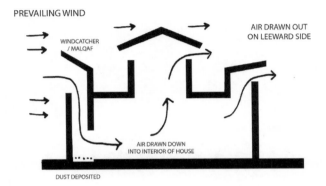

12.2.15b Diagrammatic representation of a malqaf or wind catcher for natural ventilation

Image by Fellanamedlime [Public domain], from Wikimedia Commons

> 12.2.16   Explain how landscaping can contribute to reductions in energy consumption for buildings.
>
> © IBO 2007

Energy conserving landscapes reduce energy costs in a home during summer and winter. Ideally, the landscaping should be both water efficient and low maintenance. Planned landscaping significantly reduces a building's heating and cooling costs by dealing with the sunlight before reaching the building. Savings of up to 30% of heating and cooling costs are achievable.

The reduction of building energy consumption through planned landscaping falls into the categories of; provision of shade, planted windbreaks, built structures and the use of vegetative surfaces and reflective materials (such as paths and driveways).

Carefully planned plantings of vegetation provide shade, reduce the surface temperature of building walls and roofs and prevent direct heat gain through windows. In the Northern Hemisphere evergreen trees planted on the north and west sides afford the best protection from the setting summer sun and cold winter winds. The use of deciduous trees on the southern and eastern sides of homes allows for the infiltration of winter sunlight to assist with daylighting and heat gain.

Strategic selection and group planting of trees and shrubs may also generate windbreaks and sound barriers. Grasses, groundcovers and shrubs offer a cooling effect through the process of evapo-transpiration.

Heat absorbent surfaces such as asphalt, re-emit stored heat after sunset and need to be either minimized or shaded to reduce their impact.

> 12.2.17   Explain how daylighting can contribute to reductions in energy consumption for buildings.
>
> © IBO 2007

Energy consumption as a direct result of lighting and the cooling required to deal with associated heat can be as much as 40–50% of building energy requirements. Daylighting can significantly reduce these costs through the effective use of natural sunlight. Daylighting is much more than the provision of more or larger windows or the addition of skylights. It is a complex mix of factors taking into account seasonal variations, site requirements, materials selection, heat gain and loss as well as glare control.

Solar radiation consists of approximately 44% visible light, 53% invisible infrared heat and 3% ultraviolet light. Ideally, glazing should admit the visible portion of the spectrum and block the rest.

Standard window glass is transparent and is very good at admitting both light and heat. The use of natural light reduces lighting costs but transferring incoming heat raises cooling costs. Reflective glass (with a metallic coating) is often specified to reduce heat gain. The mirror effect produced from this material also reflects much of the incoming light. Tinted glass incorporates heat-dispersing elements infused with the glass to reduce heat transfer. Unfortunately, these elements also absorb incoming light and distort its colour.

Heat mirror® insulating glass has a thin metallic films implanted between two layers of glass. This material reflects heat without affecting incoming light and, with optional gas filled voids, can achieve a U-values of 0.10, (R-value of 10).

Rooms that receive large amounts of natural sunlight during daylight hours may not need artificial lighting. Light sensors incorporating photocells can monitor ambient light levels in a room and automatically adjust overhead lighting to preset levels. Coupled with motion sensors, this technology actively minimizes the energy used for lighting.

Elements of effective daylighting include:

- selection of appropriate glazing materials
- automating dimming control of lights in daylit areas
- planning structure layouts to allow for daylighting to all zones
- orienting the building to maximize daylighting opportunities
- considering glare control, window films, curtains, awnings, wing walls etc.

12.2.18 Explain how active solar collection can contribute to reductions in energy consumption for buildings.

© IBO 2007

Harnessing the Sun's power and converting it into useable forms is the nature of active solar systems. Rooftop solar cells may gather energy for hot water storage, pool heating and space heating and even provide heat for commercial and industrial premises. Most collectors are mounted on a fixed platform, carefully aligned to improve exposure. Others 'track' the sun to maximize their efficiency. All employ a darkened surface designed to trap incoming solar radiation. Once absorbed by the collector, heat is efficiently distributed via heat transfer liquids, such as an antifreeze mix, water or oil. The heat may be used instantly or stored against future demands.

Figure 12.2.18a Solar panel

Photovoltaic panels constructed from modified silicon are also used to capture incoming solar radiation and convert this directly into electricity thus reducing dependence on the energy grid. Oversupply can be redistributed and 'sold' back to the grid offsetting costs of any future needs.

Photovoltaic and thermal collection panels can be designed to seamlessly combine with other building elements, such as roof tiles or windows. Figure 12.2.18b shows a photovoltaic array covering an entire roof.

Figure 12.2.18b Household photovoltaic panel array

Further Reading

Braat, S. (2006). *KISSTile Project,* Design Summary.

Prasad, D. & Fox, E. (1996). *Environment Design Guide,* The Royal Australian Institute of Architects.

Passive Solar Design, Briefing 09, (2003). Cement and Concrete Association of Australia.

Study for the Development of European Ecolabel Criteria for Buildings. (2009). Italian Institute for Environmental Protection and Research, First Background Report, Revised version.

Exercises

1. Intelligent buildings are:
   A. controlled by computers
   B. autonomous and think for themselves
   C. designed and constructed with embedded sensors to provide computing services to occupants
   D. optimized to provide services within a structure using energy management systems and building controls?

2. Appropriate technology may be defined as:
   A. technologies chosen for their cost effectiveness
   B. technologies targeting the needs of local consumers
   C. technology considering function, aesthetics and ergonomics
   D. technology chosen considering natural resources, financial capital, labour and skills.

3. To maximise solar efficiency, buildings should be aligned:
   A. facing north
   B. facing south
   C. along an east-west axis
   D. along a north-south axis.

4. The 'term triple bottom line' refers to:
   A. people, peace, profit
   B. improving efficiency by a factor of three
   C. social, financial and environmental sustainability
   D. social, financial and environmental development.

5. If the 'U' value of a material is 0.7, the corresponding 'R' factor would be?
   A. 7
   B. 1.43
   C. 14.43
   D. 0.1437

6. Explain the difference between sustainable architectural design and living building designs.

7. Identify the key components of appropriate technology.

8. Explain the relationship between 'U' and 'R' factors.

9. Calculate the total heat gain due to conduction through a wall with a U-Value of 4.5 W/m² K and a surface area of 10 m².
   Consider the outside temperature to be 30°C and the inside 25°C.

10. Explain why it is difficult for governments to agree on the guidelines for sustainable development.

11. Explain the difference between embodied and operational energy.

12. Discuss the importance of building orientation to passive solar design.

AHL

229

FOOD SCIENCE AND TECHNOLOGY

CONTENTS

At a purely physiological level we need food in order to provide energy to maintain a body temperature at which biological functions of growth and repair can be performed optimally. It is a basic requirement for sustaining life and unlike some species, humans and animals need to eat and drink at frequent and regular intervals to survive. Because of this, access to food is considered to be a basic human right under the 1948 Universal Declaration of Human Rights.

Beyond this level of basic needs, food has always played an important part in the social, cultural and religious parts of human civilization. Many peoples of the world identify certain culinary dishes with their national or ethic identity, while the colour, texture and smell of food can invoke strong emotional responses and memories.

Too much or too little food however can lead to system malfunction and disease. Although global trade and modern technology has helped to alleviate concerns over food quality and availability for many, the occurrence of drought, floods, disease and war continue to result in starvation in some countries, while an overabundance of convenience processed foods high in salt, sugar and fat has led to an obesity epidemic in others.

A.1 DEVELOPMENT OF THE FOOD INDUSTRY

A.1.1   Explain that food is a precious, highly seasonal and perishable commodity that has to be handled carefully and in an appropriate and timely manner to ensure that it is safe to eat.

© IBO 2007

The production of food has always been subject to the vagaries of the climate, natural pests and disease that have limited the useful yield obtained season to season. In addition to this is the limited period available beyond harvest that the nutrient value is retained before spoilage.

Until relatively recently, the means for rapid distribution of large quantities of produce to distant markets, and processing methods such as refrigeration and canning were not available. Today, technological advances have allowed the period of safe consumption following harvest

OPTION

to be significantly increased and, while many foods such as fruits and vegetables are seasonal, the global nature of the food industry means that many of these commodities remain available all year round. Food remains a perishable commodity however and some, such as 'fresh' milk, have a relatively short shelf life before spoiling.

The processes involved in the perishing of food can lead to the development of bacteria and toxins that are dangerous to health. To prevent such circumstances, food packaging usually carries a date by which consumption is recommended, such as those shown in Figure A.1.1.

Figure A.1.1 A selection of typical food use-by labels

The human body requires a regular intake of food and water to maintain an adequate level of nutrition for normal cell function and processes of growth and repair. Without adequate nutrition, as occurs during starvation, these functions begin to slow down and stop, leading to organ failure and ultimately death.

In the early stages of starvation, the body begins to burn fat reserves, however, if starvation continues, muscle tissue and liver cells are burnt in a process known as catabolysis to obtain the reserves of glycogen they contain.

Typical symptoms of starvation are:

- hair loss
- emaciation
- skin rashes
- sleep disorders

- physical weakness
- loss of bone density
- constipation or diarrhoea
- decreased concentration
- teeth decay and bleeding gums
- edema (swelling) of stomach and extremeties
- emotional changes, including depression, irritability and social withdrawal

Assuming an adequate supply of water to maintain hydration, survival under conditions of starvation is generally of the order of four to six weeks, although this is dependent on a variety of factors such as:

- metabolism
- temperature
- state of mind
- muscle content
- state of health
- level of exertion
- body fat reserves.

Survival without access to water is approximately one week.

Up until the 1700s and the beginning of the Industrial Revolution, the majority of people lived a largely subsistence life in rural communities. Peasant farmers grew food for their family on small plots of ground under traditional rights of access to land owned by the wealthy. Food was produced by labour intensive methods aided by basic tools, often made solely of wood.

Diets consisted primarily of bread, made of roughly ground wheat and rye flour, and soups and gruel made of grains and seasonal vegetables such as peas and beans. A diet largely unchanged from that of the Middle Ages.

The Industrial Revolution began in the 1700s with changes to land use. The peasants who had traditionally farmed small plots of land, owned by wealthy land owners, were excluded from these plots as the land was amalgamated and fenced into larger fields, leading to greater efficiency.

Changes to crop rotation practices were also introduced, where previously a field would be left fallow the season after a harvest to allow time for soil nutrients to be regained, it was found that by planting a crop such as clover or lucerne, nutrients were returned to the field. This practice had the additional benefit that feed for livestock was created that would help maintain animal condition through the winter.

With the introduction of Steam Power in the early 1800s, the mechanisation of industry gained pace. Steam engines operated pumps to remove water from mines, allowing increased production of resources such as coal and as a power source, freed industry from being located next to waterwheels and windmills. With steam, a factory could be built almost anywhere as long as there was an adequate supply of water and coal for the boilers. The mechanisation of industry and the growth of factories particularly, in the textiles industry, created a demand for labour and many people in rural communities were attracted to the cities in the hope of a regular wage and a better life.

The reality of life in these growing population centres was that it was often difficult, and the problems of supplying the population with food became an increasing concern. Malnutrition was common among the factory labourers, with a common diet consisting of bread, potatoes and tea with the possibility of a piece of meat on Sundays. Death as a result of scurvy and rickets claimed the lives of many, particularly the young. Sanitation was poor and living conditions overcrowded.

These conditions of an increasing population and unreliable supply of food led the political economist Thomas Malthus in 1798 to suggest that such a population could not be supported and would lead to a correction by mass starvation. While his prediction proved inaccurate, his ideas were influential in the development of Darwin's Theory of Evolution.

The increasing pace of innovation during the Industrial Revolution led to a solution to the food supply problem. The introduction of rail transport greatly increased the amount of food that could be distributed in a short period of time. The ability to rapidly move grain and meat large distances also meant that new areas of land distant from cities and towns could now be linked to markets economically and were therefore now viable locations for food production. As iron and steel production increased, farm implements previously made of wood began to be replaced by mass produced equipment made of sturdier, longer lasting, iron and steel. The efficiency of such production was also greatly improved by the introduction of mechanical tools such as the stump jump plough and combine harvester.

The beginning of the nineteenth century saw the introduction of an organised food industry as roads and improved methods of transport and storage began to appear. Canning developed at the beginning of the 1800s and later, reliable means of freezing meat increased the importance of an international food trade. This also reduced exposure to the impact of local crop failures and disease. During this period Brand Names began to become more important as trade and competition between manufacturers of mass-produced products increased and consumers began to demand greater consistency in quality and price. By the 1920s household refrigerators began to appear on the market allowing the foodstuffs such as meat and dairy foods to be stored for longer periods and reducing the need for daily shopping.

Today, international trade in foodstuffs is well established, although distribution remains a concern in many parts of the World. While technology has provided may answers to the problems of food supply since Malthus' essay in 1798 with a World population of over six billion and growing, some commentators are again asking if the resources are available to maintain such an increase. The increase in world population since 500AD is presented in Figure A.1.2, along with some significant events in the period since the Industrial Revolution.

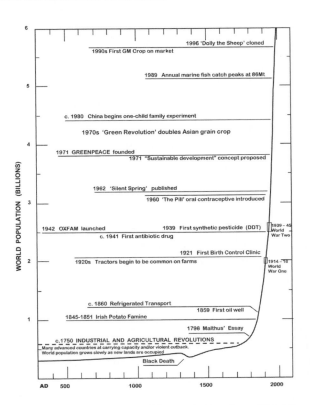

Figure A.1.2 *Change in World Population from 500 AD to 2000AD*

(Adapted from Stanton, W. (2004). The rapid growth of human populations, 1750-2000.

OPTION

Typically, food distribution follows through a complex supply chain that starts with initial agricultural cultivation and ends on the consumer's plate at home or in a restaurant. When the end product finally arrived on the dinner table it has travelled all the way down a long supply chain.

The flow chart shown in Figure A.1.5 illustrates the food chain structure. Farmers as food producers are on the top of the food chain, and can be divided into two groups:

- Small-farm agriculture supplying directly to the local market
- 'Buyer-driven' chains with high levels of private sector governance and long-term vertical coordination between producers/farmers, processors/manufactures, distributors/wholesalers and retailers.

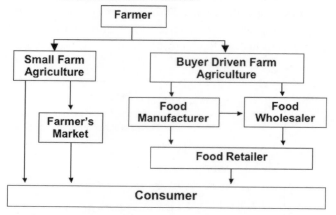

Figure A.1.5 The food chain from the farmer to consumer

Primary processing is the conversion of a crop into a product that may or may not be consumed directly. It involves the efficient handling of the crop to retain its freshness, flavour, texture and appearance. This is accomplished through efficient harvesting, cleaning, chilling and storage of the product.

Secondary processing is the conversion of an intermediate product into a final product for consumption. Within most agriculture sectors, an opportunity exists for producers to add value to their primary products through further processing to meet consumer demands. Consumers' increasing knowledge of the food industry, combined with the need for more convenience food to satisfy the ever changing lifestyle, has provided producers of primary food products with an opportunity to increase potential value through further processing. Secondary food processing can involve freezing, dehydration, extraction and preservation, fermentation etc. For example, traditional vegetable retailing only involves farmers selling their raw products such as strawberries in the local markets. Some farmers further process them into bottled jams and other preserves. Other strawberry processors take the next step to supply frozen mix berries to supermarkets. Strawberries can be processed into a non-perishable product, thus increasing their value.

There are three factors that determine a need for primary and secondary processing, they are:

- storage properties
- physical properties
- energy consumption.

For example, milk as the primary product can be directly consumed, however its storage properties are not excellent, Milk requires refrigeration to maintain its freshness. However, if it is subjected to further high temperature treatment and packaging, its storage properties can be greatly improved while eliminating the energy requirements associated with the need for refrigeration.

The physical property of milk can be defined as being a high-density liquid material. This poses some problems in terms of long-term storage and transport. If processed to remove the water content, the high density milk is transformed into a low density powder that can be easily transported and stored and which can later be reconstituted by the addition of water.

The evolution of food outlets is influenced by the social and economic conditions of a society, as may be seen in differences existing between developed and developing nations, although a number of basic stages of evolution can be identified.

Stage 1: involves the existence of simple farmers markets where the farm produce is taken by the farmer to a local market and sold direct to the consumer. Products are fresh and seasonal and consumers need to attend the markets regularly to obtain produce, unless they have the facilities to chill or freeze products such as milk and meat.

Small food stores also develop. These provide a retail outlet for farm produce, which may have been purchased from a regional market by the shopkeeper. These stores are often dispersed through a community and provide convenience with respect to travel requirements of consumers.

The farmers' markets and small food stores often provide a centre of community interaction

Stage 2: As community size increases, food shops tend to evolve from the small corner shops to larger grocery shops, although still operated by a shopkeeper who provides assistance in the purchase. In developed countries many of these shops operate on the self-service principle, by which the consumer collects their groceries from shelves and places them in a basket or trolley before proceeding to the front of the store to pay.

Stage 3: As cities increase in size, supermarkets and department stores develop which are vertically integrated, allowing them economies of scale and the development of co-ordinated distribution systems.

While supermarkets have become ubiquitous in most developed countries, in the developing countries, supermarkets have developed primarily in the larger cities in which a greater proportion of affluent consumers may be found. Transport restrictions and prices have meant that poorer members of the community still prefer local markets which provide both lower prices and centres of social contact.

A.1.9 Explain that the food industry is now the largest industry in the world.

© IBO 2007

Due to its complex and globalized nature, the size of the food industry is actually difficult to accurately establish. This is because it comprises not only the primary industries traditionally associated with food production, such as farming and fishing, but also secondary and tertiary industries such as the food processing industries

and the food and beverage industries, farm machinery manufacturers and biotechnology laboratories.

Taken as a whole, the food industry is estimated by many to be one of the largest if not the largest industry in the world, and growing. The globalized nature of the food industry has also meant that mergers and acquisitions have increasingly led to the creation of large multinational food corporations such as Kraft, Kellogg, Cadbury and Simplot.

A.1.10 Discuss the influence of market pull and technology push on the development of new food products.

© IBO 2007

Market 'pull' refers to the power of consumers, representing the market, to demand the goods and services they require. Conversely, the suppliers are considered to offer, or 'push' products toward the consumer. Food manufacturers are constantly looking for areas of unmet market demand in order to provide new food products.

Increasingly this challenge is being met by recourse to technology, where food science and engineering is being used in the selection, preservation, packaging, and distribution of food.

To this end the food industry spends a considerable amount of time analysing food trends and lifestyle issues to develop products that will attract consumers. One such development has been the appearance of pre-packaged 'ready-to-use' ethnic sauces and pastes that can be stored at room temperature in a pantry until required, and that offer the opportunity to prepare at home an exotic meal with minimal effort. A selection of these sauces is presented in Figure A.1.10.

Figure A.1.10 Selection of 'Ethnic' sauces

A.1.11 Explain that the modern food industry in developed countries is an example of a tightly controlled just-in-time system.

© IBO 2007

Just-in-time (JIT) systems operate under the philosophy that the holding of more stock than required for the next stage in a production process, or to satisfy market requirements, is an unnecessary cost. Therefore, reducing inventories to only those required to continue operations reduces costs overall. To work, this system relies heavily on careful forward planning, backed up by an efficient and reliable distribution and maintenance system. In developing countries the lack of infrastructure can result in problems in the storage and distribution system that have been blamed for food spoilage rates of between 20 to 40 percent.

A.1.12 Describe organic agriculture.

© IBO 2007

Organic agriculture is a philosophy of food production that believes that the use of artificially produced chemical fertilisers, herbicides and insecticides results in harm to the environment and the incorporation of harmful chemical residues in the produce.

To be considered organic, produce must also be free of synthetic food additives and avoid the use of processes such as artificial ripening, and measures that increase shelf life such as irradiation.

Some disagreement exists between advocates of organic farming and conventional farming methods as to the effect on yield and nutrient value of food produced this way.

A.1.13 Explain that organic production is driven by market issues and problems associated with existing agricultural practices.

© IBO 2007

Although often more expensive than conventionally grown food, organic produce represents one of the fastest growing sections of the food market. This growth has largely been driven by a number of food scares related to the use of artificial hormones and antibiotics in animals and fears regarding the presence of herbicide and pesticide

residues in fruit and vegetables. Examples of products branded as organic is shown in Figure A.1.13.

Concern has also been raised regarding the introduction of genetically modified (GM) foodstuffs onto the market and harmful effects to the local ecosystem including the run-off of artificial fertilisers from farms into rivers and streams.

Figure A.1.13 Food endorsed as organic appearing in supermarkets

Further Reading

Troops, D. (2007). *How did the food industry get (from there) to here? Accelerating New Food Product Design and Development.* Jacqueline H. Beckley, et.al. (Editors). Chapter 2, pp7-26. Blackwell Publishing Ltd, Iowa, USA.

Tannahill, R. (1973). *Food in History. Stein and Day,* New York, USA.

Ewald, J. & Moskowitz, H. R. (2007). *Market forces: The push-pull of marketing and advertising in the new product business. Accelerating New Food Product Design and Development.* Jacqueline H. Beckley, et.al. (Editors). Chapter 8, pp103-122. Blackwell Publishing Ltd, Iowa, USA.

Sarah Murray (Nov 2007), *Food: The World's Biggest Industry* . http://www.forbes.com/2007/11/11/growth-agriculture-business-forbeslife-food07-cx_sm_1113bigfood.html

Minnesota Starvation Experiment? http://en.wikipedia.org/wiki/Minnesota_Starvation_Experiment

Starvation Facts http://www.brighthub.com/health/diet-nutrition/articles/71288.aspx

A.2 DESIGNING NEW FOOD PRODUCTS

A.2.1 Describe the role of the design brief in the design of new food products.

© IBO 2007

The definition of what constitutes a 'new food product' is broad and includes a change of any sort, ranging from the development of a previously unavailable product, to the repackaging of an established product.

In order to provide some structure and focus to the process and purpose of the new food development, a design brief is a prepared outlining the goals and constraints involved. Because the definition of a new product is broad, the design brief will by necessity vary, depending on the nature of the product development.

The goals of the development may include:

- responding to competition
- taking advantage of new technology
- rejuvenation of sales of an established product
- expansion of sales, e.g. extension of product range to new flavours
- responding to societal trends, e.g. low calorie, organic, microwave meals, etc.

A.2.2 Describe how food manufacturers gain evidence to support the development of a new food product.

© IBO 2007

Traditionally, new product development involves manufacturers exploring the needs of the market and developing appropriate products in response. This process can be complex and expensive but helps to ensure market success. While incremental improvement of existing products is the most common form of product development, manufacturers still require information to assist them in determining the direction these modifications should take. Market research, data collection and analysis by manufacturers that may involve:

- competitor product analysis
- user trials to test product acceptance
- 'what-if' scenarios evaluating product profitability

- investigation of unfilled or alternative niche opportunities
- market dynamic analysis (growth/decline, recent trends etc.)
- user surveys and interviews focusing on customer buying habits and attitudes
- targeting existing customers to gather their views on an existing product to seek ways of improvement.

Manufacturers regularly observe market competition sales to test their level of comparative success. Innovation, modifications and adjustments of products by competitors may also provide clues to manufacturers of market trends.

General Source	Specific Impetus Providing Inspiration
The marketplace	Market research to identify customer needs, for example: lifestyle, health factors
	Retailer providing details of consumer's buying habits
	Handling issue raised from the distributor
Within the company	Strategic change according to sale force's observation and competitor's products
	Environment concerns and cost reduction of waste removal
	Spontaneously generated idea from employees
Outside the marketplace	Advances in science, technology, and nutritional
	New food legislation
	New market opening

Figure A.2.2 Sources of information for the development of new products

A.2.3 Construct a specification for a food product.

A.2.4 Evaluate food products against specifications.

© IBO 2007

Food products sold around the world are required to display a product specification. This. is fundamental to the quality control process and contains details about the food product, including sourcing of ingredients through to the cooking or preparation process, plus use-by information.

OPTION

This legislative requirement should not be confused with a product design specification, which will list the specific criteria required when considering the development of a new product for the food industry, as shown in Figure A.2.4. Design specifications should be based on research conducted, data collection and analysis. For example, when developing a design specification for a new flavoured ice cream, the following table will enable the food technologists or manufacturers to analyse the product against the specification.

Categories	Specification	Justification
Type of product	Banana and coconut flavored ice-cream	Research shows there are fewer banana and coconut flavored ice-cream available.
Target market	Children and families	Survey indicates that banana is the favorite fruit among children, generic milk addition was replaced by coconut milk, creating a diary free, and vegan friendly ice cream. New product is also lower calorie
Size and packaging	250g plastic tray 1kg container	Smaller package can be sold for test taste sample, while 1kg package is for family use.
Main ingredients	Water, sugar, coconut milk, banana	Diary milk replaced by the coconut milk

Nutritional information	Banana coconut milk ice cream	Average Quantity per 100g	Conventional ice cream	Average Quantity per 100g
	Energy (kJ)	226	Energy (kJ)	816
	Protein (g)	3.5	Protein (g)	4.1
	Fat- total (g)	7.5	Fat- total (g)	10.6
	Fat- saturated (g)	3.5	Fat- saturated (g)	7.0
	Carbohydrates- total (g)	18.1	Carbohydrates- total (g)	20.7
	Carbohydrates- sugar (g)	20.1	Carbohydrates- sugar (g)	20.1
	Sodium (mg)	52.9	Sodium (mg)	58

Storage instructions	Product needs to be kept at or below -18°C when stored. Shelf life under these conditions is 24 months from date of manufacture as indicated by the best before date.	
Preparing/Cooking instructions	Serve straight from the package	
Cost	$3.50/ 250g	$10.00 /kg

Figure A.2.4 Food specification example

A.2.5 Describe the role of taste panels in the development of the specification of a food product.

While the objective testing of foods for calorific value, sugar, salt and fat content, colour, pH, nutrient content, storage life and cost can be undertaken to obtain a measure against specification, the final arbiter of acceptance and success in the market place are the organoleptic factors we associate with taste. The reaction to sensory or organoleptic factors such as visual appearance, flavour, aroma and texture are primarily subjective measures that can vary not only from person to person, but between cultures.

In order to measure food for these factors, food manufacturers use taste panels comprising groups of people who evaluate food based on assessments of their reaction to the sensory aspects of the food. A taste panel may consist of professional tasters, or they may be a group of untrained customers. Typically, taste tests are carried out individually and without the knowledge of the reactions of other participants, so the testers cannot influence each other (Figure A.2.5). Under a red light that gives all samples the same colour, sensory panel members sample food supplied without information regarding the method of preparation and coded with letters and numbers. Each taster completes an evaluation form as they taste the product. These forms often include a Lickert scale by which each factor to be evaluated is rated on a five point scale, from strongly dislike through to strongly like.

Figure A.2.5 Taste test panels help determine the acceptance of new products.

Image by USDA, ARS Image Gallery

A.2.6 Describe the issues involved in the scaling up of recipes from bench scale.

A product is designed initially as a bench-top prototype and key parameters are determined using taste panels. As the volume of product increases, the recipe may need to be modified to achieve the same organoleptic characteristics. Variations in ingredients and processing may require, for example, more or less fluids or binding agents in the recipe.

The scaling up of bench-top prototype recipes to commercial scale production requires considerable 'tweaking' of quantities to reproduce the original organoleptic characteristics. This refers to any sensory properties of a product, involving taste, colour, odour and feel.

Because of the volume involved in commercial production, quantities need to be converted from measures such as pinch, teaspoon and cup to kilograms and litres. Similarly, handling issues for the mixing, transport, handling, cooking, storage and packaging of the ingredients and finished product need to be considered. These issues are important to resolve and guarantee the consumer the same experience between products processed over time. The important consideration here is repeatability and consistency of quality.

> ### A.2.7 Describe the role of market testing in the development of a food product.
>
> © IBO 2007

The success of any product, including new food products in the marketplace depends entirely on its ability to meet the tastes, trends and requirements of the target market. To maximise the chances of product success and ultimately financial viability, meeting consumers' demands is paramount. Initially, however, market surveys may be employed to determine:

- price placement
- current market solutions
- customer niche and demand
- brand recognition and product perception.

Once a market demand and initial product specification has been developed, production would be scaled up from bench scale to pilot-plant scale. This enables a larger volume trial production of product, allowing wider market testing.

A range of methods may be employed by food manufacturers to measure potential market acceptance before their products go to full-scale production. These methods may include:

- sensory evaluation methods with a trained panel or with ordinary consumers
- product rating tests involve consumers ranking product attributes on line or graphic scales
- paired preference tests are used to focus consumers on specific product criteria or characteristic by comparing two samples before being asked their preference.

Following acceptance in a test market, the product would be scaled up to industrial-scale production.

Packaging design is another way of developing new product. It can reformulate or reinforce the brand identity, separating the product from competition, while reinforcing messages judged to be important, such as

traditional values, while reducing images of being old fashioned. The provision of a number of alternate package sizes can also provide a wider range of buying options to the market. Some special offer, or promotion logo, can also be added to the original design.

Figure A.2.7 product testing

Image by USDA, ARS Image Gallery

Further Reading

Winger, R. and Wall, G. (2006). *Food product innovation, A background paper,* Food and Agriculture Organization of the United Nations, Rome.
[Retrieved from http://www.fao.org/fileadmin/user_upload/ags/publications/J7193_e.pdf]

Design Brief
http://www.secondarydandt.org/data/files/fooddesbriefsstu.pdf

BDI Design Advisory Service: Design Brief Template
http://www.britishdesigninnovation.org/new/bdi/Design_Brief.doc

Classroom Video (2009). *Developing a Design Brief.* Clickview Video library, Global ID 5526. [http://www.clickview.com.au/videolibrary/video_category.php?category_type=secondary]

OPTION

A.3 NUTRITION, BALANCED DIET AND HEALTH

A.3.1   Define protein, amino acid, essential and biological value.

© IBO 2007

Proteins are large complex molecules constructed from a sequence of amino acids. The body uses approximately 1,000,000 different types of protein to perform the various functions required in the body associated with growth and repair.

Proteins are constructed from a set of 20 amino acids that combine in different combinations to form distinct three-dimensional shapes. Some of these amino acids are constructed in the body, while others must be obtained from food. This latter group are known as the essential amino acids.

Amino acids are commonly known as the building blocks of protein and are made up of carbon, hydrogen, oxygen, and nitrogen.

The specific bodily functions performed by the protein depends upon how the strands of amino acids are arranged. Some amino acids can be produced by the body from other proteins and carbohydrates, that is, they do not need to be obtained directly from food. Because of this they are often termed non-essential amino acids. Other amino acids cannot be produced in the body but must be obtained from our food. These amino acids are known as essential or indispensable amino acids.

The body gains the amino acids it needs by breaking down the protein in food to its constituent amino acids. From these amino acids the body can produce its own proteins.

Eight amino acids (Leucine, Isoleucine, Valine, Threonine, Methionine, Phenylalanine, Tryptophan and Lysine) are considered essential for adults, while nine (those mentioned above plus Histidine) are considered essential for children. Figure A.3.1a gives a summary of the Amino acid composition of certain common food proteins.

The pairs asparagines/aspartic acid, (asx), and glutamine/glutamic acid, (glx), are closely related and are often difficult to differentiate.

Amino Acid	protein						
	egg white	beef	chicken	whey	casein	soy	yeast
alanine	6.6	6.1	5.5	5.2	2.9	4.2	8.3
arginine	5.6	6.5	6.0	2.5	3.7	7.5	6.5
aspartic acid	8.9	9.1	8.9	10.9	6.6	11.5	9.8
cysteine	2.5	1.3	1.3	2.2	0.3	1.3	1.4
glutamic acid	13.5	15.0	15.0	16.8	21.5	19.0	13.5
glycine	3.6	6.1	4.9	2.2	2.1	4.1	4.8
histidine *	2.2	3.2	3.1	2.0	3.0	2.6	2.6
isoleucine *	6.0	4.5	5.3	6.0	5.1	4.8	5.0
leucine *	8.5	8.0	7.5	9.5	9.0	8.1	7.1
lysine *	6.2	8.4	8.5	8.8	3.8	6.2	6.9
methionine *	3.6	2.6	2.8	1.9	2.7	1.3	1.5
phenylalanine *	6.0	3.9	4.0	2.3	5.1	5.2	4.7
proline	3.8	4.8	4.1	6.6	10.7	5.1	4.0
serine	7.3	3.9	3.4	5.4	5.6	5.2	5.1
threonine *	4.4	4.0	4.2	6.9	4.3	3.8	5.8
tryptophan *	1.4	0.7	1.2	2.2	1.3	1.3	1.6
tyrosine	2.7	3.2	3.4	2.7	5.6	3.8	5.0
valine *	7.0	5.0	5.0	6.0	6.6	5.0	6.2

* Essential amino acids

Figure A.3.1a Amino acid composition of food proteins (Percentage (%) by weight of amino acid) [Retrieved from http://www.food-info.net/uk/protein/bv.htm].

Biological Value is a measure of the degree to which the body is able to absorb protein from food. The higher the Biological Value of a protein consumed, the more readily it can be broken down ready for use by the body in protein synthesis. Because proteins are the major source of nitrogen, BV can also be defined as the amount of nitrogen absorbed from the protein. Nitrogen is needed to produce amino acids in the body.

BV is usually expressed in one of two ways, as a percentage of utilisation, or as a relative utilisation, where a percentage is determined relative to a scale on which egg has a value of 100%.

$$BV_{Absolute} = \frac{BV_{Abs(Rel)} \times BV_{Relative}}{100}$$

$$BV_{Relative} = \frac{BV_{Absolute}}{BV_{Abs(Rel)}} \times 100$$

Absolute BV = $(N_f / N_a) \times 100$

Where: N_a = nitrogen absorbed in proteins
            N_f = nitrogen incorporated into the body

Relative BV = (BVfood / BVegg) $\times 100$

If a protein contains all of the essential amino acids it is said to have a high BV, conversely those proteins that do not contain all essential amino acids are considered to be low BV. Figure A.3.1b gives an indication of the Absolute and Relative measures of BV for a range of foods. It should be noted that considerable variation exists in the published data and the information should be used as an indication only.

Product	Absolute BV	Relative BV
Whole egg	93.7	100
Potato	84	90
Milk	84	90
Edam cheese	83	85
Fish	81	83
Beef	78	80
Rice	78	80
Chicken	77	79
Maize	74	76
Cashew nuts	73	75
Soybeans	72	74
Rice, polished	64	66
Wheat, whole	64	66
Rolled oats	63	65
Corn	60	62
Beans, dry	58	60
Peanuts	58	59
Wheat, flour white	54	55

Figure A.3.1b Indicative absolute and relative biological value (BV) of some foods

A.3.2   Describe the role of protein in the body.

© IBO 2007

Proteins serve a number of roles within the human body by providing both essential and non-essential amino acids. Some proteins are involved in cellular regeneration and maintenance, while others are involved in hormone and enzyme production, movement, immune response, tissue fluid balance and energy production.

Because there is a constant breakdown of proteins in the body we need to consume proteins on a regular daily basis.

A.3.3 Identify foods of high biological value and low biological value.

© IBO 2007

High biological value (HBV) proteins include meat, fish, eggs, cheese, and milk. Low biological value (LBV) proteins include cereals, pulses, white flour, some nuts and vegetables.

A.3.4   Describe how low biological value foods are complemented in different parts of the world to ensure that essential amino acid requirements are met.

© IBO 2007

While low BV (LBV) foods do not contain all of the essential amino acids required by the body, it is possible to obtain all of the essential amino acids by consuming a number of different LBV foods so that the limitations of one food are compensated for by the contents of another LBV food with a different limiting amino acid. Foods combined to satisfy the requirements for full intake of essential amino acids are known as complimentary proteins, or amino acid complementarity. An example of this complementarity is shown in Figure A.3.4a.

	IsoLeu	Lis	Met	Trp
Legumes	✓	✓	✕	✕
Cereals	✕	✕	✓	✓
Combined	✓	✓	✓	✓

Figure A.3.4a Complimentary proteins

A typical example is baked beans on toast (Figure A.3.4b), in which all of the essential amino acids are obtained by the complimentary action of the protein from the bread (cereal) and the baked beans (legume). Similar complimentary combinations could be:

- nuts and cereal
- peanut butter on bread
- stir-fried vegetables & rice
- cereal and dairy - macaroni cheese
- legumes and cereal - refried beans & tacos
- legumes and dairy - bean salad and yoghurt.

Figure A.3.4b Baked beans on toast

A.3.5   Discuss the effect of low protein intake.

© IBO 2007

As protein is the most essential element of everyday diet, humans can become seriously ill without sufficient intake of protein. Most commonly found in areas experiencing limited food supply and famine, diseases resulting from a lack of sufficient protein and carbohydrates in the diet are often broadly grouped as PEM, or protein energy malnutrition diseases. Infants and children are particularly at risk of developing such conditions. Two diseases belonging to this group are Marasmus and Kwashiorkor.

Marasmus also known nonedematous PCM results from an energy deficiency and generally occurs in dry climates mainly affecting infants, causing them to become thin and weak as a result of a lack of nearly all nutrients, especially protein and calories. This condition may arise from chronic diarrhoea. When food intake decreases, the body adapts to the shortage of energy and nutrients by depleting all energy stores in order to supply the vital organs. As a result, the child with marasmus looks emaciated and may weigh less than 20% of the normal weight for its height, as shown in Figure A.3.5a. Features typical of a child suffering from Marasmus are:

* dry skin
* extensive tissue and muscle wasting,
* fretful, irritable, and voraciously hungry.

If the disease progresses to the point where the body's ability to undertake protein synthesis is degraded, a process through which the cells build proteins, the body will not be able to handle proteins. At this point the disease cannot be arrested by the supply of food.

Figure A.3.5a Marasmus

Kwashiorkor, also known as edematous PCM, occurs when the child is weaned from breast milk and the diet that replaces the milk is high in starches and carbohydrates, and deficient in protein. A typical feature of this disease is the distended bellies in children. This is a result of insufficient levels of blood serum proteins, such as albumin and globulin, which are required to maintain the integrity of capillary walls that regulate the fluid balance between the blood and tissue. If these proteins are diminished serum seeps into the soft tissues and the abdominal cavities causing diffuse body swelling or edema.

Kwashiorkor is commonly found in warm humid climates, where the conditions for mould growth are favourable. If mouldy food is ingested, aflatoxin poisoning can occur, leading to a disruption in the production of blood serum proteins such as albumin and globulin.

The large protuberant belly, formed as a result of the edema caused by the syndrome, can sometimes be confused with children appearing well-nourished, as can be seen in Figure A.3.5b.

Figure A.3.5b Kwashiorkor

A.3.6   Define monosaccharide, disaccharide and
         polysaccharide.

© IBO 2007

Most of the energy for the body comes from the consumption of carbohydrates The carbohydrates are organic compounds composed of carbon, hydrogen and oxygen with the general formula $C_m(H_2O)_n$ broken down by the body to form a simple sugar called glucose. When glucose combines with oxygen during respiration, energy is released. The carbohydrates are also known as saccharides (from Greek sacchar: sugar).

The simplest of the carbohydrate sugars is the monosaccharide. A monosaccharide cannot be hydrolysed to smaller units and forms the basic building blocks for the higher sugars disaccharide and polysaccharide and have the general formula $(CH_2O)_n$, where n is 3 or more. The monosaccharide structure is found in one of two groups consisting of either an aldehyde or ketone and are illustrated in Figure A.3.6a, where R and R' represent a group of hydrocarbons. The basic difference between these is that a carboxyl group, consisting of a carbon atom double bonded to an oxygen atom, terminates the chain of carbon atoms in the aldehydes while ketones have the carboxyl group elsewhere along the chain of carbon atoms.

Figure A.3.6a Aldehyde and Ketone

Two of the most common monosaccharides are glucose (also known as dextrose or blood sugar) and fructose (fruit sugar), which represent the aldehyde and ketone forms respectively of a six carbon monosaccharide, and are illustrated in Figure A.3.6b. While the structure of glucose and fructose are shown below, a variety of sugars are possible with the same formula but differing in the side of the molecule the OH group sits. The examples shown in Figure A.3.6b are the D or dextrose form of the structures in which the last OH group is on the same side as the oxygen as opposed to the L (or Levo) form, in which the OH group would be on the other side. It is the dextrose form that is generally found in nature and is metabolised by the body. These molecules can be found in two forms as illustrated in Figure A.3.6b, consisting of either a straight chain or a ring.

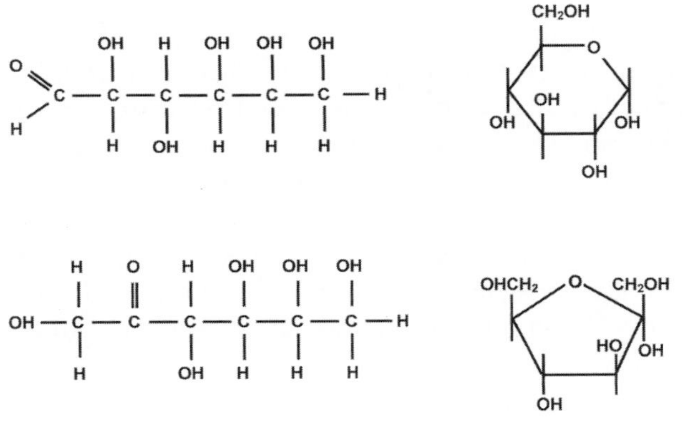

Figure A.3.6b Two forms of a six carbon monosaccharide Aldohexose (D-Glucose) and Ketohexose (D-Fructose) top and bottom respectively

Disaccharide is formed from the combination of two monosaccharides and includes the sugars maltose (corn sugar), sucrose (table sugar) and lactose (milk sugar). The bond being formed between the monosaccharides to create a disaccharide involves the dehydrogenation of the OH group, as illustrated in Figure A.3.6c.

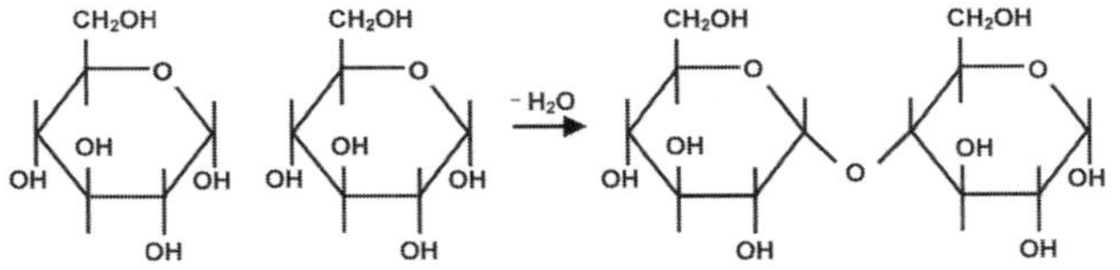

Figure A.3.6c Formation of a Disaccharide from the combination of two monosaccharides.

The polysaccharides are formed from the combination of a large number of monosaccharides, typically in the thousands, and include starch and cellulose.

Because foods such as potatoes, wheat, rice and corn contain a relatively high proportion of these saccharides, they are often referred to as being carbohydrates.

A.3.7   Describe the role of carbohydrate as an energy source in the body.

© IBO 2007

Carbohydrates are formed in plants through the process of photosynthesis, by which carbon dioxide and water react in the presence of sunlight to form the monosaccharide glucose.

$$6CO_2 + 6H_2O \xrightarrow[\text{Energy absorption}]{\text{Sunlight}} C_6H_{12}O_6 + 6O_2$$

For the stored energy of carbohydrates to be used by the body they must be capable of being broken down to the monosaccharide glucose. Specific enzymes in the body break down the disaccharides and polysaccharides to glucose. Glucose itself combines with oxygen during respiration, catalysed by the action of enzymes in the body oxidizing the glucose molecule. This effectively reverses the process of photosynthesis and releases the stored energy for use by the cells of the body, producing carbon dioxide and water as by-products.

$$C_6H_{12}O_6 + 6O_2 \xrightarrow[\text{Energy release}]{\text{Enzymes}} 6CO_2 + 6H_2O$$

OPTION

243

A staple food is one that is generally available all year round and forms the basis of a diet. Staple foods vary around the world, but are typically inexpensive and consist of grains and vegetables such as wheat, potato, corn, barley, sago, rice and milk.

Rice tends to form the basis of a staple diet in Asia, while wheat, rye and barley are used in Europe. Corn and potato based dishes are common in central and South America. North Africa also uses corn, in addition to root vegetables such as yams and cassava.

Such foods provide a source of starch and carbohydrate. Carbohydrates, basically sugar and starch, break down in the body to form glucose molecules. Used as energy, carbohydrates fuel the body. Excess glucose is converted into glycogen and stored in the liver and muscles as an energy reserve.

Low income communities across the developed world maximize their energy intake per dollar through the consumption of high carbohydrate diets. In many developed nations highly processed, energy-rich foods high in refined carbohydrate, fat (and often salt) and low in fibre are cheaper per calorie than the healthy alternatives, such as fresh fruit, vegetables, lean meat and fish. Lower incomes force families to make the choice between quality and quantity. International research literature describes this phenomenon as, 'the economics of food choice'.

Even in developing nations such as Africa, cassava, has proven a popular cultivar due to its drought resistance and tolerance of poor quality soils. However, the protein content of cassava is typically around 1%. Diets high in carbohydrates such as cassava may place individuals and population groups at risk of inadequate protein intake. While the consumption of plant-based staples provide many of the body's dietary requirements, supplementation with high protein foods such as legumes, meat and fish in the diet may still be required.

Without carbohydrates, fats burn incompletely, causing byproducts, (ketone bodies), to accumulate in the

bloodstream. While the amount of carbohydrate required to avoid ketosis is very small (about 50 g/day), carbohydrate provides the majority of energy in the diets of most people. In addition to providing easily available energy for oxidative metabolism, carbohydrate-containing foods are vehicles for important micronutrients, phytochemicals and assist in maintaining gastrointestinal integrity and function.

Unlike fat and protein, high levels of dietary carbohydrate, provided it is obtained from a variety of sources, is not associated with adverse health effects. High carbohydrate diets opposed to those high in fat, also reduce the chances of obesity.

Researchers debate the benefits and hazards of low and high carbohydrate diets. Some claim low carbohydrate diets cause muscle depletion through the consumption of glycogen stored in muscles and the liver. Others promote low-carbohydrate diets to deliberately create the condition of ketosis in the body. Proponents of this form of diet maintain properly managed, the body will thrive on dietary proteins and fats, as well as stored body fats, and glycogen thus sparing the muscles.

Lipids are organic molecules that are insoluble in water (i.e. hydrophobic), they include fats, waxes, sterols (such as cholesterol), fat-soluble vitamins (such as vitamins A, D, E and K), monoglycerides, diglycerides, phospholipids, and others. The main biological functions of lipids include energy storage and the protection of body tissues and organs.

Fats and oils are made from two kinds of molecules: glycerol (a type of alcohol with a hydroxyl group on each of its three carbons) and three fatty acids joined by dehydration synthesis, illustrated in Figure A.3.11a. Since there are three fatty acids attached, these are known as triglycerides. The lengths of the fatty acids making up the triglycerides can vary from 11 to 20 carbon atoms. Many naturally occurring fats contain a number of different triglycerides, leading to a range of melting temperatures.

The main distinction between fats and oils is whether they're solid or liquid at room temperature, and this is based on differences in the structures of the fatty acids they contain. Figure A.3.11b shows the solid saturated fat butter and a polyunsaturated oil at room temperature.

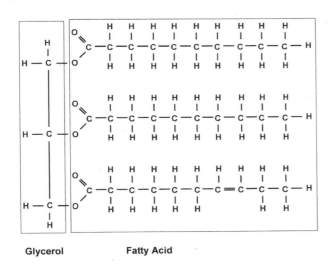

Figure A.3.11a Molecules forming fats and oils

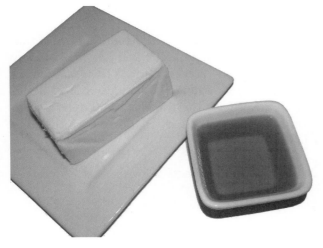

Figure A.3.11b A solid saturated fat (butter) and an unsaturated fats (olive oil) at room temperature

Glycerol is an organic compound, also known as glycerin or glycerine, and consists of three carbon atoms with an hydroxyl group attached to each for a molecular formula of $C_3H_5(OH)_3$. Its molecular structure is shown in Figure A.3.11c. Glycerol is soluble in water, due to the presence of the hydroxyl groups. Used in the food industry as a sweetener and thickening agent.

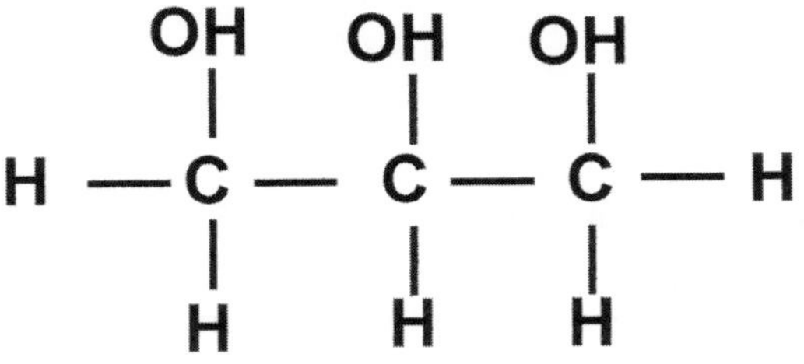

OH   OH   OH

H —C— C — C —H

H   H   H

Figure A.3.11c Molecular structure of Glycerol

Fatty acid is a carboxylic acid consisting of an unbranched aliphatic chain. The term aliphatic refers to the fact that the structure does not contain a benzene ring but are instead linear in nature. Fatty acids can be classified as either saturated or unsaturated fatty acids.

Saturated fatty acid originates primarily from animal sources and is characterized by a linear structure in which single bonds are present between the carbon and hydrogen atoms of the hydrocarbon chain, as illustrated in Figure A.3.11d. Since the structure contains the maximum possible number of hydrogen atoms, these fats are called saturated fats. Because of the single bond nature of these fats the hydrocarbon chains are fairly straight and can pack closely together, making these fats solid at room temperature. The saturated fats have been implicated as a factor in the development circulatory disease and are known to raise the level of LDL (Bad) cholesterol and reduce the levels of HDL (good) cholesterol.

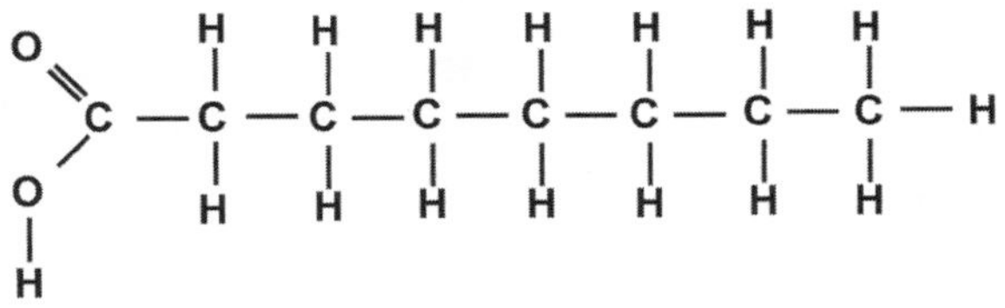

Figure A.3.11d Molecule forming saturated fat

Unsaturated fatty acid originates primarily from vegetable sources and is characterized by the presence one or more double bonds between carbon atoms in the chain. Those with one double bond are known as Monounsaturated, while those with two or more double bonds are Polyunsaturated. Because of the presence of double bonds in the structure, the maximum number of hydrogen atoms can no longer be present leading to the description of an unsaturated fatty acid.

Because of the double bond, the unsaturated fatty acids can be found with two slightly different configurations, depending upon the position of the hydrogen bonds attached to the carbon atoms on either side of the double bond.

If both hydrogen atoms are on the same side of the chain, the structure is referred to as being in the Cis configuration illustrated in Figure A. 3.11e. This asymmetric configuration tends to result in a slight kinking of the molecule as the adjacent hydrogen atoms either side of the double bond repel each other. The presence of this kink reduces the closeness of packing that can be obtained and leads to these fats being liquid at room temperature.

Figure A. 3.11e Illustrating the Cis- configuration of an unsaturated fatty acid

If both hydrogen atoms are on opposite sides of the chain however, the structure is referred to as being in the trans configuration illustrated in Figure A. 3.11f. Because the hydrogen atoms associated with the carbon double bond are on either sides of the chain, there is no repulsion between adjacent hydrogen atoms and the chain remains straight. As a result, molecular packing is good and the trans-fats are solid at room temperature.

Figure A. 3.11f Illustrating the trans- configuration of an unsaturated fatty acid

The trans-fats are not naturally occurring and are typically created by the hydrogenation of vegetable oils during industrial processing to produce margarine. The trans-fats have been implicated as a factor in the development of circulatory disease and are known to raise the level of LDL (Bad) cholesterol and reduce the levels of HDL (good) cholesterol. Changes to the process have since been introduced to reduce the level of trans-fats in products such as margarine.

Essential fatty acids, or EFAs, are fatty acids that humans and other animals must obtain from specific food sources, because the body requires them but cannot self produce them itself. The term EFA refers to fatty acids required for biological processes, and not those that solely act as fuel. The omega 3 and omega 6 fatty acids, represent some of these essential fatty acids, they are required for normal growth but cannot be synthesised by the body and must be obtained from foods such as fish and green leafy vegetables.

A.3.12 Describe the role of lipids in the body.

© IBO 2007

When the fatty acids are not combined with another molecule they are referred to as 'free fatty' acids. The free fatty acids are an important source of energy in the body, particularly the heart and skeletal muscles, providing supplies of Adenosine triphosphate (ATP), used by the body to transport chemical energy within cells.

Most of the lipids found in food are in the form of triacylglycerols, cholesterol and phospholipids. A minimum amount of dietary fat is necessary to facilitate absorption of fat-soluble vitamins (A, D, E and K) and carotenoids. Humans and other mammals have a dietary requirement for the essential fatty acids omega-3 and omega-6 because they cannot be synthesized from simple precursors in the diet.

A.3.13 Identify major sources of lipids in the diet.

© IBO 2007

There are only two EFAs: alpha-linolenic acid (an omega-3 fatty acid), and linoleic acid (an omega-6 fatty acid). Almost all the polyunsaturated fat in the human diet is from EFA. Some of the food sources of ω-3 and ω-6 fatty acids are fish and shellfish, flaxseed (linseed), hemp oil, soya oil, canola (rapeseed) oil, sunflower seeds, leafy vegetables, and walnuts.

A.3.14 Discuss the effects of low and excess lipid intakes.

© IBO 2007

Excessive lipid intake raises cholesterol and triglyceride levels above normal, inducing thrombosis, obesity and carbohydrate intolerance. Low lipid intake however can lead to a decrease in HDL (good) cholesterol and lead to a lack of antioxidant vitamins E and A. It is therefore necessary to focus on the qualitative aspects of dietary fats rather than just the effects of a low fat diet on reducing cholesterol.

A.3.15 Define vitamins and minerals.

© IBO 2007

Vitamins represent a group of essential organic nutrients that are required for the regulation of chemical reactions in the body. Deficiencies in vitamins can lead to a disruption of metabolic function. Vitamins can be divided into two basic groups based on the medium (either water or fat) in which they dissolve in the body.

Minerals consist of a number of non-organic substances that are required for healthy development of body structures such as bones and teeth, as well as normal bodily function. The minerals required by the body can be divided into two groups based on the quantities (bulk or trace) required.

- Bulk: Calcium, Chlorine, Magnesium, Phosphorus, Potassium, Sodium

- Trace: Copper, Chromium, Fluorine, Iodine, Iron, Manganese, Molybdenum, Selenium, Zinc

A.3.16 Describe the role of water-soluble vitamins (vitamin B complex, vitamin C) in the body and their food sources.

© IBO 2007

The water soluble vitamins consist of the B-complex group and Vitamin C.

The B-complex group consists of : thiamin (vitamin B1), riboflavin (vitamin B2), niacin, vitamin B6, folate, vitamin B12, biotin and pantothenic acid. These vitamins are widely distributed in foods. (See Figure A.3.16a).

Functioning as coenzymes, (helping the body obtain energy from food), they influence many parts of the body assisting with maintaining appetite, quality of vision, healthy skin and red blood cell formation. With the exception of B12, these vitamins are not stored in the body and must be continuously supplied through the diet.

Our bodies cannot make vitamin C and the human body has a limited capacity for its storage. With the body requiring a constant supply, we must consume foods containing this vitamin daily. Vitamin C-rich foods include citrus, kiwifruit, peppers, asparagus, broccoli, brussels sprouts, cabbage and tomatoes. Research suggests vitamin C may reduce the risk of certain cancers, heart disease and cataracts. The degree of its beneficial effects in these areas is yet to be fully determined.

Water soluble vitamins can be easily destroyed or removed from the food source in preparation or storage phases. Simple storage and preparation methods can reduce vitamin loss in food including:

- refrigeration of fresh produce
- shielding milk and grains away from strong light
- using vegetable cooking water as a stock base for soups.

Water-soluble vitamins can easily enter the bloodstream by diffusion, since the stomach contents, extracellular fluid, and blood plasma are all aqueous solutions. The specific role of each vitamin in the body is also summarized in Figure A.3.16.

A.3.17 Describe the role of fat-soluble vitamins (vitamins A, D, E, K) in the body and their food sources.

© IBO 2007

The fat soluble vitamins are stored in the body's fatty tissue and the liver and are not readily excreted in urine. They are not absorbed in the body unless fat digestion and absorption proceed normally. Fat-soluble vitamins can be consumed together with dietary fat to be absorbed. The vitamins are first dissolved in the dietary fat. Then, bile released from the gall bladder acts like a detergent and allows the fat (with the vitamins dissolved in it) to be solubilized in micelles. Figure A.3.17 documents the role and sources fat-soluble vitamins.

A.3.18 Describe the effects of deficiency of water-soluble vitamins on the body.

© IBO 2007

Because the water soluble vitamins (Vitamin C and B group), are easily lost from the body and need to be replenished regularly, a deficiency can develop relatively quickly.

Vitamin C deficiency was a particular problem historically for seafarers on long voyages, where the lack of access to fresh fruit and vegetables meant that a Vitamin C deficiency could develop, leading to Scurvy. This was typified by swelling and bleeding of the gums, bruising under the skin, lethargy and ultimately death. The importance of Vitamin C appears to have been known in China since the 5th Century where ginger was included in the diet. The West appears to have been aware of the need for fresh fruit and vegetables from the 17th century but, due to a reluctance to accept the additional costs, neglected to include them in ships' provisions, with the result that Scurvy remained a problem while cheaper options were trialled. The English Naval officer Lt James Cook, on his three voyages of discovery in the Pacific between 1768 and 1780, famously insisted on including sauerkraut and fruit juice among the ships' provisions, with the result that no sailors were lost to the disease.

OPTION

Water Soluble Vitamins

Nutrient (Vitamins)	Needed for	Key sources
Vitamin B1 (Thiamin)	• supplying energy to tissues • breaking down and using the energy and nutrients in carbohydrates, proteins and fats • nerve function	Fortified breakfast cereals, baking flour, wholegrains, wheatgerm, yeast, legumes, nuts, pork.
Vitamin B2 (Riboflavin)	• obtaining energy from food • making Vit B6 active in the body • reducing a key cardiovascular risk factor • production of red blood cells and body growth	Milk, cheese, yoghurt, fortified breads and breakfast cereals.
Vitamin B3 (Niacin)	• obtaining energy from food • breaking down and using carbohydrates, proteins and fats and their building blocks • maintaining healthy skin and nerves • releasing calcium from cellular stores	Beef, pork, liver, beans, wholegrain cereals, eggs, cow's milk.
Vitamin B6 (Pyridoxine)	• breaking down, using and reforming the building blocks of proteins	Muscle and organ meats, fortified breakfast cereals, brussel sprouts, green peas, beans, split peas, and fruit.
Biotin(B7)	• breaking down and using the building blocks of fats and proteins	Meats and cereals. *Note: eating raw egg whites prevents absorption of biotin.*
Vitamin B12 (Cyano-cobalamin)	• normal nerve function • normal blood function	Beef, lamb, fish, veal, chicken, eggs, milk and other dairy products.
Pantothenic acid	• making, hormones, vitamin A and D and substances that help make nerves work • helps make new fats and proteins in the body	Chicken, beef, potatoes, oat-based cereals, tomatoes, egg yolks, whole grains.
Folate	• breaking down and using the building blocks of proteins • the processes of tissue growth and cell function • maintaining good heart health • preventing neural tube defects in newborns	Cereals, cereal products, vegetables eg broccoli, legumes and fruit eg oranges.
Vitamin C (Ascorbic acid)	• protects against oxidative damage • aiding absorption of iron and copper • formation of collagen • healthy bones • helps fight infection • helps regenerate and stabilise other vitamins such as vitamin E or folate	Blackcurrants, orange, grapefruit, guava, kiwi fruit, raspberries, sweet peppers (Capsicum), broccoli, sprouts.

Figure A.3.16 Summary of the role of the water soluble vitamins in the body.

Fat Soluble Vitamins

Nutrient (Vitamins)	Needed for	Key sources
Vitamin A	• maintaining normal reproduction • good vision • formation and maintenance of healthy skin, teeth and soft tissues of the body • immune function (has anti-oxidant properties).	Milk, cheese, eggs, fatty fish, yellow-orange vegetables and fruits such as carrots, pumpkin, mango, apricots, and other vegetables such as spinach, broccoli.
Vitamin D	• absorption of calcium and phosphorus • maintenance of calcium levels in blood • immune function • healthy skin • muscle strength	Sunlight on skin allows the body to produce Vitamin D. Few foods contain significant amounts however main dietary sources are fortified margarine, salmon, herring, mackerel, and eggs.
Vitamin E (Tocopherol)	• acts as antioxidant particularly for fats • keeping heart, circulation, skin and nervous system in good condition	Oils and margarines, fats of meats, chicken, fish, wheat germ, spinach, cashews, peanuts, almonds, sunflower seeds.
Vitamin K (phylloquinone)	• normal blood clotting	Kale, collards, spinach, salad greens, cabbage, broccoli, brussel sprouts, egg yoke, bananas, kiwi fruit, soybean oil, canola oil, margarines

Figure A. 3.17 Summary of the role of the Fat soluble vitamins in the body

The first chemical compound to be identified as Vitamin C, is also known as Ascorbic Acid derived from 'a - scorbutus' meaning no scurvy.

Vitamin B1 (Thiamine) deficiency can lead to Beri-Beri, a disease of the peripheral nervous system. Symptoms include appetite loss, fatigue, irritability, depression, nausea, limb and abdominal pain, congestive heart failure, oedema.

Vitamin B2 (Riboflavin) deficiency can lead to cracks at corners of mouth, dermatitis around nose and lips and Keratitis, an ulceration of the cornea.

Vitamin B3 (Niacin) deficiency can lead to Pellagra. Symptoms include skin rash, diarrhoea, depression and dementia leading to death. Parts of Africa which depend on corn for a large part of their diet can suffer from a Niacin deficiency, as corn is the only grain that does not contain Niacin.

Folacin (folic acid) deficiency leads to Anemia; smooth tongue; diarrhoea.

Vitamin B12 deficiency leads to pernicious anemia, anemia, neurological disorders; degeneration of peripheral nerves that may cause numbness and tingling in fingers and toes.

Biotin deficiency is uncommon under normal circumstances, but can lead to fatigue, loss of appetite, nausea, vomiting; depression, muscle pains and anemia.

A.3.19 Describe the effects of deficiency or excess of fat-soluble vitamin intake.

© IBO 2007

Although the body stores the fat-soluble vitamins for an extended period, those suffering from malnutrition may develop a number of diseases related to their deficiency. Similarly, because the fat-soluble vitamins are stored within the body's fatty tissue and are eliminated from the body relatively slowly, a toxic level of these vitamins can build up if an excessive intake occurs. This may result if mega dose vitamins are used incorrectly, leading to hyper vitaminosis.

Because the absorption of Vitamin A depends on the presence of lipids in the diet, low fat diets can lead to

OPTION

malabsorptive disease, when Vitamin A ingested is not fully utilized.

Due to its role in the formation of metabolites needed for sight and its influence on the immune system, a deficiency in Vitamin A can lead to night blindness, and the formation of corneal ulcers, a reduced ability to fight infection and diarrhoea. The highest incidence of Vitamin A deficiency occurs in Southeast Asia and Africa. Vitamin A deficiency exposes children to a greater risk of dying from common infectious ailments such as measles, malaria or diarrhoea. While vitamin A deficiency is rare in the developed world, it is still the leading cause of irreversible blindness in children worldwide. Those following a Vegan diet may need vitamin A supplements to meet their daily requirements.

Vitamin A toxicity (Hypervitaminosis A) typically results from mega dose vitamin A supplements. Too much vitamin A can result in a loss of appetite, headaches, irritability, liver damage, bone pain, and neurological problems, including brain damage. An excess of Vitamin A leading to poisoning has occurred when Arctic explorers have eaten the liver of polar bears or sled dogs.

Vitamin D deficiency can lead to Rickets (long, soft bowed legs) and flattening of the back of the skull. In adults, Vitamin D deficiency is termed osteomalacia and manifests itself in the form of weakness in muscles and bones. Vitamin D deficiency has also been associated with an increased risk of; common cancers, autoimmune diseases and hypertension. Oversupply of vitamin D may cause weight loss, vomiting, irritability, destructive deposits of calcium in soft tissues like the kidneys and lungs and possibly fatal kidney failure.

Vitamin E deficiency, is a very rare problem even though our body stores limited amounts of vitamin E, because vitamin E is derived from both food and bacterial synthesis in our intestine. Some of the symptoms however include decreased sensory perception, muscle weakness and scoliosis. These symptoms can usually be reversed using Vitamin E supplementation.

Vitamin K deficiency may occur when the absorption of fat and related substances is abnormal. It can result in impaired blood clotting, easy bruising, nosebleeds, bleeding gums, blood in the urine and stools. Deficiency in infants may be life-threatening.

A.3.20 Describe the functions and sources of minerals.

© IBO 2007

Minerals are naturally occurring, homogeneous inorganic solid substances having a definite chemical composition. In contrast to vitamins, minerals do not contain the element carbon in their chemical makeup. Minerals play two major roles in the body acting both to form the hard structural parts consisting of the bones and teeth while also playing an important part in the cell function. For example, minerals are required for the transport of oxygen in the blood, and the regulation of heartbeat and blood pressure. Figure 3.20 describes role of the minerals in the body.

A.3.21 Discuss the effect of low or excessive intake of calcium and iron.

© IBO 2007

With the possible exception of iron and calcium, mineral deficiencies are rare among healthy people in developed nations.

Calcium is instrumental in the building and maintenance of bone. A constant intake of calcium is therefore required to maintain bone density. Inadequate intake can lead to the degenerative bone disease, osteoporosis. Calcium in the blood also helps regulate cholesterol levels and blood pressure. Bone stores of calcium may be used to bridge short-term dietary deficiencies, however, over the long term these bone stores can become depleted causing weakening of the bones, nerve and muscle impairment. Dietary deficiency is rarely the cause of low calcium levels, and is more commonly the result of a disruption to the body's regulating mechanisms or other causes such as insufficient levels of Vitamin D. A calcium deficiency can also be associated with some forms of hypertension, prostate and colorectal cancer and some types of kidney stones.

Because the gastrointestinal tract maintains limits to calcium levels, toxicity is rare, however if it does occur, due to long-term exposure, symptoms may include abnormal deposition of calcium in soft tissues. Very high levels of calcium can result in appetite loss, nausea, vomiting, abdominal pain, confusion, seizures, and even coma.

The World Health Organization considers iron deficiency the number one nutritional disorder in the world with up to 80% of the world's population exhibiting some degree of iron deficiency, while 30% may have iron deficiency anemia.

Nutrient (Vitamins)	Needed for	Key sources
Calcium [1]	• development and maintenance of bones and teeth • good functioning muscles and nerves • heart function	Milk, cheese, yoghurt, bony fish, legumes, fortified soy beverages and fortified breakfast cereals.
Chromium	• enhancing the action of insulin to regulate blood sugar	Widely found in foods such as yeast, eggs, meat, whole grains, cheese.
Copper	• the functioning of several enzymes • formation of connective tissue • iron metabolism and blood cell formation • nervous system, immune system and cardiovascular system function	Organ meats, seafood, nuts, seeds, wheat bran cereals, whole grains.
Fluoride	• healthy teeth and bones	Fluoridated water, fish, tea.
Iodine [2]	• normal thyroid function (important in the growth and development of central nervous system) • energy production • oxygen consumption in cells	Salt water fish, shellfish, seaweed, iodised salt, vegetables (if there is iodine in the soil where they are grown).
Iron [3]	• Haemoglobin in red blood cells (important for transport of oxygen to tissues) • component of myoglobin (muscle protein)	Red meats – beef, lamb, veal, pork, fish, chicken and wholegrain cereals.
Magnesium	• the functioning of more than 300 enzyme systems • energy production • regulating potassium levels • the use of calcium • healthy bones	Green vegetables, legumes, peas, beans, lentils, nuts, wholegrains and cereals
Manganese	• healthy bones • carbohydrate, cholesterol and protein metabolism	Cereal products, tea, vegetables.
Molybdenum	• breakdown of proteins	Legumes, wholegrain products, nuts.
Phosphorus	• forms part of DNA and RNA • buffers the acidity of urine • protection of acid/base balance of blood • storage and transport of energy • helps activate some proteins	Widely distributed in natural foods eg dairy, meat, dried fruit, eggs, cereals.
Potassium [4]	• nerve impulses • muscle contraction • regulates blood pressure	Leafy green vegetables, tomatoes, cucumbers, zucchini, eggplant, pumpkin, root vegetables. Also moderately abundant in beans, peas, bananas, avocados, milk, yoghurt
Selenium	• antioxidant • thyroid metabolism • part of several functional proteins in body	Seafood, poultry, eggs and to a lesser extent other muscle meats and cereal foods (content varies widely with soil condition).
Sodium [5]	• maintain water balance throughout the body • nerve impulses • transport of molecules across cell walls	Found in most take-away and processed foods eg bread, butter, margarine, deli meats, cheese, cereals. It is also a major component of table salt and baking soda
Zinc	• component of enzymes that help maintain structure of proteins and regulate gene expression • needed for growth, immunity appetite and skin integrity	Beef, pork, lamb, shellfish, wheat germ, milk, cheese, nuts, avocado.

Figure A.3.20 Summary of the role of minerals in the body

OPTION

Iron deficiency can be associated with a low dietary intake of foods rich in iron, such as meat, or problems associated with poor absorption. In this respect, the gastrointestinal tract is also important in the uptake of iron by the body since most iron is absorbed in the small intestine. Gastrointestinal disorders can therefore lead to low absorption of iron, leading to an iron deficiency. An Iron deficiency can lead to anemia, typified by fewer and smaller red blood cells than normal, resulting in symptoms such as fatigue, breathlessness, pallor of hands and eyelids, fainting. Individuals undergoing dialysis treatment, females of child bearing age and children are most at risk of developing iron deficiency anemia, while adult males and menopausal women have a low risk of iron deficiency.

An apparent iron deficiency can be caused by a deficiency of Vitamin A, which is necessary to mobilise iron stored by the body.

Pernicious anemia, in which the red blood cells are larger than normal by poor absorption of vitamin B12 due to a lack of intrinsic factor, secreted by the parietal cells of the stomach lining.

Iron excess is a greater risk than iron deficiency, with even a small amount of excess iron potentially leading to gastrointestinal distress, heart attack or stroke.

A.3.22 Define micronutrient deficiency and malnutrition.

© IBO 2007

Micronutrient deficiency refers to a deficiency of those nutrients that, while required in only small (or trace) amounts, are essential for healthy growth and development. Common Micronutrient deficiencies involve iron, iodine, Vitamin A, folic acid and zinc. Those most vulnerable to micronutrient deficiency are pregnant women and young children.

Iron (present in red meat, fish and whole grain cereals) deficiency can result in anemia and insufficient production of haemoglobin to transport oxygen in the blood, leading to fatigue. (RDA 7-18µg/d pregnancy 27µg/d).

Vitamin A (present in dairy products, fish and vegetables) can lead to poor vision, diarrhoea and lowered immunity to disease. Poor absorption of Vitamin A may result from low levels of fat or oil in the diet.

Iodine (present in shellfish and iodized salt) deficiency in pregnancy has long been linked to intra-uterine brain damage and possible foetal wastage. It is an essential

element for the proper functioning of the thyroid gland. (RDA 90-150µg/d pregnancy 220µg/d).

Folate (present in green vegetables and fortified cereals) deficiency can lead neural tube defects in a developing foetus.

Zinc (present in shellfish and green leafy vegetables) is essential for the normal function of the immune system. (RDA 3-11µg/d pregnancy 12µg/d).

Malnutrition is the insufficient intake of nutrients, either through an unbalanced diet or digestive disorder that reduces absorption of nutrients from a diet. Malnutrition can arise even if adequate supplies of food are available to prevent hunger if that food is deficient in adequate levels of nutrients, such as vitamins and minerals.

Some people have digestive disorders that limit the absorption of nutrients from food, such as those indicated below.

Celiac disease: sensitivity to gluten found in cereal crops such as wheat. An immune response to the gluten causes damage to the villi in the intestine.

Lactose intolerance: inability of the body to break down lactose in the diet (present in dairy products). Lactose not broken down in the small intestine travels to the large intestine where bacteria digest it producing gases and acid leading to abdominal pain, flatulence and diarrhoea.

Crohn's disease: an autoimmune disease in which the body's immune system typically attacks the lining of the large intestine (Colon), although it may occur anywhere along the gastrointestinal tract, causing inflammation and ulceration. Decreased food consumption due to pain means that patients often suffer from malnutrition.

Social and psychological factors also lead to malnutrition through eating disorders, such as those indicated below.

Anorexia Nervosa: represents an eating disorder in which the sufferer has a distorted view of their body image, in which they believe they are overweight when, in fact, they are dangerously underweight. Sufferers avoid food and often engage in strenuous exercise in an attempt to continue losing weight. While affecting both sexes adolescent girls make up the largest group to be affected and often follows a period of illness or dieting.

Bulimia Nervosa: Similar to Anorexia in some respects, Bulimia sufferers attempt to maintain control over their weight by restricting their food intake. In contrast to Anorexia, those suffering from Bulimia may eat normally or even binge eat before purging the food by vomiting or taking laxatives.

The effects of Anorexia and Bulimia are similar and include excessive weight loss, dry skin, hair loss, and anemia. Vomiting can lead to loss of tooth enamel and oesophagus damage.

While those suffering from an eating disorder may recover unaided in time, those affected often require hospitalisation in order to stabilise weight and obtain professional counselling to affect a recovery. Left untreated these conditions can lead to death through organ failure including cardiac arrest, depression and suicide.

> **A.3.23** Explain what is meant by a balanced diet and how various food-group systems can be used to help achieve a balanced diet.
>
> © IBO 2007

A balanced diet is one in which all the nutritional needs for a healthy body are being provided. While individual requirements will vary with age and levels of physical activity, a number of guidelines have been developed to simplify the process of creating a balanced diet.

One of the most well known of these is the Food Pyramid developed by the US Department of Agriculture (USDA) in 1992 in order to provide some dietary guidance to reduce diet related diseases such as coronary heart disease. The pyramid developed is shown in Figure A.3.23a. The Food Pyramid divides food into six basic groups consisting of:

- breads and cereals
- vegetables and fruits
- dairy and protein
- fats and oils.

The position on the pyramid represents the amount of each group that should make up a healthy diet, with those at the base forming a good foundation for a balanced diet and those at higher positions on the pyramid being required in lesser quantity.

The food pyramid had the advantage of being easy to understand although a number of compromises were required to achieve this simplicity. One of these compromises was that both saturated fats (associated with animal products) and polyunsaturated fats (associated with plants and fish) were both grouped together as fats and oils at the top of the pyramid. Similarly, red meat and fish were grouped together, even though it was known at the time, that it was the intake of saturated fats and trans-fats (made from the hydrogenation of polyunsaturated

oils to make them solid), that were implicated in coronary heart disease rather than the polyunsaturated and monounsaturated fats. The USDA pyramid also aggregated all complex carbohydrates at the bottom of the pyramid, even though highly processed carbohydrates such as white rice are more easily processed by the body and can lead to obesity. Similarly potatoes were also grouped with other vegetables despite being high in starch and easily metabolised.

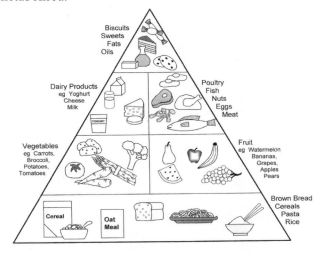

Figure A.3.23a The food Pyramid introduced in 1992 by the United States Department of Agriculture USDA

In order to accommodate some of the research into healthy eating and a balanced diet accumulated since 1992, Willett & Stampfer (2003), published a modified version of the food pyramid that left saturated fats at the top of the pyramid while introducing poly and monounsaturated fats at the base to recognise the beneficial effects of these fats on reducing the ratio of High Density Lipoprotein (HDL) to Low Density Lipoprotein (LDL). They also redistributed potatoes and refined carbohydrates such as white bread and rice to the top of the pyramid, as illustrated in Figure A.3.23b.

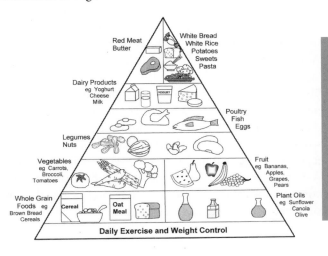

Figure A.3.23b Alternative food Pyramid suggested by Willett & Stampfer (2003)

Both of the pyramid guides are of necessity generalized and simplified by their nature, as they do not take into account differences in gender and age, although specific versions of the pyramids to cater for these concerns could be produced.

In 2005, the USDA created a new advisory guide to healthy eating and, although they maintained the symbolism of a pyramid, avoided a fixed image of food portions. Instead, they created 'MyPyramid.gov', a Web based calculator that uses information about gender, age and height, (weight optional), to provide a guide to a healthy diet.

The logo for this guide, shown in Figure A.3.23c, no longer uses the hierarchy of food groups of previous representations, but suggests a balance, while the figure climbing the stairs conveys the need for exercise, a feature of the Willett & Stampfer pyramid.

Figure A.3.23c USDA 'My Pyramid' logo for the 2005 guide to a balanced diet [MyPyramid.gov]

'Five a day'

The 'five a day' programme was developed on advice from the World Health Organization in 1990, that a diet rich in fruits and vegetables such as those shown in Figure A.3.23d was beneficial for a healthy diet.

To this end, it was recommended that at least five 80g portions of fruits and vegetables should be included in the daily diet. It was suggested at the time, that such a diet would have a beneficial effect of reducing cancer, although it has since been found that such benefits are marginal. A benefit was however found in reducing obesity and coronary heart disease if the fruits and vegetables are substitutes for higher calorie foods.

Figure 3.23d Five a day system

'The plate system'

A number of systems are available that use a plate as a visual indication of the portion size and food groups that should be included daily to achieve a balanced diet. Two of these are the 'Eat Well Plate' and the 'Diet Plate®' shown in Figures A.3.23.e and f respectively.

The systems are very similar, as might be expected, although some differences exist, with the following general divisions indicated:

- between one quarter and a third of the plate = high starch foods such as bread, rice, potatoes and pasta,
- between one fifth and a quarter of the plate = high protein foods such as meat fish and eggs,
- between one fifth and a quarter of the plate = dairy foods such as milk, cheese and yoghurt,
- remainder = fruit and vegetables.

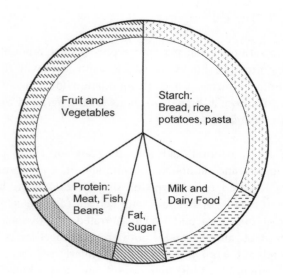

Figure A.3.23e The Eat Well Plate

One of the major differences between the two concepts is that while both illustrate the division of food groups that should be included in a healthy diet the 'diet plate®' system uses a physical plate of the sort illustrated in Figure A.3.23f, to help control portion sizes, with the sauce circle being used as a measure of pasta or rice portions.

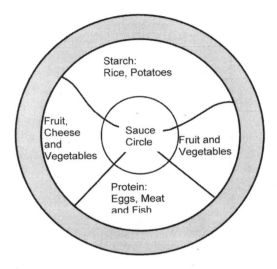

Figure A.3.23f The diet plate system

A.3.24 Explain how nutritional requirements and food choice change as a person gets older.

© IBO 2007

As we age, our nutritional requirements also changes as our energy requirements change.

In infancy a period of rapid growth requires a high energy intake along with protein, vitamins and minerals for growth and development. This need for high nutritional intake continues through adolescence, as rapid growth continues along with the onset of hormonal changes associated with puberty.

During pregnancy females have additional requirements for the minerals calcium and iron and the vitamins A and Folic acid to assist in the development of the baby, while maintaining a healthy nutritional intake for the mother.

With old age, energy requirements decline substantially, due largely to a reduction in physical activity. At this time physiological changes associated with aging can arise reducing the efficiency with which the body previously absorbed nutrients. The onset of age related diseases and an increase in the use of medication can also affect both the desire to eat and the metabolising of food. The changes in nutrient requirements with age are outlined in Figure A.3.24.

Life Stage	Change in Nutrient Needs
Pregnance*	**Increased requirements:** energy protein, essential fatty acids, vitamin A, vitamin C, B-vitamins (B1, B2, B3, B5, B6, B12, folate, choline) & calcium, phosphorous**, magnesium, potassium, iron, zinc, copper, chromium, selenium, iodine, manganese, molybdenum.
Lactation*	**Increased requirements:** vitamins A, C, E and B-vitamins, sodium, magnesium** **Decreased requirements:** iron
Infancy childhood	**Increased requirements:** energy, protein, essential fatty acids
Adolescence	**Increased requirements:** energy, protein, calcium, phosophorous, magnesium, zinc, (females only)
Early adult (ages 19-50)	**Increased requirements for males compared with females:** vitamins A, K, B1, B2, B3, and choline; magnesium, zinc, chromium, manganese **Increased requirements for females compared with males:** iron
Middle ages (ages 51-70)	**Increased requirements:** vitamin B6, vitamin D
Elderly (age 70 +)*	**Increased requirements:** vitamin D **Decreased requirements:** energy; iron (females only)

* Relative to adult requirementfor those 19-50 tears of age ((and on a per kg basis for macronutrients)
** Applies only to individuals under age 18

Figure 3.24 Change in nutrition requirements with age.

(Source: Nutritionmd Nutritional Requirements Throughout the Life Cycle)

A.3.25 Identify the nutrient content of typical foods

© IBO 2007

Figure 3.25 identifies nutritional content for a range of common foods. Foods are listed from all of the major food groups and for an identified quantity, data is provided on:

- iron
- energy
- total fat
- protein
- calcium
- sodium
- total sugar
- saturated fat
- carbohydrates
- poly unsaturated fat
- mono unsaturated fat
- DHA Omega 3 fatty acid cholesterol.

food	Weight	Energy	Protein	Carbohydrate	Total sugar	Total fat	Saturated fat	Mono unsaturated fat	Poly unsaturated fat	DHA, Omega 3 fatty acid	Cholesterol	Calcium	Iron	Sodium
	g	kJ	g	g	g	g	g	g	g	g	mg	mg	mg	mg
Salmon-smoked	40	196	7	0	N/A	2	0.4	-	0.4	0.11	9	4	0.3	314
Tuna canned in water	75	364	19	0	N/A	1	0.2	-	0.3	0.17	23	8	1.1	254
T- Bone, Steak, - Lean	75	903	22	0	N/A	13	5.6	6.6	0.4	N/A	54	N/A	2.1	51
Pork Tenderloin - Lean, roasted	75	452	21	0	N/A	2	0.8	0.9	0.4	N/A	52	N/A	1.0	44
Chicken Breast - Roasted	75	499	25	0	N/A	2	0.4	0.5	0.3	N/A	64	N/A	0.4	56
Tofu - Silken soft	75	345	7	4	2	4	0.5	0.8	2.3	N/A	-	47	1.2	8
Baked Beans - Canned	188	738	9	40	17	1	0.2	0.2	0.2	N/A	-	64	2.2	633
Hummus - Commercial	57	394	4	8	-	5	0.8	2.3	2.1	N/A	-	22	1.4	215
Peanut Butter - Natural	31	770	7	7	1	16	2.2	7.8	4.9	N/A	-	17	0.7	2
Burrito beef, cheese & chilli	152	1322	20	32	N/A	12	5.2	-	-	N/A	85	111	3.9	1046
Spaghetti with meat sauce	262	1678	19	50	9	14	4.5	-	-	N/A	56	101	4.7	1008
Butter	5	144	Tr	Tr	-	4	2.5	1.0	0.1	N/A	10	1	Tr	28
Milk, whole	258	647	8	12	14	8	5.4	-	-	N/A	26	291	0.1	103
Yoghurt - drinkable	207	607	5	24	24	3	2.1	-	-	N/A	12	191	0.2	81
Cheese, Brie	50	699	10	Tr	Tr	14	8.7	-	-	N/A	50	92	0.3	315
Jams, preserves	20	234	Tr	14	10	Tr	Tr	Tr	Tr	N/A	0	4	0.1	6
Potato chips - plain	43	964	3	21	-	15	1.8	-	-	N/A	0	9	0.7	229
Cola- carbonated	262	461	Tr	28	24	0	0	0	0	N/A	0	8	0.1	10
Bread, white - commercial	35	389	3	18	2	1	0.3	-	-	N/A	0	53	1.3	238
Peas, green, - canned	90	260	4	11	4	Tr	-	-	-	N/A	-	18	0.9	226
Potato, no skin - boiled	135	486	2	27	1	Tr	-	-	-	N/A	-	11	0.4	7
Tomato, raw	123	92	1	5	3	Tr	-	-	-	N/A	-	12	0.3	6
Orange	131	258	1	15	12	Tr	-	-	-	N/A	-	52	0.1	0
Rice, white - boiled	83	454	2	24	Tr	Tr	0.1	0	-	N/A	-	8	0.2	1
Corn Flakes - Kellogg's™	26	430	2	23	2	Tr	0	-	-	N/A	0	2	4.4	192
Weetabix™	35	543	4	29	2	1	0.1	-	-	N/A	0	14	1	126

Figure A.3.25 Nutrient content of selected foods

[Extracted from http://www.hc-sc.gc.ca/fn-an/alt_formats/pdf/nutrition/fiche-nutri-data/nvscf-vnqau-eng.pdf]

OPTION

A.3.26 Discuss how health awareness affects food choice with reference to fat (quality and quantity), fibre, sugar and salt content.

In many countries, governments have initiated healthy lifestyle programs in an effort to better inform consumers about healthy food and lifestyle choices. The coupling of lifestyle advice with legislation requiring manufacturers to provide consistent product information that is easily interpreted and which allows for direct product comparison, is a powerful tool for both manufacturers and consumers.

Product information in the form of food labels carry information helping consumers to make food choices, as shown in Figure A.3.26. Depending on the food and the legislative requirements labels list additives, ingredients and nutrition information such as fat, fibre and protein content, sugar and salt intake, as well as cholesterol levels. Foods that have a shelf life of less than two years must also carry a 'use-by' or 'best before' date. Food labels can help people with food allergies, and may also make nutrition and health claims. A food label should list the country of origin of the food product, but this statement is not always easy to interpret.

Approx. serving per pack: 1		Avg. serving size: 320g	
	Avg. Quantity Per serving	% Daily Intake Per serving**	Avg. Quantity Per 100g
Energy	1560kg 371 Cal	18%	486kJ 116 Cal
Protein	18.9g	38%	5.9g
Fat - Total*	12.5g	18%	3.9g
- Saturated	2.9g	12%	0.9g
- Trans	<0.3g		<0.1g
- Polyunsaturated	2.6g		0.8g
- Monounsaturated	7.0g		2.2g
Cholesterol	0.3mg		0.1mg
Carbohydrates	43.8g	14%	13.7g
- Sugars	14.1g	16%	4.4g
Sodium	864mg	38%	270mg
Calcium	102mg	13%	32.0mg

Figure A.3.26 Nutrition label showing fat, fibre, sugar and salt content

A.3.27 Discuss the social impacts resulting from a change from traditional diets and the effect on consumer health.

Societal changes such as employment, work patterns, ease of transportation and communication have effected, among other things, diets and eating patterns.

While Paleo-biologists claim the shift from traditional hunter-gatherer societies to other forms of settlement have resulted in dietary changes that have impacted on the overall health of communities over generations, until recently, a traditional Western diet was arranged around the pattern of three meals a day with snacking in between. Mealtimes were opportunities for families to gather, especially for the evening meal and maybe even breakfast. More complex work patterns mean individuals within households may all eat at separate times.

Today, cheap, high calorie, food is readily available, often high in fat, salt and sugars, as well as being low in fibre. This dietary change has arisen through a greater reliance on convenience or pre-prepared meals and so called 'fast foods'. Busy lifestyles and the habit of purchasing the quickest and cheapest food available does not necessarily make a nutritious meal. Microwave technologies have also allowed for the fast preparation of highly processed foods in the home. Kitchens and dining rooms have been replaced as preferred eating areas by lounge rooms, bedrooms, cafes or grabbing food 'on the run' outdoors.

These dietary changes. along with a generally more sedentary lifestyle have led to a rapid rise in obesity in many western cultures such that, in 2010, the World Health Organization (WHO) reported that, 'Globally, there are more than 1 billion overweight adults, at least 300 million of them obese.' With the rise in obesity an increased risk of chronic diseases also occurs, including type 2 diabetes, heart disease, hypertension, stroke, and certain forms of cancer.

Further Reading

Black, R. (2003). *Micronutrient deficiency—an underlying cause of morbidity and mortality.* Bulletin of the World Health Organization, 81(2), p 79.

de Benoist, B. (2007). *Preventing and controlling micronutrient deficiencies in populations affected by an emergency.* World Health Organization.

Price W. A. (2002). *Nutrition and Physical Degeneration: A Comparison of Primitive and Modern Diets and Their Effects.* A Project Gutenberg of Australia ebook.

Méndez C. D., and Benito, C. G. (2008). *Food, Consumption and Health*, Social Studies Collection No. 24, The 'la Caixa' Foundation, Barcelona.

Miller, G.D. et.al. (2009). *It Is time for a positive approach to dietary guidance using nutrient density as a basic principle.* Journal of Nutrition, Vol.139, pp1-5.

OPTION

A.4 FOOD SPOILAGE AND FOOD PRESERVATION

Foods are described as spoiled if irreversible organoleptic changes (relating to taste, sight, smell, and touch) make them unacceptable to the consumer. Changes may take the form of changes in appearance (discolouration), the development of off-odours, slime or mold formation. Such changes can be caused by physical, chemical and microbiological means.

Any damage sustained by the natural protective layer of a food (such as the skin of an apple), or to its artificial packaging, can result in spoilage through chemical and microbiological changes.

Physical Spoilage – is the result of a physical injury or disruption to the natural protective layer or packaging that subsequently leads to the food being exposed to changes in its environment (e.g. humidity, temperature, air, etc). Once exposed, the food is more susceptible to spoilage from chemical and microbiological factors.

Chemical Spoilage - chemical reactions within the food are responsible for changes in the colour and flavour of foods and begin to occur after harvesting or slaughtering and continue through processing and on to storage. These reactions lead to deterioration in the original food structure. The two major chemical changes that occur are lipid oxidation (rancidity) and enzymic reaction.

Microbiological Spoilage – is the result of the growth of microorganisms such as yeasts, moulds and bacteria. Microorganisms in the air can settle on food. They can remain, due to inadequate removal of soil or animal waste, or they can be transferred to the food by poor sanitation or contaminated water. Once present, these microorganisms will grow and multiply changing the smell, taste and colour of the food.

The two major chemical changes that occur during the processing and storage of foods and which lead to a deterioration in sensory quality are lipid oxidation (rancidity) and enzymic reaction. Chemical reactions are also responsible for changes in the colour and flavour of foods during processing and storage.

Enzymes are organic catalysts that are produced by the cells of animals, plants, or bacteria. Foods, including plants and animals have their own enzyme complement. They help speed up or slow down chemical reactions. In many fruits and vegetables the enzyme polyphenoloxidase undergoes a redox reaction, producing the familiar browning of the surface, (Figure A.4.4a), and is responsible for up to 50% of the losses of fruit and vegetables.

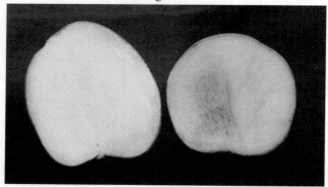

Figure A. 4.4a Enzymatic browning

Typically phenol oxidase enzymes catalyse these reactions. These oxidase enzymes react with phenol compounds and oxygen to form undesirable brown colour pigments on the food product. For example, the enzymes in a tomato help it to ripen and further enzymes produced by the tomato cause softening and staining. The final stage of the enzymatic reaction is that fungal and bacterial spoilers on it cause it to decay or rot, as shown in Figure A.4.4b.

Figure A.4.4b Rotten tomato due to enzymatic reaction

Enzymic action is clearly visible in a ripening banana. The change from green to yellow to black is evidence of enzymatic activity. Similar activity is seen in maturing apples, peaches and tomatoes. Enzymic activity may however be halted through the application of heat, hence blanching operations performed on some vegetables.

Bacteria also produce enzymes that break down food, allowing them to obtain nutrients through their cell walls. Therefore, lowering the temperature reduces the rate of enzyme action, as well as the rate at which bacteria can multiply. In this way refrigeration increases the time required to spoil food. As the number of bacteria increases, the amount of enzymes produced increases. Higher temperatures can cause increased enzymatic activity. With large numbers of bacteria and high temperatures, a food will spoil very rapidly. When bacterial contamination is high and the storage temperature is low, a food will keep for a moderate period of time; when the bacterial contamination is low and the storage temperature high, food will keep for a moderate period of time. However, if the contamination of bacteria is low and the storage temperature kept low, the food product will have the longest possible shelf life.

Many foods contain carbohydrates in the form of sugars, while others contain amino acids in the form of proteins. Some foods (such as raw meat and bread dough) contain both sugars and amino acids. The Maillard reaction, a form of browning which happens due to non-enzymatic activity was named after French chemist Louis-Camille Maillard. It occurs through the addition of heat.

When bread dough or meat is introduced to a hot oven, a complex chemical reaction occurs on the surface. The carbon molecules contained in the sugars, or carbohydrates, combine with the amino acids of the proteins. This combination cannot occur without the additional heat source. The end result of this chemical recombination is the Maillard reaction. The surface of the heated bread dough is now brown, as is the outer layer of the roasted meat.

Not only do the combined sugars and amino acids change the appearance of the food, but they change the flavour as well. The Maillard reaction is responsible for the savoury flavour of roasted meats, as well as the toasted flavour of baked breads. It is also associated with loss in nutritional value, along with the browning and change in the texture of food products.

Specifically, when bread is placed in a toaster, the Maillard reaction causes the outer layer of carbohydrates and proteins to combine. The result is a piece of browned toast (Figure A.4.5). Recipes containing both eggs, which contain protein, and flour, which contains carbohydrates, benefit from the Maillard reaction to achieve a pleasing browned appearance.

The Maillard reaction is not limited to the food sciences. Self-tanning products also rely on the reaction between amino acids and sugars to create a brown skin tone.

One of the main reasons that older photographs develop brown spots is the Maillard reaction. The albumin-based photographic process used in early photography often reacts negatively to heat and light exposure over time, causing brown patches to form.

Figure A.4.5 Maillard browning of toast

A.4.6   Describe three types of rancidity, and outline how rancidity can be prevented.

© IBO 2007

Most fats and oils can develop unfavourable flavours and odours known as rancidity. Rancidity can be caused by several factors:

- absorption rancidity
- oxidative rancidity
- hydrolytic rancidity

Absorption Rancidity: When oils and fats are stored next to strong smelling foods e.g. onions or garlic or products such as paints, detergents and disinfectants. The smell is absorbed by the fat or oil, making it unpleasant to eat.

Oxidative Rancidity: Oxygen from the air can oxidize unsaturated fats producing objectionable flavours. This is the most important and common type of rancidity. In this process the long-chain fatty acids are degraded and short-chain compounds are formed. One of the reaction products is butyric acid, which causes the typical rancid taste.

Hydrolytic Rancidity: This is caused by the presence of water. The hydrolysis split the fat into glycerol and fatty acids. The rate of hydrolysis in the presence of water alone is negligible but can be accelerated if enzymes (lipases) and micro-organisms (bacteria, moulds and yeasts) are present. As a result, the oil/fat develops a soapy taste/texture. This is a less common type of rancidity but is quite common in emulsion systems such as butter, margarine and cream.

> A.4.7   Explain the importance of rancidity in the shelf life of food products.
>
> © IBO 2007

The prediction of shelf life is based on an estimation of the rate of chemical reactions at the temperature of storage and assumes a number of environmental factors, such as humidity, oxygen content of the atmosphere, and exposure to sunlight.

In order to delay the process of rancidity and improve shelf life, packaging is designed to reduce exposure to sunlight and protect the product from the general environment. In addition, antioxidants are often included along with antimicrobial agents to delay the growth of bacteria.

> A.4.8   Define water activity (a_w).
>
> © IBO 2007

Water activity (a_w) is a measure of the amount of unbound water in a food. That is, it is a measure of the water in food that is not bound to food molecules, and is available to support the growth of bacteria, yeasts and fungi. If this unbound water is reduced below certain levels microbial growth can be stopped.

Water activity is calculated as the ratio of the water vapour pressure in food to the water vapour pressure of pure water under the same conditions, where a value of zero represents the 'bone dry' condition and 1.0 is pure water.

> A.4.9   Describe the importance of water activity in microbial spoilage.
>
> © IBO 2007

Because water activity (a_w) can be related to the growth of bacteria, yeasts and fungi responsible for food spoilage it is a critical measurement to determine and to control shelf life of the food product. The water activity of most fresh foods is 0.99. In order to prevent the growth of micro-organisms in a food, the water activity of the food must be reduced. The level to which water activity needs to be reduced to slow the growth of a number of micro-organisms is indicated in Figures A.4.9a and b.

Micro-organism	a_w
Clostridium botulinum	< 0.93
Staphylococcus aureus	< 0.86
Yeast	< 0.75
Mould	< 0.70

Figure A.4.9a Water content (a_w) below which growth of various micro-organisms stops

> A.4.10 List the major reasons for preserving foods.
>
> © IBO 2007

Extended safe storage life

Foods are preserved to prolong their shelf life. As soon as animals have been slaughtered, or plant foods have been harvested, deterioration of these products begins. This involves the breakdown of cells due to the presence of enzymes and the disruption of cell structure due to micro-organisms, causing the changes in odour, flavour, colour and texture of food.

Safety

Many processing techniques ensure the safety of foods by reducing the numbers of harmful bacteria that can cause

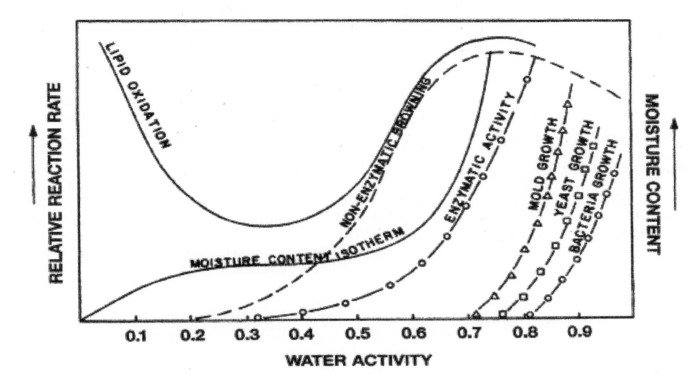

Figure A.4.9b Stability map of foods as a function of water activity.

[Labuza, T. P. (1979). A theoretical comparison of losses in foods under fluctuating temperature sequences. Journal of Food Science, 44(4), pp1162-1168.]

illness (e.g. pasteurisation of milk). Drying, pickling and smoking reduce the water activity (i.e. water available for bacterial growth) and alter the pH of foods and thereby restrict the growth of pathogenic and spoilage micro-organisms and retard enzyme reactions. Other techniques such as canning, pasteurisation and Ultra-High Temperature (UHT) destroy bacteria through heat treatment.

Acceptability

The organoleptic (sensory) quality of some foodstuffs benefits directly from processing techniques. For example, baked beans derive their creamy texture from the heat treatment during canning. Extruded and puffed products like breakfast cereals or crisps would be almost impossible to make without large scale modern food processing equipment.

Nutritive value

Processing, such as freezing, preserves the nutrients that are naturally present in foods. Other processes, like cooking, can sometimes improve the nutritional value by making nutrients more available. For example, cooking and canning tomatoes to make tomato paste or sauce

renders the bioactive compound lycopene more available to the body

Availability

The limited shelf life and seasonal nature of many foods means that availability requires some form of preservation.

Economic Viability

Similar to availability, the shelf life limitations of many foods has required the use of various food preservation techniques to ensure that products maintain their quality during transport to markets with sufficient shelf life to be bought by consumers. Today, food production is often on a large scale to reduce costs and markets can be not only in a nearby town, but thousands of kilometres away.

A.4.11 Describe five methods of preserving food, including chilling, irradiation (pasteurization, sterilization, canning), vacuum packing, use of acids and preservatives, and removal of water (dehydration, use of sugar and/or salt).

© IBO 2007

Freezing and Chilling

By reducing the temperature of food, microbial growth is inhibited, freezing, stops or slows bacterial growth brought about by enzymes present in the foods. Fast or 'snap' freezing in commercial plants enable foods to retain more of their natural appearance and taste. Quick freezing prevents the formation of large ice crystals, reducing damage to the cell walls of the food and preventing textural changes that would otherwise occur on thawing. Most foods can be preserved by freezing for long-term preservation, however, short term preservation may be obtained by chilling food between 0 to 5°C to reduce growth of micro-organisms. A variety of freezing techniques are employed including:

- plate-freezing - food packed between refrigerated plates
- blast freezing - food is exposed to a blast of air at - 40°C
- immersion freezing - food is immersed in a refrigerant such as brine
- fluidized bed freezing - refrigerant passed through a bed of small particle size food such as peas
- cryogenic freezing - food is exposed to cryogenic temperatures using liquid nitrogen or carbon dioxide (-78°C).

Heat Treatment (Pasteurization, Sterilization, Canning)

Heat treating of food is achieved by exposing it to elevated temperatures for a defined period of time with the aim of inactivating micro-organisms. Heat treating processes include pasteurization, sterilization and canning.

Pasteurizing is a process used in the treatment of food to kill pathogenic micro-organisms and involves heating food to a temperature below boiling point (72°C). At this temperature the majority of micro-organisms are eliminated yet bacteria and yeasts are unharmed.

Sterilization uses high temperatures in order to try and kill all micro-organisms e.g. UHT milk

Canning was an invention of Nicolas Appert in response to a prize offered by Napoléon in 1795, Originally developed for preserving fruits and vegetables during long sea voyages, the process used glass jars. The canning process still known as 'Appertization' is named after him. The process was later commercialized by Peter Durand, (1910), using metal cans. These cans would later prove to be problematic due to the toxic nature of the lead used to solder cans together.

Canning has a similar aim to sterilization with the food being sealed in an airtight container which has had the air excluded. The process involves heating the contents of the can to a high temperature before sealing and cooling. As the sealed can and its contents cool a vacuum is formed excluding oxygen and bacteria.

Irradiation

The process of food irradiation involves exposing food to an ionizing radiation source such as:

- Gamma-rays from the nuclides; Co-60 or Cs-137
- X-rays generated from 5 MeV machine sources
- electron beams generated at or below 10 MeV.

Food treated in this fashion has agents of spoilage such as bacteria and insects eliminated. Irradiation requires less human handling of foodstuffs and therefore reduces the risk of contamination. Because irradiation does not heat the treated material, frozen or dried products also retain their physical state. This makes the process just as applicable for dried herbs as it does frozen fish. Irradiation slows the ripening of fruit and, in conjunction with refrigeration, extended shelf life can be achieved. The process is relatively energy efficient when compared to other food preservation techniques. It also reduces the need for food additives and fumigants, the reduction of which is also advantageous for factory workers packaging food. Irradiation techniques are regularly used to extend the shelf life of strawberries.

Although the colour and texture of some fruit and vegetables may be affected, irradiation does not make food radioactive. A summary of the application of irradiation to a number of food products is provided in Figure A.4.11a.

Benefit	Dose (kGy)	Products
Low – dose (up to 1 kGy)		
(i) Inhibition of sprouting	0.05 – 0.15	Potatoes, onions, garlic, root ginger, yam etc.
(ii) Insect disinfestation and parasite disinfection	0.15 – 0.5	Cereals, and pulses, fresh and dried fruits, dried fish and meat, fresh pork, etc
(iii) Delay of physiological processes (e.g. ripening)	0.25 – 1.0	Fresh fruits and vegetables
Medium – dose (1 - 10 kGy)		
(i) Extension of shelf-life	1.0 – 3.0	Fresh fish, strawberries, mushrooms etc.
(ii) Elimination of spoilage and pathogenic microorganisms	1.0 – 7.0	Fresh fish and frozen seafood, raw or frozen poultry and meat, etc.
(iii) Improving technological properties of food	2.0 – 7.0	Grapes (increasing juice yield), dehydrated vegetables (reduced cooking time), etc.
High – dose (10 - 50 kGy)		
(i) Industrial sterilization (in combination with mild heat)	30 – 50	Meat, poultry, prepared foods, sterilized hospital diets.
(ii) Decontamination of certain food additives and ingredients	10 – 50	Spices, enzyme preparations, natural gum, etc.

Figure A.4.11a Food irradiation applications

[Facts about food irradiation, International Consultative Group on Food Irradiation, 1999]

Vacuum packed

Foods such as meat or cheese are packed in impermeable plastic material, and the air is sucked out under vacuum, as shown in Figure A.4.11b. This method prevents the growth of aerobic micro-organisms because of the absence of oxygen.

Figure A.4.11b A view of a range of vacuum packed foods

Modified atmosphere packaging (MAP):

This form of packaging is a relatively recent development and involves the creation of a package in which an atmosphere is created with modified proportions of carbon dioxide, oxygen, nitrogen, water vapour and trace gases that retards the growth of micro-organisms. Products such as bacon, red meat, poultry and vegetables use this method to increase the shelf life of the product. Examples of typical products employing MAP technology are shown in Figure A.4.11c.

Figure A.4.11c Food packaging using MAP

The combination of gases chosen and their relative proportions are determined by the food to be protected and is largely dependent on the process of decay or change the process is attempting to inhibit.

Acids and Preservatives

Micro-organisms grow rapidly in specific ranges of pH, outside these ranges however their growth is severely restricted. It has been known for centuries, that food could be preserved for long periods of time if submerged in an acidic (low pH) environment such as that provided by vinegar, a modern example of which is shown in Figure A.4.11d. The low pH environment prevents the growth of micro-organisms.

Figure A.4.11d Preservation in vinegar

The addition of some chemicals to food can also act to slow down or prevent the process of oxidative rancidity, and inhibit bacterial growth , such as benzoic acid, sulfur dioxide, sodium nitrite and ethanol.

Removal of Water (dehydration, use of sugar and/or salt)

Dehydration is the removal of moisture from food by exposure to the sun, although low temperature drying in a controlled air environment is often used today. As indicated previously, (section A.4.9), the presence of water has a significant influence on the microbial spoilage of food, thus the removal of water can have a significant influence on the shelf life food.

Ancient peoples are known to have had dried fruits, vegetables, and meats. The Pemmican of Native Americans and the jerky consumed by present-day campers and hikers are both prepared by drying. The drying process can include smoking, which may actually add antibacterial agents. Modern of processes of dehydration and freeze-drying used today to produce such foods as powdered coffee and soup are variations of drying.

Among the earliest preservatives were sugar and salt (NaCl). These produced food environments of high osmotic pressure that denied bacteria the aqueous surroundings they needed to live and reproduce.

Sugar is traditionally used in the manufacture of jams and the canning of fruit. Sugar in concentrations exceeding

50% stops the growth of most microorganisms that cause spoilage. Through the creation of a syrup, high in sugar, there is less water available for the growth of micro-organisms. Jams and jellies are preserved as solutions of high sugar content, and many meats (e.g., hams) and fish are still preserved by salting. Unlike other microorganisms, moulds can often withstand the effects of high salt or sugar concentrations in foods. Fortunately, they seldom cause illness.

Salt draws moisture from food, consequently, less water provides less opportunities for microorganisms to grow. Salt also reduces enzymic activity. In this fashion, salt has been used for centuries, to prolong the shelf life of meats such as beef and bacon as show in Figure A.4.11e.

Figure A.4.11e Beef jerky

A.4.12 Explain how food preservation methods affect the organoleptic properties of foods.

© IBO 2007

Toward the end of the shelf life of a product, it can be expected that the organoleptic characteristics such as taste, texture, colour or smell may be changing. These changes are the result of microbial growth and typically begin to be detected at the levels indicated in Figure A.4.12a.

Micro-organism	Count
Bacteria	≥ 10 million/gram
Yeast	$\geq 100,000$/gram
Mould	Visible

Figure A.4.12a Typical threshold levels of microbial growth for changes in organoleptic properties

Method	Type	Action	Effect on Organoleptic Properties
Low temperature	Freezing and Chilling	Slows enzyme activity of microbial growth	Texture changes may occur. Some fruits may become mushy due to collapse of cell walls due to ice crystals
Irradiation	Gamma radiation (Cobalt 60)	Kills Microbes	No Change Although not suitable for all fruits and vegetables due to changes in colour and/or texture.
Heat Treatment (Pasteurization, Sterilization, Canning)	Pasteurization	Kills most Microbes	Milk shows no effect. Some products show reductions in their natural organoleptic properties while other such as cereals often derive their familiar organoleptic properties from processing eg puffed rice.
	Sterilization	Kills Microbes	May affect taste and appearance gaining a sweet taste from caramalisation of natural sugars
	Canning	Kills Microbes	May benefit some products eg baked beans gain a 'creamy' texture during canning
Vacuum packing	Vacuum	Water removal leads to reduction in microbial growth	No change Refrigeration is also required
Acids and Preservatives	Acid Pickling eg Vinegar	Low pH reduces enzyme activity of microbes	Produces a sour taste
	Common Preservatives: Sorbic Acid (E200-E203] Benzoic Acid [E210-213] Sulfur dioxide [E220-228] Potassium & Sodium Nitrate [E249-E250] Propionic Acid [E280-283]	Reduces enzyme activity or disrupts microbe cell wall	Nitrates produce a reddish colour in meats
Drying	Salt	Draws water from microbes by process of osmosis	Alters the cellular structure of food, alters texture and taste.
	Sugar		Adds characteristic flavours to food
	Spices		
	Temperature eg Sun drying		May intensify flavours in fruit
Smoking	Smoke	Chemicals in smoke kill microbes. May be followed by drying	Applied to meats such as bacon and fish. Produces a smoky taste.

Figure A.4.12b Common methods of food preservation and changes in organoleptic properties

In order to delay microbial growth and extend shelf life preservatives are added to food. A summary of common methods of food preservation and effects on organoleptic properties is presented in Figure A.4.12b.

> **A.4.13** Explain how food preservation methods affect the nutritional properties of foods.
>
> © IBO 2007

Preservation by its nature aims to extend the shelf life of a material as well as maintain its nutrient value. Depending on the method used some are more successful than others. Over time vitamin and mineral quality will often degrade but, in some cases, foods actually become more nutrient dense.

During the freezing process water content turns to ice. In its entirety, (freezing, storing, thawing) this process may cause a loss of 20-25% of nutrients in fruits and vegetables. Dehydrated foods, reconstituted by cooking in water, may incur further loss of nutrients through leaching out. As a result of dehydration or drying, between 10-25% of water soluble vitamins, such as vitamin C, will be lost while at the same time sugars turn to starch and carbohydrates will become more dense. Dehydrating also has the effect of concentrating fibre.

Salting increases nutrient density when used as a drying process. When used as a solution treatment through immersion in brine, nutrient density decreases.

Canned foods, having gone through pressure cooker like preservation, have their nutrient value significantly reduced. Water soluble vitamins, in particular, are sensitive to high temperatures. Many people believe that canned foods are not as nutritious as their fresh counterparts; however, this is not always the case, as fresh food often deteriorates more rapidly than canned foods.

Pickling or fermenting processes are commonly employed to preserve foods such as wine, bread, cheese, miso and pickles. While there is some loss of vitamins and minerals, overall the influence of fermentation is positive for our health. The nutritional value of Vitamin B may be increased as part of the process as well as antibacterial and digestive properties.

The heating of milk to destroy micro-organisms using the process of Pasteurisation leaves the nutrient value of milk largely unaffected. In the case of Pasteurised fruit juices however, some losses of Vitamin C may occur.

Method	Effect on Nutritional Properties
Freezing and Chilling	Some vitamins may be lost during thawing.
Yeast	No change
Heat treatment (Pasteurization, sterilization, canning)	Reductions in nutritive value can be expected especially of ascorbic acid, Vitamin C and B group vitamins during sterilisation.
Vacuum packing	No change
Acids and Preservatives	
Drying	Retinol (vitamin A), thiamin (B1), ascorbic acid (C), and vitamin E - lost

Figure A.4.13 Effect of various preservation methods on nutritional properties

Further Reading

Astyk, S. (2009). *Independence Days: A Guide to Sustainable Food Storage & Preservation*. New Society Publishers. Canada.

Branen, A. L. (2002). *Food Additives, 2nd edition*. Marcel Dekker. New York.

Madison, D. (1999) *Preserving Food without Freezing or Canning: Traditional Techniques Using Salt, Oil, Sugar, Alcohol, Vinegar, Drying, Cold Storage, and Lactic Fermentation*. Chelsea Green Publishing Company. White River Junction Vermont.

Rahman, M. S. (2007). *Handbook of Food Preservation, Second Edition (Food Science and Technology)*. CRC Press. Florida.

van Kooi J., *Food preservation by irradiation*, IAEA Bulletin Vol. 23 (3), pp33-36.

van Kooij, J., *Food preservation makes progress*, IAEA Bulletin Vol. 26 (2), pp17-21.

A5 FOOD SCIENCE

A 5.1   Describe the role of sugar and artificial sweeteners in the design of food products.

A 5.2   Identify two artificial sweeteners.

Figure A.5.1b Image of common artificial sweeteners

Artificial sweeteners are used to replace sugar for two reasons: they have less or no calorific value, and they are cheaper to produce. Due to the increasing demand for low calorie food products, the use of sugar replacement artificial sweeteners has increased.

A selection of commonly available artificial sweeteners on the market is presented in Figures A.5.1a and b. With the exception of Aspartame, the other sweeteners shown can have a slightly bitter aftertaste when used in large amounts. Other additives are often added to mask this taste.

Sucralose and Acesulfame Potassium are both stable under heat and a broad range of pH, so can be used in baking, compared to Saccharin and Aspartame which break down under heat and elevated pH.

Name	Brand Name	Sweetness by weight relative to Sugar	E Number
Acesulfame Potassium	Sweet One	200	E950
Aspartame	Nutrasweet Equal	160 - 200	E951
Saccharin	Sweet'N Low	300	E954
Sucralose	Splenda	600	E955

Figure A.5.1a Table of common artificial sweeteners

While all of the artificial sweeteners have been the subjects of some controversy regarding potential carcinogenicity, no credible scientific evidence has substantiated such a link and they remain approved for use by the US FDA along with agencies in Europe and Australia.

A 5.3   Describe the role of thickeners in the design of food products.

Thickeners are food additives used to increase the viscosity of liquids in a process called gelatinisation. A variety of common gelling agents are described below.

Agar-Agar (E406) is a unbranched polysaccharide extracted from red algae and is often used as a vegetarian alternative to gelatine. Agar melts at a temperature of 85°C and solidifies to a semi-translucent gel from 32-40°C. Used in desserts and jelly toppings for cakes.

Carrageenans (E407a) is a complex mixture of polysaccharides extracted from red seaweeds. Depending on the form of Carrageenan used, the gels produced vary from hard and brittle to soft and elastic.
Used in meats, desserts and glazes.

Pectin (E440) is a Polysaccharide obtained from apple residue and citrus peel. It has a long chain molecular structure that easily entangles, causing thickening in low sugar liquids. If sugar is added, water in the structure is displaced forming three dimensional gel networks that resist dissolution. In order to facilitate this reaction, a low pH environment is required. High sugar products, such as jam, use this process to form a sugar-acid-pectin gel. Gel hardness is dependent on the pH of the food, being softer at higher pH. Commonly used in jams.

Starch (Wheat flour, Corn flour, Arrowroot) In the presence of hot water the intermolecular bonds of starch molecules breakdown. The starch molecules then begin to attract water into the structure beginning the gelatinization process. As the starch particles absorb more water they swell in size, increasing the viscosity of the liquid. The temperature at which this begins varies depending on the

OPTION

267

source of the starch and can vary between 55° and 85°C. Used in gravies and stews

Gelatine/Gelatin (E441) is obtained through the hydrolysis of animal collagen and has a long-chained amino acid structure. The bonds connecting gelatine are easily broken on heating however, forming a liquid. On cooling, the bonds are easily reformed to create a translucent, tasteless gel with good elasticity. It does not require the use of sugar, salt or acid to set. Gelatine is used extensively as a gelling agent in soft gummy confectionary and desserts.

A.5.4   Describe the function of preservatives in food.

© IBO 2007

Food preservatives act to extend the life of food by reducing the rate of normal means of deterioration. Preservatives used in food can be divided roughly into three groups based on their action in suppressing decay. These are:

- Anti-microbial agents – reduce the growth of fungi, moulds and bacteria
- Anti-oxidative agents – prevents the oxidation of fats and oils
- Chelating agents – bind with ions of the metals copper and iron, preventing them from oxidizing and spoiling food.

A.5.5   List two commonly used food preservatives.

© IBO 2007

Some people are sensitive to the presence of chemical preservatives in food. Among the most commonly encountered is a sensitivity to the sulfites and benzoates. Sulfur dioxide (often used to preserve wines) can also cause irritation to those with asthma. Nitrites have also been implicated as carcinogens.

Two preservatives belonging to each of the three groups of preservative action are presented in Figure A.5.5.

Name	Chemical	Use	E No.
Anti-microbial	Potassium Benzoate	fruit juice, soft drinks, vinegar	E212
	Sodium Nitrate	Meat, fish	E250
Anti-Oxidative	Sodium Metabisulfite	Wine, beer	E223
	Butylated Hydroxyanisole	butter, meats, baked-goods, potato crisps	E320
Chelate	Disodium EDTA	Soft drinks	E385
	Sodium Polyphosphate	dips, freshly-peeled fruit	E425i

Figure A.5.5 Examples of commonly used food preservatives

A.5.6.   Describe the role of antioxidants in foods.

© IBO 2007

The oxidation of food results in the formation of free radical molecules that can subsequently lead to the oxidative damage of other molecules. Antioxidants act to stop this chain reaction inhibiting further oxidation damage.

A.5.7 List two commonly used antioxidants

© IBO 2007

In addition to those listed in A.5.4, two commonly used antioxidants are:

- Ascorbyl palmitate (E304) also known as 'Vitamin C ester', is a fat soluble form of Vitamin C used both as an antioxidant preventing the rancidity of vegetable oils and a source of Vitamin C.
- Sodium Ascorbate (E 301) is a water soluble salt of Ascorbic acid (Vitamin C) - preserves the colour of freshly cut fruits and vegetables.

A.5.8   Describe an emulsion.

A.5.9 List two examples of food emulsions.

An emulsion is a mixture of two immiscible liquids in which one liquid is suspended as a fine globular form within the other.

Oil-in-water emulsions are common in food. Notable examples include:

- Vinaigrette – vegetable oil in vinegar; if prepared with only oil and vinegar (without an emulsifier), yields an unstable emulsion

- Mayonnaise – vegetable oil in lemon juice or vinegar, with egg yolk lecithin as emulsifier.

A.5.10 Describe the role of emulsifiers in stabilizing food emulsions.

A.5.11 List two commonly used emulsifying agents.

Oil and water do not mix naturally but if they are 'forced' together by thorough mixing, they stay in an emulsion (in suspension) for a very short time. If left, they will separate out, with oil floating on top of the water. Emulsifiers are soluble in both fat and water. They enable fats and oils to be uniformly dispersed in water as an emulsion through the creation of a chemical bond to bridge the 'gap' between the two substances. Foods benefiting from the use of emulsion technology include butter, margarine, salad dressings, mayonnaise, and ice cream.

Egg yolk is one of the most common emulsifying agents and is commonly used in mayonnaise and hollandaise sauces. Albumin (egg white), casein, and gelatine are also popular emulsifying agents.

Further Reading

Artificial sweeteners myths
[Retrieved from http://www.canserwa.asn.au/resources/cancermyths/artificial-sweeteners-myths]

What is Pectin?
http://www.ippa.info/what_is_pectin.htm

Starch
http://www.food-info.net/uk/carbs/starch.htm

A6 FOOD PROCESSING

A.6.1   Define aeration, coagulation of protein and gelatinizing (gelling).

Aeration involves the incorporation of gas into a food product. This may be accomplished by the whipping or beating of a liquid protein such as egg whites to incorporate air or, the introduction of a gas such as carbon dioxide (CO_2), under pressure (carbonated drinks), or as a by-product of an aerating agent such as yeast or baking soda.

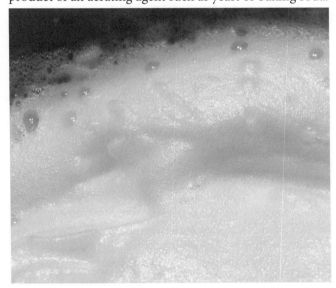

Figure A.6.1a Aeration of egg whites

Coagulation of protein occurs when the molecules of a liquid protein, such as those present in egg white, are exposed to heat or acid. This results an irreversible change occurring during which the molecules lump together leading to a reduction in solubility and change optical characteristics. Because it coagulates, egg protein is used in baking, along with flour and milk.

Gelatinizing (gelling) involves the formation of a gel through the use of gelatine or by the heat-treatment of starch and water to break open the starch granules. Starch gelatinization is often used to thicken liquids, such as custards and gravy, while gelatinization using gelatine, results in the formation of a jelly having a soft springy consistency, popular in desserts.

Figure A.6.1b Meringue formed by the aeration of egg whites and sugar that has been exposed to heat leading to protein coagulation and caramelization of the sugar

> A.6.2 Explain how the processes of aeration, protein coagulation and gelatinization have been used to affect the physical and/or chemical properties of bread.
>
> © IBO 2007

The production of bread has been undertaken from the earliest days of civilisation and is manufactured as a staple part of the diet throughout the world. While a wide range of varieties and recipes are available, there are two basic forms in which it is found - Leavened and Unleavened. A selection of leavened and unleavened breads is shown in Figure A.6.2a. Both forms of bread involve the production of dough made with flour, water and salt.

Figure A.6.2a Selection of different types of bread

Unleavened or flat bread does not allow the formation of any gases so that aeration does not occur. Leavened bread on the other hand, contains yeast in order to produce CO_2 gas and promote aeration. The gluten network in the dough, formed by the mixture of flour, salt and water is strong and elastic enough to contain the gas produced, resulting in a low density dough. When baked, the protein in the dough coagulates and the starch gelatinizes. When sliced, the bread exhibits a light airy structure, shown in Figure A.6.2b.

Figure A.6.2b Pores in bread are results of aeration

> A6.3 Explain the control systems used in the manufacturing process of bread.
>
> © IBO 2007

Production processes may be broken down into their component parts and organized in a linear fashion, generally comprised of three interrelated parts: input, process and output.

Input: Ingredients are gathered into bulk storage containers. These containers allow for direct, controlled distribution of the raw ingredients into mixing chambers. Sampling and testing of these ingredients is undertaken to ensure quality and consistency

Process: This stage represents those procedures involved in the conversion of the raw materials into a finished product. In bread manufacture this involves:

- mixing of the raw materials in large batches to form a dough
- resting of the batch in a temperature controlled environment to assist the yeast to rise
- removal of the batch from the mixer to be carefully divided into measured amounts
- rolling of each measure into a ball and resting to allow continued rise (proofing stage)
- placement in baking tins shapes the dough
- final proofing under precisely controlled temperature and humidity

- baking in ovens
- removal from ovens and cooling
- slicing operations if required.

Output: Loaves are packaged and prepared for distribution.

> **A.6.4** Outline the influence of scale of production on the organoleptic properties of bread.
>
> © IBO 2007

Commercially manufactured (or mass produced) bread contains a range of various preservatives and additives. So-called bread improvers are added to dough to reduce rising times and enhance bread volume and texture. Preservatives are added to improve overall shelf life.

Homemade (or small batch) bread production is often made with a specific consumer in mind. In this situation, greater control and variation of the product ingredients are obtained. Additives such as salt etc. may be carefully monitored and controlled.

Because bread manufactured in this fashion is made to order, preservatives are also not required to lengthen the product shelf life.

> **A.6.5** Explain how food processing enhances the value of food commodities.
>
> © IBO 2007

Historically, value adding came about from the need of producers to better preserve their produce for transport to markets. This may have taken considerable time and resulted in considerable loss due to deterioration.

In addition to this form of value adding, that extends the life of the raw material, consumers use these raw materials to produce new products, such as jams, bread, cakes, all the way to a finished meal. By processing the raw materials partially or completely into the final form desired by consumers, manufacturers add value to food commodities and gain the benefits of economy of scale, while providing convenience to the consumer.

In recent years an explosive growth has occurred in the production of pre-packaged ready to reheat and serve meals, along with the sale of meat and fish products

prepared and marinated in a variety of sauces ready for cooking.

Because of this value adding, the largest part of the 'food dollar' today is associated with the secondary processing.

> **A.6.6** Explain how on-farm processing can enhance farm sustainability.
>
> © IBO 2007

The pressures on the sustainability of farms come from a number of directions, ranging from perennial concerns about the weather and insects to increasing fuel and seed prices and market volatility. In order to provide some protection against these forces, many farms follow a diversified approach in which several different crops may be grown, along with some livestock.

In addition, a number of farms are adopting on-farm processing in order to retain more of the 'food dollar'. By processing some of their produce on the farm into a form desired by consumers, farmers are able to largely eliminate the 'middle-man' and add value to their produce. Such ventures often focus on niche markets and rely on direct marketing to businesses in local communities and tourists who are willing to support local growers and who appreciate the benefits of high quality, fresh products. On-farm processing might entail the milling of grain into flour, conversion of berries into jam or grapes into wine.

The rise of the Internet has given such ventures an added boost as on-line marketing and sales has greatly increased the reach and lowered the costs of operations. Although additional cost associated with processing and packaging can pose problems not normally encountered by farmers in their traditional role, this sort of value-added agriculture can be one way of preserving small farm enterprises while benefiting the local community.

Further Reading

Danielson R. and Park D. (2001) Value-added, *On-farm Processing, Summer's Harvest – Hope, North Dakota*, North Dakota State University.
[Retrieved from http://www.und.edu/org/ndrural/case%20study%2011.summer's%20harvest.pdf]

OPTION

271

A.7 FOOD PACKAGING AND DISTRIBUTION

A.7.1 Identify the functions of food packaging.

© IBO 2007

Food packaging serves a number of important functions. Among these is the purely functional requirement of containing the food product in a convenient form for transport, storage, display and purchase. More importantly perhaps, packaging allows the branding of the product. Through branding, packaging fulfils an important role in the marketing and promotion of products in the market place, by attracting the attention of consumers over and above that of competitor products. This is often achieved by appealing to emotional cues that establish and reinforce brand recognition and loyalty. It is this aspect of packaging that has lead to its description as the 'silent salesman' and resulted in packaging becoming an important part of the marketing process. It has been estimated that a product needs to be recognised by the consumer from a distance of 3 to 5 metres in less than 10 seconds if it is to be selected over its competition.

A brand can be anything that distinguishes the product from it competitors and may be a name, sign, logo, colour or symbol. The type or form of packaging required of course varies significantly, depending on the foodstuff. Some foods are provided with efficient primary packaging by nature, such as nuts, oranges, eggs and the like. In packaging this type of food product, only a secondary outer protection packing is required, for example a box, wrap or drum to hold units together, see Figure A.7.1a.

Other foods such as milk, dried eggs and fruit concentrates often will be filled into primary packaging containers such as plastic liners, which are then packaged within protective cartons or drums. In this case the secondary container provided by the carton or drum greatly minimises the requirements that must be met by the primary container. Examples of foods requiring secondary packaging are shown in Figure A.7.1b.

Except in special instances, secondary containers are not designed to be highly impervious to water vapour and other gases, especially at zones of sealing, dependence for this being placed upon the primary container.

Figure A.7.1b Examples of secondary packaging

Different food packaging materials can be fashioned into different types of food packages and containers. Examples are given in Figure A.7.1c.

Packaging type	Type of container	Examples of foods packaged
Aseptic packages	Primary	Fruit juice
Plastic trays	Secondary	Portion of fish
Glass Bottles	Primary	Bottle of a soft drink
Cardboard box	Secondary	Box of soft drink bottles
Plastic lined steel can	Primary	Tomato soup
Pulp cartons	Secondary	Carton of eggs

Figure A.7.1a Examples of foods with Primary packaging and which require only secondary protective packaging

Figure A.7.1c Examples of different forms of food packaging

A.7.2 Identify a range of materials used for food packaging.

A.7.3 Describe how different packaging materials affect food.

©IBO 2007

Food packaging styles vary enormously based on fitness for purpose, materials availability, technology, culture and point in time and target consumer. Traditional materials such as leaves and plant fibres are still in use today alongside metal cans, earthenware, textiles, cardboard and polymers.

Metal containers

There are two basic types of metal cans: those that are sealed using a 'double seam' and are used to make cans for canned foods; and those that have push-on lids or screw-caps that are used to pack dried foods or cooking oils respectively. Double-seamed cans are made from tinplated steel or aluminium and are lined with specific lacquers for different types of food in order to prevent contact between the contents and the metal surface that might otherwise cause corrosion and taint the food. The advantages of double seam cans over other types of containers is that they are impermeable to moisture, odours, light and micro-organisms, and provide an excellent barrier to gases.

Figure A.7.3a Metal food containers

Glass bottles and jars have some of the advantages of metal cans: they are impervious to micro-organisms, pests, moisture, oxygen and odours; they do not react with foods or have chemicals that migrate into food. The fragile nature of glass containers, however, can create some safety issues, and the cost of transporting is comparatively high.

Glass containers are still widely used for foods such as juices, wines, beers, pickles/chutneys and jams and are often preferred because the contents are visible. A selection of glass food containers are shown in Figure A.7.3b.

Figure A.7.3b Selection of products packaged in glass

Paper and cardboards are made from wood pulp with additives mixed into the pulp to give particular properties to the packaging. While made in a similar way, cardboard is thicker and stiffer than paper and is more resistant to damage. Several forms of paper and board are used in the food industry, depending on the application.

'Sulphate' paper is made using the Kraft process in which the wood pulp is treated with sodium hydroxide and sodium sulphide. The paper formed from this process is generally stronger than that made by other processes and finds use as sacking material for products such as flour, sugar and vegetables due to its strength. Kraft is German for strength.

'Sulphite' paper is made using the Sulphite process in which salts of sulphurous acid are used to create a pulp. The paper formed from the sulphite pulp is weaker than that formed by the Kraft process and finds use as grocery bags or is treated to be resistant to oils and greases.

Cardboard or paperboard packaging is a generic term for a stiff, heavy-duty paper and includes not only single thickness paper used to package foods such as cereal, but also the composite material formed by the sandwiching of corrugated paper between flat sheets and sometimes referred to as corrugated board.

White board is a high quality thick paper which is often coated with wax, or laminated with plastic, to make it heat sealable. It is commonly used for ice cream, chocolate and frozen food cartons.

A selection of products packaged in paper and cardboard is shown in Figure A.7.3c.

Figure A.7.3c Paper and cardboard packaging

Plastic and in general, flexible plastic films, have relatively low cost and good barrier properties against moisture and gases. They are heat sealable to prevent leakage of contents. Plastics add little weight to the product and fit closely to the shape of the food, thereby wasting little space during storage and distribution. They have wet and dry strength, are easy to handle and convenient for the manufacturer, retailer and consumer.

The main disadvantages are that, (with the exception of cellulose), they are produced from non-renewable oil reserves and are not biodegradable. Concern over the environmental effects of non-biodegradable oil-based plastic packaging materials has increased research into the development of 'bioplastics' that are derived from renewable sources, and are biodegradable. However, these materials are not yet available commercially in developing countries.

A range of plastics used for packaging are shown in Figure A.7.3d.

Figure A.7.3d Selection of products packaged in plastic

A.7.4 Explain the impact of alternative packaging decisions on product cost and the environment.

© IBO 2007

While many containers intended as single use disposable packaging items are found in the food industry, an increasing trend has been for such packaging to be replaced with biodegradable and/or recyclable materials such as cardboard. The move toward this packaging has been driven largely by community concerns about the damage to the environment represented by the non-biodegradable and non-recyclable packaging originally used, particularly polystyrene foam containers that were ubiquitous throughout the industry due to their ability to be used for both hot and cold foods.

While the production of cardboard itself is an energy intensive process when the ability to compost or recycle is taken into account, it becomes a much more environmentally friendly option.

A.7.5 Identify current developments in packaging.

© IBO 2007

With the aim of providing convenience products to the consumer, a number of developments have occurred in packaging.

Plastic bags have recently been introduced to provide a pre-packaged meal sized selection of salads. Rather than the consumer buying the individual components of the salad, which required subsequent washing and processing, a variety of salads are available ready for the plate with minimal waste. Small sachets of sauce and even plastic eating utensils may also be included to complete the presentation, as shown in Figure A.7.5a.

By sealing the salad vegetables in the bag using a technology known as MAP, (Modified Atmosphere Packaging), the atmospheric conditions within the plastic bag are controlled, slowing the rate of deterioration and allowing chilled storage for a period of time before use. See also section A.4.11. While some have criticised the appearance of such packaging on the grounds of reduced nutritional value and as a further sign of a convenience culture that further disconnects consumers from real produce, others have credited such innovations as leading to an increased consumption of salad vegetables.

Figure A.7.5a MAP packaging of ready to serve salad

Aseptic packaging also known as 'Tetra Paks' is the packaging method commonly used in the beverage and liquid food system. This method allows perishable food products to be distributed and stored without refrigeration for a long period of time. Foods such as milk, soup and fruit drinks are commonly packaged using this technology. An example of aseptic packaging is shown in Figure A.7.5b.

Figure A.7.5b Aseptic packaging of fruit drink boxes

Image by Tetra Pak (Tetra Pak[1]) [CC-BY-SA-3.0 (www. creativecommons.org/licenses/by-sa/3.0) or CC-BY-SA-3.0 (www.creativecommons.org/licenses/by-sa/3.0)], via Wikimedia Commons

The Tetra Pak system uses a laminate of several materials to provide an impermeable barrier. Approximately 70% of the thickness of the laminate is paper card, from which the carton gains its strength and rigidity. Approximately 24% of the packaging material is polyethylene plastic, provided to effect a sealable liquid-tight boundary on the inner layer, and a protective water-proof coating on the external surface. The remaining 6% of material is Aluminium film, which forms a barrier against light and oxygen, eliminating the need for refrigeration and preventing spoilage, without using chemical preservative. A section through a Tetra Pak wall is provided in Figure A.7.5c.

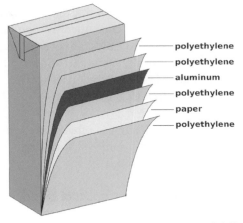

Figure A.7.5c Aseptic packaging with layers of different materials

A.7.6 Outline how food packaging is used as a promotional tool for other products.

In order to gain attention and create interest, food packaging often incorporates promotional techniques such as competitions, puzzles, recipes, in-package collectibles (cards, toys, etc). Cross-promotional packaging might also include reference to current events such as the Olympic games, or a recently released movie. The MacDonald's restaurant chain is perhaps the most famous of these with their popular child sized meal pack known as a 'Happy Meal' that incorporates a child-sized burger or wrap, drink and toy. The release of a new movie is often celebrated by promotional packaging and a toy character from the film, see figure A.7.6.

Figure 7.6 Cross-promotion packaging

A.7.7 Explain how packaging of food products contributes to the development of brands

Brand identity is regularly quoted as a company's most valuable asset. Product packaging and prominent brand placement allows a manufacturer to expand their product range while maintaining consumer recognition and loyalty over lesser-known brands. Innovative packaging can break this brand loyalty cycle and allow trial of new and different brands. Well-designed packaging also plays a role in facilitating impulse buying.

While the shape of packaging is often generic in nature to provide functionality, some shapes have become synonymous with their brand.

> **A.7.8** Discuss the global impact of branded products, for example, Coca-Cola®.
>
> © IBO 2007

Apart from yielding economies of scale, globalization pragmatically increases consumers around the world to develop similar preferences and speeds up a brand's time to market globally instead of local modifications

Global brands can have the effect of stifling competition and reducing diversity in the marketplace. They may also replace local brand names. The shift towards global brands is also attributed to the consumer's preference for brands with global image over local competitors, even when quality and value are not visibly superior

Research shows that, from a consumer's perspective, global brands: espouse quality, represent cultural or social ideals and come with expectations of ethical responsibility. In this case, global brands may be selected by consumers in the belief the products are of higher quality and the company possesses greater credibility. Ownership of globally branded products may convey prestige and social status in the eyes of many consumers.

Coca-Cola® is a global leader in the beverage industry. It offers hundreds of subsidiary brands involving itself in the soft drink, water, fruit juice and sports drink markets. It has a brand identity recognized the world over. It does this through carefully and consistently presented, standardized packaging and graphics.

It has not always been plain sailing for globally branded and marketed products. Anti-globalization campaigners have targeted the likes of Coca Cola®, Nestle® and Macdonalds®. Demonstrators have attacked transnational companies over their policies relating to exploitation of workers, pollution and the exporting of western corporate capitalism.

> **A.7.9** Describe the purpose of food labels and the information provided on them.
>
> © IBO 2007

Food labels are required by legislation and are designed to inform consumers and assist them in making an appropriate purchase based on mass (or volume), nutritional value, health requirements or country of manufacture. Food labels list ingredients, additives and nutritional information. Foods with a limited shelf life or 'use by' dates must also display this information. Labeling should also assist consumers with particular dietary requirements by documenting fat, fibre, food allergens or those ingredients that may produce severe adverse reactions.

Food labels should list the country of origin but this information can often be misleading or open to interpretation due to sourcing, processing and packaging issues.

> **A.7.10** Discuss the impact and effectiveness of legislation governing what should appear on food labels as a means of altering diet.
>
> © IBO 2007

In June 2010, members of the European Parliament supported a moved to create more uniformity in the labeling of food within in the EU. Guideline Daily Amounts (GDAs) could now appear on food labels within the next three years. All-important nutritional information, including salt, fat and sugar content, will also appear on the front of packages.

Issues surrounding 'country of origin' were also discussed and the often-misleading statements made by manufacturers. Under the new law, country of origin information will become compulsory for dairy products, poultry, meat, fish, fruit and vegetables. These details are considered important. This new legislation mandates consistent front-of-package labels detailing energy, fat, saturated fat, salt, sugar and carbohydrates, all reported in ratios per 100g/100ml. Complications however, may arise from too much information and legibility.

Supporters of clearer labeling point to rising obesity rates and assert consumers require accurate information to assist them in making appropriate choices. Colour coding schemes have been trialed as a means of easily communicating to consumers healthy and unhealthy choices. This approach has concerned some food producers who see their products being 'demonized'.

While the addition of clear, unambiguous information regarding the nutritional content of food will be of value to consumers in making an informed choice, healthy changes to diets only occur when consumers make that choice.

Further Reading

Abreu, M. *Recycling of Tetra Pak Aseptic Cartons.* Tetra Pak Canada Inc., Markham Canada.

Beaudoin, C. (2006). *Food packaging materials for takeout: The industry and the alternatives.*

Hartmann, J. (2007). *Brands: A Discussion on the Difference Between Creating Good Brands and Meaningful Brands. Accelerating New Food Product Design and Development.* Jacqueline H. Beckley, et.al. (Editors). Chapter 7, pp87-102. Blackwell Publishing Ltd, Iowa, USA.

Miller, G.D. et.al. (2009). *It is time for a positive approach to dietary guidance using nutrient density as a basic principle.* Journal of Nutrition, Vol.139, pp1-5.

Steenkamp, J.E., Batra, R. and Alden, D. (2002). *How perceived brand globalness creates brand value.* Journal of International Business Studies, Vol.34(1), 53-65.

Williams, P.G. et.al. (2003). *Nutrition and related claims used on packaged Australian foods - implications for regulation.* Faculty of Health & Behavioural Sciences, University of Wollongong, Research Online.

Vazquez, D., Bruce, M. and Studd, R. (2003). *A Case Study Exploring the Packaging Design Management Process within a UK Food Retailer.* British Food Journal, Vol.105(9), pp602-617.

Yip, G. S. (1995). *Total Global Strategy: Managing for Worldwide Competitive Advantage.* Englewood Cliffs, NJ: Prentice-Hill.

Food Packaging
[http://www.thesite.org/healthandwellbeing/fitnessanddiet/food/foodpackaging]

Packaging Materials for Foods
[http://practicalaction.org/docs/technical_information_service/packaging_materials.pdf]

A8 PEOPLE AND FOOD – LIFESTYLE ISSUES

A 8.1 Discuss how religion and other cultural factors affect food choice and impact on health.

Before the current era of globalized food supply, the only foods that were available were those produced locally. Because of this, provincial recipes developed taking advantage of this produce and, in the process, developed a provincial characteristic, becoming an integral part of the community culture. Similarly, various parts of the world can be identified with similar dietary characteristics. The Mediterranean diet, for example, includes fresh vegetables, seafood and legumes with a small amount of meat cooked with olive oil, while the diets of those living in Asian countries has typically been based around rice and noodles, supplemented with fresh vegetables and fruit, with a small amount of seafood or meat.

Superimposed on these regional characteristics are the influences of religious beliefs, that identify certain restrictions to the diet and stipulate when, where and how food is to be prepared and eaten. A brief outline of some of these practices is provided below.

The Islamic faith avoids the consumption of pork and requires that only meat slaughtered in a prescribed way can be considered to be 'halal' and therefore permitted under the dietary laws. In addition, food should be eaten only when one is hungry. Ceremonies such as Ramadan, observed in the ninth month of the Muslim calendar, involve the observance of a fast between dawn and dusk followed by a feast.

Judaism avoids the consumption of 'non-kosher' (unclean according to the dietary laws) foods such as pork and certain fish such as sturgeon and shellfish, including crustaceans such as prawns. A number of religious fasting days are observed such as Yom Kippur (the Day of Atonement) during which eating and drinking is forbidden from sundown to sundown. Another important celebration in the Jewish calendar is Passover, which begins on the 15th day of the month of 'Nisan', (typically in March or April), and runs for eight days, commemorating the Exodus of the Israelites from ancient Egypt and slavery. During the eight days of the Passover festival leavened bread is not

OPTION

eaten, to observe that the Exodus occurred in such a hurry the Israelites did not have time to wait for it to rise.

While a specific diet is not prescribed in Buddhism, many follow a vegetarian diet based on the teaching 'do no harm'. Many Buddhists do however eat meat and fish, although certain foods may be excluded in order to avoid traits linked to that animal, that is, as an obscuration. Tibetan Buddhists, for example, avoid the consumption of fish as an obscuration of aggression. The Buddhist practice of the offering of food to a Monk is an act of piety.

Those following Hinduism typically avoid the consumption of meat fish and fowl, preferring a vegetarian diet while abstaining from mushrooms, onions and garlic as obscurations for ignorance and passion. Religious ceremonies often involve the offering of food to God (prasada) through which purification of the body, mind and spirit is obtained.

Christianity has few dietary limitations. Fasting is observed by some denominations on days such as Easter Friday (Good Friday), while special foods such as Easter buns are also commonly eaten during the Easter period, shown in Figure A.8.1a.

Figure A.8.1 Hot Cross buns baked at Easter

A.8.2　Discuss how vegetarian and/or vegan diets affect food choice and impact on health.

© IBO 2007

Vegetarian diets do not contain meat, poultry or fish; vegan diets further exclude dairy products and eggs. People choose to be vegetarians for a variety of reasons such as insufficient income, lack of animal products, ethical issues, environmental concerns, religious and cultural beliefs.

A number of religions, notably those originating in India (Buddhism, Hare Krishna, Jainism) advocate a vegetarian diet while others, such as Jewish and Muslim faiths, avoid only selected meats such as pork, based on their religious beliefs.

Outside of religious observance, many people have adopted a vegetarian diet based on ethical considerations of animal rights and the cruelty involved in the growth and processing of animals for food or a desire to follow a healthy diet low in saturated fats and cholesterol.

Whatever the reason for adopting a vegetarian diet might be, the dietary requirements for continued health and the need to maintain a balanced diet remain. If meats are excluded from the diet substitutions need to be made to ensure that an adequate intake of protein and minerals such as iron are included. Diets rich in both fruits and vegetables will be high in fibre and low in fat. Protein can be obtained from legumes and grains, while iron can be obtained from whole grains, chick peas, soy products and green vegetables such as broccoli and spinach.

Similarly, the intake of calcium can be supplemented by fortified orange juice and baked beans along with soy products such as tofu and soymilk.

A8.3　Define lifestyle.

A.8.4　Explain how lifestyle factors affect food choice and impact on health.

© IBO 2007

Lifestyle is defined as a way of life or style of living that reflects the attitudes and values of a person or group.

The increased inclusion of fast foods in the diet, along with a more sedentary lifestyle in many Western countries, has resulted in high protein, high carbohydrate diets. This results in an energy imbalance leading to an increase in the proportion of the population classified as overweight or obese. Increasingly, this trend is being seen in younger children.

Obesity can result in an increased risk of developing Type 2 diabetes and cardiovascular disease (CVD), high blood pressure, gallstones and a number of cancers such as renal, colorectal, prostate and breast cancer. Chronic diseases such as sleep apnoea and back pain are also related to obesity.

A.8.5 Explain how lifestyle factors have led to the development of new food products, such as snack foods and individual convenience foods.

The Göteburg Adolescent Study, which examined nutrition and lifestyle factors of school age adolescents, found that many adolescents did not have breakfast and that this was '...related to lifestyle factors and poor food choice and nutrition'. One of these factors was smoking, where it was found that those who smoked were more likely to not eat breakfast. Studies of adult smokers have also found that they made poorer food choices, consuming larger amounts of chips, alcohol and coffee and lower intakes of fibre and micronutrients. Those adolescents who missed breakfast were also more likely to consume snack foods between meals.

While high sugar snacks and fast foods have been available for a considerable time and have been implicated in the growing problem of obesity, a large market has developed for those consumers who want a ready to serve meal but were concerned about the heath and quality aspects of the food they purchased. TV dinners and low calorie meals, controlled for portion size and calorie content, have been available for many years. Recently, however, meals of higher quality and variety have appeared on the market to cater for busy consumers who no longer know how to cook but want the convenience of dining at home rather than at a restaurant.

A.8.6 Explain how travel, the media and lifestyle factors have led to increased consumption of foods from other cultures and the development of an international cuisine.

A.8.7 Explain how (ironically) many of the most popular ethnic dishes consumed in the developed world were traditional staple foods.

The increased ease of international travel and immigration has lead to a greater awareness of culinary styles from around the world. The demand for traditional ingredients by immigrant populations, in order to cook traditional meals, has led, in many countries, to the development initially of specialty outlets catering to this population, and eventually the availability of such items in mainstream supermarkets. In addition, international tourism exposes the traveller to new tastes, cooking styles and ingredients while encouraging the development of restaurants to offer meals familiar to the traveller. The media coverage of different cooking styles, and the increasing popularity of international foods, also influenced the development of an international cuisine which may include ingredients from anywhere in the World. Many of the most popular ethnic dishes consumed in the developed world were traditional staple foods in their countries of origin.

A.8.8 Define food allergy and food intolerance.

A food allergy is a hypersensitivity to dietary substances and involves an immunological reaction to food proteins. Symptoms usually appear within minutes to one hour after eating the offending food and can include local swelling and burning around the mouth and throat followed by nausea, vomiting and diarrhoea. There are many food allergies occurring childhood such as peanuts, wheat, milk, eggs, and soy.

Food intolerance is not an immune response but rather is a chemical reaction and is more common than food allergies. The symptoms of food intolerance can occur immediately following consumption, or may occur several hours later and require a threshold of the non-tolerated food to be exceeded before a reaction occurs.

A.8.9 Explain how food allergies impact on diet.

Food allergies affect up to 10% of school-age children and are an emerging public health issue in the world. The impact of this disorder is felt in daycare, preschool, school, and camp settings — environments that are integral to a child's life. The most common food allergies in childhood are milk, eggs, peanuts, tree nuts, wheat, and soy

Food allergies, such as those associated with reactions to peanuts, have a significant impact on the sufferers' diet and lifestyle in general. Allergic reactions to peanuts are particularly common. Appearing at an early age, allergic reactions to peanuts are often apparent at first exposure. In cases where the individual is highly sensitive, even trace quantities can induce severe reactions. Children with such allergies are discouraged from sharing food and schools must be both well educated and prepared. Many schools request that parents do not pack school lunches or snacks for their children that might contain nuts, in order to protect their classmates from exposure. Avoiding peanuts can prove to be very difficult however as evidenced by the number of accidental exposures. In the case of young children, the burden of supervision weighs heavily on parents. Ingredients on all food packaging must be read carefully and enquiries at eateries made to avoid the effects of cross-contamination. Even with these precautions, peanuts may be present as a result of contaminant remaining on processing equipment used previously to process food that contained peanuts.

Today, many children who are prone to severe allergic reactions to nuts carry their own Epipen® (see Figure A.8.9) in case of emergency. These pens consist of a syringe with a dose of Adrenaline in order to counter a severe allergic reaction, known as anaphylaxis, that can result in restricted breathing due to the swelling of the airways.

Figure A.8.9 Epipen® used to deliver a dose of adrenaline (Epinephrine) in the emergency treatment of anaphylactic shock from an allergic reaction

A.8.10 Explain why a number of products not containing nuts are labelled with warnings that they may contain traces of nuts.

© IBO 2007

The similarity between peanuts and other nuts means that people allergic to peanuts may also be allergic to other types of nuts such as almonds, walnuts, macadamias, pecans, etc.

Unfortunately, nuts are often added to foods either as deliberate additions, or through cross-contamination of machinery when switching from the processing of one product to another. Because the presence of even a small degree of nut contamination can have significant health effects, warning labels are placed on product packages, regardless of whether the products actually contain nuts and/or the factories where the products are processed have nuts onsite.

An example of this form of warning statement is presented in Figure A.8.10. Foods containing such labels need to be avoided by those with a nut allergy.

any allergies?
CONTAINS WHEAT AND MILK PRODUCTS.
MADE ON EQUIPMENT THAT ALSO PROCESSES PRODUCTS CONTAINING PEANUT, SESAME, EGG, FISH AND CRUSTACEA.

Figure A.8.10 Example of food warning label

A.8.11 Explain how food intolerances impact on diet.

© IBO 2007

Gluten is a complex protein found is in grain crops such as wheat, rye, barley and oats. These grains are used extensively in the food industry in the form of flour and find their way into a wide range of foods. Avoidance of gluten in the diet can therefore be difficult and, as previously noted for allergic reactions, requires vigilance and close attention to food labeling to avoid consumption.

An intolerance to gluten can be difficult to diagnose as symptoms can vary from headaches, poor weight control and dermatitis, to diarrhoea and flatulence. In cases of severe intolerance, an immune response is triggered, damaging the villi of the small intestine and resulting in a diagnosis of Celiac Disease.

A.8.12 Explain how to achieve a gluten-free diet.

© IBO 2007

Today, many products are manufactured specifically for this market and are labeled as gluten-free as shown in Figure A.8.12. Reading all labels on prepared foods is important and those pursuing a gluten-free diet should not eat any foods that contain the following:

- hydrolysed vegetable protein
- flour or cereal products
- vegetable protein
- malt and malt flavourings
- starches (unless specified as corn starch, which does not contain gluten)

- various flavourings, which can be derived from cereals containing gluten
- vegetable gum
- emulsifiers, stabilizers derived from cereals containing gluten.

Figure A.8.12 Examples of food labeled a gluten free

Further Reading

Sjöberg, A. etal. (2003). *Meal pattern, food choice, nutrient intake and lifestyle factors in the Göteborg Adolescence Study.* European Journal of Clinical Nutrition, Vol.57(12), pp1579-1578.

Walters, K.S and Portmess, L. (1999). *Ethical Vegetarianism: From Pythagoras to Peter Singer.* State University of New York Press.

Aboriginal Food Rules & Laws
http://www.indigenousaustralia.info/food/food-rules-a-laws.html

Convenience food from Flanders
[http://www.flanderstrade.com/site/internetEN.nsf/0/82a8360411c57921c125750f004ac1d1/$FILE/English.pdf]

Faith and Food
http://www.faithandfood.com/

Food allergy and intolerance
[http://www.betterhealth.vic.gov.au/bhcv2/bhcarticles.nsf/pages/Food_allergy_and_intolerance]

Food culture and religion
[http://www.betterhealth.vic.gov.au/bhcv2/bhcarticles.nsf/pages/Food_culture_and_religion?OpenDocument]

Health and Nutrition. Vegetarian Society
[http://www.vegsoc.org/page.aspx?pid=760]

A.9 ISSUES AND RESPONSIBILITIES

A.9.1 Define body mass index (BMI), overweight and obesity.

The body mass index (BMI), is a statistical measure of body mass based on the ratio of the person's weight (in kilograms) and height (in metres). The BMI is commonly used to estimate a person's health condition based on their weight relative to a healthy norm. The calculation has the advantage of being easy to calculate and the relationship between weight and health has been well established.

$$BMI = \frac{mass}{height^2}$$

Overweight generally refers to those who have a greater body weight than considered to be healthy, when including fat, bone and muscle. Measurement is often referred to the BMI index or by performing the 'Pinch test' in which a roll of flesh at the triceps or waist is pinched between the forefinger and thumb and measured by callipers, although these methods do not include assessments of bone and muscle. A measurement of a more than 2.5cm indicates overweight.

Obesity is a chronic disease in which an abnormally high level of body fat has accumulated to the extent that a significant impact on health can be expected.

A.9.2 Identify values of BMI indicating overweight and obesity.

A typically encountered representation of the regions defined by BMI as underweight through to obese is shown in Figure A.9.2. A BMI value between 25-30 is considered overweight, while a value exceeding 30 would be considered obese. Persons with a BMI above 35 and 40 would be considered to be severely obese and morbidly obese respectively. Some adjustment of these measures is required for children under 18 year old, body builders, and pregnant or lactating women.

OPTION

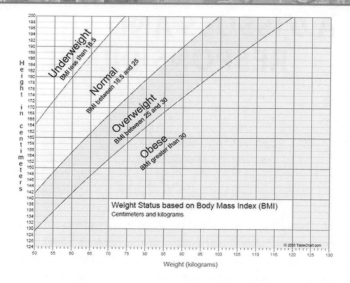

Figure A.9.2 Weight and Height ratio and classification of weight condition [Retrieved from http://myheartrisk.net/bmi-and-heart-disease/]

A.9.3	Explain how overweight and obesity are caused.

© IBO 2007

A number of factors can lead to becoming overweight or obese. The most commonly encountered is a result of excess calorie intake. This can be as a result of the consumption of energy dense foods high combined with low physical exercise. Many people in developed countries have unhealthy diets as a result of the ready availability of convenience foods that reduce the need to produce a meal from raw ingredients. Similarly, the reliance on cars for transport, and entertainment provided by movies, television and computer games has reduced physical exercise.

Some chronic diseases such as an under-active thyroid gland or adrenal gland can lead to obesity, while some medications can slow the body's metabolism leading to weight gain.

A.9.4	Discuss the physiological and psychological conditions associated with overweight and obesity.

© IBO 2007

Both overweight and obesity have been found to be associated with a greater risk of developing chronic health conditions such as high blood pressure, sleep apnoea and back pain as well as Type 2 diabetes, cardiovascular disease (CVD), and a number of cancers such as renal, colorectal, prostate and breast cancer. Some research also indicates

that overweight individuals may also have a greater risk of developing Alzheimer's disease.

Those considered to be overweight often suffer from low self-esteem and this is particularly true of those who fall into the obese category who report high levels of institutional and interpersonal discrimination. This is exacerbated by the negative stereotypes and stigmatisation they are subjected to in the media. Some transport and entertainment venues require the obese to purchase additional seating or refuse service outright, while employers may deny employment based on concerns about performance and health.

A.9.5	Explain that total energy intake, especially of fat-rich foods, can be an important indirect factor in determining cancer incidence.

© IBO 2007

Cancer is the second most common cause of death, after cardiovascular disease, (CVD), and like CVD, is believed to be the result of a number of factors associated with genetic predisposition and environmental exposure. As might be expected, one of the environmental exposures linked to both the cause and prevention of cancer, is nutrition. Foods high in saturated fats and chemical changes that occur to these fats when cooked are known to produce carcinogens. A high fat diet particularly one rich in saturated fats and processed meats containing nitrates, can also lead to conditions of overweight and obesity which are positively linked with a number of cancers as previously indicated in section A.9.4.

Conversely, diets rich in fruits, vegetables and unrefined cereal are believed to protect against many cancers by reducing oxidative damage to DNA.

A9.6	Explain that some naturally occurring components of food have been identified as carcinogenic.

© IBO 2007

Meat products are of course not the only foods found to contain potentially carcinogenic substances, plants too can contain these agents among which are the mycotoxins and plant alkaloids.

Mycotoxins are a family of secondary fungal metabolites produced when the fungi secrete enzymes into food to break it down. Mycotoxins and are found to contaminate a large number of agricultural commodities either before harvest or under post-harvest conditions. Fourteen mycotoxins have been identified as being carcinogenic, among them Aflatoxin and Ochratoxin.

Pyrrolizidine alkaloids are naturally occurring plant toxins produced by the plant to protect it from insect attack. Some of the Pyrrolizidine alkaloids have been shown to be carcinogenic particularly in relation to the liver.

> A9.7 Explain that cooking of food can result in the production of carcinogenic substances.

If food is overcooked or burnt, a number of chemical compounds can be formed which have been identified as being carcinogenic. Among such substances are the Polycyclic Aromatic Hydrocarbons (PCH's) and Heterocyclic Amines (HCA's). These compounds are produced when fat burns and can form in the fat of the cooking meat or, when grilling, rise as a vapour from fat that has dripped onto the heat source, infusing the meat above. Figure A.9.7 shows a typical barbecue in which some of the meat has begun to burn and fat vapours are rising from the hot charcoal below.

The formation of carcinogenic substances is not restricted to the overcooking of meat. The high temperature cooking of starchy vegetables such as potato and corn have also been found to produce carcinogenic substances in the form of Acrylamide. This substance has been found in roasted cereals and deep fried vegetable dishes such as tempura.

As a general guide, the hotter the temperature and longer the food is cooked, the more of these substances are formed.

Figure A.9.7 Burnt sausages on a BBQ

> A.9.8 Explain that some foods, for example, garlic, contain substances that can protect against cancer.

A number of compounds contained in foods, have been found to provide some protection from cancer. One avenue for this protection is provided by an anti-oxidant action in which free radicals that otherwise act to damage DNA are neutralised.

Among the antioxidants are the chemicals Beta-carotene, Ellagic Acid, Anthocyanocides, Lutein and Lycopene along with the Vitamins A, C and E and phytochemicals such as Sulforaphane. Other chemical such as Indole-3-carninol and Isothiocyanate regulate enzymes that protect against cancer, while the enzyme Alliinase, found in garlic slows or prevents tumour growth. The phytochemical Sulforaphane belongs to the family of isothiocyanate.

Several food sources are known to contain one or more of the substances that can protect against cancer.

Dark green-leafy vegetables such as collard greens, spinach and kale contain carotenoids and lutein.

Berries such as strawberries, blueberries, blackberries and raspberries are good sources of the antioxidants such as Vitamin C and phytochemicals. Raspberries are also rich in Ellagic Acid, while blueberries and blackberries are good sources of anthocyanocides.

Cruciferous vegetables such as broccoli, cauliflower, cabbage and brussels sprouts, contain indole-3-carbinol and isothiocyanates such as Sulforaphone which provide both an antioxidant and stimulation of natural enzymes that protect against cancer. Broccoli and brussels sprouts are particularly rich in Sulforaphane.

Tomatoes contain the antioxidants Lycopene and Vitamin C as do carrots, watermelons and chilli peppers.

Garlic has antibacterial properties, which may prevent the formation of cancer forming substances. Garlic also contains the chemical diallyl sulphide, which stimulates the production of the enzyme Alliinase, believed to be responsible for the slowing or prevention of tumour growth. The enzyme Alliinase is activated when garlic is chopped of crushed.

OPTION

A.9.9 Explain that chronic and acute food-related issues impact on health services.

© IBO 2007

Chronic diseases are often complex medical conditions that have developed over a long period of time and have a significant impact on health and include diseases such as cardiovascular disease (CVD), cancer, diabetes and arthritis. These diseases are the leading causes of death and disability and are generally found to increase in number with age.

As previously indicated these diseases are strongly linked to the balance struck between a healthy diet, exercise and lifestyle choices such as smoking and alcohol consumption.

Chronic diseases account for up to 70% of Australia's disease burden. With patients living longer, a large part of this burden is borne by GP services who manage these conditions on an ongoing basis, or until they reach the stage that hospitalization is required. Figure A.9.9a shows the relationship between lifestyle choices and some chronic diseases.

Modifiable risk factors		Broad influences	
Behavioural	Biomedical	(may or may not be modifiable)	non-modifiable factors
Tobacco smoking	Excess weight	Socio-environmental factors	Age
Excess alcohol use	High blood pressure	Psychosocial factors	Gender
Physical activity	High blood cholesterol	Early life factors	Indigenous status
Poor diet	Other	Political factors	Ethnic background
Other			Family history
			Genetic makeup

Figure A.9.9a Risk factors and determinants for chronic diseases. (Source: AIHW (2006). Chronic diseases and associated risk factors in Australia, 2006. Australian Institute of Health and Welfare, Canberra)

In Australia more than half of all potentially preventable hospitalizations are from chronic conditions related to lifestyle issues and approximately 22% of total allocated health expenditure in 2000—01 (both Government and non-government) in Australia was spent on treating chronic diseases. The impact of these diseases on health services can be see in the number of patient days spent in hospital, with longer periods in hospital

In contrast to chronic disease, acute diseases usually have a rapid onset of severe pain which is of relatively short duration following treatment. They include conditions such as a heart attack or food poisoning or respiratory diseases such as SARS (Severe Acute Respiratory Syndrome). Treatment is usually obtained through hospital emergency services or acute illness centres. An outbreak of an acute disease can require a significant mobilization of emergency service, hospital and public health resources. Figure A.9.9b shows chronic diseases managed by General Practitioners, while Figure A.9.9c shows hospitalization days for chronic diseases.

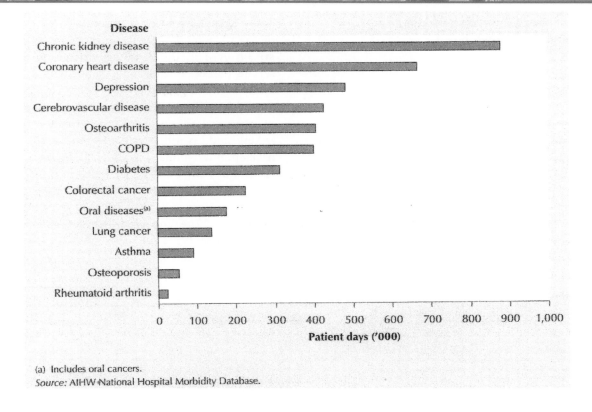

Figure A.9.9b Chronic diseases managed by General Practitioners. (Source: AIHW (2006). Chronic diseases and associated risk factors in Australia, 2006. Australian Institute of Health and Welfare, Canberra)

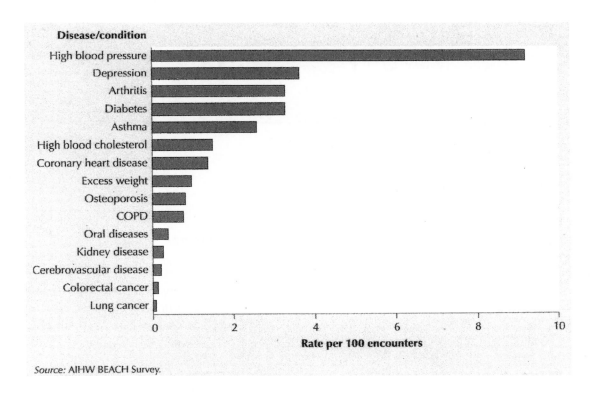

Figure A.9.9c Hospitalization days for chronic diseases. (Source: AIHW (2006). Chronic diseases and associated risk factors in Australia, 2006. Australian Institute of Health and Welfare, Canberra)

A.9.10 Explain the role of governments in promoting public health.

© IBO 2007

Governments play an integral role in ensuring public health by developing policies relating to the operation of the health system, trade and agriculture. Direct responsibilities for food safety are typically the responsibility of the Health Departments within the various tiers of federal, state and local government. Figure A.9.10a outlines the Australian and New Zealand Food Regulatory Model developed by the Council of Australian Governments' (COAG).

These agencies provide a framework for the regulation of food standards and the inspection of facilities that are involved in the handling, storage, preparation and serving of food. In addition to national food standards, an international organisation was created in 1963 known as the Codex Alimentarius Commission as a joint initiative of the United Nations Food and Agriculture Organization (FAO) and World Health Organization (WHO), to develop international standards. The *Codex Alimentarius* (Latin for 'Food book') is designed to provide a point of reference for consumer protection in international trade.

Figure A.9.10 The Australian and New Zealand Food Regulatory Model

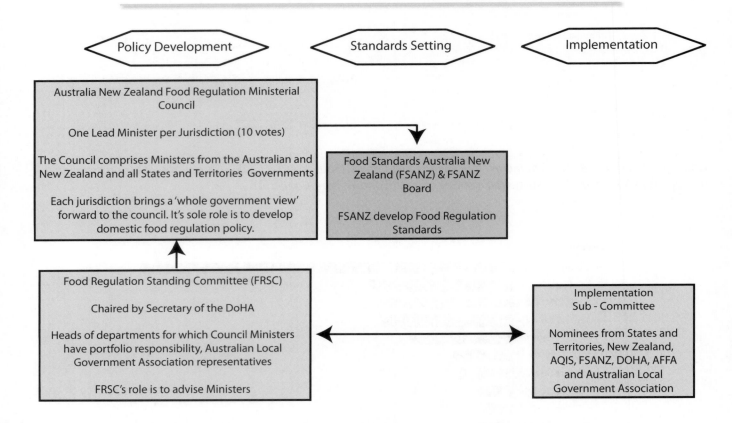

A.9.11 Explain that a major role of government is to raise public awareness of food-rlated health issues.

© IBO 2007

In order to raise the public awareness of health and food-related health issues, governments organize education campaigns for the general public and health professionals. These campaigns are promoted through the media and the education system to raise awareness of the links between lifestyle behaviours such as exercise, smoking and nutrition and the risk of chronic disease, along with advisory messages regarding acute illnesses related to food handling and preparation.

Further Reading

Nicholls, T. (2001). *Government policy on public health, food safety and environmental issues- lessons from BSE in Europe (emergency management, mad cows, anxious politicians, science and the media!).* Australian Journal of Emergency Management, vol.16(1), pp15-17.

Uauy, R. and Solomons, N. (2005). *Diet, nutrition, and the life-course approach to cancer prevention.* Journal of Nutrition, Vol.135(12), pp2934S-2945S.

A.10 FOOD POISONING

Diseases developed as a result of consuming food fall into two general categories: food borne infections and food poisoning. The distinction between these categories lies in the origin and nature of the causative agent.

Food-borne illnesses are caused by the ingestion of parasitic organisms such as worms, protozoa, bacteria and viruses that are present in food or have been transferred to it prior to being consumed. The subsequent infection with these organisms and their growth within the body leads to the disease.

Commonly encountered bacteria include Salmonella, Shigella and Listeria. Contaminated water is a typical source of these infections and is particularly of concern in areas suffering natural disasters where access to clean water and sanitation is disrupted. If infected water is not boiled, or food adequately cooked, diseases such as Cholera, Typhoid, Amoebic Dysentery, Shigellosis and Haemorrhagic Colitis can occur.

Viruses responsible for food-borne infections include Norovirus, Rotovirus and Hepatitis A, all of which can cause moderate to severe illnesses characterised by nausea, vomiting and diarrhoea.

In contrast to food-borne infections, food poisoning, or 'toxic' food poisoning, occurs as a result of the consumption of foods that contain a natural toxin or through the consumption of toxins produced by bacteria.

The natural toxins fall into three general groups: the alkaloids, bioactive amines and fungal toxins.

Plants that contain toxins of the alkaloid group include the nightshade family that include tomatoes, eggplant and chilli peppers, although these are relatively benign. Other foods widely consumed such as mushrooms, include varieties that contain toxic alkaloids that produce reactions ranging from the mild to life threatening.

Fugu, also known as Pufferfish, contains a potent alkaloid that acts as a neurotoxin and can be deadly if not prepared correctly.

Bioactive amines cause changes in blood vessels and include caffeine. An overdose of caffeine, consisting of amounts in excess of 600mg, can result in symptoms that include an increased heart rate, vomiting, tremors, headache and anxiety. Figure A.10.1 shows the range of caffeine levels that may be present in some commonly consumed beverages. It should be noted that the serving size of these beverages could vary considerably.

Beverage	Caffeine mg/100ml
Cola soft drink	10 - 15
Tea	20 - 70
Energy drinks	30 - 40
Instant coffee	20 - 80
Percolated coffee	30 - 110
Espresso coffee	60 - 225

Figure A.10.1 Caffeine content of some popular beverages

Fungal toxins known as mycotoxins can contaminate cereals, nuts, fruits and vegetables. The contamination of rye in the Middle Ages with the mycotoxin 'Ergot', resulted in symptoms of convulsions, hallucinations, tinnitus, vertigo and headaches and came to be known as Saint Anthony's Fire.

Food poisoning arising from toxins produced by bacteria are commonly associated with poor sanitation, food handing and storage practices. The toxins, once produced, are not neutralised by cooking.

Infective bacterial food poisoning occurs when certain bacteria detrimental to human health contaminate food and are subsequently consumed with the food. Once in the body, these bacteria continue to grow and act to disrupt normal cell function, causing illness. Among the most commonly encountered causes of infective bacterial food poisoning are contamination with Salmonella, Shigella and Listeria resulting from the inadequate storage and

HL

OPTION

handling of raw foods such as poultry, meat, eggs, seafood and dairy products

Toxin-type food poisoning occurs as a result of toxins produced by the bacteria, rather than direct bacterial action. Among the most commonly encountered causes of contamination are:

- Staphylococcus aureus (Golden Staph) – carried on the skin and transferred to food by poor sanitation
- Clostridium perfringens – spores are present in soil and dust and grow rapidly in foods that can cool slowly. Represents a common form of food poisoning although usually mild in nature
- Clostridium botulinum - typically present in poorly preserved foods - causes the food poisoning known as botulism
- Escherichia coli (E.coli) – transferred to food by poor sanitation.

A.10.3 Outline the signs and symptoms of food poisoning.

The indications of food poisoning can vary greatly from those of mild flu-like symptoms to acute pain. The most common symptoms of food poisoning typically include:

- weakness
- diarrhoea
- headaches
- fever and chills
- abdominal pain
- nausea and vomiting

A.10.4 Explain how lifestyle factors contribute to the increased incidence of food poisoning.

Lifestyles in which food is prepared or eaten outdoors have a potentially greater exposure to windblown contamination, while crowded living conditions also raise the possibility of cross contamination and pathogen transmission within a community.

The inadequate reheating of consumption-ready meals and the maintenance of servery foods under inadequate temperature control conditions for extended periods, as may occur in bain-marie cabinets, can also result in food poisoning

A.10.5 Describe how food poisoning can be avoided.

In preventing food poisoning, it is recommended to assume that all foods may cause food-borne illness and the following steps be taken:

- wash hands, or wear disposable gloves when handling food
- sanitize food preparation surfaces and utensils thoroughly before and after handling raw foods to prevent recontamination of foods
- refrigerate foods below 5°C. Serve hot foods immediately or keep them heated above 60 °C
- use separate utensils, containers and equipment for raw food and read-to-eat food.

A.10.6 Define food hygiene.

The World Health Organisation (WHO) has defined food hygiene as 'all conditions and measures necessary to ensure the safety and suitability of food at all stages of the food chain.'

Under this definition food hygiene ranges from the production (grown and harvested or raised and slaughtered) through processing, storage, distribution and preparation to serving.

A.10.7 Explain how good personal hygiene can help to prevent the contamination of food with food-poisoning bacteria.

An important way to prevent food contamination is to maintain a high standard of personal hygiene and cleanliness. Even healthy people can carry food poisoning bacteria, for example many people carry Staphylococcus aureus in the nose, mouth and skin. Bacteria can be easily spread through human-to-human contact, and good personal hygiene is essential to prevent food contamination.

Personal hygiene, such as the washing of hands after going to the toilet, is essential to avoid contamination of food through direct contact or the contamination of food utensils.

A.10.8 Explain how the design of food preparation areas can help to prevent the contamination of food with food-poisoning bacteria.

© IBO 2007

Food safety can be managed through process controls or controls that affect the way food moves through food preparation areas. During food preparation, the following basic requirements have to be met to prevent the contamination of food:

- institute and maintain pest control measures
- provide adequate space for food production and equipment
- maintain adequate refrigeration capacity and temperature control
- Maintain a linear workflow direction from raw material to finished product
- segregate equipment and utensils washing areas from food production areas.

The design of premises must reduce potential for contamination of food, food-contact surfaces, and packaging material. It must also permit users to protect against contamination of food from clothing or personal contact through separation of operations.

A.10.9 Describe 'high-risk' foods.

© IBO 2007

The FAO defines 'high risk foods as 'those foods that are capable of transmitting food poisoning micro-organisms to consumers.' Australia's Priority Classification System for Food Businesses' (ANZFA 2001b) defines high-risk foods as those that 'may contain pathogenic microorganisms and will normally support formation of toxins or growth of pathogenic microorganisms.' These foods include raw meat, fish, oysters, poultry, milk, dairy products, egg products tofu, fresh filled pasta, meat pies, frankfurts, salami, cooked rice, and uncooked or partly cooked pastry and dough products.

A.10.10 Describe the temperature danger zone for bacterial growth.

© IBO 2007

Bacteria grow quickly in high-risk foods when kept at a temperature between 5°C and 60°C. This is called the Temperature Danger Zone. Below this temperature range the growth of bacterial pathogens is reduced substantially while above 60°C, they are killed. If high-risk food is

contaminated with food poisoning bacteria and then left in the Temperature Danger Zone for more than 4 hours, it can cause food poisoning.

Figure A.10.10 Temperature danger zone (Australia VIC Department of Human Services, 2007)

A.10.11 Explain that cooking is an important means of controlling bacterial growth.

© IBO 2007

In order to avoid the presence of bacteria in food, it must be cooked with four things in mind:

- food must be raised to a temperature sufficient to kill contaminating bacteria
- cooking time must adequately adjust for the mass of food being cooked
- time at temperature must be sufficient to ensure all areas of the food have reached the desired temperature
- frozen foods need to be defrosted prior to cooking to ensure that the centre has reached the desired temperature and does not lag behind the rest.

A.10.12 Explain how an understanding of food poisoning influences the design of individual convenience foods.

© IBO 2007

The rapid development of the convenience food industry has led to an increased risk of food poisoning. In order to avoid such problems the designers of these foods need to be aware of the various avenues for contamination and method of avoidance. This may involve the careful selection of foods to be processed, the methods by which they are to be cooked, the packaging materials and storage conditions, the use of preservatives and the determination of use-by dates.

A.11 GENETICALLY MODIFIED ORGANISMS AND FOOD PRODUCTION.

A.11.1 Define genetically modified organism (GMO).

© IBO 2007

Genetically Modified Organisms, also known as GMOs, are organisms whose original genetic characteristics have been modified using molecular biology techniques.

A.11.2 Identify the factors underpinning the genetic modification of foods.

© IBO 2007

Genetic modification of food was made possible by the discovery of the DNA molecule and the description of its structure in 1953 by James Watson and Francis Crick. Subsequent techniques to remove and insert specific genes have allowed DNA modification.

One of the fundamental underpinnings of genetic modification is that specific genes from one species, identified as being advantageous, can be inserted into the DNA of an unrelated species, and that by using such techniques the development of new and improved plants and animals can be produced that result in an improved yield and/or nutritive value.

A.11.3 Explain the principles underpinning genetic modification.

© IBO 2007

In one sense the genetic modification of food has been undertaken for centuries, through selective breeding, where plant varieties with desired characteristics were selected for propagation and cross-bred with other varieties of that species in the hope of developing a new improved variety. Selective breeding basically emulated natural processes that could occur in the wild, although at an accelerated rate and in a more directed manner. The technique is illustrated in Figure A.11.3a and involved the

identification of a related species, often found in the wild, that exhibited a desired characteristic not shown in the original domesticated variety, such as drought resistance or resistance to a specific disease. The wild variety was then cross-bred with the domestic variety, resulting in a mixture of genes from both. By selecting individuals from this union that showed evidence of the new trait and cross-breeding these with the original variety, over a number of generations the new variety could be developed.

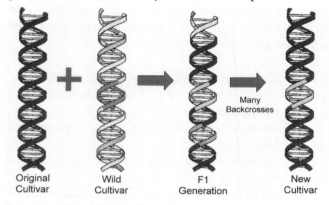

Figure A.11.3a Selective breeding

Genetic modification of food involves the insertion of genes taken from one organism and the insertion of those genes into the DNA of another organism, producing a transgenic organism, with the aim of producing an improvement such as increased drought, frost, herbicide or insecticide resistance. This modified organism is subsequently capable of passing on the inserted genes to subsequent generations. The technique is illustrated in Figure A.11.3b and involved the identification of a species with a desired characteristic and isolating the gene responsible. This gene is subsequently transferred to a plasmid, which is used to carry the gene to the DNA of the cultivar, creating a new cultivar. Because the isolated gene can come from any species related or unrelated to the cultivar, the new cultivar may not have been possible in the wild. The direct nature of the gene transfer also means that the new cultivar is created much more rapidly than might be possible using selective breeding techniques, although regulatory procedures to confirm its safety and efficacy can slow release onto the market considerably.

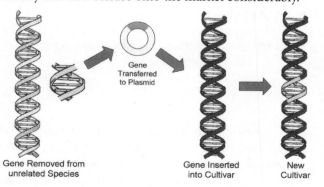

Figure A.11.3b Genetic modification

A.11.4 Discuss issues relating to the traceability of genetically modified crops.

In order to trace genetically modified foods a unique identifier is assigned to the GM food documentation that must accompany that product through the various stages of processing. In addition, the GM food itself is traceable through DNA testing for the inserted gene. Biotechnology companies have used this form of tracing to protect intellectual property rights over their GM crops.

A.11.5 Discuss the ethical issues underpinning public concerns about the safety of genetically modified foods.

The debate over genetically modified foods has raged for over a decade. Scientists, consumers, religious leaders and farmers all have opinions. Below are outlined some of the major considerations from both sides of the debate.

Advocates of genetically modified foods argue:

- GM foods offer hope of feeding a starving world
- decreased use of pesticides and no-till crops are better for the environment
- scientific studies have shown no ill-effects on human health from eating GM crops
- continued population growth and existing hunger across the world makes GM crops an imperative.
- crops better engineered for a range of climatic conditions, (e.g. drought resistant), will increase yields and seasonal availability
- higher yielding crops require less land and therefore less wholesale clearing of landscapes, therefore less erosion and better water retention
- farmers have been practising a form of crop modification (altering the gene pool) when adopting their traditional practice of selecting the most hardy or best yielding crops for seeding
- less pesticide, less land clearing, (burning), and higher yields equate to less greenhouse gas production.

Opponents to genetically modified foods argue:

- there has been a general lack of transparency in the development of GM foods with regard to testing and introduction into the marketplace
- GMOs offer little extra benefit to the consumer
- the process is 'unnatural'.

- contamination of non-transgenic varieties by GM crops
- reliance on a few GMO varieties may reduce biodiversity
- long-term affects of modified crops on humans and the environment is unpredictable and testing has not been performed over a long enough period of time to adequately evaluate adverse consequences
- there already exist historically successful methods for improving crop properties and yields
- from a socio-economic perspective, concerns have been expressed about large corporations dominating the development of GMOs, reaping the profits and potentially exploiting less technologically advanced nations and communities
- acceptance of genetically modified foods provides tacit acceptance for transgenic animals and eventually humans – the slippery slope argument
- some biotech companies have produced a 'terminator seed' that do not produce fertile seeds in the next generation requiring annual purchase from the industry potentially increasing world hunger

A.11.6 Discuss the importance of acceptance by the general public in establishing a market for a food product.

Confidence in the security and safety of the food supply is of prime concern to consumers. If some uncertainty exists over these, the general public will show great reluctance in accepting such foods on the market. If government reassurances of safety and quality are not sufficiently convincing and no driving need for the new product is perceived, public protest and poor sales are likely to result. This situation has been exacerbated in recent years with revelations regarding poor inspection practices and accusations of government cover-ups that have diminished confidence in official pronouncements of food safety.

The introduction and acceptance of GM foods in Europe has suffered from such uncertainty. While GM foods are widely used in the USA, surveys of European consumers suggest that they are unlikely to accept GM foods unless they can be seen as offering health, environmental or price benefits. European consumers have protested that GM foods are being introduced surreptitiously into the food supply without adequate response to consumer concerns regarding its long-term safety.

HL

OPTION

A.11.7 Describe the significance of the FlavrSavr™ tomato.

The FlavrSavr™ tomato was the first genetically modified food approved for human consumption by the US Food and Drug Administration (FDA) and, as such, marked a milestone for GM food.

It was produced by the American biotechnology company, Calgen, using antisense technology.

A.11.8 Describe the advantages of FlavrSavr™ tomatoes over traditionally grown tomatoes.

Traditionally, tomatoes are picked from the vine while still firm and green. This assists in reducing damage during transportation. The fruit is then ripened artificially by spraying with ethylene gas.

The genetically altered FlavrSavr™ tomato contained an antisense RNA that inhibited the expression of an enzyme (polygalacturonase) that would normally cause fruit to soften. The effect was that the fruit could be allowed to ripen on the vine and still remain firm for longer. The FlavrSavr™ therefore provided both a firm fruit that resisted damage during transport, and extended shelf life and the elimination of the need for ripening in artificial atmospheres.

A.11.9 Explain how antisense technology impacts on gene expression.

The normal sequence of nucleotides within single strand of DNA or RNA is called 'sense' and carries a message regarding how proteins are to be manufactured. In the FlavrSavr™ tomato an 'antisense' version of the RNA, responsible for the production of the enzyme polygalacturonase (PG) was introduced. This enzyme is responsible for the softening of the skin of the tomato, making it more susceptible to fungal infection.

The normal (sense) sequence of RNA that provides a template for protein production is often referred to as messenger RNA (or mRNA). Transfer RNA (or tRNA) subsequently 'reads' the information represented by the mRNA sequence.

The antisense gene consists of a single strand of RNA that contains a sequence of nucleotides which is reverse to that of the mRNA. The 'antisense' RNA gene combines with the 'sense' form, interfering with the production of the protein. By blocking the production of the enzyme polygalacturonase (PG), in the FlavrSavr™ tomato, a reduction in the breakdown of pectin in the cell walls occurred. The resultant slowing of cell wall breakdown delayed softening of the fruit. FlavrSavr™ tomatoes had improved harvest and processing properties. They were able to remain longer on the vine to ripen while still maintaining firmness for transport purposes. Being firmer, the tomatoes produced a thicker, more viscous consistency when processed.

A.11.10 Explain how FlavrSavr™ tomatoes were produced.

The first step in producing FlavrSavr™ tomatoes involved the isolation of the PG gene from the tomato. This gene was then cloned using reverse transcriptase to produce the antisense PG gene. The antisense PG gene was then introduced into a plasmid (a bacterial virus). In this case the cauliflower mosaic virus (CaMV) was chosen.

This plasmid was then transferred to Escherichia Coli (E-Coli) bacteria to multiply the number of antisense genes and subsequently transferred to the Agrobacterium Tumefaciens by triparental mating with E-Coli. The bacteria Agrobacterium Tumefaciens (also known as Crown gall disease) is able to transfer some of its DNA or RNA into the cells of a host and, because of this, has been used for the introduction of new genes into plants. In an organism with both sense and antisense mRNA, the two will encounter one another, binding due to their complementary sequences and cancelling each other out.

A.11.11 Explain how the seeds carrying the antisense PG gene were identified.

Kanamycin is an antibiotic. Resistance to this antibiotic was employed as a selectable marker to identify plants carrying the antisense PG gene. Plants containing the antisense gene, and thus the antisense marker, were easily identified by sowing seedlings in a medium such as agar containing approximately 75 picograms per millilitre (pg/ml) Kanamycin. If the seedling has the antisense gene, which would mean it also has Kan-R gene, then it will grow on this selective medium. If the plant does not have the Kan-R gene (this means the antisense sequence was not incorporated into the genome of the plant), then it will not grow on the growth medium. Another method used for identification of genetically modified organisms can involve the use of fluorescent markers that are visible using fluorescent microscopy.

> **A.11.12** Explain why kanamycin-resistant genes are approved as selectable markers for crop genetic engineering.

In 2004 the European Food Safety Authority (EFSA) GMO Panel used the importance of antibiotic treatments as a criterion for approval of individual antibiotics for use as genetic engineering markers. The panel determined Kanamycin to be of 'limited importance' to medicine. This provided major support for the approval of Kanamyacin in GM plants, but in a more recent determination, (2009), the GMO Panel found the use of antibiotic-resistant markers was 'unlikely' to have an adverse effect on humans or the environment. The GMO panel also found a low probability of transferring antibiotic resistance from modified plants to bacteria and the number of antibiotic resistant genes already existing in the environment.

> **A.11.13** Explain how public concerns resulted in the withdrawal of the FlavrSavr™ tomato from the market.

Public concern over the safety of the FlavrSavr™ tomatoes was raised because the tomatoes contained marker genes that gave resistance to the antibiotic Kanamycin. Consumers were concerned that if the genes were transferred from tomatoes and entered bacteria, the modified bacteria could develop resistance to the antibiotic. Scientists were also concerned that research had shown that GM tomatoes had a potential to cause stomach lesions. After only three years on the market, (1994-1997), the FlavrSavr™ tomato was withdrawn from sale.

Case study: Roundup Ready™

> **A.11.14** Describe the significance of the resistance of crops to the herbicide Roundup™.

Crops resistant to Roundup™ can be sprayed with this herbicide to kill weeds that would compete for space with the crop, without damaging the crop itself.

> **A.11.15** Identify a range of crops that have been genetically modified to make them Roundup-resistant.

Roundup™ is the brand name of a series of herbicide products developed by the American company Monsanto, and first marketed in 1973, to aid in agricultural weed control. The active ingredient of Roundup™ is glyphosate, which is combined with the surfactant POEA to increase plant penetration. Glyphosate acts to inhibit the production of the enzyme EPSP synthase, required by the plant to form proteins necessary for growth.

Monsanto has also patented a number of genetically engineered seeds that are tolerant to glyphosate, so that crops grown from these seeds are unaffected by the spraying of Roundup™. This was achieved by the insertion of genes from a bacteria that was capable of synthesising an enzyme with a function similar to EPSP synthase but is not affected by glyphosate. These seeds are marketed as being Roundup Ready™ and include such crops as alfalfa, soybeans, maize (corn), canola and sugar beet.

> **A.11.16** Explain how the testing of the safety of Roundup Ready™ crops is undertaken.

A principle adopted internationally by the World Health Organization (WHO), and the United Nations Food and Agricultural Organization (FAO) for assessing genetically modified crops involves comparing the composition, including the level of key nutrients, of the food derived from a GM plant with food derived from the same plant cultivated in the traditional manner. When a food is shown to be substantially equivalent, in safety and quality, to a food with a history of safe use, the GM food is deemed to be as safe as its conventional counterpart (FA/WHO:1996).

The commonly used measures of comparison include content of protein, oil, ash, fibre, carbohydrates, and amino acids. According to the systematic comparison of the research data, it was indicated no significant differences existed between the Roundup Ready™ crops and the range of values reported in literature for the same crop variety.

HL

OPTION

> **A.11.17** Explain the importance of independent evaluation in assessment of the appropriateness of the testing of GM crops.
>
> © IBO 2007

The conventional scientific process involves the independent confirmation of new research findings. It is particularly important that independent assessment of the experimental procedures and data analysis is undertaken in instances where modifications to the food supply are involved in order to avoid any charges of data manipulation.

Independent assessment is considered particularly important in the case of GM foods to ensure their introduction into the food chain does not have any long term health effects or impact on the environment.

> **A.11.18** Discuss the ethical issues underpinning the labeling of GM crops and their products.
>
> © IBO 2007

Research shows that most shoppers read food labels for a number of reasons. It may be due the concern of a specific allergy or intolerance to a food or additive. Some consumers read labels for health reason, for example, reducing their fat, sugar or energy intake.

Many consumers, particularly in Europe, remain uneasy and distrustful of the adequacy of the research showing that GM food products are safe. The underpinning of the push for labeling is to provide consumers with information, regarding the presence of GM ingredients, allowing each consumer to make their own decision about its purchase. The ethical underpinning of the push for GM labeling, as for any labeling, therefore involves the right to know.

Further reading

Millstein R. L., *Natural Selection, Genetically Modified Food, and the Environment*, Department of Philosophy California State University, Hayward, California, U.S.A.

Streiffler, R. & Rubel, A. (2002). *Choice versus autonomy in the GM food labeling debate: Comment*. AgBioForum, 6(3), 141-142. [Retrieved from www.agbioforum.org.]

Sand, P. H. (2006). *Labelling Genetically Modified Food: The Right to Know*. Reciel, 15(2), pp185-192.

A.12 FOOD SECURITY

> **A.12.1** Define poverty and human development index.
>
> © IBO 2007

Poverty is one of those terms which is difficult to reduce to a single universal expression. Definitions of poverty vary from country to country. A person deemed to be living in poverty in a wealthy nation in Europe, the USA or Australia, although suffering hardship, could be considered to be relatively well-off compared to a person living in a poor, underdeveloped country. Sociologists have therefore suggested the term 'relative poverty' be used for those living in a wealthy country, whose income and living conditions are low compared with the rest of the community. The term 'absolute poverty' is recommended for use where individuals survive at the very margins and life is characterized by malnutrition, illiteracy, disease and low life expectancy.

With this in mind, poverty can be considered primarily as 'a deprivation of choices and opportunities for living a life one has reason to value.' (Human Development Report, 1990).

The Human Development Index, (HDI), is a composite statistic that takes into account measures of the average achievements in a country in three basic dimensions of human development: life expectancy, education and living standards to create a single numerical value or index. The index is used to rank countries in terms of their development. The rankings for the top 30 countries for 2010 are shown in Figure A.12.1.

Country + Rank	Country + Rank	Country + Rank
Norway 1	Japan 11	Hong Kong 21
Australia 2	Korea (South) 12	Greece 22
New Zealand 3	Switzerland 13	Italy 23
United States 4	France 14	Luxemborg 24
Ireland 5	Israel 15	Austria 25
Liechtenstein 6	Finland 16	U K 26
Netherlands 7	Iceland 17	Singapore 27
Canada 8	Belgium 18	Czech Rep. 28
Sweden 9	Denmark 19	Slovenia 29
Germany 10	Spain 20	Andorra 30

Figure A.12.1 Human and income poverty: OECD countries (Source: Human Development Report 2010)

Of the 169 countries evaluated, the top 42 ranked were considered to have achieved Very High Human Development while the remaining countries were divided between High, Medium and Low.

A.12.2 Explain the significance of poverty.

Poverty results in a loss of human potential through death and reduced opportunity for education, while contributing to lower national productivity and increased crime. Poverty is the world's biggest killer, with death through malnutrition and disease resulting in about 25,000 deaths every day, with children representing the highest proportion, according to the United Nations.

While poverty in wealthy countries may not have the consequences of the order, or scale, of that in developing countries, the relative poverty and high inequality in many wealthy nations creates significant social issues. According to the OECD, the gap between rich and poor has grown in more than three-quarters of member countries over the past two decades. Figure A.12.2a demonstrates the significant gap between the rich and poor in some of the wealthiest nations.

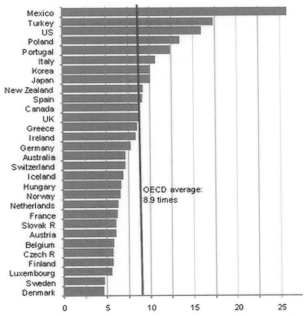

The gap between rich and poor in 2005

OECD average: 8.9 times

Average incomes of richest 10%, multiple of average incomes of poorest 10%

Source: *Growing Unequal?* OECD, 2008.

Figure A.12.2. The gap between rich and poor in 2005 (Source: Growing Unequal? OECD, 2008)

A.12.3 Outline the importance of targeted policy interventions.

Targeted policy interventions involve the direction of resources to a specific 'target' group within society to alleviate poverty. Targeted interventions may be broad in nature, such as the provision of subsidy assistance for primary education and health, or narrow in nature, such as the provision of focused expenditure on areas specific to the poor such as the price of staple foods.

The broad approach to targeted policy intervention can have the problem that many poor often lack the resources, or live in geographically remote regions that reduce their opportunities, to take advantage of such programs. For example, East Africa has an estimated 87.8 million poor with approximately 70.9 million living predominantly in rural areas (ECA 2005).

Agrarian reform policies and other targeted interventions designed to address land distribution, have often involved the forced redistribution of land from the rich to the poor based on political rather than market force considerations. The results of this redistribution in many instances was a need for costly agricultural subsidies. Current approaches to agrarian reform favour government programs that remove obstacles to investment by farmers in their land.

A.12.4 Identify the Millennium Development Goals (MDGs) in relation to poverty and food security.

The Millennium Development Goals (MDGs) were officially established in 2000, at the United Nations Millennium Summit. The 189 Member States of the United Nations agreed to a broad set of eight international development goals to achieve by the year 2015. They include:

1: Eradicate extreme poverty and hunger
2: Achieve universal primary education
3: Promote gender equality and empower women
4: Reduce child mortality
5: Improve maternal health
6: Combat HIV/AIDS, malaria and other diseases
7: Ensure environmental sustainability
8: Develop a Global Partnership for Development

HL

OPTION

Goal 1 was identified as the eradication of extreme poverty

In establishing this goal the importance of interrelationship with many of the other goals was also recognised.

'*The Millennium Development Goals, particularly the eradication of extreme poverty and hunger, cannot be achieved if questions of population and reproductive health are not squarely addressed. And that means stronger efforts to promote women's rights, and greater investment in education and health, including reproductive health and family planning.*'

United Nations Secretary General Kofi A. Annan
Message to the Fifth Asian and Pacific Population Conference
Regional conference on ICPD+10, Bangkok, December 2002

In order to achieve the eradication of extreme poverty the following targets were set:

- Halve, between 1990 and 2015, the proportion of people whose income is less than $1 a day.
- Achieve full and productive employment and decent work for all, including women and young people.
- Halve, between 1990 and 2015, the proportion of people who suffer from hunger.

A.12.5 Evaluate progress towards the MDGs.

According to UN's MDGs report 2010, 'the number of people who are undernourished has continued to grow, while slow progress in reducing the prevalence of hunger stalled—or even reversed itself—in some regions between 2000-2002 and 2005-2007. About one in four children under the age of five are underweight, mainly due to lack of food and quality food, inadequate water, sanitation and health services, and poor care and feeding practices'. As the world is recovering from the global financial crisis, poverty rates are forecasted to be higher in 2015, or even 2020. However, many countries in the East Asia, for instance China and India have showed significant reduction in poverty rate.

A.12.6 Explain how the human development index combines key poverty-related issues into a holistic measure that can be used at a country level to evaluate poverty alleviation strategies.

The Human Development Index (HDI) was created to re-emphasize that people and their capabilities should be the ultimate criteria for assessing the development of a country, not economy growth.

For example if two countries with the same level of income per person have significantly different results in their HDI levels, significant differences in factors such as life expectancy and educational levels, it would indicate that the government policies on health and education in the lower HDI country require review for a better outcome. The HDI can also highlight the internal differences within countries, including gender, ethnicity, religion background etc.

A.12.7 Define food insecurity, undernourishment and undernutrition.

Food insecurity: The FAO defines food insecurity as existing 'when people lack access to sufficient amounts of safe and nutritious food, and therefore are not consuming enough for an active and healthy life'. This may be due to the unavailability of food, inadequate purchasing power, or inappropriate utilization at household level.

Under-nourishment: A health condition with insufficient quantity or quality of nourishment to sustain proper health and growth.

Under-nutrition: inadequacy of diet, resulting in a low calorie intake, along with possible vitamin and mineral deficiencies which, if continued over a long period, results in either loss of normal bodyweight or reduction in physical activity or both.

A.12.8 Describe undernourishment and undernutrition as distinct measures used to estimate the numbers of hungry people.

The Food and Agriculture Organization of the United Nations (FAO) defines undernourishment and under-nutrition in terms of the calories that a person consumes a day. A person is considered to be undernourished if their daily food intake is below approximately 1900kcal a day, while those suffering from under-nutrition have endured a prolonged period of low food consumption.

The relation between hunger and under-nutrition and under-nourishment is relatively clear, the amount of people suffering under-nourishment and under-nutrition can be used as a measure to estimate the extent of hunger within the region.

A.12.9 Explain how under-nourishment and under-nutrition are calculated.

The FAO calculates undernourishment based on three criteria:

(i) the average amount of food available for human consumption: based on FAO estimates of the food produced, imported and withdrawn for non-food purposes. A food energy equivalent (in kcal) is calculated which is then divided by the total population to determine average daily energy consumption.

(ii) the level of inequality in accessing food: is derived from household surveys of food usage to determine a coefficient of variation.

(iii) the minimum number of calories required for an average person: taken from data supplied by FAO/WHO/UNU for those of different sex and age and following a sedentary lifestyle.

The nutritional status of a person is calculated based on a number of factors including: anthropometric, clinical and biochemical measurement.

- anthropometric measures include assessment of mid-upper arm circumference (MUAC) and the ratio of height to weight (W/H) based on age and sex.
- clinical indicators include pallor of palms or mouth, evidence of night blindness, goitre
- biochemical indicators include deficiencies of micronutrients in blood and urine.

A.12.10 List the criteria for food security.

Food security is generally assessed according to four factors:

Food Availability – Food is physically available and of sufficient amount.

Food Access – Food is accessible through different avenues, including home production, buying, borrowing, sharing etc.

Food Utilization – Food quality, preparation facilities and storage conditions are suitable.

Food Stability – Food is secure, so people can access food at all times.

A.12.11 Identify the global extent of undernourishment.

The FAO has developed an index by which factors affecting undernourishment are evaluated and distilled into a single number which can be used to assess progress in meeting targets. A graph of this index is presented in Figure A.12.11a. As can be appreciated, the number of undernourished people in the world varies in response to Global factors and the index shows that undernourishment was relatively stable between 1969 and 2006, averaging around 850 million. Between 2006-2008 however, food prices soared as Western nations committed a greater proportion of grain crops to the production of bio fuels. The global financial crisis of 2008-2009 further exacerbated the problem as financial markets contracted and loans for the purchase of food became increasingly difficult to obtain. Projections for 2010 suggest that a reduction in the number of people suffering undernourishment will fall but will remain high due to 'recurrent natural disasters or conflict'.

Number of undernourished people in the world, 1969–71 to 2010

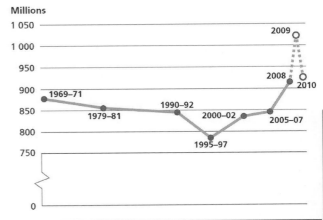

Note: Figures for 2009 and 2010 are estimated by FAO with input from the United States Department of Agriculture, Economic Research Service.

Source: FAO.

Figure A.12.11a The distribution undernourished population around the world (Source: The State of Food Insecurity in the World, FAO 2010)

The distribution of undernourishment by region is presented in Figure A.12.11b and shows the largest

HL

OPTION

number of undernourished to be living in the developing nations of Asia-Pacific and Sub-Saharan Africa. While the greatest number of undernourished people is shown to be in the Asia-Pacific region, Sub-Saharan Africa has the greatest number of undernourished by proportion of population, as can be seen in Figure 12.11c.

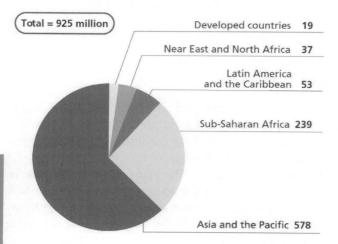

Figure A.12.11.b The distribution undernourished population around the world (Source: The State of Food Insecurity in the World, FAO 2010)

Many of the countries with a high proportion of their population undernourished were also those involved in conflict, in which problems of food distribution and displacement of the population arose. Indeed, it has been noted food insecurity may be one of the factors leading to conflict, such that '… more than 80 percent of wars and civil strife in recent years have taken place in countries ranked in the lower half of the United Nations Human Development Index (HDI)'.

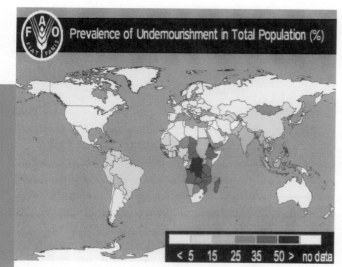

Figure A.12.11.c The distribution undernourished population rate around the world (Source: The State of Food Insecurity in the World, FAO 2009)

While undernourishment is a problem often associated with only the under-developed countries of the world, even the most developed nations experience problems of undernourishment in the midst of plenty, with those suffering depression being particularly at risk, along with the elderly, who may have lost their appetite or developed problems with chewing.

| A.12.12 | Explain the importance of local, national, international and global strategies in combating food insecurity. |

© IBO 2007

Food insecurity is a global phenomenon, which requires strategies implemented at all levels of government to combat. The FAO has proposed several strategies to be undertaken over a number of time scales and geographical reach.

Short term strategies include the improvement of safety nets and social protection programs targeted at the people most in need. Agricultural development in terms of facilities and technologies should also be improved, as should dissemination of knowledge on the principles of nutrition

Medium-long term strategies include the establishment of effective policies to ensure a sustainable food supply is maintained; this would include the promotion of agricultural investment and development of infrastructure.

In food insecure regions, transparent and accountable policies and legislation should be developed, and need to be based on the principles of the Right to Adequate Food established by FAO.

'Right to adequate food is a human right, inherent in all people, to have regular, permanent and unrestricted access, either directly or by means of financial purchases, to quantitatively and qualitatively adequate and sufficient food corresponding to the cultural traditions of people to which the consumer belongs, and which ensures a physical and mental, individual and collective fulfilling and dignified life free of fear.'

Source FAO Guiding principles: Right to Food

At the international level, the Committee on World Food Security should be acting as the cornerstone to integrate operations in the area of food security. The Committee acts as the leading political body to combat hunger, and ensure the transparency of the policy-making process, and the scientific and statistic support, before each policy is established.

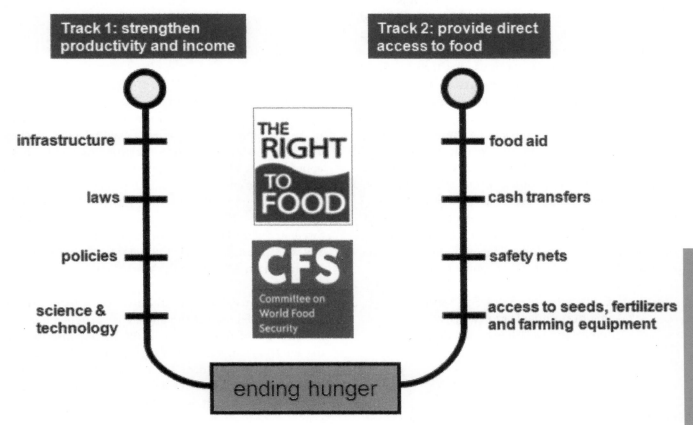

Figure A.12.12. The strategies to combat world hunger (Source: FAO-The States of Food insecurity in the World 2009).

A.12.13 Discuss the ethical issues surrounding the development of a global policy concerning food security.

While many countries are able to produce far more food than they require to sustain their populations, many other countries cannot regularly produce sufficient food to prevent hunger, often for reasons beyond their control such as flood, drought and war.

A consequence of this is that malnutrition and starvation leading to death and disease takes a large toll on human life and potential, often falling disproportionately on infants and young children.

In the 1970s, it was proposed through the United Nations that an Official Development Assistance (ODA) goal of 0.7% of GDP should be adopted by developed nations to address the growing needs of developing countries. In 2000, this target was again proposed as one of the Millennium goals.

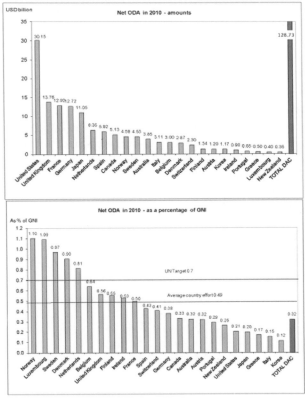

Figure A.12.13 Net official development assistance in 20010

Source: OECD April 2011

HL

OPTION

299

While some countries such as Sweden, Norway, Luxembourg, Denmark and the Netherlands had achieved this level by 2009, other countries have set a date of 2015, while others are still to commit to a time frame for adoption. Figure A.12.13 shows the net official development assistance levels reached by a number of countries in 2009, in both dollar and percentage terms.

It is argued that by not contributing more, the wealthy nations are allowing the poor to remain in poverty and that leading an affluent lifestyle and spending money on non-essential commodities, while others starve, is unethical. Ethical issues also arise, however, regarding the best way that such situations should be addressed. Global policy on food security aims to provide developing countries with the technological means by which they can produce sufficient food for their ongoing needs.

> A.12.14 Explain the role of the Food and Agriculture Organization (FAO) of the United Nations (UN) in combating food insecurity.
>
> © IBO 2007

Founded in 1945, the Food and Agriculture Organization of the United Nations (FAO) leads international efforts to combat world hunger and food insecurity. Its motto 'Fiat Panis' or in English 'Let there be bread' symbolizes its objective to act as a neutral agency for the provision of agricultural knowledge and where all nations can meet as equals to negotiate agreements and policies. The mandate of the FAO is to 'raise levels of nutrition, improve agricultural productivity, better the lives of rural populations and contribute to the growth of the world economy'. Under this mandate, the FAO provides help to developing countries to improve their agriculture, forestry and fisheries practice in order to defeat food insecurity. The FAO's activities comprise four main areas:

- sharing policy expertise
- bringing knowledge to the field
- putting information within reach
- providing a meeting place for nations.

Figure A.12.14. Symbol of the FAO

> A.12.15 Evaluate the progress of the work of the FAO in relation to food security.
>
> © IBO 2007

The Food Security program is the key initiative of FAO to reach the goal of reducing the poverty and hunger as part of the Millennium Development Goal (MDG). Currently 102 countries are engaged in the program, and of these, approximately 30 have begun shifting from pilot to national programs. Many donors have supported the food security programme, including Austria, the European Commission, IFAD, Italy, the Netherlands, Spain, Sweden, Switzerland, the United Kingdom, the United States of America, the UN's Office for the Coordination of Humanitarian Affairs and the World Bank.

The Food Price Index for the period 1990 to 2011 is presented in Figure A.12.15 and shows a sudden increase in the price of food in 2007-2008. In response to this, the FAO took urgent action by launching the Initiative on Soaring Food Prices to help small farmers boost production. In 2008, FAO delivered US$600 million in short- and long-term assistance. The assistance directly benefited nearly seven million smallholder farmers and their 35 million dependents.

In addition, the FAO Council held a World Summit of Heads of State and Government on Food Security at FAO headquarters in November 2009. The Summit set a new goal for the eradication of hunger from the Earth by 2025, and established an agenda to develop a more coherent and efficient system of governance of World food security. This was to include a greater proportion of Official Development Assistance being dedicated to investment in the agricultural sector. Despite this action the Food Price Index again began a rapid increase in 2010-2011 as shown in Figure A.12.15.

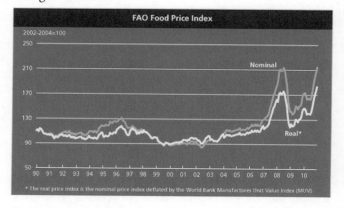

Figure A.12.15 Graph of the FAO Food Price Index for the period 1990 to 2011

Source: FAO

Further Reading

Cousins, B. (2007). *Land and agrarian reform in the 21st century: Changing realities, changing arguments?* Keynote address Global Assembly of Members, International Land Coalition. Entebbe, Uganda, 24-27.

Feldblum, I., Germa, l., Castel, H., Harman-Boehm, I., Bilenko, N., Eisinger, M., Fraser, D. and Shahar, D. (2007). *Characteristics of Undernourished Older Medical Patients and the Identification of Predictors for Undernutrition Status.* Nutrition Journal, 6 (1) pp37-45.

Gaud, A. (2005). *Spatial maps: Targeting & mapping poverty.* United Nations Economic Commission for Africa.

Kaufman, F. (July, 2010). *The food bubble: How Wall street starved millions and got away with it.* Harpers Magazine, pp. 27-34.

Myatt, M. & Duffield, A. (2007). *Weight-for-height and MUAC for Estimating the Prevalence of Acute Undernutrition?*

Notaris, M. (31 January, 2011). *A food price crisis, if not in name.* World and media.

FAO (2006). *The right to food in practice: Implementation at the national level.* Food and Agriculture Organization of the United Nations, Rome: Italy.

FAO (2001). *Undernourishment around the World. The State of Food Insecurity in the World.*

Health Policy Initiative, Task Order 1. (2010). Equity: Target Resources and Effort to the Poor. Washington, DC: Futures Group, Health Policy Initiative, Task Order 1.

*IMF Survey online (April,2008). Progress toward MDGs off track*United Nations (2010). The Millenium Development Goals Report 2010. New York.

United Nations Development Report (2003). *Millennium Development Goals: A Compact Among Nations to End Human Poverty.*

Exercises

1. Modified atmosphere packaging preserves food by:

   A. preventing enzyme activity
   B. altering the gases that surround the food
   C. preventing the entry of oxygen to the product
   D. limiting water available for micro-organisms.

2. Which of the following would best demonstrate an appropriate use of technology in a small bakery?

   A. bread-slicing machine
   B. computerised labeling machine
   C. fully automated production line
   D. automatic bread-buttering machine.

3. Identify the factor most affecting the price structure of food products?

   A. environment
   B. distribution systems
   C. level of staff expertise
   D. nature of target market.

4. Food additives are designed to:

   A. enhance food quality
   B. disguise inferior ingredients
   C. reduce environmental impacts
   D. reduce the risk of food allergies.

5. Milk is pasteurised to:

   A. improve safety
   B. change its colour
   C. assist with packaging
   D. improve nutritional value.

6. Discuss impact of polystyrene packaging (used for perishable foods) on the environment.

7. Explain how the production of carcinogens can be avoided in certain foods. Provide examples.

8. Explain the causes of food spoilage and deterioration. Support your answer with examples.

9. Identify one diet-related disorder linked to overnutrition and explain the physical effects on a suffering individual.

10. Discuss the implications of wholesale approval of genetically modified organisms.

HL

OPTION

HL

OPTION

ELECTRONIC PRODUCT DESIGN

B

CONTENTS

Electronics is a division of engineering. It grew from humble beginnings when attempts were first made to tame and manipulate electricity. Conduction, or the so called 'Edison Effect', discovered by Thomas Edison in 1883, showed that electrons will flow from one metal conductor to another through a vacuum. Developments in the vacuum tube, transistor and now the integrated circuit, chart the progress of the 20th Century as new materials, processes and applications are explored and developed. Today, we see the convergence of a range of technologies and applications as multi-function products serve as personal computers, media readers and communications devices.

Figure Intro Early vacuum tube or valve technology

B1 GENERAL PRINCIPLES

> B.1.1   Define voltage, current, charge and resistance.

© IBO 2007

Voltage

Potential difference is a measure of the work that must be done to move an electric charge from one point to another. Potential difference is measured in volts and is symbolized by the capital letter 'V'. The relationship can be represented by the relationship below.

$$V = \frac{W}{Q}$$

Where W is work expressed in joules, required to move the charge Q.

Current

Electrical current is a measure of the flow of electrons past a point in a unit of time and can be represented by the relationship below.

OPTION

$$I = Q / t$$

Where I is the electrical current measured in amperes and expressed in the units amps symbolized by the capital letter 'A'.

Charge

The electric charge Q on an electron is measured to be: 1.6×10^{-19} Coulombs.

Resistance

Resistance is related to voltage and current by Ohm's law stated as;

$$V = I R$$

Resistors are components within an electrical circuit that retard or resist the free flow of electrons. Resistance is measured in ohms and is symbolized by the Greek letter omega (Ω). When drawing circuits, resistors are represented by a saw tooth line or rectangle (Figure 1.55).

Figure B.1.1a Graphic representation of a resistor

B.1.2 Calculate I, Q or t based on the equation I = Q/t.

© IBO 2007

What is the current in an electric circuit in which 30 coulomb of charge flows past a given point in 5 seconds.

$$I = \frac{Q}{T} = \frac{30}{5} = 6A$$

If 10A of current passes through the filament of a light bulb how many coulombs have moved through the filament in 0.5 seconds.

$$Q = I \times t = 10 \times 0.5 = 5C$$

B.1.3 Describe Ohm's law.

© IBO 2007

George Simon Ohm (1787-1854) determined by experiment that a relationship existed between voltage, current and resistance that could be expressed by the simple equation:

$$V = I R$$

This relationship has come to be known as Ohm's Law.

This relationship demonstrates that if the resistance increases and current remains unchanged, the voltage will increase. Alternatively, if the voltage is to remain constant as the resistance increases, the current must decrease.

This can be easily memorized using the Ohm's Law triangle shown in Figure B.1.3a.

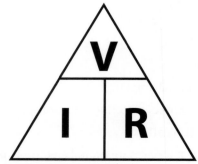

Figure B.1.3a Ohm's Law triangle

B.1.4 Calculate V, I or R based on the equation V = IR.

© IBO 2007

If a circuit has a current of 5 amps and a resistance of 2 ohms, what is the circuit voltage?

Using Ohms Law:

$$
\begin{aligned}
V &= I \times R \\
&= 5 \times 2 \\
&= 10V
\end{aligned}
$$

Assuming a circuit voltage of 14V, what circuit resistance would be required to produce a current of 0.2A?

Rearranging Ohms Law for Resistance:

$$
\begin{aligned}
R &= V / I \\
&= 14 / 0.2 \\
&= 70\Omega
\end{aligned}
$$

B.1.5 Identify resistors using colour codes.

© IBO 2007

Resistors have been classified by the Electronic Industry Association (EIA) into preferred value series, with groupings based on resistor tolerance. There are a number of preferred series in use and are commonly referred to as E12, E24, E48 and E96. These series are arranged in a table in which the columns, moving from left to right, represent an increase of a power of 10. The number of resistors needed to cover the range of values in each column (taking into account the relevant tolerance) constitutes the number of rows in the table and supplies the series name. The E24 series for example is presented in Figure B.1.5a and has twenty-four (24) rows. Each resistor in this series has a tolerance of 5%. If we were considering the E12 series, it would contain only twelve (12) rows, consisting of only those rows shaded in Figure B.1.5a, and each member of the series would have a tolerance of 10%.

1R0	10R	100R	1K0	10K	100K	1M0
1R1	11R	110R	1K1	11K	110K	
1R2	12R	120R	1K2	12K	120K	
1R3	13R	130R	1K3	13K	130K	
1R5	15R	130R	1K3	13K	130K	
1R6	16R	160R	1K6	16K	160K	
1R8	18R8	180R	1K8	18K	180K	
2R0	20R	200R	2K0	20K	200K	
2R2	22R	220R	2K2	22K	220K	
2R4	24R	240R	2K4	24K	240K	
2R7	27R	270R	2K7	27R	270K	
3R0	30R	300R	3K0	30K	300K	
3R3	33R	330R	3K3	33K	330K	
3R6	36R	360R	3K6	36K	360K	
3R9	39R	390R	3K9	39K	390K	
4R3	43R	430R	4K3	43K	430K	
4R7	47R	470R	4K7	47K	470K	
5R1	51R	510R	5K1	51K	510K	
5R6	56R	560R	5K6	56K	560K	
6R2	62R	620R	6K2	62K	620K	
6R8	68R	680R	6K8	68K	680K	
7R5	75R	750R	7K5	75K	750K	
8R2	82R	820R	8K2	82K	820K	
9R1	91R	910R	9K1	91K	910K	

Figure B.1.5a The E24 series of resistors is shown, with the E12 series highlighted by shading

With so many resistors available, the rapid and accurate identification and discrimination between them is important. Resistors are often very small components and their identification would be difficult if it only consisted of alphanumeric characters along the surface. In order to provide clear identification, a system of colour-coded bands along the surface is used.

The colour code system assigns a numerical value to each colour as indicated in Figure B.1.5b.

The colour code system may consist of four, five or six bands. When four or five bands are present the last band represents the tolerance and the preceding bands represent the resistance. In a six band code, the sixth band represents a temperature coefficient.

	1st Digit	2nd Digit	3rd Digit	Multiplier	Tolerance	Temperature Coefficient
4 bands	1	2		3	4	
5 bands	1	2	3	4	5	
6 bands	1	2	3	4	5	6
Black	0	0	0	$\times 10^0$		
Brown	1	1	1	$\times 10^1$	± 1%	100 ppm/ °K
Red	2	2	2	$\times 10^2$	± 2%	50 ppm/ °K
Orange	3	3	3	$\times 10^3$		15 ppm/ °K
Yellow	4	4	4	$\times 10^4$		22 ppm/ °K
Green	5	5	5	$\times 10^5$	± 0.5%	
Blue	6	6	6	$\times 10^6$	± 0.25%	10 ppm/ °K
Violet	7	7	7	$\times 10^7$	± 0.1%	5 ppm/ °K
Grey	8	8	8	$\times 10^8$	± 0.05%	
White	9	9	9	$\times 10^9$		
Silver				$\times 10^{-2}$	± 10%	
Gold				$\times 10^{-1}$	± 5%	
None					± 20%	

Figure B.1.5b Resistor colour code system

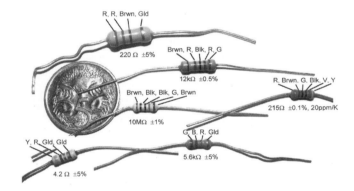

Figure B.1.5c Colour coded resistors

An alternative system of alphanumeric identification is also used to identify resistance. In this system the letter R is used to indicate a decimal point and the letters F, G, J, K and M used to indicate tolerance as indicated below.

F	G	J	K	M
± 1%	± 2%	± 5%	± 10%	± 20%

Code	Resistance
6R8M	6.8Ω ± 20%
3301G	3300Ω ± 2%
2302J	2302Ω ± 5%

Figure B.1.5d Alternative system of alphanumeric identification

OPTION

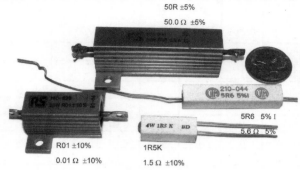

Figure B.1.5e Alphanumerically coded resistors

B.1.6 Calculate total resistance for resistors in series.

© IBO 2007

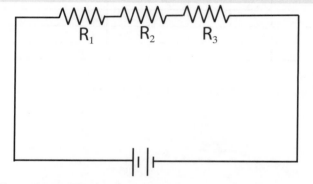

Figure B.1.6a Total resistance in series

A simple electric circuit is presented in Figure B.1.6a in which three resistors are present arranged in series. The total resistance of the circuit (R_T) is obtained by adding the resistors as shown in equation below.

$$R_T = R_1 + R_2 + R_3$$

B.1.7 Calculate total resistance for resistors in parallel.

© IBO 2007

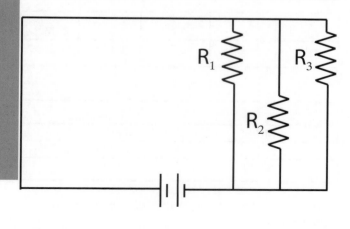

Figure B.1.7a Total resistance in series

A simple electric circuit is presented in Figure B.1.7a in which three resistors are present arranged in parallel. The total resistance of the circuit (R_T) is obtained by adding the reciprocal of each resistor to obtain the reciprocal of the total resistance. Taking the reciprocal of this result gives R_T.

$$\frac{1}{R_T} = \frac{1}{R_1} + \frac{1}{R_2} + \frac{1}{R_3}$$

B.1.8 Explain electrical power in terms of voltage and current.

© IBO 2007

Power is the rate at which energy is used and can be expressed as shown in equation below.

$$P = \frac{Work}{Time} = \frac{W}{t}$$

Combining the three equations:

$$V = \frac{W}{Q} \quad Q = I\,t \quad \text{and} \quad P = \frac{W}{t}$$

We can derive the relationship between Power, Volts and Amps.

$$P = VI$$

B.1.9 Calculate P, V or I based on the equation P = VI.

© IBO 2007

As shown previously is section B.1.8 the power generated by an electric circuit can be expressed by the equation:

$$P = VI$$

By using Ohm's Law, two other relationships can also be obtained as shown in the equations below.

$$P = I^2R \quad \text{and} \quad P = \frac{V^2}{R}$$

Collectively, these three equations are known as Joule's Law and the power generated by a circuit can be easily determined.

What is the power of a circuit in which the voltage is 14V and current is 0.5A?

$$
\begin{aligned}
P &= V \times I \\
&= 14 \times 0.5 \\
&= 7\,\text{Watts}
\end{aligned}
$$

What is the power of a circuit in which the resistance is 5Ω and the current is 3A?

$$P = I^2 \times R$$
$$= 3^2 \times 5$$
$$= 45 \text{Watts}$$

B.1.10 Explain the importance of power ratings for components.

© IBO 2007

Resistors begin to heat when a current flows through a circuit due to the collision of electrons. Consequently, the components within a circuit are rated for the amount of heat or power they can accommodate without damage. This rating relates to the amount of heat that can be dissipated and is determined largely by the physical dimensions of the component, as this relates to the surface area available for heat dissipation to the environment.

The power rating of a component must exceed the power generated in the circuit if damage is to be avoided, and ideally should be rated at more than twice the power generated in the circuit.

B.1.11 Identify suitable power ratings for components in circuits.

© IBO 2007

For the simple circuit shown in Figure B.1.11a with a single 5Ω resistor and a source voltage of 6V, the power can be readily calculated.

$$P = \frac{V^2}{R} = \frac{6^2}{5} \quad 7.5W$$

In determining the power rating of a resistor the power to be dissipated is rounded up to the nearest whole number. In the case illustrated, a rating of at least 8W is required. However, to ensure overheating that might damage the resistor will not occur, a power rating of at least double this figure, at 16W would be specified.

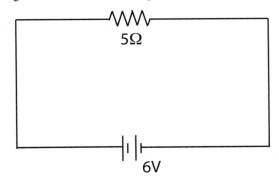

Figure B.1.11a Single resistor circuit

If a larger resistor, say 14Ω, was used in place of the 5Ω resistor of Figure B.1.11a, the power to be dissipated would be only 2.57W, so that a power rating of only 3W would be necessary, with an extension to 6W to provide an adequate safety factor.

$$V_x = \frac{R_x V_T}{R_T}$$

For the circuit presented in Figure B.1.11b, a similar process is followed, only modified by taking into consideration the voltage drop experienced across each of the resistors, where V_x is the voltage drop across resistor R_x, and R_T and V_T represent the total circuit resistance and source voltage.

See section B.4.6 for further discussion of voltage drop across resistors.

Using the equation from section B.1.6, the total circuit resistance of the series circuit shown in Figure B.1.11b is:

$$R_T = R_1 + R_2 + R_3 = 14\Omega$$

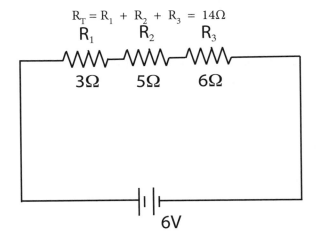

Figure B.1.11b Multiple resistor circuit

The power requirements of each resistor can be calculated after determining the voltage drop associated with each resistor.

Resistor R1

$$V_1 = \frac{R_1}{R_T} \times V_T = \frac{3}{14} \times 6 = 1.29V$$

A minimum power rating of at least 1W would be required with a desired capacity of 2W.

$$V_2 = \frac{R_2}{R_T} \times V_T = \frac{5}{14} \times 6 = 2.14V$$

Power dissipation through R_2

$$P = \frac{V_2^2}{R_2} = \frac{2.14^2}{5} = 0.92W$$

A minimum power rating of at least 1W would be required with a desired capacity of 2W.

Resistor R_3

$$V_3 = \frac{R_3}{R_T} \times V_T = \frac{6}{14} \times 6 = 2.57V$$

Power dissipation through R_3

$$P = \frac{V_3^2}{R_3} = \frac{2.57^2}{6} = 1.10W$$

A minimum power rating of at least 2W would be required with a desired capacity of 4W.

Note that adding the individual power dissemination requirements of the circuit shown in Figure B.1.11b, which had a total circuit resistance of 14Ω, comes to (0.55 + 0.92 + 1.10) 2.57W, the same as that determined when using a single 14Ω resistor in the Figure B.1.11a circuit.

B.1.12 Distinguish between alternating current (ac) and direct current (dc).

© IBO 2007

Alternating current gets it name from the way that the direction of electron flow changes or alternates. In this process, the positive and negative charges at either end of the conductor switch positions resulting in reversals of electron direction. As shown previously, by Ohm's law, for a given resistance, voltage and current maintain a constant ratio i.e. they vary in unison. Each reversal of current is termed a cycle. Alternating current is generated using rotating-coil generators in which a cycle is completed for every complete rotation of the generator shaft. At various times during a cycle, the value of current or voltage can be determined by sin θ, where θ represents the angle of rotation of the generator shaft. The variation of current and voltage in an AC circuit can therefore be represented by a sine wave moving with respect to time as shown in Figure B.1.12a.

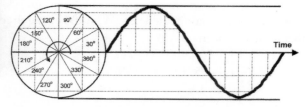

Figure B.1.12a Variation in current and voltage with rotation of rotor in AC power generation

DC involves the movement of current in only one direction, and so results in a constant current.

B.1.13 Measure the amplitude of a given alternating waveform using an oscilloscope.

© IBO 2007

The oscilloscope allows visualization of an alternating waveform by essentially drawing a graph of voltage versus time, in which voltage is displayed on the vertical or Y-axis, and time on the horizontal or X-axis. Figure B.1.13a shows the typical sine waveform of voltage versus time showing both the peak amplitude and peak-to-peak amplitude. Figure B.1.13b shows the typical square waveform of a voltage versus time plot showing both the peak amplitude and peak-to-peak amplitude.

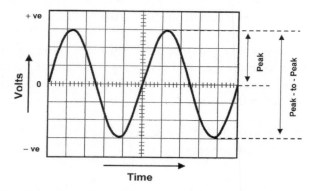

Figure B.1.13a Typical sine wave form of voltage versus time.

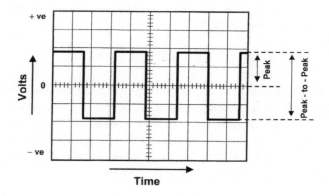

Figure B.1.13b Typical square, voltage/time wave form

B.1.14 Deduce the frequency of a given alternating waveform having measured its period using an oscilloscope.

© IBO 2007

The frequency (f) of an alternating waveform is related to a fundamental characteristic of the waveform, the wave period (T). As illustrated in Figures B.1.14 a and b, the wave period represents the time for one complete cycle or wavelength (λ) to pass and is measured in seconds.

Because frequency is defined as the number of cycles per unit time, the expression shown in Eqn B.1.14a can be used to relate frequency and period. As can be appreciated from the equation, the units of frequency are s^{-1} or Hertz (Hz).

$$f = \frac{1}{T}$$

Similarly, the wavelength and frequency of a waveform are related to the wave velocity, (v), as shown below.

$$V = \lambda f$$

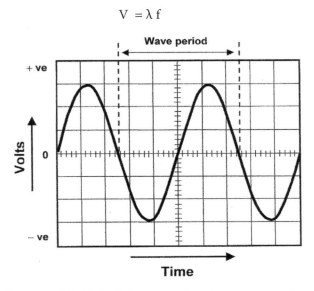

Figure B.1.14a Typical sine wave showing a wave period

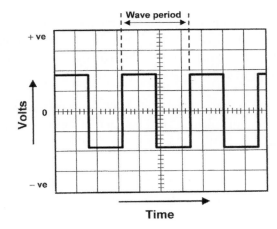

Figure B.1.14b Typical square wave showing a wave period

Power supplies throughout the world are delivered in a variety of ways. The supply systems and mechanisms vary from national grids, to regional or local supplies to none at all.

The quality of electrical supply networks is often used as means of measuring a country's developmental progress due to the fact that industrialization and technological growth relies on a reliable supply of energy. In remote areas or indeed large areas of developing nations, power supplies may be unreliable. Power outages, rationing and unreliable voltages (including voltage spikes) plague centrally based systems.

In an attempt to provide reliable power, many regions resort to a localized supply. Solar, biomass, hydro-electric, geothermal, battery and diesel generators are all systems used to either enhance the national system or run independently. As always, cost is a major factor in determining which system will be employed but maintenance, repair, local knowledge and expertise are all factors influencing the success of any venture. Additional complications arise through incompatibilities between power sources and power appliances. Some systems provide AC, (220-volt, 50-Hz), while others DC, (solar-powered or backup batteries). In these instances, AC to DC transformers or DC to AC inverters may be used where necessary to allow operation from either type of power.

Figure B.1.16a shows how the world tends to be divided into those countries using 230V/50Hz (most countries) and those using 120V/60Hz (favoured by North and South America and parts of Japan). These differences are largely historical in nature and relate to decisions made by Edison regarding the balancing of distribution costs, lamp life for early carbon filament lights and retrofitting costs associated with moving to a higher voltage.

OPTION

Country	Voltage	Frequency	Voltage	Frequency	Plug
Afghanistan	220	50			C & F
Argentina	220	50			C & I
Australia	240	50			I
Austria	230	50			F
Belgium	230	50			E
Bermuda			120	60	A & B
Brazil			110/220	60	A, B & C
Brunei	240	50			G
Cambodia	230	50			A & C
Canada			120	60	A & B
Chile	220	50			C & L
China	220	50			A, G & G
Colombia			110	60	A & B
Cuba			110/220	60	A, B & C
East Timor	220	50			C, E, F & I
Egypt	220	50			C
France	230	50			E
Germany	230	50			A. I & G
Indonesia	127/230	50			C, F & G
India	230	50			C & D
Iran	230	50			C
Italy	230	50			C, F & L
Japan			100	50/60	A & B
Kenya	240	50			G
Malta	240	50			G
Malaysia	240	50			G
Mexico			127	60	A & B
Russia	220	50			F & C
Rwanda	230	50			C & J
Saudi Arabia			127/220	60	A, B, F & G
South Africa	220/230	50			M
Thailand	220	50			A & C
United Kingdom	240	50			G
USA			120	60	A & B
Venezuela			120	60	A & B
Vietnam	127/220	50			A, C & G

Figure B.1.16a Voltage variations across the world

While the nominal voltages shown vary, they basically fit into the tolerances allowed for either 230V ±10% or 120V ±5%.

As indicated in Figure B.1.16a, differences in electrical voltage supplied in different countries not only leads to voltage incompatibilities that may cause damage if ignored, but national decisions made regarding the system of connectivity (plug and socket design) also impact on the design of electrical and electronic products. Figure B.1.17a shows a selection of plug types.

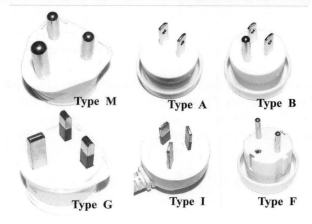

Figure 1.17a Power plug variations

Aid agencies are often required to work is remote areas with no connections to the national grid and where the supply of locally generated power can be unreliable. Because of this, Aid Agencies often need to supply their own power using diesel generators. These systems may be supplemented with solar power and rechargeable battery operated devices.

A capacitor is an electrical component composed of two charged metal plates separated by a layer of insulating material. The capacitor allows the temporary storage of charge (Q) in a circuit.

Capacitance is the amount of charge that a capacitor can store per unit of voltage. The basic unit of capacitance is the farad (F).

Where: $F = \dfrac{Q}{V} = \dfrac{A \times s}{V}$

Because the farad is a large unit, capacitance is usually expressed in terms of micro-farads (μF).

Two circuit symbols commonly used to represent a capacitor are illustrated in B.1.19a.

Figure B.1.19a Common symbols used to represent a capacitor in an electric circuit

B.1.20 Calculate total capacitance for capacitors in series.

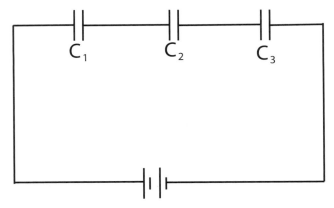

Figure B.1.20 Capacitors arranged in series

The total series capacitance is always less than the smallest individual capacitance because, when arranged in series, the effect is considered to be similar to an increase in the separation of the capacitor plates.

$$\frac{1}{C_T} = \frac{1}{C_1} + \frac{1}{C_2} + \frac{1}{C_3}$$

B.1.21 Calculate total capacitance for capacitors in parallel.

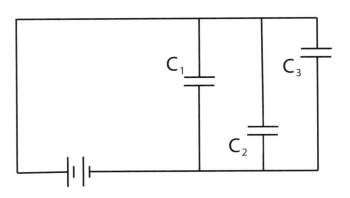

Figure B.1.21 Schematic representation of a circuit with capacitors in parallel

The total parallel capacitance is the sum of the individual capacitors as indicated by the equation, because this arrangement effectively increases the area of the plates.

$$C_T = C_1 + C_2 + C_3$$

B.1.22 Define time constant.

Capacitance cannot exist in a circuit without the presence of a resistance, even if this resistance is just the resistance of the wire. The circuit shown below contains a resistor and a capacitor. Such a circuit is known as an RC circuit.

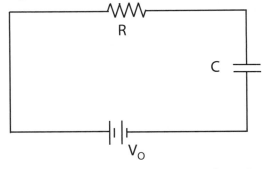

Figure B.1.22a Schematic representation of an RC circuit

Because a resistor acts to slow the flow of charge, the charging and discharging of a capacitor is not instantaneous, but rather is determined by a factor known as the time constant of the circuit represented by the Greek letter tau, (τ), which in turn is dependent on the size of the resistance. The time constant is defined as the period of time represented by the product of the circuit series resistance and the capacitance:

$$\tau = RC$$

The charging and discharging of a capacitor follows an exponential curve with time, of the form shown in the two equations following. Because it is an exponential relationship it theoretically takes an infinite time to complete. In practical terms however, completion is generally considered to be achieved after five time constant intervals (5τ). In order to comply with Ohms Law, as a capacitor is charging, the voltage rises and the current across the capacitor falls. On discharging, the voltage falls and the current increases.

The relationship for the charging of a capacitor in a circuit with a battery voltage V_o, through a resistor after one time constant, is as follows:

$$V = V_o\left[1 - e^{\frac{-t}{RC}}\right] = V_o\left[1 - e^{\frac{-t}{\tau}}\right] = V_o\left[1 - e^{\frac{-1x}{\tau}}\right] = V_o\left[1 - \frac{1}{2.718}\right] = 0.63\,V_o$$

OPTION

311

The relationship for the discharging (decay) of a capacitor from an initial maximum voltage Vo through a resistor after one time constant, will be as follows:

$$V = V_o e^{\frac{-t}{RC}} = V_o e^{\frac{-t}{\tau}} = V_o e^{\frac{-1\tau}{\tau}} = V_o \frac{1}{2.718} = 0.368 V_o$$

A graphical representation of the charge and discharge curves for a capacitor in an RC circuit is presented in Figure B.1.22b and c.

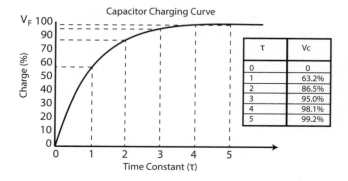

τ	Vc
0	0
1	63.2%
2	86.5%
3	95.0%
4	98.1%
5	99.2%

Figure B.1.22b Graphical representation of the charge curve for a capacitor in an RC circuit

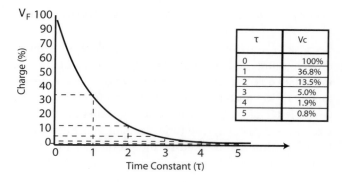

τ	Vc
0	100%
1	36.8%
2	13.5%
3	5.0%
4	1.9%
5	0.8%

Figure B.1.22c Graphical representation of the discharge charge curve for a capacitor in an RC circuit

B.1.23 Calculate the time constant for circuits.

© IBO 2007

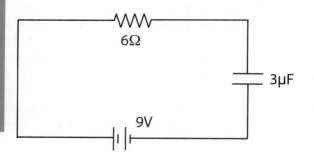

Figure B.1.23a Sample circuit

For the series circuit shown in Figure B.1.23a:

$$R = 6\Omega$$
$$C = 3\mu F = 3 \times 10\text{-}6F$$

Therefore the time constant for the series circuit shown in Figure B.1.23a is:

$$\tau = RC = 6 \times 3 \times 10\text{-}6 = 18 \times 10^{-6} \text{ seconds}$$

For the series circuit shown in Figure B.1.23b:

$$R = 1\Omega + 3\Omega + 5\Omega = 9\Omega$$
$$C = 2\mu F = 2 \times 10\text{-}6F$$

Therefore the time constant for the series circuit shown in Figure B.1.23b is:

$$\tau = RC = 9 \times 2 \times 10\text{-}6 = 18 \times 10^{-6} \text{ seconds}$$

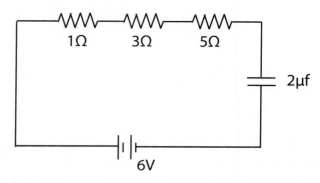

Figure B.1.23b Series circuit

B.1.24 Explain the importance of the time taken for a capacitance to lose half its voltage.

© IBO 2007

Starting with the equation for the discharge of a capacitor shown below, seen previously in section B.1.22.

$$V = V_o e^{\frac{-t}{RC}} = V_o e^{\frac{-t}{\tau}} = V_o e^{\frac{-1\tau}{\tau}} = V_o \frac{1}{2.718} = 0.368 V_o$$

The time taken to reach half the voltage (also known as the half life of the charge decay) $t_{1/2}$, can be represented as shown below.

$$1/2 \frac{V}{V_o} = V_o e^{\frac{-t_{1/2}}{RC}}$$
$$1/2 \frac{V}{V_o} = V_o e^{\frac{-t_{1/2}}{RC}}$$
$$1/2 = e^{\frac{-t_{1/2}}{RC}}$$
$$\ln 1/2 = \frac{-t_{1/2}}{RC}$$
$$t_{1/2} = RC \ln 1/2$$

By decaying to the half voltage level before switching to recharge and again decaying, a regular pulse for a logic circuit is provided, as illustrated in Figure B.1.24a. This pulse can be used as a timing switch to activate operations.

Logic Switching Circuit

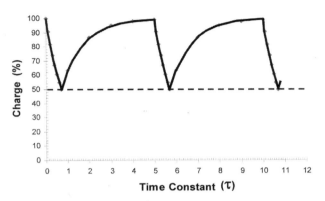

Figure B.1.24a Logic switching circuit

Further Reading

Gerrish, H. H., Dugger Jr., W. E. & Roberts, R. M. (2008). *Electricity and Electronics. 10th edition.* Goodheart-Willcox Co.

Gibilisco, S. (2011). *Teach Yourself Electricity and Electronics, 5th Edition.* McGraw-Hill/TAB Electronics. California. USA.

Slone, G. R. (2000). *Tab Electronics Guide to Understanding Electricity and Electronics. 2nd Edition.* McGraw Hill companies Inc. New York. Electric Power Around the World
http://www.kropla.com/electric2.htm

Mains Electricity
http://en.wikipedia.org/wiki/Mains_electricity

AC Power Plugs and Sockets
http://en.wikipedia.org/wiki/AC_power_plugs_and_sockets

B2 DIGITAL LOGIC

B.2.1 Explain the differences between a digital and an analogue signal.

Digital signals are made up of two basic conditions of being 'off' or 'on'. These conditions can be represented numerically as the numbers zero (0) and one (1) for 'off' and 'on' respectively.

Analogue signals by contrast are continuously and infinitely variable between an upper and lower limit, and can include both positive and negative values.

B.2.2 Explain how a digital signal can be generated from an analogue signal.

By setting threshold values for the switching of an analogue signal, a digital signal can be generated. In such a setup, when the analogue input voltage is below the threshold value the output voltage is driven to an upper or lower saturation position. When the analogue input voltage rises above the threshold, the output voltage is driven to the opposite saturation position. In this way a square waveform is produced in which the voltage varies between only two positions, forming a digital output.

Switching of this sort is often accomplished with a logic gate known as a Schmitt trigger. The Schmitt trigger is a comparator circuit that incorporates positive feedback in order to switch between positions when the threshold value from an analogue signal is reached. In this way the Schmitt trigger generates a digital signal from an analogue signal.

The circuit symbol for a Schmitt trigger is shown in Figure B.2.2a

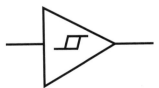

Figure B.2.2a Schmitt trigger circuit symbol

B.2.3 Describe the significance of binary code in digital electronics.

OPTION

A binary code is one based on two states such as 'on' or 'off', 'up' or 'down' 'true' or 'false.' If these two states are represented numerically, the two options are the digits '0' or '1'. Arithmetic based on these two digits is called base-2 arithmetic also known as binary arithmetic.

In the decimal (base 10) system, the position of digits within a number represent powers of 10, as illustrated below.

The number 1549.25 may be shown in base 10 as:

$$1\times10^3 \quad 5\times10^2 \quad 4\times10^1 \quad 9\times10^0 \quad 2\times10^{-1} \quad 5\times10^{-2}$$

$$1000 + 500 + 40 + 9 + 0.2 + 0.05$$

$$= 1549.25$$

Similarly, in the binary (base 2) system the position of digits within a number represent powers of two as illustrated below.

The base 2 number 11000001100.01 may be shown in base 10 as:

$$1\times2^{10} \quad 1\times2^9 \quad 1\times2^3 \quad 1\times2^2 \quad 1\times2^0 \quad 1\times2^{-2}$$

$$1024 + 512 + 8 + 4 + 1 + 0.25$$

$$= 1549.25$$

Because electronic devices operate in a binary fashion, that is, current flows or doesn't, they are particularly suited to binary code.

B.2.4	Describe how the two possible output states of a logic gate can be used as a switch.

© IBO 2007

Logic gates act as digital switches in which an output of '0' or '1' is produced. Depending on the combinations of logic gates used, various operations can be performed within a circuit.

The common logic gates encountered are shown in section B.2.5. Note that for every operation there is a logic gate that performs an inverse version of that operation. The symbols for both are similar, with the exception of the inclusion of a small circle on the output side known as an 'inversion bubble'.

B.2.5 Draw circuit symbols for digital logic gates.

© IBO 2007

As may be seen from Figure B.2.5a, there are three basic gate symbols representing a NOT gate an AND gate and an OR gate. The other gate functions are modifications of these symbols to represent some modification to the output that takes place. Note that the NOT or inverted form of the gates is represented by the addition of the 'inversion bubble'.

Logic Gate	Traditional Symbol	IEC Symbol	Function
NOT		=1	Also known as an **inverter**. Output (Q) is opposite to input.
AND		&	Current output (Q=1) only if **both** inputs are equal to 1.
NAND		&	Current outputs opposite to **AND** gate.
OR		≥1	Current output (Q=1) if **any** input equals 1.
NOR		≥1	Current outputs opposite to **OR** gate.
XOR		=1	Current output (Q=1) only if the inputs are different to each other.
XNOR		=1	Current output (Q=1) only if the inputs are the same.

Figure B.2.5a Symbols and functions of various digital logic gates

The AND gate can be thought of as analogous to a simple electric circuit in which switches are present in series. If even one of the switches is open (input 0), no current flows. However if both switches are closed (both inputs 1), current flows.

Similarly the OR gate can be thought of as analogous to a simple electric circuit in which switches are present in parallel. If even one of the switches is closed (input 1), current flows, even if all of the other switches are open.

B.2.6 Draw truth tables for digital logic gates.

© IBO 2007

Only if all switches are open (all inputs 0), will there be no current A truth table represents the output of a circuit under all possible combinations of input and output conditions. For n inputs there will be 2^n rows, each representing the output for a unique combination of input values. Each input value will be either a '0' or '1' as shown below. By convention the output is labeled 'Q'.

Logic Gate	Traditional Symbol	Truth Table		
NOT	A ▷o Q	A	Q	
		0	1	
		1	2	
AND	A ⊐ Q B	A	B	Q
		0	0	0
		0	1	0
		1	0	0
		1	1	1
NAND	A ⊐o Q B	A	B	Q
		0	0	1
		0	1	1
		1	0	1
		1	1	0
OR	A ⊐ Q B	A	B	Q
		0	0	0
		0	1	1
		1	0	1
		1	1	1
NOR	A ⊐o Q B	A	B	Q
		0	0	1
		0	1	0
		1	0	0
		1	1	0
XOR	A ⊐ Q B	A	B	Q
		0	0	0
		0	1	1
		1	0	1
		1	1	0
XNOR	A ⊐o Q B	A	B	Q
		0	0	1
		0	1	0
		1	0	0
		1	1	1

Figure B.2.6a Logic gate truth tables

An alternate representation of a truth table often employed is known as a Karnaught Map which rearranges the truth table into a two dimensional array. An example of the Truth table (top) and corresponding Karnaught Map (lower) for a two input AND gate is presented in Figure B.2.6b.

Truth table

A	B	Q
0	0	0
0	1	0
1	0	0
1	1	1

Karnaught Map

		B	
		0	1
A	0	0	1
	1	1	1

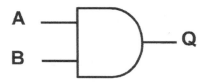

Figure B.2.6b Two input AND Gate showing the Truth table and Karnaught Map

The truth tables presented in figures B.2.6a and b illustrate the case where two inputs are involved. More than two inputs can of course be present and in such a situation the same tabulation can be followed, as illustrated below for an AND gate with three inputs shown in Figure B.2.6c.

A	B	C	Q
0	0	0	0
0	0	1	0
0	1	0	0
0	1	1	0
1	0	0	0
1	0	1	0
1	1	0	0
1	1	1	1

Truth table

		B C			
		00	01	11	10
A	0	0	0	1	0
	1	1	1	1	1

Karnaught Map

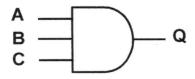

Figure B.2.6c Three input AND Gate showing the Truth table and Karnaught Map

B.2.7   Identify Boolean expressions for digital logic gates.

© IBO 2007

While truth tables can be used to show the operational outcomes associated with each of the logic gates, they can also be represented by Boolean algebra expressions. Where a true statement is represented by a 1, and a false statement by 0.

Logic Gate	Boolean Expression	Algebraic Notation
NOT	$Q = (A)$	( ) or ' or —
AND	$Q = A \cdot B$	$\cdot$
NAND	$Q = (A \cdot B)$	
OR	$Q = A + B$	$+$
NOR	$Q = (A + B)$	
XOR	$Q = A \oplus B$	$\oplus$
XNOR	$Q = (A \oplus B)$	

Figure B.2.7a Boolean algebraic expressions

Logic expressions use algebraic notation. The NOT form of each expression can be indicated in a number of ways:

- enclosing expressions in brackets, eg $Q = (A \cdot B)$
- adding a prime symbol, eg $Q = A' \cdot B'$
- using an over-bar, $Q = \overline{A \cdot B}$

Boolean arithmetic follows the general algebraic rules of being Associative, Commutative and Distributive while also including a special rule as indicated below.

Associative:

$$(A \cdot B) \cdot C = A \cdot (B \cdot C)$$

$$A + B + C = A + (B + C)$$

Commutative:

$$A \cdot B = B \cdot A$$

$$A + B = B + A$$

Distributive:

$$A \cdot (B + C) = A \cdot B + A \cdot C$$

Special

$$A + (B \cdot C) = (A + B) \cdot (A + C)$$

Some other rules associated with the simplification of expressions are also involved but are not treated in the present text.

The brackets shown above do not represent the NOT form but are used here in the algebraic sense of order of operational precedence. Boolean algebra follows an order of precedence in its operation as indicated in Figure B.2.7b.

Operation	Operation	Operation
Brackets	( )	First
NOT	'	Second
AND	$\cdot$	Third
OR	$+$	Fourth

Figure B.2.7b Order of precedence in Boolean algebra.

B.2.8 Design solutions to practical problems using digital logic gates.

© IBO 2007

Assume that we have decided to go hiking tomorrow provided that it is not raining AND not too hot. The word equation for such a decision might read as follows:

$$(hiking) = (NOT\ hot)\ AND\ (NOT\ Raining)$$

or

$$A' \cdot B' = Q$$

This simple condition can therefore be represented as shown in Figure B.2.8a.

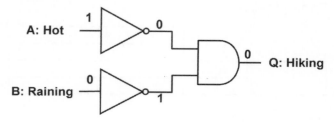

Figure B.2.8a AND NOT logic gates

Since a True statement is represented by 1 and a False statement by 0 in Boolean expressions, the input values show that while it wasn't raining (input 0) it was hot (input 1). Because we did not want either of these situations a NOT gate was used resulting in a reversal of the numerical outputs feeding in to the AND gate. Since one of our conditions was not met, the hike was cancelled.

The truth tables for Figure B.2.8a are shown in Figure B.2.8b.

Hot	Rain			
A	B	$U_1 = A'$	$U_2 = B'$	$Q = U_1 \cdot U_2$
0	0	1	1	1
0	1	1	0	0
1	0	0	1	0
1	1	0	0	0

Figure B.2.8b Truth table for Figure B.2.8a

From a comparison of the truth table shown in Figure 2.6a and Figure B.2.8a, the circuit could have been represented as a NOR gate as indicated below in Figure B.2.8c. Circuit manipulation of the sort suggested below is often performed to simplify a diagram and to find the most economical arrangement.

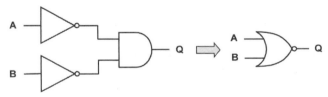

Figure B.2.8c Equivalent circuits

Note that this same decision could have been expressed without the use of NOT gates by formulating the terms indicated below:

(hiking) = (mild temperature) AND (dry)

or

$A \cdot B = Q$

Let us assume that we want to make conditions under which the hike will be cancelled, such that the hike will only go ahead if we are healthy on the day it is not raining or too hot. We rephrase the conditions into the word equation form below.

(cancel hike) = (NOT healthy) OR (raining) OR (too hot)

or

$(A + B) + C' = Q$

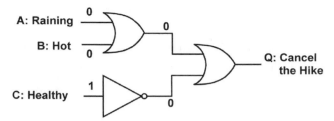

Figure B.2.8d Hike cancellation diagram

In this instance the conditions were good, it was not 'raining' OR 'too hot' so both inputs were zero, and health was good (so C was false) so that the inputs to the last OR gate did not satisfy the conditions to cancel the hike.

Hot	Rain	Health			
A	B	C	$U_1 = A+B$	$U_2 = C'$	$Q = U_1+U_2$
0	0	0	0	1	1
0	0	1	0	0	0
0	1	0	0	1	1
0	1	1	1	0	1
1	0	0	1	1	1
1	0	1	1	0	1
1	1	0	1	1	1
1	1	1	1	0	1

Figure B.2.8e Truth table for Figure B.2.8d

> **B.2.9** Design time delays by applying switches and RC circuits as the input to logic gates.
>
> © IBO 2007

Each mechanical switching component within a circuit has inherent in its operation an associated delay arising from the time taken to firmly establish terminal contact. This is sometimes referred to as contact bounce or chatter. As a consequence of contact bounce, the leading edge of the signal can exhibit fluctuations or spikes before a clear signal is established.

In order to reduce the effects of contact bounce and the signal delay associated with it, an RC circuit is often used in order to adjust the timing of the inputs so that they arrive at the same time at the logic gate. This circuit consists of a resistor in series with the voltage and a capacitor in parallel. The half-life charge decay associated with an RC circuit, previously shown in section B.1.24 and represented by the equation below, can be used to compensate for such circuit delays, by using it to filter the leading edge signal. As the capacitor charges, the output voltage increases steadily until the switching voltage is reached and discharges, providing a cleaner signal.

$$t_{1/2} = RC \ln 1/2 = 0.7RC$$

The circuit shown in Figure B.2.9a represents a circuit in which inputs are arriving at a logic gate due to contact bounce.

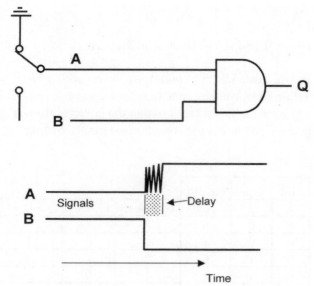

Figure B.2.9a Circuit delay

By the inclusion of an RC circuit, the time delay can be eliminated and the spurious input signals filtered out, producing a cleaner signal, as indicated in Figure B.2.9b.

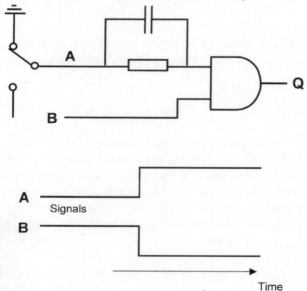

Figure B.2.9a Eliminating circuit time delay

Compensation for timing delay is also often provided by the inclusion in the circuit of a component known as a 555 timing chip. Such chips, available in an eight pin configuration shown in Figure B2.9c, or fourteen pin configuration were introduced in the 1970s and find continued widespread use because of their low cost and reliability. The chips can be purchased for operation over two different temperature ranges, with the SE type

operating in the range −55°C to 125°C and the NE type operating in the range 0°C to 70°C.

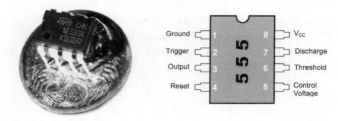

Figure B.2.9c Views of an eight pin 555 timing chip

With the 555 timer in the circuit, a regular timing pulse can be generated, with the frequency of pulses controlled by the RC circuit. In this way the input to the logic gate can be controlled to a precisely adjustable rate. These chips can also be added to the output to provide a clean, precisely timed, signal.

Further Reading

Gassend, B., Clarke, D., van Dijk, M. and Devadas, S. (2003). *Delay-Based Circuit Authentication and Applications.* Massachusetts Institute of Technology. USA.

Godse, A.P. & Godse, D.A. (2010). *Digital Logic Circuits.* Technical Publications. Pune. India.

Hamer, F., Lavelle, M. & McMullan, D. (2006). *Boolean Algebra and Logic Gates.* The Higher Education Academy. University of Plymouth. Plymouth. United Kingdom.

Holdsworth, B. & Woods, C. (2002). *Digital logic design.* Newnes. Jordan Hill. Oxford.

Matloff, N. S. (2003). *Introduction to Digital Logic.* University of California. California. USA.

Shannon, C. (2003). *The Essentials of Computer Organization and Architecture.* Boolean Algebra and Digital Logic.

Null, L. & Lobur, J. (2006). *The Essentials of Computer Organization and Architecture,* 2nd ed. Jones & Bartlett Publishers. Sudbury, Massachusetts

B3 CONTROL

B.3.1 Draw a block diagram for an open loop system.

In an open loop system an input is accepted and operated on before an output is created, as illustrated in Figure B.3.1a.

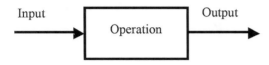

Figure B.3.1a Open loop block diagram

B.3.2 Describe the limitations of open loop systems.

An open loop does not monitor the output in order to modify the input signal. Because of this, any changes in the processing of the input that might affect the output are not taken into account.

B.3.3 Draw a block diagram for a closed loop control system.

In a closed loop system the output is fed back and compared with the desired result. This information is then used to adjust the input in order to modify the output. The block diagram for a closed loop is shown in Figure B.3.3a.

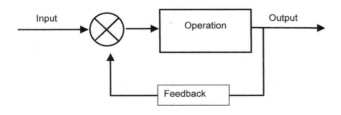

Figure B.3.3a Closed loop block diagram

B.3.4 Explain how feedback is used in a closed loop control system.

There are two basic forms of feedback encountered in electronic systems, known as positive and negative feedback.

Both forms of feedback return part of the output signal to a comparator circuit which compares the output produced with the desired output, If the signals differ, an error signal is produced that is used to adjust the input signal and the cycle continued until the desired output requirements are achieved.

B.3.5 Explain the advantages of closed loop systems over open loop systems.

Because closed loop systems employ feedback, the output is monitored and can be adjusted in response to system changes.

B.3.6 Explain why most systems use negative rather than positive feedback.

In positive feedback, the return signal is added to the input signal. This can result in a cycle of amplification leading to system overload or saturation. The annoying squeal sometimes encountered with a microphone is an example of positive feedback. Positive feedback is used in systems where rapid transition between positive and negative saturation is desired.

In negative feedback, the return signal is used to reduce the input and tends to result in a self-correcting loop forming that will drive the system to stabilisation at the aim. Such systems can be prone to 'hunting' in which the output overshoots the aim and oscillates towards its goal, if an excessive delay in the feedback signal is present.

Further Reading

Buso, S. & Mattavelli, P. (2006). *Digital Control in Power Electronics*. Morgan & Claypool Publishers. USA.

OPTION

B4 OPERATIONAL AMPLIFIERS

B.4.1 Draw the circuit symbols for, and describe the functions of, a range of electrical components.

© IBO 2007

Figure B.4.1 Functions and symbols of typical circuit components

Component	Function	Symbol	
		American	**International**
Aerial (Antenna)	Device used to send or receive signals		
Amplifier	Symbol for a circuit that amplifies input signals		
Battery	Device supplying direct current and composed of two or more cells		
Bell	A transducer operating a bell		
Buzzer	A transducer operating a buzzer	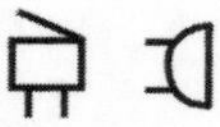	
Capacitor	Component that stores electrical energy	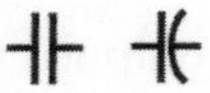	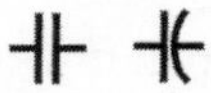
Diode, general	A device that allows only current to move in one direction		
Fuse	Safety device		
Inductor (Solenoid)	Coil creating a magnetic field		
Light Dependent Resistor (LDR)	A transducer that converts light to electrical resistance		
Potentiometer (Variable Resistor)	Device of variable resistance used to control voltage		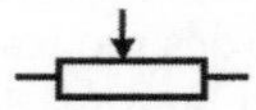
Push-to-Break Switch (PTB)	Switch that only stops current flowing when the button is pushed		
Push-to-Make Switch (PTM)	Switch that only allows current to flow when the button is pushed		
Resistor	Restricts the flow of electricity	 RES	
SPDT	Single Pole Double Throw switch	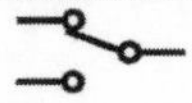	
SPST	Single Pole Single Throw switch		
Transformer - Air Core	Device used to step up and step down AC voltage		

B.4.2   Draw the circuit symbol for an operational amplifier (op amp).

© IBO 2007

An operational amplifier (op amp) is a high gain amplifier meaning that a large amplification of the input signal is obtained and fed as the output. The op amp received its name from its original purpose of performing mathematical operations in early computers.

To achieve its task, the op-amp contains a number of components including transistors and resistors through which the two input voltages are compared and the difference between them amplified. Because the op-amp has become an indispensable component itself, it is usually represented by a simple block diagram symbol shown in Figure B4.2a. All of the voltages shown are measured with respect to the ground, although for convenience the ground terminals are not shown in the standard representation.

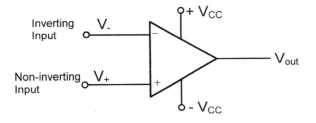

Figure B4.2a. Op amp circuit symbol

As indicated by the labels in Figure B4.2a, one input (V-) has a negative sign and is known as the inverting input and the other (V+) has a positive sign and is known as the non-inverting input. The power supplies +Vcc and –Vcc are often omitted from the diagram for the simpler form shown in Figure B4.2b.

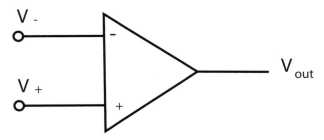

Figure B.4.2b. Simplified Op amp circuit symbol

Op amps are typically controlled by negative feedback by which the output is fed back to the negative input in an attempt the make the difference between the inputs zero.

B.4.3   Define positive saturation and negative saturation.

© IBO 2007

If the output voltage is as positive as it is capable of being, it is said to have reached its cut-off or positive saturation level.

Similarly, if the output voltage is as negative as it is capable of being it is said to have reached its cut-off or negative saturation level.

B.4.4   Draw a circuit for an op amp used as a comparator.

© IBO 2007

When used as a comparator, positive feedback is used rather than negative feedback.

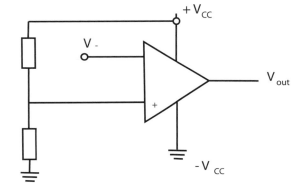

Figure B.4.4a Op amp used as a comparator

B.4.5 Explain the operation of a comparator.

© IBO 2007

An op amp will be positively saturated if the +ve input is more positive than the −ve input, and negatively saturated if the −ve input is less positive than the −ve input. That is, if there is an imbalance or difference between the input voltages, the output will be amplified as much as it can, (saturation), in the direction of the highest input value.

That is:

+ve saturation $V_+ > V_-$, $V_{out} = +V_{CC}$

−ve saturation $V_- > V_+$, $V_{out} = -V_{CC}$

OPTION

B.4.6   Describe how resistors can be used to produce a voltage divider circuit.

When resistors are present in series within a circuit such as that shown in Figure B.4.6a, there is a voltage drop associated with each resistor such that the total voltage drop can be divided among the resistors in the circuit in proportion to the value of each resistor. The larger the resistor, the larger the voltage drop.

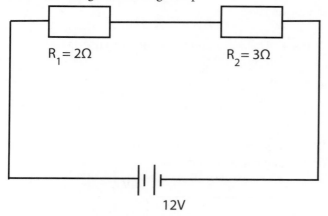

Figure B.4.6a Voltage divider circuit

Because the voltage drop across any resistor is:

$$V_x = I_x R_x$$

and current in a series circuit is

$$I_T = \frac{V_T}{R_T}$$

By substituting I_T for I_x, the voltage drop across any resistor in a series circuit can be expressed as shown below.

$$V_x = \frac{V_T R_x}{R_T}$$

or

$$V_x = \frac{R_x V_T}{R_T}$$

Therefore the voltage across any resistor in a series circuit is the resistance of that resistor divided by the total circuit resistance multiplied by the source voltage.

Calculate the voltage drop V_1 and V_2 across the resistors R_1 and R_2 of Figure B4.6a.

$$V_1 = \frac{R_1 V_T}{R_T} = \frac{2}{5} \times 12 = 4.8V$$

$$V_2 = \frac{R_2 V_T}{R_T} = \frac{3}{5} \times 12 = 7.2V$$

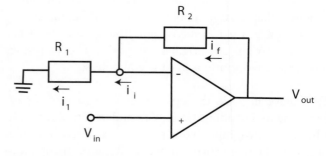

Figure B.4.6b Sample voltage circuit

This voltage drop can be expressed as a percentage of the total circuit voltage so that, in the example above, R_1 represents a voltage drop of 40% while R_2 represents a voltage drop of 60%. A circuit of this sort is known as a voltage divider circuit.

Assuming the resistors remain unchanged, if the voltage is changed (increased or decreased) the percentages to which each resistor drops the voltage remains unchanged. That is, if the circuit voltage of Figure B.4.6a was increased to 24V, the percentage voltage drop at R1 and R2 would still be 40% and 60 % respectively,

The equation: $V_x = I_x R_x$ is known as the voltage divider or potential divider formula.

Voltage divider circuits are widely used in electronic circuits in order to adjust or divide the circuit voltage into smaller values. They find extensive use in providing a stable input reference voltage for op amps.

B.4.7 Describe how $\frac{V_{in} R_2}{(R_1 + R_2)} = V_{out}$ can be used to generate a reference voltage for one input of a comparator.

A voltage divider circuit is shown in Figure B.4.7a, where two resistors are connected in series to a voltage source (V_{in}). In a divided circuit an output voltage (V_{out}) is taken across resistor R_2.

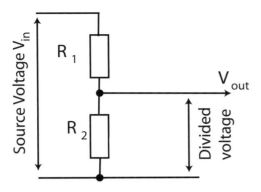

Figure B.4.7a Voltage divider circuit

This circuit can also be represented as shown in Figure B.4.7b below

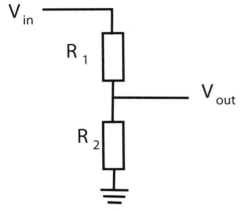

Figure B.4.7b Voltage divider circuit alternative

For a divider circuit where the two resistors are the same, the voltage out is half that of the voltage in:

$$V_{in} = 24V, \quad R_1 = 10k\Omega \text{ and } R_2 = 30k\Omega$$

$$V_{out} = \frac{V_{in} R_2}{(R_1 + R_2)} = \frac{24 \times 30}{(10 + 30)} = 18V$$

For a divider circuit where resistor R_2 is lower than R_1 the voltage out is lower than half the input voltage:

$$V_{in} = 24V, \quad R_1 = 10k\Omega \text{ and } R_2 = 0.10k\Omega$$

$$V_{out} = \frac{V_{in} R_2}{(R_1 + R_2)} = \frac{24 \times 0.10}{(10 + 0.10)} = 0.24V$$

connect a resistive divider circuit such as the one shown to one of the inputs of an op amp.

B4.8 Explain how a thermistor or a light-dependent resistor (LDR) can be used as either of the two resistors in $\dfrac{V_1 R_2}{(R_1 + R_2)} = V_{out}$ to produce a temperature or light sensor.

Thermistors allow accurate temperature control as their resistance changes rapidly in response to changes in temperature. The inclusion of a thermistor in a circuit can therefore be used for temperature compensation or control. Similarly, an LDR changes its resistance with exposure to light, such that when exposed to light its resistance decreases and when in the dark, resistance increases. It can easily be imagined therefore from the preceding examples in B.4.7, that when an LDR or thermistor are placed in a circuit, different output voltages will be obtained depending on the environmental conditions of temperature or light exposure.

In the circuit shown in Figure B.4.8 an LDR is included in the R_2 position. In bright light, the resistance will be relatively low, and the output voltage will be low, while in dim light, resistance will be relatively high and the output voltage will be high.

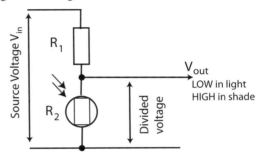

Figure B.4.8 Temperature or light sensor

It will also be appreciated from the preceding explanation that placing the LDR or thermistor in the R_1 position instead of the R_2 position just reverses the response to light or heat. That is instead of V_{out} being low in light and high in shade, it will be high in light and low in shade.

B.4.9 Draw a circuit for an op amp used as a non-inverting amplifier.

The circuit diagram for a non-inverting amplifier is presented in Figure B.4.9a and shows the input signal being fed into the positive (non-inverting) terminal of an op amp.

In an attempt to make the difference between the inputs zero, part of the output signal is fed back to the negative terminal, and is therefore known as negative feedback. In passing through the voltage divider, the signal returned to the negative terminal is reduced. Because it is different from the positive terminal, the op amp acts to try and bring the difference between the two inputs to zero by boosting the output.

OPTION

The resistors R_1 and R_f represent a voltage divider across the output voltage driving the current to zero at point a.

Because the input resistance of an op amp is very large, for practical purposes the input current is considered to approach zero and indeed the inputs of an ideal op amp are considered to draw no current.

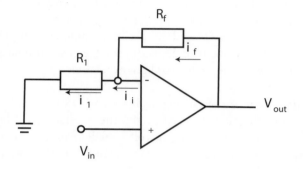

Figure B.4.9a Non-inverting op amp

B.4.10 Calculate the gain of a non-inverting amplifier.

© IBO 2007

A diagram of a non-inverting op amp is presented in Figure B.4.9a.

Because there is no voltage difference between the input terminals

$$V_{in} = V_a = I_1 R_1$$

$$I_1 = \frac{V_a}{R_1}$$

Because of the voltage divider, the output voltage will be as shown below.

$$V_{out} = i_a (R_1 + R_f)$$

$$i_a = \frac{V_{out}}{(R_1 + R_f)}$$

Since $i_a = i_1$ then $i_a = \frac{V_{out}}{(R_1 + R_f)} = \frac{V_{in}}{R_1}$

Leading to: $V_{out} = \left(1 + \frac{R_f}{R_1}\right) V_{in}$

The amount by which the input voltage is magnified is known as the gain A and as shown above the gain for a non-inverting op amp is.

Gain (A) $= 1 + \frac{18}{2} = 10$

B.4.11 Draw the transfer characteristic for a non-inverting amplifier.

© IBO 2007

The voltage transfer characteristic refers to the way in which the input voltage is transferred to an output voltage and is shown graphically for a non-inverting op-amp in Figure B.4.11.

The transfer characteristic moves from the extremes of negative saturation and positive saturation. Between these two extremes a region exists where a linear relationship exists between the input voltage and output voltage, in which the output is the differential between the two inputs magnified by the gain (A).

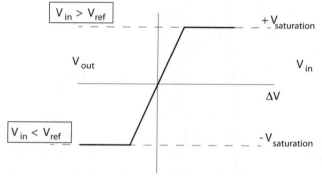

Figure B.4.11 Transfer characteristic for a non-inverting op amp.

B.4.12 Draw an output waveform of a non-inverting amplifier, for a given input waveform and gain.

© IBO 2007

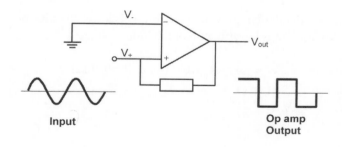

Figure B.4.12 Drawing of an output waveform of a non-inverting amplifier, for a given input waveform and gain

B.4.13 Explain the effect that saturation has on the output waveform for a non-inverting amplifier.

© IBO 2007

When the input voltage is higher or lower than the reference voltage, the output voltage moves to either the positive or negative saturation positions such that a continuously variable input is transformed into a square wave that undergoes abrupt step changes of positive to negative. This is sometimes referred to as 'clipping'.

B4.14 Calculate the gain of an inverting amplifier.

© IBO 2007

A diagram of an inverting op amp is presented in Figure B.4.14 and shows the input signal being fed into the negative (inverting) terminal of an op amp.

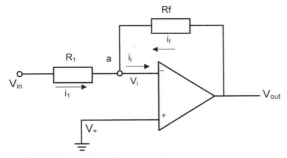

Figure B.4.14 Inverting Op amp diagram

As previously indicated, when considering the non-inverting op amp, because the input resistance (R1) of an op amp is very large, for practical purposes the input current (ii) is considered to approach zero. Similarly, because the op amp gain is very large the input voltage (Vi) is considered to approach zero.

Therefore
$$I_1 = \frac{V_{in}}{R_1} = 0$$

and
$$I_f = \frac{V_{out}}{R_f} = 0$$

Summing the inputs gives:

$$I_1 + I_f = \frac{V_{in}}{R_1} + \frac{V_{ou}}{R_f} = 0$$

Leading to:
$$V_{out} = -\frac{R_f}{R_1} V_{in}$$

$$\text{Gain (A)} = -\frac{R_f}{R_{in}}$$

B4.15 Draw the transfer characteristic for an inverting amplifier

© IBO 2007

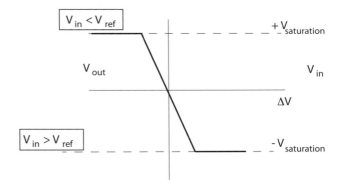

Figure B.4.15 Transfer characteristics af an inverting amplifier

B.4.16 Draw an output waveform of an inverting amplifier, for a given input waveform and gain.

© IBO 2007

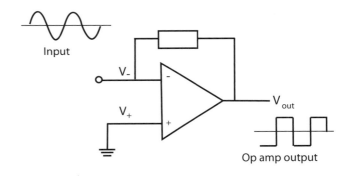

Figure B.4.16 Output waveform for an inverting amplifier

B.4.17 Explain the effect that saturation has on the output waveform of an inverting amplifier.

© IBO 2007

If the input varies as is the case with an AC input which has a sinusoidal wave form, the output voltage will rapidly transition from positive saturation to negative saturation resulting in a square wave output. Because an inverting amplifier is being used, a positive input results in a negative saturation and a negative input creates a positive saturation.

OPTION

325

B5 PROGRAMMABLE INTERFACE CONTROLLERS

B.5.1 Define programmable interface controller (PIC).

A programmable interface controller (PIC) is a small computer complete with input, output and memory that can be programmed to perform simple tasks. Input and output are typically voltages.

Alternatively known as a Peripheral Interface Controllers and trademarked as PIC chips by Arizona Microchip Technology.

B.5.2 Describe why PICs are ubiquitous in almost all modern electronic products.

Because the PIC is capable of storing and running a simple program, many modern electronic devices incorporate PICs to provide the various programmable options. The flexibility of the PICs allows high performance and low cost.

The programme options available in modern washing machines and microwave ovens are provided through PICs.

B.5.3 Explain why in many design contexts only a small proportion of the capacity of a PIC is utilized.

The flexibility of the PIC comes from the wide range of functions for which it can be utilized. In any one application where a PIC is suitable, however, this capacity is largely unnecessary. The use of a purpose-built controller for each and every application, to ensure that full use of capability is made, would be time consuming and expensive to build and maintain compared with the convenience of a single component that can satisfy a large number of different requirements, albeit with redundant capabilities.

B.5.4 Identify reasons why PICs are particularly applicable for portable electronic products.

PICs are popular with both designers and manufacturers because they are:

- compact
- inexpensive
- widely available
- flexible in their use
- flash memory advantages
- access to free development tools.

B.5.5 Discuss why PICs can be regarded as a sustainable technology.

The inclusion of PICs in a product can allow the reduction of other circuitry. Because PICs can replace many circuit components, stock levels can be reduced and assembly can be simplified.

This reduction of components and simplification of assembly can lead to lower cost and greater product reliability.

The ability to reprogram PICs also gives them an extended life.

B.5.6 Explain how PIC technology has improved the electronic systems in car design.

As electronic systems continue to proliferate in modern vehicles, so do the opportunities for PICs to improve, monitor, control or manage the performance of these sometimes-complex components. PICs can manage systems independently or coordinate multiple systems.

PICs find application in the following areas of vehicles:

Lighting - LEDs are replacing incandescent globes throughout vehicles. They are appearing as: headlight systems, interior lights, indicators, warning lamps and are also used for dashboard illumination. PICs find use in voltage management, protection from overheating and controlling efficient energy usage.

Motor control - A large number of motors require managing based on constantly changing situations. PICs not only monitor these motors and their performance, but can turn them on, vary their speed or turn them off, based on pre-programmed performance management criteria. PICs assist in the control and management of vehicle motors such as power steering, washer/wipers, water, fuel and oil pumps.

Sensors – while temperature sensors have previously been the most common application of this technology, PICs are now used in conjunction with humidity, ambient light, pressure and force sensors to manage a range of vehicle operations. Systems employing these include climate control, anti-lock braking, battery health, pollution control and airbags.

Remote control - Low-frequency communication systems negate the need for complex and weighty wire looms. Wireless communication also allows for some measure of control even when the driver is away from the vehicle. Systems using the features of wireless remote include; remote entry devices, tire pressure monitors and GPS units.

B.5.7	Explain how an audiogram represents an individual's hearing, which may be normal at some frequencies and with losses at other frequencies.

© IBO 2007

Our ability to hear sound results from the stimulation of thousands of fine hairs located in the cochlea, a fluid filled spiral shaped organ of the inner ear. Movement of these hairs in response to sound of various frequencies moving through the fluid stimulates the cochlear nerve, leading to the transmission of electrical impulses to the brain. Sound of high frequency (high-pitch), is detected by the hairs at the entrance of the cochlea, while low frequency sound is detected deeper into the cochlear.

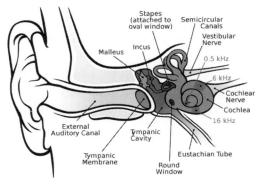

Figure B.5.7a Anatomy of the Human ear [Chittka, L. & Brockmann, A. (2005). Perception Space-The Final Frontier. PloS Biol 3(4)]

Human hearing is typically found to be able to detect sounds in the frequency range of 20Hz to 20000Hz. As we age, the response to the higher frequency end of the spectrum begins to deteriorate due to damage to the fine hairs of the cochlea. Hearing can also be compromised by exposure to loud noise over an extended period of time, which damages the hairs. A hearing test or audiogram provides a measure of hearing acuity detailing the extent to which hearing has been compromised.

An audiogram is a pictorial representation of hearing obtained, based on responses to a spectrum of sound frequencies. Tests are performed with the subject isolated in a quiet room or booth to eliminate extraneous noise. A technician known as an audiologist then feeds a range of pure tones at differing frequency (pitch) and volume (loudness) to either the right or left ear to measure reception, as indicated by the subject. Such a test is known as a Pure Tone Audiogram (PTA).

A plot of the left and right ear responses to these tests measured on an X-Y graph of the sort shown in Figure B.5.7b is produced with loudness in decibels (dB) on the Y-axis and frequency over the range 100Hz to 8000Hz on the X-axis.

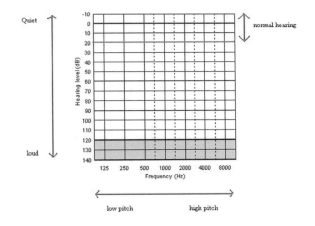

Figure B.5.7b Audiogram [Source: Wikipedia]

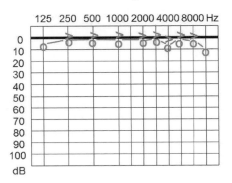

Figure B.5.7c An audiogram showing typical slight hearing variation [Source: Wikipedia]

OPTION

327

> **B.5.8** Explain that digital hearing aids are able to divide incoming sound into distinct bands, which are individually selected for amplification.
>
> © IBO 2007

A hearing aid can be used to regain some of the hearing that has been lost. Older analogue style hearing aids operated by boosting the volume which could have the effect of making some sounds too loud and others too soft. Modern digital devices however can be programmed, based on the results of an audiogram, to correct the specific frequencies affected.

Sounds entering the microphone of a digital hearing aid are converted to an analogue electrical signal and then via an A/D converter to a digital signal. This signal is the sent to the core where it is filtered into various bands, which are individually adjusted for volume based on the personalised program of the wearer. The adjusted signal is the sent to a D/A converter and on to a receiver to be converted to an acoustic signal.

> **B.5.9** Identify the key elements of a digital hearing aid.
>
> © IBO 2007

Microphone: Converts acoustic signal to an analogue electrical signal

Analogue-to-digital (A/D) converter

Core containing filters to separate frequency bands and processed to amplify certain frequency bands

Digital-to-analogue (D/A) converter

Receiver: Analogue signal converted to an acoustic signal

> **B.5.10** Explain how a PIC can contribute to the customization of a hearing aid.
>
> © IBO 2007

A PIC allows the programming of digital hearing aids based on the results of an audiogram, effectively customizing the response of the hearing aid to the requirements of the user.

Further Reading

Maini, A. K. (2007). Digital electronics: principles, devices and applications. John Wiley & Sons Ltd. England.

B6 COMMUNICATION SYSTEMS

> **B.6.1** Define bandwidth, multiplexing, modulation and demodulation.
>
> © IBO 2007

Bandwidth

The difference between the upper and lower frequencies of a band of electromagnetic radiation is called the 'bandwidth'. It is sometimes used to describe the amount of information that can be transmitted over a communications channel within a period of time.

Multiplexing

Multiplexing is the transmission of multiple signals over a single communications channel. A multiplexer therefore performs the task of merging several low-speed transmissions into one high-speed transmission.

Modulation

The successful transmission of information (or intelligence) requires a carrier. Rather than a pigeon, as in former times, modern communication uses electromagnetic radiation as the carrier. In order to add information to electromagnetic radiation, however, we need to modify or modulate the radiation in a controlled manner. It is important to note that the transmission of information is therefore dependent on the process of modulation.

Modulation can be achieved by the variation of some aspect of the electromagnetic signal. The parameters available for control are:

- amplitude or power level
- frequency
- phase of the waveform relative to a standard.

Modulation is the process by which the amplitude, frequency, phase, or intensity of the carrier wave is made to vary in a regular way, allowing the transition of a signal (intelligence) wave.

Demodulation

This is the conversion of a modulated carrier wave into a current equivalent to the original signal. Also called detection.

B.6.2 Explain the principles of frequency division multiplexing.

© IBO 2007

Frequency division multiplexing, (FDM), involves the transmission of different data streams simultaneously over the same channel using different frequencies, (sub-channels), for each stream. At the other end, filters separate out the different frequencies.

Wavelength division multiplexing (WDM), also known as colour multiplexing, can be used.

B.6.3 Explain the principles of time division multiplexing.

© IBO 2007

Time division multiplexing (TDM) is one of the most popular means of increasing the number of signals that can be carried by a fibre. The individual pulses of the various signals are interspersed in a regular manner, increasing the number of signals that are being carried at any time, as illustrated in Figure B.6.3a. The more the signal pulses can be reduced in length, the more signals that can be transmitted simultaneously. A limitation of the technique is that with the shortening of the length, bandwidth increases.

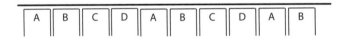

Figure B.6.3a Time division multiplexing (TDM)

B6.4 Explain the limitations of copper wires for information transfer.

© IBO 2007

Size and weight: lengths of copper are significantly heavier than fibre. Copper cable weighs approximately 1190g/m compared to 10.7g/m for optical fibre.

High losses: In copper wires signal losses increase with increasing frequency while signal loss remains stable in optical fibre.

Limited bandwidth: Copper wires are limited to a bandwidth of approximately 500MHz whereas fibre can reach levels of 10GHz.

Variable magnetic field can induce electrical interference and crosstalk: copper wires radiate electromagnetic radiation. The radiation from adjacent wires can interfere with the signal in each wire.

Security: because copper wires radiate electromagnetic radiation information can be intercepted.

More wires require: Because a signal can only be sent in one direction at a time over copper. Copper systems require two wires in order to send signals in opposite directions while fibre can send signals in opposite directions over the same fibre.

B.6.5 Describe an optical fibre.

© IBO 2007

Just as metal wires could be thought of as guides or conduits for information transmitted by electrical current, optical fibres act as guides for light or photons. Optical fibres consist of thin flexible, transparent, fibres of glass or plastic, which make use of the phenomenon of total internal reflection to convey information.

Figure B.6.5a Optical fibres

Image by BigRiz the Creative Commons Attribution-Share Alike 3.0 Unported license.

When a light ray, travelling through one medium, of refractive index η_1, encounters the surface of another medium, of different refractive index η_2, normal to that surface, the light passes from one medium to the other without deviation as illustrated in Figure B6.5b.

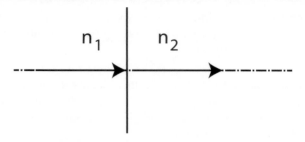

Figure B.6.5b Optical fibres

If, however, the light ray meets the second medium at an angle to the surface, known as the angle of incidence (θ), that is it deviates from normal, some of the light will enter the second medium and be refracted and some will be reflected from the boundary, as shown in Figure B6.5c.

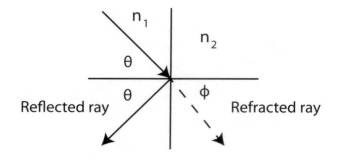

Figure B.6.5c Optical fibres

The path followed by these two light rays will be as follows:-

Reflected: The angle of incidence equals the angle of reflection.

Refracted: Snell's Law

$$\eta_1 \sin\theta = \eta_2 \sin\varphi$$

If $\eta_2 < \eta_1$
the light ray will be refracted away from the normal

If $\eta_2 > \eta_1$
the light ray will be refracted toward the normal

For light approaching a boundary with a medium of lower refractive index, a position is reached where the refracted ray deviates so far from the normal that it does not enter the second medium at all, but rather will travel along the boundary between the two media. A further increase in the angle of incidence results in the beam being reflected totally back into the first medium for 'total internal reflection'. The angle of incidence at which total internal reflection occurs is known as the 'critical angle'.

An optical fibre therefore typically consists of a core through which the light passes and a cladding of lower refractive index. Light satisfying the conditions for total internal reflection will continue a zigzag path along the fibre as indicated in Figure B.6.5d.

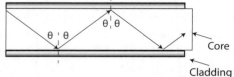

Figure B.6.5d Sectional view of light travelling through a glass fibre by total internal reflection

Adjustments are made to the refractive index of the media used for the core and cladding combination in order to influence the critical angle, and hence the amount of light that can travel down the fibre. The combination influences this by changing the Numerical Aperture (N.A.) of the fibre, and is calculated as indicated below.

$$N.A. = \sqrt{(\eta_1)^2 - (\eta_2)^2}$$

For example if the core had a refractive index (η_1) of 1.484 and the cladding a refractive index, (η_2), of 1.470 the Numerical Aperture (N.A.) would be 0.203.

Calculating the arc sine ($\sin^{-1}$) of 0.203 indicates a critical angle of 11° 43'.

Multiple fibres are usually bundled together and encased in a protective jacket, (usually consisting of PVC or polyurethane), to protect the fibres from moisture and physical damage.

> **B.6.6 Describe how fibre optic cables are able to transfer information.**
>

Although light can be used to transmit data in an analogue form (by varying the intensity or frequency of an optical signal), information is usually converted into digital form. The digitized signal is then converted into an optical signal using a diode laser. Laser light is introduced into the end of the fibre through a connector at the appropriate angle for total internal reflection. Because loss of light within the fibre is very small, information can be sent efficiently over long distances. At the terminus the light pulses are detected and reconstituted into a digital electrical signal.

While optical fibres provide a high quality transmission media, some loss of signal still occurs due to impurities, which act to disperse the signal. Because of dispersion, the signal undergoes attenuation or reduction in strength. Periodic amplification of the signal is required. Amplification of optical fibre signals may be attained by an electronic amplifier situated in the line, or an optical amplifier.

> B.6.7 Explain how fibre optics are able to transfer information in large quantities.

Because optical fibres are capable of transmitting very high frequencies, (of the order of 3×10^{14}Hz), a correspondingly wide bandwidth is available for the transmission of information.

> B.6.8 Draw a block diagram for an optical fibre transmission link.

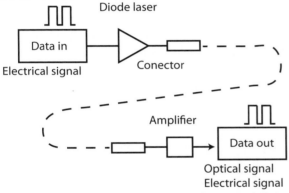

Figure B.6.8a Schematic illustration of an optical fibre system

> B.6.9 Identify three types of optical fibre.
>
> B.6.10 Explain the difference between a single-mode and a multimode optical fibre.

The electromagnetic wave that carries the signal in a fibre forms a pattern known as a mode.

In multimode fibres more than one mode travels along the fibre as shown in Figure B.6.10a. In this Figure, three light rays, (electromagnetic waves), are shown travelling along the fibre, one is travelling at the critical angle, one is travelling axially and the third is travelling in a mode somewhere between these two. Those rays taking a zigzag path take longer to reach their destination than the ray taking an axial path, due to the difference in distance

travelled. It will be appreciated therefore that a myriad of speeds can be present. The presence of multiple modes results in a broadening of the signal called intermodal dispersion.

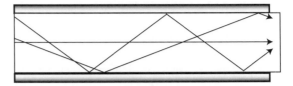

Figure B.6.10a Intermodal dispersion within a fibre

The number of modes that are present in a fibre depend on a number of factors such as the numerical aperture (N.A.), wavelength of the light (λ) and the core diameter and can be determined using the equation below. It can be shown from this equation that the biggest factor influencing the number of modes present is the core diameter, such that as the core diameter decreases the number of modes can be reduced to a single mode.

$$Number\ of\ modes = \frac{\left(Diameter\ of\ core\ x\ NA\ x\ \frac{\pi}{\lambda}\right)^2}{2}$$

For example, if the core diameter were 80μm and N.A was 0.203 and the light source was a laser with a wavelength of 850nm.

$$Number\ of\ modes = \frac{\left(80\ x\ 10^{-6}\ x\ 0.203\ x\ \frac{\pi}{850\ x\ 10^{-9}}\right)^2}{2}$$

$$= 1801.374$$

Only a finite number of modes can be contained in a fibre, so that in any calculation the result is rounded down to the nearest whole number. In the present example 1801 modes are present.

A core diameter of 40μm and other factors remaining the same as the example above would have 450modes.

Fibres that carry more than one mode are known as multimode fibres.

There are three basic types of optical fibre available, each with its advantages and disadvantages. These are Multimode (MM), Single mode (SM) and plastic optical fibre (POF).

Multimode (MM) Fibre

Multimode fibre is available in two forms and represents different ways in which problems with the presence of differentials in the speed of light rays as they travel through the fibre, and the resultant signal dispersion, are dealt with.

Stepped Index (SI) Multimode fibres

These fibres represent the traditional form of fibre optic construction and are made of fused silica often doped with varying percentages of elements such as titanium and germanium and consist of a core fibre surrounded by cladding of distinctly different refractive index. Core fibres are typically in the range 50 to 100µm in diameter, while the cladding material is typically 125 to 150µm diameter. This cladding is of lower refractive index forming a distinct step with respect to refractive index and facilitates the passage of the light along the fibre as shown in Figure 6.10b.

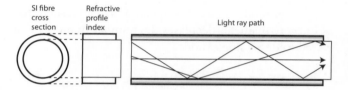

Figure B.6.10b Construction of a Stepped Index (SI) Multimode fibres

Graded Index (GI) Multimode fibres

In these fibres, the refractive index is not uniform but undergoes a gradual change on moving from the centre toward the fibre surface. As a light ray passes through this graded index, it is continuously refracted slightly into a curved path (illustrated in Figure B.6.10c), as compared to the straight path followed in a stepped index fibre shown previously in Figure B.6.10b.

The number of modes in a GI fibre is approximately half that of a stepped index fibre, so the equation for mode number in a GI fibre is divided by 4 rather than 2 as was the case for SI fibres.

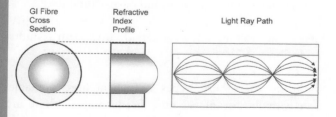

Figure B.6.10c Construction of a Graded Index (GI) Multimode fibres

Single mode (SM) optical fibre also known as monomode fibre

These fibres are also of the stepped index type, but differ in that the core diameter has been reduced to such a small diameter (<10µm) that only one mode of light can be transmitted, as illustrated in Figure B6.10d. Because the dispersion is very low and transmission over long distances is possible.

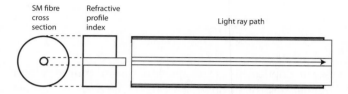

Figure B.6.10d Construction of a Single mode (SM) optical fibre also known as monomode fibre

Plastic Optical Fibre (POF)

These fibres are typically manufactured from a core of Polymethylmethacrylate (PMMA) and a cladding of fluorinated polymer. These fibres are much larger than those previously discussed, commonly being 1mm (1000µm) in diameter, with the greater proportion (approximately 96%) of the cross-section consisting of the core, as illustrated in Figure B.6.10e.

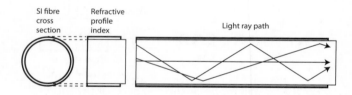

Figure B.6.10e Construction of Plastic Optical Fibre

B.6.11 Identify the advantages and disadvantages of each type of optical fibre.

Single mode optical fibres

Advantages:
- flexible
- thickness allows bundling
- no arrival time disparity so cleaner signal
- less loss over length due to small refraction
- higher speeds and greater bandwidth possible
- can carry ×100 more information than multimode fibre.

Disadvantages:
- more difficult to couple
- manufacturing cost high
- laser diode connection required.

Applications:
- long distance transmission 40-120km.

Multimode optical fibres

Stepped Index (SI)

Advantages:
- easy to connect
- cheap to manufacture.

Disadvantages:
- limiting bandwidth
- limited to short distances due to pulse broadening (dispersion).

Applications:
- LAN network & video surveillance.

Graded Index (GI)

Advantages:
- light travels slowly in high-index region, compared with low-index region equalising transit times and reducing the broadening of the pulse.

Disadvantages:
- more expensive to manufacture than SI fibres
- intermediate distance

Applications:
- Limited to short distances due to pulse broadening, (dispersion), limiting bandwidth.

Single mode optical fibres

Advantages:
- flexible
- thickness allows bundling
- no arrival time disparity so cleaner signal
- less loss over length due to small refraction
- higher speeds and greater bandwidth possible
- can carry ×100 more information than multimode fibre.

Disadvantages:
- more difficult to couple
- manufacturing cost high
- laser diode connection required.

Applications:
- long distance transmission 40-120km.

Plastic Optical Fibre (POF)

Advantages:
- strong
- easy to use
- good stability

- difficult to bend
- inexpensive to produce.

Disadvantages:
- attenuates signal more than glass making it unsuitable for long distances.

Applications:
- lighting
- motor vehicles
- consumer electronics
- limited to low speed transmission and distances less than 100m.

B.6.12 Explain the advantages of optical fibres for information transfer.

© IBO 2007

Traditionally, copper wire has been used for telecommunications, however, fibre optics offer significant advantages compared to the metal counterpart. Today optical fibre is the defacto standard for land-based transmission of data.

Compared with conventional metal wire (copper wire), optical fibres are:

- light weight
- low dispersion
- crush resistant
- low attenuation
- high bandwidth
- resistance to kinks
- high degrees of flexibility
- unaffected by power surges
- unaffected by electromagnetic interference
- difficult to tap, leading to increased security.

Satellite telecommunication systems rely on the positioning of a communications satellite in an orbit around the Earth to transmit from one location to another. Information is sent in a digital form between a ground station and satellite using microwave signals, see Figure B.6.13a. Due to their height above the earth, satellite systems can service a wide area and are particularly suited to the provision of telecommunication services to isolated areas. This is sometimes described as having a large 'footprint', in that the area on the ground accessible by the satellite is large.

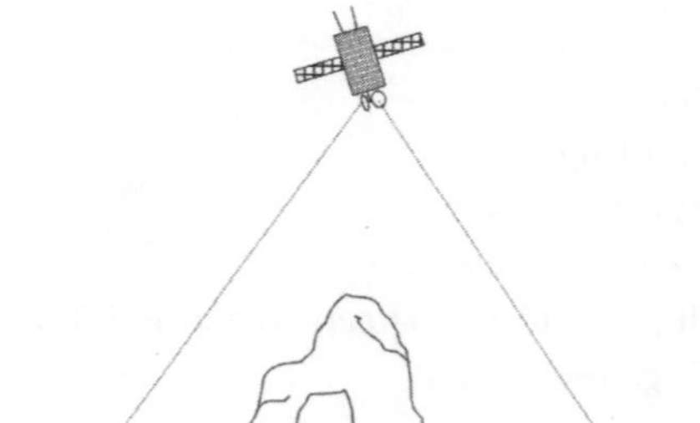

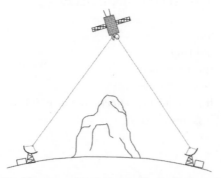

Figure B.6.13a Communication satellite in geostationary orbit in communication with Earth stations.

Analogue signals coming into an earth station via the wire telephone system undergo analogue-to digital conversion (ADC) before being transmitted by microwave. On receipt at its final destination, the microwave signal is converted back to an analogue signal by digital to analogue conversion (DAC) and sent via the wire telephone system.

B.6.14 Identify the advantages and disadvantages of satellite systems.

© IBO 2007

There are many types of telecommunication satellite systems. These systems rely on the positioning of a communications satellite in an orbit around the Earth. Through the use of differing orbits, frequencies and the transmission of very different types of signals using a range of power levels, satellites systems vary according to their intended purpose.

There are four general system designs, which are differentiated by the type of orbit in which the satellites operate: Geostationary Orbit (GEO), Low-earth Orbit, Medium-earth Orbit (MEO), and Highly Elliptical Orbit (HEO). Each of these system designs has various strengths and weaknesses in its ability to provide specific communications services.

Geostationary earth orbit (GEO) satellites (Figure B.6.14a) are placed in orbit directly above the equator at an altitude of approximately 35,700km and have a period of rotation similar to that of the Earth. This means that once placed in orbit they retain their relative geographic position, appearing to be stationary, hence the name geostationary. These satellites are also known as geosynchronous satellites. Because of the height of their orbit and size of their broadcast footprint, fewer GEO satellites are required for global coverage. Geostationary satellites typically cover one third of the Earth's surface at a time.

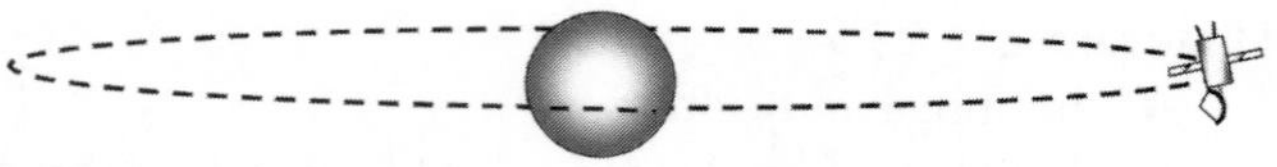

Figure B.6.14a Communications satellite in geostationary orbit.

Most weather and communications satellites such as those used for 'live' television transmission, maintain a geostationary orbit. A geostationary satellite provides the advantage for remote sensing that it always views the Earth from the same perspective, which means that it can record the same image at brief intervals. This option is interesting in connection with observations of constantly changing weather conditions. Their fixed location also means that the sophisticated tracking equipment needed for the MEO and LEO satellites is not required. The disadvantage of the geostationary orbit is the great distance to the Earth. It sets limits upon how high a spatial resolution can be achieved, while also increasing the consequences of failure.

Advantages:

- higher bandwidth
- allows remote sensing
- a fixed antenna link can be maintained with the satellite
- lower gravitational pull means they can stay in orbit longer.

Disadvantages:

- resolution limited
- higher costs to put into orbit
- require line-of-sight communication
- greater dependence on fewer satellites
- higher orbit leads to transmission delay
- common track above the equator poses problems in managing old satellites
- increased damage to electronics due to exposure to radiation and charge accumulation.

Medium earth orbit (MEO) requires more satellites for global coverage than GEO but less than LEO. Orbiting at between 2000 and 35786 km these satellites fly in three orbital planes at an orbit inclined at an angle of approximately 55 degrees, providing mobile phone and data communications. GPS satellites orbit at an altitude of approximately 20,000km.

Because MEO satellites spend only a short time overhead (approximately 20 minutes), several satellites are required to maintain coverage. A typical network may require around 27 satellites. Continuous coverage is obtained by the 'hand-off' of data from satellite to satellite. Such communication requires sophisticated tracking and switching equipment.

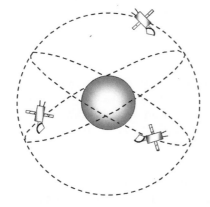

Figure B.6.14b Communications satellite in MEO orbit.

Advantages:

- require fewer satellites than LEO
- higher capacity than LEO

Disadvantages

- shorter orbital life than GEO
- require line-of-sight communication
- higher orbit leads to some transmission delay.

Low earth orbit (LEO) satellites are smaller and cheaper to launch than their counterparts. The biggest advantage of these satellites is that there is little or no signal delay.

While the low earth orbit satellite is revolving in its orbit, the Earth rotates on its axis below. Every time the satellite makes a complete rotation, a new strip of the Earth's surface is scanned, and after a certain number of rotations the entire surface of the Earth will have been scanned. The satellites orbit at an altitude of approximately 160 to 2000km.

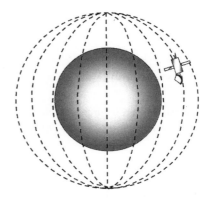

Figure B.6.14c Communications satellite in LEO orbit

A telecommunication satellite in low Earth orbit will appear in the west and move towards the east, being visible for about 10 minutes at a time. Should a transmission take more than the few minutes that any one satellite is in view, a LEO craft must 'hand off' between satellites in order to complete the transmission. In general, this can be accomplished by constantly relaying signals between the satellite and various ground stations, or by communicating between the satellites themselves using inter-satellite links.

In the last decade other system concepts have been developed around the use of large numbers of low Earth orbiting satellites. These systems guarantee the continuity of their services by ensuring the constant availability of at least one satellite (in most cases two, three or even four satellites) over the user's line of sight. This collection of LEO satellites is designed to maximise the ability of ground equipment to 'see' a satellite at any time, which can overcome the difficulties caused by earth-based obstructions such as trees and buildings.

Unfortunately LEO satellites have a shorter life span than other systems.

Advantages:

- little or no signal delay
- smaller and cheaper to launch than their counterparts.

Disadvantages

- sophisticated tracking equipment needed
- LEO satellites generally have a shorter battery life than others
- shorter life span than other systems due to the increased gravitational pull.

Further Reading

Carlson, A. B. (2009). *Communication Systems 5th edition.* Mcgraw Hill Higher Education.

Fitz, M. P. (2007). *Fundamentals of Communications Systems* (Communications Engineering).

Fulay, P. P. (2010). *Electronic, Magnetic, and Optical Materials (Advanced Materials and Technologies).* CRC Press Inc.

Haykin, S. (2009). *Communication Systems.* John Wiley & Sons Inc. USA.

Maini, A. K. & Agrawal, V. (2010). *Satellite Technology: Principles and Applications. 2nd Edition.* John Wiley & Sons Ltd. United Kingdom.

Maral, G. Bousquet, M. & Sun, Z. (2010). *Satellite Communications Systems: Systems, Techniques and Technology, 5th Edition.* John Wiley & Sons Ltd. United Kingdom.

Fleming, J. W. France, P. W. Sigel, G. H & Takahashi, S. Editors. (2011). *Optical Fiber Materials and Processing: Volume 172 (MRS Proceedings) Materials Research Society.* Pasadena. California. USA.

B7 GLOBAL STANDARDS FOR DIGITAL ELECTRONIC PRODUCTS

> **B7.1** Explain the importance of global standards for digital electronic product manufacturers.
>
> © IBO 2007

Standardization allows the technology to be used anywhere in the world. Conflicts are reduced due to the commonality and interchangeability between devices, of software, protocols and interfaces. These features make international trade easier and more efficient

Generic standards also allow a large number of developers to produce equipment and software, allowing greater functionality, along with faster development and innovation. Standardization also assists with moves towards convergence as economies of scale and potential market size come into play.

> **B7.2** Describe how companies either exploit a generic data system or develop their own system.
>
> © IBO 2007

By producing products with new features that exploit generic data systems, a company potentially gains customers interested in upgrading without the need to completely change their device platform.

Company-specific standards can initially maximize profits if competitor devices are not available, however, as competitors begin to appear using different standards, market segmentation may occur, forcing customers to choose one system over another. Extra costs are also potentially involved and innovation may be slower.

> **B.7.3** Explain how standards have impacted on multifunctionality of personal entertainment products. .
>
> © IBO 2007

The multifunctionality of today's personal entertainment products has only been possible through the introduction of standards that have allowed some commonality and interoperability between systems. Such standards have allowed agreement in a very competitive market on the introduction of common interfaces (USB, HDMI, etc) and protocols for the use of third party plug-ins and peripherals.

This connectivity has allowed additional functions to be accessed. Games consoles such as the Sony Playstation 3 for example, can be used not only as a games console but also to act as an entertainment hub by playing DVDs, connect to a television, video player or the Internet.

> **B.7.4 Explain the benefits of the adoption of generic standards for the manufacturer.**

Common standards allow manufacturers to develop devices that benefit from the software developments of others. Consumers can also purchase devices confident of connectivity with peripheral devices. The consumer confidence generated by the adoption of generic standards effectively increases the market for the products.

> **B.7.5 Explain the benefits of the adoption of generic standards for the user.**

Generic standards mean that digital electronic products can be used anywhere in the world with confidence that they will continue to operate. Generic standards also provide consumer confidence that parts and repairs are readily available. Connectability between systems is improved, as is the consumers' ability to migrate from one device to another with greater confidence.

> **B.7.6 Discuss the implications of company specific standards in the marketplace.**

Company specific standards provide companies with a competitive advantage in the market place by limiting the number of competitors that have access to the technology. Patent protection can make access by competitors expensive.

While company specific standards can lead to brand identification and the development of brand loyalty based on familiarity, the presence of several competing standards in the marketplace can lead to market fragmentation. In such a market consumers may be reluctant to commit to a purchase for fear of it losing the struggle for survival.

Many consumers to this day remember the competition for market supremacy between Sony's Betamax and JVC's VHS format videotape fought out in the 1970s.

Today, company specific standards in software cause issues surrounding data transfer and connectability. Both Microsoft® and Apple® have taken steadfastly different directions when developing their operating systems. This causes third party developers to choose to develop around one system or both. The result of this is either some programs not being readily available on both platforms or a good deal of duplication in the development of two opposing systems to perform the same goal.

Further Reading

Ludwig-Becker, M. (1998). *Electronic systems quality management handbook.* McGraw-Hill. London

Rosenau, J. N. & Singh, J. P. (2002). *Information technologies and global politics: the changing scope of power.* State University of New York Press.

Owen, D. (2008). *The Betamax vs VHS Format War* http://www.mediacollege.com/video/format/compare/betamax-vhs.html

Bylund, A. (2010). *The Format Wars: Laser and (Creative) Destruction.* http://arstechnica.com/gadgets/guides/2010/01/is-the-end-of-the-format-wars-upon-us.ars/

Weaver, G. (2006). *A Technology Environment Overview.* Kaldus Consulting http://www.kaludisconsulting.com/pdf/823.KAL.techoverview2.pdf

OPTION

337

B.8 THE SMART HOME

B.8.1 Outline the concept of a smart home.

B.8.2 Identify two electronic systems that could be incorporated into a smart home environment.

© IBO 2007

A smart home is one that integrates a number of automated devices to control functions such as air-conditioning, lighting, security and entertainment systems. Devices are often connected through a computer system allowing their programming and monitoring from either a central control system or distributed systems.

Two electronic systems that could be incorporated in to a smart home include heating/cooling as well as security systems.

B.8.3 Identify input–process–output devices appropriate to the design of heating and lighting systems in a smart home.

© IBO 2007

Figure B.8.3 shows simple input/output systems schematics for the management and control of heating and lighting.

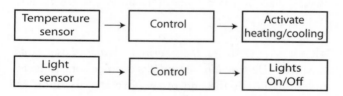

Figure B.8.3 Input/output schematics

B.8.4 Explain how modern electronic computer systems are used to monitor and perform functions in the home.

© IBO 2007

To date, the full potential of the smart house concept has found only limited penetration into the consumer market. Most modern electronic equipment, however, has incorporated a measure of computer control for some time, through the use of programmable systems that allow a 'set and forget' operation.

Such equipment includes DVD players that allow the programming of disc and track playback, TV controls that allow automatic recording of programs, ovens that offer a selection of various cooking options and air conditioning systems that control room temperature at a desired level.

As this market continues to mature, more systems, currently used in industry for sophisticated management of equipment and environments, will filter through into the domestic marketplace for use in households.

B.8.5 Identify a range of applications relevant to the implementation of a smart home.

© IBO 2007

Smart home control systems can be installed to monitor and sense before providing an automated, pre-programmed response. Systems or operations that may be integrated into a smart home include controls for:

- heating and cooling
- opening or closing blinds.
- security - video surveillance, alarms, locks
- lighting - sensors for efficient management
- energy conservation - timers for off-peak usage
- entertainment systems - control and distribution of media
- smoke detectors - automated fire suppression or alarms
- inventory control - (e.g. food), through Radio Frequency Identification (RFID).

B.8.6 Explain how PICs are integrated into control circuits to implement the smart home concept.

© IBO 2007

Each of the devices in a smart home uses PICs to perform the programmable functions of the control circuit.

B.8.7 Identify a range of input options for locking and/or unlocking a door.

© IBO 2007

Security systems vary widely in their cost and level of sophistication. At a basic level, most systems for locking and unlocking of a door use a mechanism that advanced or retracts a pin between the door and the doorframe. When advanced the pin prevents the door from opening.

Security features for such a mechanism require that the pin remains in place and the door locked until the lock is released and the pin can be easily retracted. The effectiveness of this system in terms of security therefore relies on the security of the lock release mechanism.

Such mechanisms can be divided into three basic levels:

Physical possession: Keys, ID badge, Swipe card
This represents the lowest level of security since the loss, damage or unregulated copying of the physical item can compromise security.

Items range from the metal key used for centuries, to the swipe card made of plastic with a magnetic strip or electronic chip, familiar to most people with credit cards today, used to activate the door unlocking system (Figure B.8.7a). Card entry technology is widely used in the hotel industry to allow guests into their rooms. Because this technology operates electronically, the system can recognise levels of access authority and maintain records of time and date of use. The security of systems using physical items however relies on the item being protected from theft or unauthorised copying.

Figure B.8.7a Physical possession level of door entry represented by metal keys and swipe cards

Memory: Password, PIN code: Relies on the users memory and confidentiality of the code. Such systems, while offering a greater level of security than the level of physical possession, are still not secure against criminal interception. Such a system is shown in Figure B.8.7b where a numerical code must be entered via a keypad to unlock the door.

Figure B.8.7b Memory based door security system represented by a keypad and requiring the entry of a numerical code

Biometrics: Systems based on biometric data use information unique to an individual's physical characteristics rather than physical possessions or memory. Biometric devices are among the more sophisticated technologies available today and use pattern recognition algorithms to match characteristics unique to an individual such as a fingerprint, speech or iris pattern.

Two examples of biometric systems, a fingerprint sensor and iris scanner are presented in Figures B8.7c and d. Such systems verify the entry of a specific individual rather than just the use of a valid key or code and are based on three basic properties of the biological data:

- universality - all people possess the characteristic
- distinctiveness – no two people are alike, that is, the data is unique to each individual
- permanence – the characteristics are consistent and unchanging over time.

Figure B.8.7c Biometric finger print recognition lock

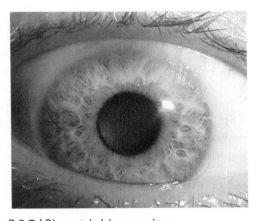

Figure B.8.7d Biometric Iris scanning

A comparison of some of the features of several selected biometric systems is presented in Figure B.8.7e. Security systems operating biometric sensors as identity verification mechanisms are capable of storing pattern data for a large number of individuals with various levels of security access rights. As may be seen from Figure B.8.7e one of the most reliable systems available uses fingerprint recognition.

HL

OPTION

339

	Facial Recognition	Fingerprints	Hand Geometry	Iris Recognition	Retinal Scan	Speaker Verification	Vascular Biometrics
Universality	Low	High	Medium	High	Very High	Low	Medium / High
Accuracy	Low	High	Medium	Very high	High	Low	Medium
Permanence / Stability	Medium	High	Medium	High	High	Medium	High
Ease of use	High	High	High	High	Low	High	Medium / High
Public Acceptability	Medium	High	High	Medium	Low	High	High
Limitation	Changes with age, Lighting, Make-up	Damage to fingers	Diseases eg Arthritis	Diseases eg Iritis	Diseases eg Retinitis, Diabetes, Hypertension	Background noise, colds, etc.	Affected by Drugs

Figure B.8.7e Comparison of Biometric systems [Source: Biometric Technology Application Manual Volume One: Biometric Basics. http://www.nationalbiometric.org/]

B.8.8 Explain how a door can be locked and/or unlocked electronically.

© IBO 2007

In a conventional door lock, a cylinder containing a number of tumblers with pins positioned at various heights is secured in the door frame. When the correct key is introduced into the lock the notches on the key push the pins in each tumbler to a height sufficient so that the cylinder is free to rotate - unlocking the door. A number of electronic locking systems are available, but one common form uses keypad technology and an access code. When an access code is entered on the keypad that code is electronically compared with the expected code. If accepted as valid, the door is unlocked.

B.8.9 Explain the role of valves to control water flow, for example, into a bath.

© IBO 2007

A valve represents a device that allows the flow of a fluid passing along a pipe to be regulated. When we turn the handle of a tap, we are opening or closing a valve.

The operation of a valve can be electronically controlled and, if connected to a computer system, programmed to open and close at specific times or under specific conditions. Temperature sensors linked to the computer system can be used to coordinate the relative amount of hot and cold water entering a bath to achieve and maintain a desired temperature. Similarly, level sensors can be used to control the fill rate and volume.

B.8.10 Identify reasons for using smart technology to open and close windows or blinds.

© IBO 2007

Smart technology in homes and businesses may be employed to automate processes in response to a range of stimuli in an effort to manage and optimize environments or systems. Sensors may be deployed to measure conditions that allow for the control of temperature or noise through the opening and closing of windows and blinds. The system may be programmed to respond to light, sound and/or temperature sensors so it may also act to manage energy efficiency. This form of technology may provide assistance for people with a disability.

B.8.11 Explain how a motor could be applied to open or close ventilators, windows or blinds.

© IBO 2007

If environmental conditions exceed a set point, an electric motor can be activated to open or close ventilators, windows or blinds to control interior conditions, based on information received from temperature sensors.

In the same fashion, noise sensors may be connected to motors, driving gears to open and close windows in an

HL

OPTION

attempt to reduce excessive noise as may be associated with peak hour traffic or overpassing aircraft. Time-based security systems may also open and close blinds to give the appearance of occupancy.

> **B.8.12 Identify a range of input sensors applicable to a home security system.**

Strategically placed sensors that blend into, or are embedded into, the architecture of a home can provide secure surveillance and monitoring of interior and exterior environments. Input sensors include:

- gas
- laser
- smoke
- glassbreak
- infra-red heat
- video camera
- pressure sensor
- motion detector.

Depending on their purpose, these sensors may be linked secondary systems such as alarms or 'back to base' systems, designed to protect the home from intruders. Other sensors and systems may secure the home from damage caused by fire or smoke.

> **B.8.13 Identify a range of output devices applicable to a home security system.**

Output devices are designed to provide an indication that an event has occurred, a limit tripped or response has been delivered. Output devices appear in a range of visual, audio and electronic responses including:

- data logging
- video monitors
- LED warning lamps
- printouts and reports
- space or spot lighting
- alarms - buzzers, bells
- automated communications e.g. SMS.

> **B.8.14 Describe the role of video monitors in a home security system.**

Video monitors allow surveillance of outdoor areas without the need to physically investigate. In this way occupants can remain safe inside their home while conducting a scan for intruders or identify visitors before opening the door. Cameras may be located inside buildings and connected to service providers or the internet to allow real time remote surveillance of interiors.

> **B.8.15 Define bit rate, resolution and refresh rate.**

Bit Rate: is the amount of data transmitted by a video camera per second. The bit rate is measured in terms of bits per second (bps).

Resolution: is a measure of the number of pixels used to create the image on a CRT or LCD screen, where a pixel represents the smallest screen picture element and which in combination are used to create an image.

Refresh rate: is the rate at which an image on a CRT or LCD monitor is redrawn or refreshed. The refresh rate is typically expressed in terms of Hertz (Hz). Refresh rates of greater than 60Hz are required to avoid noticeable screen flicker.

> **B.8.16 Calculate the bit rate requirement in a given situation.**

The bit rate is related to the system requirements by the relationship below.

Bit rate required = number of rows × pixels per row × bits per pixel × refresh rate × number of monitors using link

Many governments have introduced CCTV Video surveillance of public areas as a means of reducing crime. Such systems rely on offenders being identified from the surveillance video, however, the resolution of such images particularly under low light conditions can make such identification difficult. This is because under low light conditions many cameras increase the gain to amplify the signal. In doing this, the image becomes 'noisy' and the compression software used (MPEG, JPEG etc) cannot determine what is useful information and what is not. A consequence of this is that bit rate requirements increase as the image quality decreases. Some use of infra-red illumination in low light conditions has been used in special applications and this can reduce bit rate requirements by reducing the signal noise.

HL

OPTION

B.8.17 Explain the significance of the limited bit rate capacity of a home security data link.

As can be seen from the relationship presented in B.8.16, the limited bit rate of home security systems can mean that transmission is slow and can produce images of low resolution and poor quality.

B.8.18 Explain how the specification for security systems would differ for different applications.

The cost and complexity of security systems varies a great deal depending on the level of security desired, assessment of the security threat and the consequences of inadequate security. The requirements of an average family living in a suburban home will be significantly different from those of a Prime Minister or President, or those charged with the security of nuclear weapons.

Security systems for the home may be limited to motion-activated lighting at night and a simple alarm system to alert of a break-in. High priority security systems may incorporate a number of different systems operating in combination, including sound and motion detectors, pressure sensors, video surveillance, time locks and biometric security.

B.8.19 Discuss the ethical issues relating to the use of home security systems.

The installation of a home security system carries with it an obligation to ensure that the privacy and comfort of neighbours is not affected. Camera surveillance systems that are installed to monitor the exterior grounds of a property should not include in their scope of view neighbouring properties, effectively 'spying' on neighbours. Similarly, video systems that may be legitimately set-up within a home to monitor a sleeping infant or its daily activities, from another room or by internet access, can be fraught with ethical issues of invasion of privacy if extended to adolescents or adults.

Movement activated lighting systems can also disturb and annoy neighbours if not situated such that they do not continually activate at night from spurious signals such as tree branches moving in the wind.

Some of the issues raised extend past ethical and moral consideration and may even have legal implication. Careful consideration may be required when establishing home security systems to ensure they were not in breach of human rights legislation.

Ethical issues surrounding home security arise from questions such as:

- are the surveillance sytems covert or visible?
- do people know they are being viewed and/or recorded?
- is information stored for later use?
- how long is data held for?
- who has access to this data?
- is the system recording vision and sound?

Further Reading

Crosby, I. *Benefits of using infrared (IR) illumination in modern surveillance environments.* Bosch Security Systems.
[http://www.sourcesecurity.com/news/articles/co-289-ga.5492.html]

Biometric Security Overview
http://www.technology.com/ct/Technology-Article.asp?ArtNum=10

National Biometric Security Project
http://www.nationalbiometric.org/

Briere, D. & Hurley, P. (2007) *Smart Homes For Dummies.* For Dummies. Wiley Publishing Inc. Hoboken. NJ.

Meyer, G. (2005). *Smart Home Hacks: Tips & Tools for Automating Your House.* O'Reilly Media Inc. USA.

Goodwin, S. (2010). *Smart Home Automation with Linux.* Springer-Verlag. New York.

Elsenpeter, R.C. & Velte, A. (2003). *Build Your Own Smart Home* Anthony. McGraw Hill/Osborne. California. USA

B9 DISPOSAL OF ELECTRONIC PRODUCTS

> **B.9.1** Define product stewardship, dematerialization, service costs and upgradeability.
>
> © IBO 2007

Product Stewardship is a program being undertaken in most developed countries aimed at reducing the impact of consumer electronics on the environment. Product stewardship involves both redesign of products by manufacturers taking into account end-of-life issues associated with e-waste, and provision for its effective collection and safe disposal. Initial focus has been on computers and TVs.

Influenced by factors such as:

- lack of landfills
- collection costs
- cost of disposal
- elimination of hazardous materials from waste.

Dematerialization can be defined as the progressive reduction in the amount of energy and/or materials used in the production of a product. Some of the interrelated factors associated with dematerialization are indicated in Figure B.9.10a.

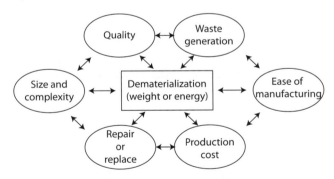

Figure B.9.10a Factors affecting, and affected by, the dematerialization process. Economic and population growth, of course, also strongly interact with many of the factors.

Herman, R. et al. (1990). Dematerialization http://phe. rockefeller.edu/dematerialization/

Dematerialization does not mean a decline in the use of materials will occur, as increased production may result in a growth of material use overall, although the individual use of material per unit decreases with design changes and miniaturization. This phenomenon is sometimes referred to as Jevons' Paradox or the rebound effect. In 1865, the English economist, William Stanley Jevons, found that the increased efficiency of newer steam engines resulted in an increased use of coal rather than a reduction. This was because the increased efficiency led to the increased expansion of steam power.

Service costs refer to product maintenance or repairs. Repair of electronic equipment requires the attention of skilled technicians and can necessitate a significant amount of time to diagnose the problem. The costs of repair can therefore be high and the decision to repair is usually based on an assessment of the relative costs of repair versus the purchase of a new and possibly more capable replacement. Service costs also include the possibility of regular maintenance due to wear and tear or simply as a function of use. Products such as digital cameras and automobiles have regular service programs that should be met to keep the item working at peak efficiency. Lack of attention to appropriate maintenance could lead to product failure.

Upgradeability is the extent to which the functionality of a system can be modified to the latest performance standards without the need for it to be completely replaced.

> **B.9.2** Discuss the issues associated with advanced electronic technology and product life cycle.
>
> © IBO 2007

Electronic products have evolved rapidly over the last several decades, and this evolution has resulted in the rapid rise of electronic products that are considered obsolete and in need of replacement after a relatively short life. The rate at which electronic obsolescence is occurring exceeds that of any other technology in human history and this phenomenon has resulted in a significant and growing amount of electronic waste.

Apart from filling land fills, many of these products contain materials that could cause environmental damage if they were to leach into the surrounding soil and ground water.

In order to counteract this, trend legislation has been enacted requiring manufacturers to make provision for the collection and safe disposal of end-of-life (EOL) electronic waste. This strategy is known as the Extended Product Responsibility (EPR).

The strategies employed for dealing with the large amount of end-of-life (EOL) electronic waste consist of:

- reuse
- disposal
- recycling
- remanufacture.

B.9.3 List the implications of product stewardship for manufacturers.

© IBO 2007

To successfully meet their responsibilities under product stewardship, manufacturers must consider:

- legislation to the product category
- design/redesign for easy dismantling
- strategies and systems for disposal of e-waste responsibly
- mechanisms and systems for collection of products at end-of-life
- marking of components for ease of identification and separation in end-of-life phase.

B.9.4 Explain why electronic products are designed for disassembly.

B.9.5 Discuss strategies that can be used for the disassembly of electronic products.

© IBO 2007

Products are specifically designed for disassembly to allow them to be easily dismantled and separated into parts that can be, reused, recycled or disposed of. Some components, within electronic products in particular, must be disposed of using particular protocols. These components, such as batteries, may contain toxic or hazardous materials.

Strategies employed to assist with design for disassembly include:

- design for easy access
- reduce the number of parts
- clearly label component materials
- use standard components were possible
- avoid or reduce the use of toxic materials
- eliminate the use of adhesives and screws were possible and replace with snap connections.

B.9.6 Explain how legislation controls the disposal of electronic products.

© IBO 2007

The legislation shifts responsibility and costs of the collection and disposal of electronic products to the original equipment manufacturer (OEM), through the establishing guidelines for the effective disposal of e-waste and setting targets for product recovery.

B.9.7 Explain the impact of product take back legislation on the design of electronic products.

© IBO 2007

Because the responsibility of end-of-life disposal of electronic waste is made the responsibility of the manufacturer, market forces act to encourage designs that need less material or have fewer parts, making recycling easier and cheaper. Designers may also consider making products that are more durable and last longer, to reduce the need for constant product recovery.

B.9.8 Discuss the advantages and disadvantages of electronic disposal legislation for the designer, consumer and manufacturer.

© IBO 2007

The advantages and disadvantages of electronic disposal legislation for designers, consumers and manufacturers are documented in Figure B.9.8.

Because the OEM is held to be responsible for costs of e-waste recycling, market forces act to encourage design changes that improve recyclability and reduce costs. Unfortunately increases in the costs of products may be passed on to consumers due to end-of-life recovery expenses.

The use of less material, or material substitutions with less toxic materials, are strategies that will both have positive affects on the environment. Material substitutions, however, may come at an increased cost.

Improved product life through more durable products means consumers are not constantly replacing products before they are ready. Improved product life unfortunately reduces sales volumes for manufacturers and consumers may miss the availability of regular technological changes or changing fashion trends.

In response to legislation, manufacturers produce products that are more easily recycled and larger percentages of devices are recovered. The challenge for designers and manufacturers is to meet the legislative requirements for sometimes very complex pieces of equipment.

> **B.9.9 Compare reuse and recycling of electronic products.**
>
> © IBO 2007

Product reuse involves the refurbishing or remanufacture of products, reducing the need to dispose of electronic devices at end-of-life. These programs allow the repackaging for sale or donation to communities that may not otherwise be able to afford such equipment. Under a program of reuse, the electronic products are repackaged and resold at reduced cost. Some reuse programs may only use certain components from an obsolete device that can still be used in a new product, while others will employ a technological upgrade to extend the life of the product.

Recycling projects may recover components and casings of electronic products to be separated and broken down into their raw materials to be remanufactured into new products.

> **B.9.10 Explain how the miniaturization of electronic components has helped promote design for dematerialization.**
>
> © IBO 2007

One of the most remarkable examples of dematerialization has been in the production of electronic devices through the process of miniaturization. The miniaturization of electronics dates from the development of the solid-state transistor in 1949 by William Shockley, John Bardeen and Walter Brattain, an achievement that earned them the 1956 Nobel Prize for Physics.

The transistor replaced the larger vacuum tube amplifiers that, in addition to being relatively large, were fragile and generated considerable heat. Subsequent developments in the production of transistors using Photolithographic techniques have allowed integrated circuits (computer chips) to be produced. The size of transistors has steadily decreased allowing evermore transistors to be placed on a computer chip.

> **B.9.11 Discuss how rising service costs are key contributors to the replacement of electronic products in preference to repair.**
>
> © IBO 2007

The complexity and interconnectedness of electronic products often means that the time taken to diagnose and repair electronic products exceeds the cost of replacement, assuming spare parts are available to allow repair.

The decision of repair needs to take into account the cost of repair relative to replacement, and whether repairs are covered by a guarantee.

A general guideline is often employed such that if repair would cost >50% of a new replacement or the device is >3 years old, a new device should be purchased.

> **B.9.12 Outline how new developments in technology enhance the upgradeability of electronic products.**
>
> © IBO 2007

Many electronic products today allow for increases in functionality through their software, which can be upgraded by installing the latest version. Computers are an obvious example of this, where the latest version of Microsoft® or Apple Mac® software provides increased functionality. Similarly, the modular design of most computers allows the replacement of components such as processors, RAM, sound and graphics cards to the latest faster or more powerful versions.

> **B.9.13 Discuss the advantages and disadvantages of upgradeability for the designer, manufacturer and consumer.**
>
> © IBO 2007

For designers, the opportunities to incorporate upgradeability into a product assists with their endeavours to develop the functionality of devices and provide regular product developments. These developments assist manufacturers to reinvigorate product lines and maintain sales. Consumers also benefit from extended product life at a reduced cost, while at the same time keeping up with technological advances.

Disadvantages surrounding upgrades, particularly software or hardware revisions, include restrictions around the use of current architecture and compatibility problems and 'bugs' associated with upgrades. This causes problems for both designers and consumers. Upgrading a product usually deals with issues of functionality and may lead to products externally looking 'tired' or outdated. Consumers not only want a functional upgrade but the latest fashionable appearance as well, which may only associated with the newest or latest product.

B.9.14 Describe digital photography.

© IBO 2007

Until recently, the production of a photographic image relied on a photochemical reaction occurring when a silver based emulsion on a celluloid film substrate was exposed to light. When the film was processed through a number of chemical baths, an image would appear.

Today, film based photography has been largely superseded by digital photography, in which an image is captured by the exposure of a mosaic of small picture elements (known by the contraction PIXELS). Each pixel consists of a small square of silicon (typically 9μm square) on which is mounted three metal-oxide semiconductor (MOS) capacitors separated by a narrow channel. These MOS capacitors operate as photodiodes and electron storage devices. The pixels are typically arranged in a rectangular mosaic known as a charged coupled device (CCD) that acts to store image information, shown in Figure B.9.14a.

Figure B.9.14a View of a CCD from a 2.1 megapixel Argus digital camera.

Each pixel contains information on light and colour of part of the image. After exposure to light each pixel is transferred to an amplifier and then to an analogue-to-digital converter (ADC) where the signal is converted to binary code, with each pixel storing a numerical value from 0 to 255 for the three colours of red, green and blue. These values are stored in binary form as an 8bit (2^8 = 256) sequence or byte.

That is, the base 10 number 255, is the 8bit (1byte) sequence 11111111 in base 2. Each pixel therefore contains 3bytes of data.

The colour stored by each pixel is then a combination of the values held for red, green and blue. Because of this, there are over 16 million (2^{563}) colours possible and a 3MP (mega pixel) CCD chip generates over 9 million bytes (9MB) of data. This code is sent to a digital signal processor (DSP), which adjusts the image for contrast and colour and compresses the file for storage.

A schematic representation of the digital camera image processing sequence is presented in Figure B.9.14b. A number of storage formats are used, the most common being JPG, TIF and BMP.

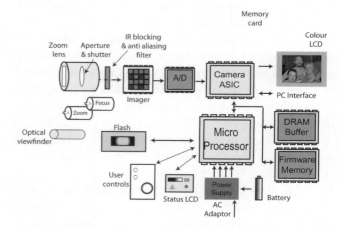

Figure B.9.14b Schematic representation of the processing of image by a digital camera

As may be appreciated, the detail or resolution of an image depends in large part on the number of pixels that make up the CCD chip. This is not the only factor that determines the quality of a digital image however.

Another important factor is the size of the CCD chip. For the same number of pixels the larger the CCD chip and hence the larger the pixel size, the better will be the image quality. This is because a larger pixel can store more light, meaning that less amplification of the signal is required and signal noise is minimized.

Traditionally, one of the most popular formats for film was 35mm (actually 24 × 36mm). This film is generally considered to have a digital equivalent of 20MP. However, the quality of images taken by digital cameras over 3MP capacity are often indistinguishable from 35mm film when viewed at up to 10 × 8' enlargement. Enlargement past this point can begin to reveal pixilation of the image.

A comparison of the size of a 35mm film and a CCD chip from a 3MP digital camera are shown in Figure B.9.14c.

Figure B.9.14c Comparison of 35mm film with a 3MP CCD chip

One feature of digital photography, in common with traditional photography, is the dependence of image quality on the quality of lens (Figure B.9.14d) used and the stability of the camera during exposure.

Figure B.9.14d Digital camera lens

B.9.15 Discuss how digital photography can be used to minimize waste.

© IBO 2007

The digital photography process has many advantages most of which revolve around waste minimization. They include such things as:

- no chemicals are needed to process film
- film is not wasted on unwanted images
- only those images specifically wanted as 'hard copies' are printed
- photographs can be stored electronically, sent by email and shared with friends to be viewed on an LCD screen.

Further Reading

Herman, R., Ardekani, S. A. & Ausubel, J. *Dematerialization* http://phe.rockefeller.edu/dematerialization/

An Introduction to Product Takeback http//:ce.Berkeley.sd/~horvath/NATO_ARW/FILES/ Klausner.pdf

B10 CONVERGING TECHNOLOGIES

B.10.1 Define converging technology and nanotechnology.

© IBO 2007

The term 'to converge' describes the process of things from different areas coming together and the term 'converging technology' refers to the coming together of a number of formerly separate technologies. Perhaps the most commonly encountered area of converging technology has been in the field of electronics, where modern communication systems increasingly provide greater personal access to communication, information and entertainment. In fact, the telecommunication industry has moved from a mere provider of communications channels to one of 'information provider' with the advent of computer networks such as the internet.

This change is being seen perhaps most clearly in the mobile phone. Today there are more mobile phone connections than fixed line connections and mobile phones offer an increasing array of functions such as text messaging, MP3 player, digital camera, games, personal organizer, e-reader, GPS services and internet access along with thousands of applications specifically written for mobile phones. This interconnectedness of telecommunications and computer technology is sometimes described as 'convergence'.

In recent years, consideration has been given to the convergence expected to occur between a broader range of technologies including nanotechnology, biotechnology, information technology and cognitive science (represented by the acronym NBIC), and the changes that might accompany such developments. The interaction of these areas is represented in Figure B.10.1a.

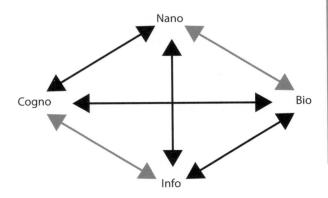

Figure B.10.1a Representation of interaction expected as a result of NBIC technology convergence [NBIC report 2003]

HL

OPTION

Nanotechnology involves the engineering of particles in the nanometre scale, that is particles of the order of one billionth (10_{-9}) of a metre in size. While a strict definition of the particle size range constituting a nanoparticle is yet to be made, a range of 1 to 100nm is often quoted, although an upper limit of 200nm is sometimes found.

To place this into perspective, a virus particle is approximately 100nm in size and a human hair is between 50000 and 100,000nm in thickness. Figure B.10.1b provides a size comparison.

When reduced in size to the nano scale materials have been found to exhibit unique physical and mechanical properties unavailable on the macro scale.

Nanoparticles are typically encompassing particles, crystals and clusters of between 1 and 100nm in size, to create new and improved properties and products. Through nanotechnology, molecular sized mechanisms are envisaged. These will be built atom by atom and will be capable of powering small machines, while structures such as nano-tubes will find a wide range of applications in engineering, medicine and national security.

It is hoped that machines will be constructed on the nano scale capable of performing a variety of tasks such as injectable machines capable of targeting and destroying cancer cells or blood clots. Figure B.10.1c shows a scanning electron microscope image of a nano-machine approximately 100nm across.

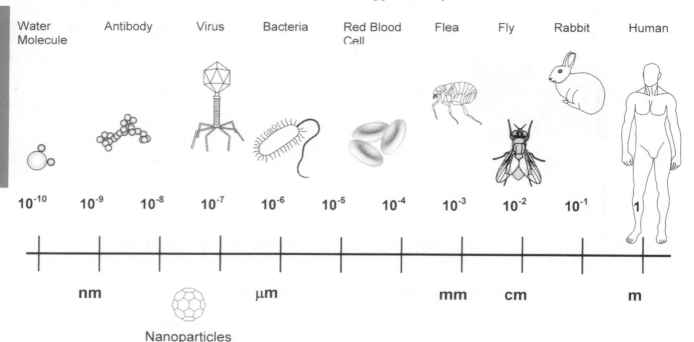

Figure B.10.1b

Figure B.10.1c Scanning Electron Microscope image of a nano-machine [Sandia National Laboratories]

B.10.2 Identify current nanotechnology applications.

© IBO 2007

While nanoscience and nanotechnology are relatively recent areas of study, many products boasting nanotechnology components are available on the market. To date, most of these involve the use of nanoparticles as a bulk colloidal suspension. An overview of some of the applications currently available and envisioned is indicated in Figure B.10.2a and include:

- zinc oxide nano-particles have found uses in sunscreens and UV protective fabrics
- alumina particles have been used in cosmetic products such as face powder, eye shadow and

lipstick in addition to high temperature lubricants and mould release agents

- aluminium silicate nanoparticles have been used in scratch resistant coatings for polymers
- silver nanoparticles have been used as an antibacterial agent in toothpaste, facemasks, bandages, socks, underwear, surface sprays and refrigerator linings
- medical diagnostic test kits using carbon nano-tubes.

While many advantages have been envisioned from the use of products containing nanoparticles, some concerns have been raised as to the safety of such products intended for skin contact. The majority of these concerns to date have involved the cosmetics industry and the presence of ZnO and TiO nano-particles. Some consumer groups have called for improved product labeling to provide consumers with sufficient information to make an informed choice regarding these contents. While such labeling is currently not required, some manufacturers in Australia have begun advertising their products as 'micronised' or nano free; as shown in Figure B.10.2b, a description not entirely free of controversy itself. Such labels indicate that the particle size is of the order of 1 micron (1µm) or 1000nm.

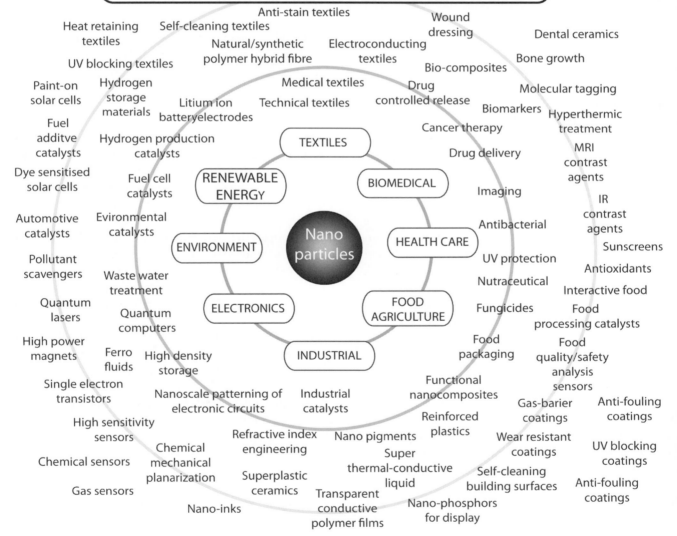

Figure B.10.2a Applications of Nanoparticles [www. deakin.edu.au/itri/nanotechnology/Nanoparticles.php]

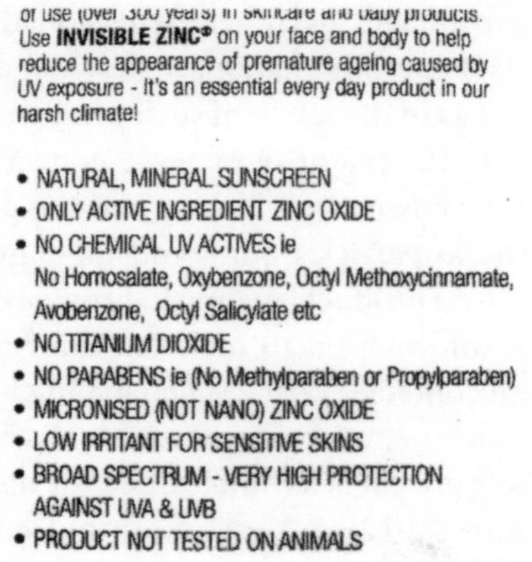

of use (over 300 years) in skincare and baby products.
Use **INVISIBLE ZINC®** on your face and body to help
reduce the appearance of premature ageing caused by
UV exposure - It's an essential every day product in our
harsh climate!

- NATURAL, MINERAL SUNSCREEN
- ONLY ACTIVE INGREDIENT ZINC OXIDE
- NO CHEMICAL UV ACTIVES ie
  No Homosalate, Oxybenzone, Octyl Methoxycinnamate,
  Avobenzone, Octyl Salicylate etc
- NO TITANIUM DIOXIDE
- NO PARABENS ie (No Methylparaben or Propylparaben)
- MICRONISED (NOT NANO) ZINC OXIDE
- LOW IRRITANT FOR SENSITIVE SKINS
- BROAD SPECTRUM - VERY HIGH PROTECTION
  AGAINST UVA & UVB
- PRODUCT NOT TESTED ON ANIMALS

*Figure B.10.2b Sunscreen labelImage by Supermaster2011
(Own work) [CC-BY-SA-3.0 (www.creativecommons.org/
licenses/by-sa/3.0) or GFDL (www.gnu.org/copyleft/fdl.
html)], via Wikimedia Commons*

B.10.3 Identify how converging technologies might enhance human performance.

Wearable sensors may allow the monitoring of the wearer's physical condition allowing early warning of a medical problem, collecting data and communicating it to emergency rescue or medical personnel.

Sensors and assistive technologies may provide increased assistance to the aged, and those with disabilities, by providing increased sensory capabilities. Examples of these include artificial hearing and sight and communications along with exoskeletons providing increased mobility and independence.

B.10.4 Explain how converging technologies might expand human cognition and communication.

Enhancement of sensory capabilities may improve communication between individuals and groups. It may also allow for the creation of improved interaction between the mind and tools (mind/machine interfaces).

Through a greater understanding of neuroscience and cognitive function, the creation of a visual language could also greatly improve communication across cultural and language barriers. Figure B.10.4a shows how visual language, created by a merger of vocabularies from many different fields, may assist communication.

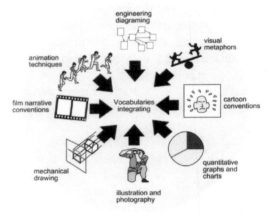

Figure B.10.4a Visual language created by a merger of vocabularies from many different fields. [NBIC report 2003]

B.10.5 Explain how converging technologies might improve human health and physical capabilities.

Ingestible machines and new medicines that could more accurately target and treat disease. Diagnostic tests that rapidly and cheaply test for numerous conditions that currently are time consuming and expensive to perform, requiring the resources of specialty facilities.

Technologies that compensate for some of the limitations currently imposed by aging and various disabilities.

Electronic signage, electronic Braille displays, speech to Braille conversion for those who are both deaf and blind.

Body part replacements such as an artificial heart, eliminating the need for donor organs and reducing complications associated with rejection.

B.10.6 Explain how converging technologies might benefit national defence.

Converging technologies may supply improved communications capabilities and sensory systems, providing greater capabilities to detect, analyse and respond rapidly to national security threats.

Other areas of development include intelligent weapons systems and unmanned weapons platforms.

Nanotechnology is expected to be part of the standard equipment supplied to soldiers of the future. Light-weight smart materials may also provide a climate controlled environment for soldiers which supply greater protection and real time information about the battlefield, while monitoring the health of the combatant.

Figure B.10.6a Nanotechnology will be part of the equipment of the soldier of the future.

Image by US Army Natick Soldier Center. Future Force Warrior System

> **B.10.7 Describe 'The Communicator'.**
>
> © IBO 2007

'The Communicator' represents a vision of a system arising from the convergence of NBIC technologies through which, greater communication between individuals and groups could result. The Communicator would act to remove barriers to communication that currently exist associated with differences in:

- age
- society
- culture
- religion
- language
- physical disability.

> **B10.8 Identify the key components of 'The Communicator'.**
>
> © IBO 2007

The three key components of 'The Communicator' are the individual information, avatar and environmental interface elements. Each of these are designed to work together in a cooperative and efficient fashion.

The individual information component would consist essentially of every piece of information that defines an individual. As much data as possible would be included to inform the system not only of skills, values and attributes but ways of thinking, preferences and social skills.

The avatar component allows for the human-like manifestation of a person within the system. Importantly, as part of the communication process, these 'creations' should assist with interaction and social discourse between individuals and groups within the projected environment. Avatars could be used in situations potentially dangerous to their flesh and blood counterparts.

The environmental interface component is perceived to be a part of the system that would automatically and seamlessly enhance our ability to communicate and relate to individuals, groups, technology and information.

'The Communicator' will facilitate presentations to groups by allowing presentations prepared with different software packages to be used, automatically detecting and resolving incompatibilities seamlessly.

Barriers to communication due to physical disabilities and language differences will be detected by sensors and automatically supplemented with appropriate aids such as captioning, Braille and simultaneous translation.

> **B.10.9 Identify key design considerations in the implementation of 'The Communicator'.**
>
> © IBO 2007

'The Communicator' will require high-speed data transfer systems. The device itself will probably take the form of some kind of wearable technology offering services on-demand in real time. It may consist of a number of interconnected modules providing a discrete interconnected network.

B.10.10 Explain how technologies will be used in the implementation of 'The Communicator'.

© IBO 2007

A range of technologies present themselves as potential candidates for inclusion in realization of technology such as 'The Communicator'. These include:

- neural interfaces that allow thought directed control of tools. Such systems are expected to require nanotechnologies to both create the devices and to measure their performance
- adaptive software systems that learn and adapt to changing societal and cultural situations
- personal and environmentally distributed systems of sensors that allows the collection and analysis of sensory data
- software systems that analyze, filter and prioritize data based on personal preferences and importance
- systems that will present information in a form that enhances flexibility.

Many of these developments require advances in cognitive science. While non-invasive technologies such as functional Magnetic Resonance Imaging (fMRI), Positron Emission Tomography (PET), and Magnetoencephalography (MEG) provide some insight into those areas of the brain that are working during specific tasks, they currently only provide limited insight into how this activity relates to cognition. That is, they don't provide the link between brain activity generated by sensory data and understanding.

If computing power continues to increase, as it has historically, it is possible that within the next 20 years, processing capacity approaching that of the human brain, (10^{14} operations per second), may be attained. If in addition, an understanding of the link between computational power and understanding can be achieved – a true mind in the machine might arise from what has been called a 'computational theory of mind'.

Since the earliest days of computer development, questions about the ability of machines to think have been raised. In 1950, the British computer scientist Alan Turing proposed a test for artificial intelligence now known as The Turing Test. Future Computer systems operating in an environment of NBIC convergence envisioned will undoubtedly raise questions of what constitutes consciousness and self awareness, and what does it mean to be alive?

B.10.11 Identify potential applications for avatars.

© IBO 2007

An avatar is a computer generated image used to represent a person in a virtual environment. An advanced communication system such as 'The Communicator' might use avatars as personal assistants to provide information. Such an assistant could be used to research information from the internet, arranging it into an accessible form. The avatar would also allow the virtual representation of individuals in meetings held in distant places or under dangerous circumstances.

Many people are familiar with the use of an avatar through digital role-play games and social simulations such as Second-life, 'The Communicator' concept would extend and broaden the use of avatars.

B.10.12 Explain the advantages of 'The Communicator' for global cooperation.

© IBO 2007

It is suggested that through 'The Communicator', barriers to understanding between the peoples of the World would be removed and the ability and opportunity for cooperation enhanced. Geographical barriers to education would be eliminated, allowing the general level of education to be increased, possibly through the use of augmented reality systems. Through a greater understanding of human interaction as a result of developments in neuroscience, global cooperation may also be enhanced. Work on the development of 'The Communicator' itself will require extensive global consultation and cooperation.

B.10.13 Explain the challenges of converging technologies for education systems.

© IBO 2007

The development of new curricula that take a more holistic approach to science and technology to create an informed and capable population, with a broader appreciation of the interconnectedness of the NBIC fields in preparation for the challenges and promise of their convergence.

The development of virtual environments to facilitate the education of children needs to be explored. In addition, methods to safely simulate potentially life threatening scenarios for the training of professionals in fields such as medicine, defence, mining, aerospace and plant, design and operation, need to be developed.

B.10.14 Explain the responsibilities of governments in the development of converging technologies.

© IBO 2007

The convergence of NBIC technologies will create the possibility of a technological revolution to rival that of the Industrial Revolution. While promising the benefits of increased productivity, improved health care and wealth generation, governments will need to manage these developments carefully if social disruption is not to accompany their introduction in areas of employment, education and training and social equity.

Increased emphasis on international co-operation and understanding will be required to ensure that the benefits of technological convergence are shared between nations and are adapted with sensitivity to political, social, cultural and religious differences. Systems will need to be introduced that address concern for privacy and that regulate how, when and where information is collected and stored.

B.10.15 Evaluate progress towards converging technology concepts.

© IBO 2007

Convergence of consumer digital and electronic technologies continues apace. Combinations of web, audio, digital television, video on demand, streaming media, text, print and data continue to be amalgamated into single, multi-purpose devices. New materials and technologies introduced into cables and adaptors improve connectivity speeds allowing for faster more reliable data transmission and real-time viewing. These technologies, devices and systems permeate not only the world of the consumer, but the workplace as well. Banking, international commerce, education, medicine, leisure activities and game playing all benefit. Future directions and opportunities for convergence will continue to evolve as new materials, technologies and market needs arise.

Further Reading

The Project on Emerging Nanotechnologies
http://www.nanotechproject.org/inventories/consumer/

Roco M. C. & Bainbridge W. S. (Eds). (2003). *Converging Technologies for Improving Human Performance: Nanotechnology, Biotechnology, Information Technology and Cognitive Science*. NSF/DOC sponsored report. Kluwer Academic Publishers, Dordrecht, The Netherlands.

Exercises

1. Which ball provides an example of kinetic energy?

   A.   a ball laying on the ground
   B.   one rebounding from a racquet
   C.   a ball held in the hand above the ground
   D.   one at the top of its flight at the point of falling downwards.

2. Which voltage source converts chemical energy to electrical energy?

   A.   solar cell
   B.   wind turbine
   C.   alkaline battery
   D.   electronic power supply.

3. Which electronic component is designed to be temperature sensitive?

   A.   rheostat
   B.   capacitor
   C.   thermistor
   D.   potentiometer.

4. The distance that a signal's energy travels in the time it takes for one cycle to complete is called?

   A.   waveform
   B.   frequency
   C.   amplitude
   D.   wavelength.

5. The unit for frequency is the:

   A.   watt
   B.   hertz
   C.   farad
   D.   coulomb

6. Compare AC and DC forms of energy.

7. Explain how legislation for the disposal of electronic products may disadvantage some consumers.

8. Explain how miniaturization has improved dematerialization. Provide appropriate examples.

9. Compare optical fibre to more traditional metal media used for communication connections.

10. Explain why the successful convergence of technologies will require extensive global consultation.

HL

OPTION

CAD/CAM

CONTENTS

The basis for machinery as we know it today originated in the 18th century. Wilkinson, in England, developed a horizontal boring machine in 1775 to machine the cylinders of the newly created steam engine. While Whitney, the inventor of the cotton gin, and popularly known as the inventor of interchangeable parts for the musket, implemented a form of mass production known as the 'armoury' or American system of manufacturing.

Throughout 19th century the development of milling, turning, gear cutting and grinding machines mechanized many operations. Mechanization also spread to agriculture and associated manufacturing with harvesting, weaving and sewing machines being developed and refined.

With the early 20th Century, came the development of automation and mass production. Products could now be manufactured even faster, cheaper and with greater consistency. Mass markets were created around the production of automobiles and other consumer items. Demand for consumer products increased as did the need for greater levels of quality and accuracy. From this need was borne the introduction of the first tape-controlled machinery. Improvement over time saw the introduction of multi-axis machines, new cutting tool technologies, faster operational speeds and innovative lubricants.

As computer systems developed and started to permeate manufacturing plants, computer numerical systems and robotics reduced workforce requirements and relieved many workers of the arduous jobs previously associated with manufacturing. As a direct result of the associated computer software development, designers were able to quickly develop a product through the conceptual stages of rough sketch to 3D visualisation. This streamlining of product development processes, starting with conceptual design through to market release, is regarded as a strategic imperative in every manufacturer's search for competitive advantage. A vital link in that strategy has been the adoption of CAD/CAM technology in an effort to:

- eliminate errors
- reduce cycle times
- remove duplication of effort
- improve quality control and decrease labour content.

C1 THE IMPACT OF CAD ON THE DESIGN PROCESS

> **C.1.1** Outline the use of different software applications.
>
> © IBO 2007

Computer aided design software may be used to create either 2D or 3D drawings. These drawings may be technical or conceptual in nature. They may incorporate additional information through the inclusion of tables, dimensions, tolerances assembly notes, materials lists or flowcharts. There are essentially two types of computer graphics:

- raster or bitmap graphics composed of pixels (or patterns of individual dots)
- vector graphics generated by mathematical relationships describing points, lines and shapes.

Paint programs use bitmap images whereas most drawing, animation and modelling packages use vector graphics. Vector graphics are more flexible and contain more detail. They may be scaled, stretched or resized and most often produce a file of smaller size than their bitmap counterpart.

> **C.1.2** Discuss the advantages and disadvantages of using software applications in different design contexts.
>
> © IBO 2007

CAD drawings exist as electronic data files that are created using specialist CAD software. Advantages of CAD drawings include their ability to be:

- stored in a variety of formats
- corrected or altered very quickly
- created as 2-D or 3-D representations
- rescaled, zoomed, cropped etc. for detail
- presented as paper printouts, virtual models or rapid prototypes
- electronically distributed for collaboration as part of a group project
- used in conjunction with numerical control machinery for CAD/CAM production.

The ability of CAD software to produce drawings in layers allows details to be viewed either separately or as a whole. Architectural drawings often make use of this layering feature allowing: foundations, wiring or plumbing services to be viewed individually or with complementary layers that aid interpretation and reduce complication. Rendered architectural drawings may also be placed in photorealistic settings or have digital 'people' added to provide a sense of human scale. 'Nesting' functions incorporated in CAD programs automatically lay out individual parts (when manufacturing in sheet materials) optimizing the use of material by fitting smaller components inside voids in others and reorienting parts for 'best fit'.

Levels of difficulty, steep learning curves and non-compatibility between software packages and computer platforms can make the introduction to, and early stages of adopting CAD drawing packages challenging. Some files may only be viewed using the proprietary software used to create it, which can be very expensive.

> **C.1.3** Define animation and virtual reality.
>
> **C.1.4** Compare animation and virtual reality.
>
> © IBO 2007

Computer animation is a way of automating the process of linking graphic elements that change slightly over time and when played consecutively simulate motion. Animation and virtual reality presentations add realism to CAD models. The animation of the complex engine and crankshaft assembly, shown in Figure C.1.4, illustrates the benefits associated with animation. Not only does the graphic show a great degree of detail but, through animation, shows the complexity of movement associated with each rotation of the shaft.

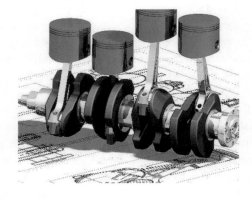

Figure C.1.4 Engine animation

OPTION

CAD-generated virtual models can be reviewed, modified, and altered as required. Computers may perform virtual machining operations allowing designers to choose the optimum manufacturing process and sequence of operations. Full size physical prototypes may then be machined identical to the virtual construct.

Virtual or augmented reality can range from a simple arrangement of elements on a computer desktop to a more immersive experience. Virtual reality simulates environments and may give the user an opportunity to interact with the environment. Walk-through or fly-over simulations are an example of this type of digital material where the user is able to 'walk around' mathematical models and view them as if they existed in a three dimensional space. They are designed to provide an off-site viewer with an in-context impression of projected designs that may not even exist. These digital constructs provide detail, perspectives and interaction not necessarily available with a physical model without any of the costs associated with physical models or transport to remote sites. Virtual technologies are used to test vehicle aerodynamics, train astronauts and even simulate road conditions for learning drivers.

In applications where assembly instructions or movement of parts is required, these are best supplied visually though a staged/timed assembly presented through an animation. This type of presentation would also be the fastest to produce, generate the smallest file size and be the least expensive option.

The required outcome of the initial brief and anticipated returns will often determine whether the considerable time and costs associated with generating a realistic and effective virtual environment can be justified.

> **C.1.5   Discuss the cost-effectiveness offered by animation and virtual reality.**
>
> © IBO 2007

The ability of computers to either convert 2D drawings or 3D models into virtual reality environments has enhanced the designer's ability to perceive potential design flaws, test for materials suitability, examine ergonomic compatibility and make modifications before the first physical component is produced. Recent developments see CAD programs incorporating 'assessment of sustainability algorithms' that can determine and compare the environmental impact of a range of viable alternatives.

Virtual reality technologies generating computer models of real components or systems are finding application in architectural modelling, remote control of robotics, machining, ergonomic design and vehicle prototyping.

Virtual reality can be used to simulate the interaction of components on-screen, without incurring the costs of physical prototypes. Static or dynamic loads may be modelled to analyze the performance of a particular design or modification. Virtual reality constructs also allow designers to predict how the model will perform in use and when exposed to variety of real world forces.

Virtualization of products allows designers to evaluate efficacy of design in a responsive, immersive environment. It is often employed in conjunction with computer-based testing such as finite element analysis, (see C.1.20). In the transport industries, (air, sea and land), designers are able to use virtual tests to examine fluid dynamics and review the efficiency and viability of their designs. Both time and money are saved in these virtual 'proof of concept' simulations. Designers are able to test a variety of factors such as lift, draft, turbulence, fluid flow patterns, heat transfer fields, momentum etc. All of this done using the CAD package's embedded mathematical modelling and driven by a physics engine maintaining the laws of physics.

In a practical, consumer-based application, Japanese customers of Matsushita can submit architectural plans for processing into a virtual simulation of a range of kitchen design alternatives.

All of these operations save costs, allow for real-time training, testing and development at considerable cost savings and reductions in time compared to traditional approaches to model making, testing and evaluation. Virtual Reality technology has the potential to:

- advance real-time training
- reduce product development cycles
- save resources by removing reliance on physical modelling.

Simulated robot production lines such as the example shown in Figure C.1.5, may be programmed off-line. This pre-programming of robotic movements, cycle times, interactions with humans and anti-collision paths can be constructed to reflect real time operations and viewed as an animation. In this situation, the animation process saves time and expensive errors. It may also be conducted off-site without access to any expensive robotic hardware.

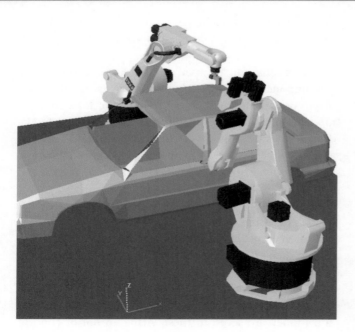

Figure C.1.5 Animated simulation of robotic movement

Image by L. Beyer at the English Wikipedia project [GFDL (www.gnu.org/copyleft/fdl.html) or CC-BY-SA-3.0 (www.creativecommons.org/licenses/by-sa/3.0/)], via Wikimedia Commons

C.1.6 Describe haptic technology.

The word 'haptic', originates from the Greek, 'to touch.' Haptic technology is commonly referred to as 'force feedback' or 'force reflection' technology because of the sense of touch or force communicated through the system. These devices approximate the physical 'feel' of the environment, providing real-time feedback in the form of pressure and spatial information. This ability allows users to interact with virtual environments accessed through computer connections.

Based on haptic or 'force response' devices, telepresence systems allow for control of processes remotely. Used in medicine, robotics and for the operation of industrial equipment, these systems rely on sensors to feedback visual and/or tactile information to the operator.

Research is underway to further develop haptic design into touchscreen technology. Some smartphones already provide a click-like response when the screen is pressed and computer game controllers activate 'rumble packs' to pass on vibrations to gamers. Devices employing tactile feedback may be used to simulate keyboards or other tactile sensations like texture.

C.1.7 Define motion capture technology.

Motion capture technology is used to record, track and analyze movement. The process records movement through a series of snapshots generated many times per second. Special markers may be applied to strategic points of a moving body to identify key pieces of geometry. The resultant changes in position of the figure(s) are recorded and easily digitized for playback or analysis. Once recorded, motion capture images may then be translated to digital constructs for the purposes of animation such as in filmmaking (as shown in Figure C.1.17) or used directly for the purposes of motion study.

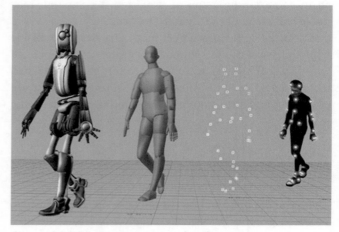

Figure C.1.7 Motion capture technology

Image by Hipocrite at en.wikipedia [Public domain], from Wikimedia Commons

C.1.8 Outline how various input devices are used by a CAD system.

The computer mouse is a digital pointing device that locates the cursor or point of insertion for information on a screen. In CAD work it may be used for: selecting objects, modifying object size and shape, locating a reference point on the screen, moving objects, selecting tools, accessing menus. It may also be used to create lines, curves, shapes etc. An optical mouse with reprogrammable functions also allows for greater drawing accuracy and speed of access to tools and operations.

A scanner is an optical device used to convert digital documents into graphic images. These documents may take the form of the written word, graphics, photos or slides. Once converted, the image may be manipulated by any of the graphic editing programs available or optical character recognition programs to make the information more accessible.

Digital cameras record images without the use of film. Using flash memory or optical discs, digital photographs may be reviewed before deleting or downloading to a computer for storage or further processing. The flash memory in a camera once erased, can be reused repeatedly.

Graphics tablets allow computer users to recreate the feel of a pencil using a stylus when creating drawings. The stylus can perform the same functions as a traditional mouse, but may also incorporate the additional benefit of a pressure sensitive tip. This allows the user to define heavier or thicker lines when sketching.

3D scanning converts real objects into computer data that is three-dimensional. Using 3D computer modelling programs, 3D-scanned objects can be rotated, manipulated, tested in virtual environments and even animated on a computer screen. Once an object has been 3D scanned, the computer model can be converted into industry-standard computer formats. Once objects have been digitized, files can be viewed and manipulated in a variety of different programs.

Almost anything can be 3D scanned. Examples of objects that can be 3D scanned include large buildings, mine sites, vehicles, people, household products, tooling, toys, archaeological artifacts, room interiors, art works and body parts. Traditional methods of inspection and dimensional data recovery are much slower and can be can be very time consuming.

Technology, such as the FARO Arm, recovers data on detailed features within its reach (up to 7 metres). For larger items, it may be interfaced with a laser system to accurately recover information over extended distances. The most dramatic reductions in the time taken for this process and inherent cost of resources occur if some or all of the following conditions exist:

- inspection with hand tools is prohibitively time consuming
- complex surfaces or profiles are difficult to measure with hand tools
- relationships between different features of equipment is difficult to measure
- equipment to be measured is too large or awkward to get accurate measurements.

The use of 3-D scanning in engineering applications is increasing as the acceptance of the technology becomes more widespread.

Uses for this technology include:

- design
- animation
- manufacturing
- quality inspection
- dimensional reverse engineering.

Scans of people or casts of body parts can be used by designers to design better-fitting products such as helmets and facemasks. Scanning can also be used to create datasets of human sizes for anthropometric applications. A complete scene could also be scanned to assess a work environment for health and safety issues.

> **C.1.9** Explain how haptic technology and motion capture have enhanced design capability.

Haptic technology allows designers to interact with computer models assisting them to analyze the performance of the product under simulated use. The data obtained from this form of experimentation allows designers to consider the ergonomic 'feel' of the device when tested with multiple users. This allows for digital sculpting and redesign of the product before prototyping or any form of manufacturing begins. Used in conjunction with motion capture technologies, the physiological requirements or anthropometric data of users may also be recorded and assessed including elements such as, fatigue, need for physical support etc.

Figure C.1.9a shows an innovative force-sensing 'glove' incorporating a tactile pressure sensing system used for ergonomic research and analysis. This prototype device shown has been used to test a range of projects including consumer, industrial and medical product design.

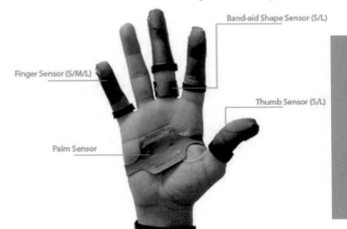

Figure C.1.9a Force sensing glove - market version

Image by AirMouse.com

As an example, records of measurement of forces applied over time for particular fingers when operating various controls on products (e.g. touchscreen versus five-way controller) is input automatically through the device. Besides benchmarking product controls, the relative strengths of different types of users (e.g. children, adults or users with a disability) can be analyzed to provide data to designers for more appropriate control designs.

Figure C.1.9b shows the AirMouse2 and clearly demonstrates the transition from prototype to marketable product.

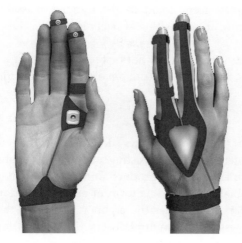

Figure C.1.9b Force sensing glove - market version

Image by AirMouse.com

> **C.1.10** Outline how 3D pictorial drawings are the primary mode of design in CAD.
>
> © IBO 2007

CAD drawing packages allow users to design in 3D to give designers the opportunity to view models as they would appear in real life. No longer are complex orthographic drawings created and converted into 3D figures. These 3D models can quickly be viewed as wire-frame or solid. They are able to rotated and viewed from any direction, as well as resolved into oblique, isometric or perspective views. These 3D models such as the one shown in Figure C.1.10 instantly provide recognition and realism for designers, clients and consumers. Notice how the features in the CAD drawing (upper), are instantly recognizable in the final manufactured part (lower).

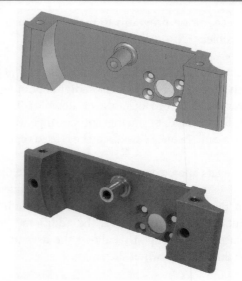

Figure C.1.10 CAD model and CNC machined part

Image By Mike1024 [Public domain], via Wikimedia Commons

The ability to sketch directly in 3D has also enhanced the designer's ability to perceive potential design flaws. This process known as virtual design is increasingly used in industry to generate computer models of real components or assemblies. Animation of moving and mating components can show areas of non-alignment or 'clashing'. Flow simulation software can analyse effects, such as turbulence and drag, without recourse to expensive models and wind tunnel tests. Stress analysis can also be performed on these virtual products to identify weaknesses and make modifications before the first physical component is produced.

While 3D CAD design software has revolutionized product design, manufacturers still require engineering drawings for production purposes. CAD packages allow for the easy transformation of 3D graphics into detailed workshop drawings, with all the attendant documentation.

> **C.1.11** Explain how the initial 3D drawings can be used to generate other types of drawing.
>
> © IBO 2007

3D drawings created in CAD packages may be viewed in a variety of forms including wire frame, isometric, oblique, perspective, showing hidden lines, shaded, textured and toned. They may also be reworked at the click of a mouse button to be viewed as orthographic, exploded isometric, fully dimensioned, sectioned or animated assembly/ disassembly etc.

OPTION

C.1.12 Describe the processes used to revolve and extrude sketches in CAD.

© IBO 2007

The revolve tool rotates a profile around a singular axis. The path of revolution may be from 0° to 360°. To create a revolved solid, a selected piece of geometry is revolved around a predetermined axis. The axis may even be offset from the original sketch.

The extrusion process starts with a basic profile sketch that is then projected along one axis, (of given length), to generate a solid section with the same cross sectional area throughout. Figure C1.12 shows a series of vertical and horizontal profiles extruded or revolved before final assembly.

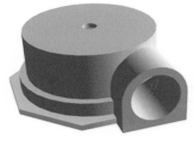

Figure C.1.12 Assembly of a variety of extruded and revolved profiles

Image by Nicholas John

C.1.13 Annotate a 3D CAD drawing to identify workplanes, faces, edges and features.

© IBO 2007

Figure C.1.13a shows the initial startup screen for a CAD package asking the user to identify the workplane on which to start drawing. Until a suitable workplane is selected, a drawing cannot start.

Workplanes not only provide a starting point for the orientation of a new drawing, but allow the user to immediately 'snap' to a particular view for confirmation of part alignment or 3 dimensional review of a model.

The management 'tree' on the far left of the screen shows the features applied to the model while the features tab displays the various options that can be selected.

Figure C.1.13b shows a shaded CAD 3D model of a generic pump cover. Features include an extruded profile as the basis for the model. The 3D extrusion has then been 'shelled' to produce a hollow item with a specified wall thickness. Holes have been drilled and fillets applied to selected edges.

Figure C.1.13a CAD workplanes

Image by Belinda Jane

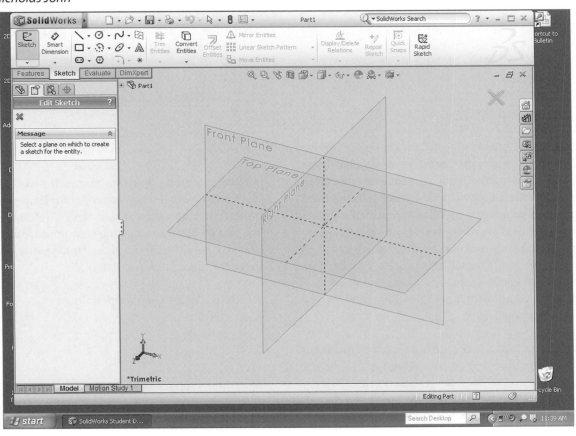

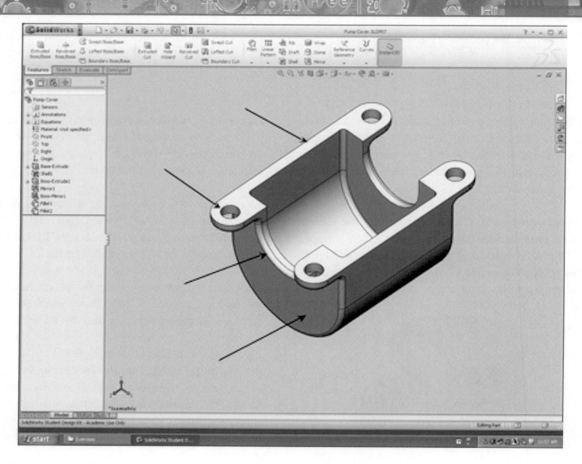

Figure C.1.13b 3D CAD model

C.1.14 Define 'top down' modelling.

C.1.15 Define 'bottom up' modelling.

C.1.16 Compare 'bottom up' and 'top down' CAD modelling.

'Bottom up' design involves creating parts before joining (mating) them together to form an assembly. These parts may be: constructed from scratch, imported from established libraries or downloaded designs from third party suppliers of standard components. Each of these parts contains independent geometry and any modifications to individual components will not be distributed to others that may be affected. Overall, the process can be time consuming particularly when one change may affect a variety of other components that must first be identified then modified manually.

'Top down' design relates to the use of a hierarchy involving locking-in information critical to a design at the earliest stage and relying on this structure to inform the design at later or lower levels of product design. Top-down design, involves the addition of new parts to assemblies through the application of relationships. As a simple example - two cylindrical parts may be mated around their centres using the relationship of concentricity. This maintains the alignment of the two parts regardless of changes to circle diameters. This automatic modification of related components saves considerable time throughout the evolution of a design and reduces the chance of error in complex assemblies.

C.1.17 Define surface modelling.

Surface modelling software shapes the surface or 'skin' of a CAD object. It enables very complex geometries and produces a more detailed view than wireframe modelling. The aim of surface modelling is to produce as realistic an effect as possible, however, no information is recorded about the object's interior detail.

C.1.18 Define solid modelling.

Solid modelling contains the most geometric information of all CAD model types. Solid models contain all the wire frame and surface information to fully define faces and

OPTION

edges of models, as well as associative information known as topology.

C.1.19 Explain the differences between solid and surface modelling techniques.

© IBO 2007

Based on external appearance, there may seem to be little difference between surface and solid models. Surface modelling is used to quickly generate complex shapes and is extensively employed in the consumer product design industry. These shapes however, possess no thickness or interior information therefore they cannot be cut to provide interior details or used as the basis for rapid prototyping. Conversely, solid modelling is often used in conjunction with rapid prototyping technologies to build a physical 3D model. Solid modelled objects contain more information in the form of primitive geometry (planes, cones, cylinders etc.).

C.1.20 Define finite element analysis (FEA).

© IBO 2007

Most often used for stress calculations, Finite Element Analysis (FEA) is a tool used to test virtual models under a variety of load conditions. It may be used to test the design of new products or analyse existing products in new situations.

C.1.21 Explain how FEA can be used to show the forces acting upon an object while in use.

© IBO 2007

FEA can be used to simulate how an object would react under service loads or conditions. Under the FEA process, a virtual model shows how loads would be distributed within the object. These reactive forces may be in response to loads generated by: expansion due to temperature variations, external loads, pressures or vibration. Through the action of dividing the model up into a series of simple but discrete elements joined through nodes, the program is able analyse a complex object by considering it as a series of resolvable units. Observations are then made as to how the object may perform under a variety of conditions. FEA can be used to study the interactions of assembled components on-screen, before incurring the costs of physical prototypes. Static or dynamic loads may be simulated to evaluate a design's performance under stress, strain, and displacement. FEA often finds applications in the car industry, where simulated collisions using components, assemblies or whole-of-vehicle designs can

show the result of various crash scenarios. The data would show distributed forces, twisting, buckling, movement and even failure of various elements of the design.

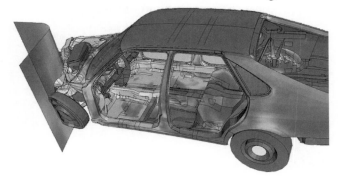

C.1.21 Finite element analysis of an asymmetrical collision

C.1.22 Compare finite element analysis with real-life testing.

© IBO 2007

FEA is very cost and time effective. Manufacturing and physical testing costs far outweigh those of producing and testing a computer simulation. FEA, however, cannot take into account the complexity and variability of: materials, manufacturing processes, environmental conditions or human influence. To this end, FEA analysis can inform designs to a point where physical testing may be required to confirm the specifications of the final product.

C.1.23 Outline how CAD can aid cost analysis in the planning to manufacture.

© IBO 2007

CAD programs have the ability to export data in spreadsheet form. Selected objects, components or assemblies may thus be exported in a form that communicates: materials, volumes and quantities etc. A complex materials list may then be generated and costs established when materials are matched with financial data. A similar process applies to the production phase. CAD software can also generate production flow charts, allowing manufacturers to predict production times and allocate hourly rate estimates.

Further Reading

Cleminshaw, D. (1999). Sea Change, Visualizing Strategy, Inovation.

Gaggioli, A., Breining R. (2001). *Perception and Cognition in Immersive Virtual Reality, Identity Community and Technology in the Internet Age*, IOS Press: Amsterdam.

C2 CAM SYSTEMS

C.2.1   Describe additive manufacturing techniques.

C.2.2   Describe subtractive manufacturing techniques (wasting).

C.2.3   Compare subtractive and additive manufacturing techniques.

© IBO 2007

Additive manufacturing processes build physical models by fusing, sintering or polymerizing separate pieces of material together. Modern additive manufacturing is often referred to as rapid prototyping, solid free form fabrication, layered manufacturing or direct digital manufacturing. It consists of a range of processes used to produce solid components through the deposition and fusing of consecutive layers of material. Initially designers create a CAD model, which is then converted into an STL (STereo Lithography) file. This format was originally developed for stereo lithographic manufacturing. The process converts surfaces into polygons with their geometry recorded as mathematical coordinates. In some situations, IGES, (Initial Graphic Exchange Specifications), formatting of the data may also be appropriate. The advantage of rapid prototyping lies in its ability to quickly and cost-effectively produce any shape that can be modelled in a CAD program. Once started, the build operation requires no operator input.

The production of physical models is done through the slicing of the formatted 3D CAD models into multiple layers ready to be sequentially rebuilt, without the use of any tooling or complex toolpaths, thus significantly reducing the amount of time to produce a prototype or fully functioning model. While there are at least 20 different commercial additive manufacturing processes, they all are encompassed in four major groups involving:

- lamination
- photopolymers
- deposition (fibre and inkjet)
- powders (layered and sprayed).

Use of these technologies significantly reduces the lead-time required to bring a design to market.

Subtractive prototyping may also be used to create prototypes. In this process, material is removed often using traditional manufacturing tools such as drills, lathes, routers and milling machines. Starting with a block

or blank, subtractive manufacturing continues to remove material until the part is finished. These machines and processes may also be automated.

The major advantage of subtractive technologies is the range of materials suitable for processing and the fact that the object is produced in the final production material. Amongst its other merits, subtractive manufacturing also produces objects with:

- high degrees of accuracy
- very smooth surface finishes
- smaller per part costs when mass produced
- larger dimensions and greater range of materials than additive prototyping methods.

Figure C.2.3 Additive and subtractive manufacturing processes

Image by Fabbers.com

Subtractive or machining processes strike some difficulties with varying thickness sections, deep slots, square corners and features such as undercuts. As parts become more complex, so to do toolpaths. The number of tool changes also increases. Although issues such as these are resolvable, they require great skill, creativity and problem-solving abilities. From designing tool paths and machining strategies to operating and monitoring the cutting, machining is the work of experienced craftsmen.

Additive manufacturing processes are less limited in their ability to reproduce physical shapes. However, rapid prototyping can be sensitive to environmental conditions such as temperature and humidity. CNC machining processes are much more consistent in their repeatability.

C.2.4   Describe a laser cutter.

© IBO 2007

Laser cutting uses a high power laser directed towards flat sheet surfaces to be cut. A high quality surface finish is generated as the laser vaporises the sheet material. Laser cutters may also be used for piping or structural shapes. Through the adjustment of power levels laser cutters may also be used for 2D cutting, welding, boring and engraving. A variety of laser cutters are employed dependent on their application. Examples include:

- CO_2 — Boring and engraving
- Nd — Low energy-repetitious cutting
- Nd-YAG — High power engraving or boring

When repetitive, complex or long production runs are required, a computer may be employed to direct the laser.

C.2.5 Describe rapid prototyping (RP).

C.2.8 Explain how RP (rapid prototyping) machines can be used to manufacture a variety of outcomes (additive).

© IBO 2007

As the name suggests, rapid prototyping is simply a process employed to produce prototype models quickly. Rapid prototyping has the ability to quickly translate a 3D computer model into a physical model. 3D computer models of components can be downloaded to specialized equipment able to manufacture components in resin or a polymer, as shown in Figure C.2.5. The prototype model shown has been produced by an additive or incremental process, where the model is built up by fusing material together.

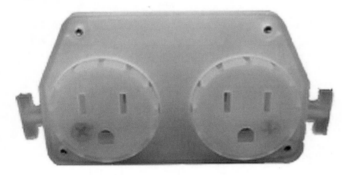

Figure C.2.5 Prototyped electrical component

Rapid prototyping processes can produce a wide variety of outcomes including:

- sand casting moulds
- fully functional prototypes
- patterns for investment casting
- metal, ceramic or polymer prototype parts.

Figure C.2.8 shows an excellent example of a complex part manufactured using rapid prototyping.

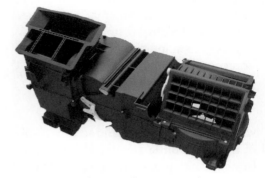

Figure C.2.8 Complex rapid prototyped part.

Rapid prototyping continues to develop as new materials and processing techniques generate new applications including:

- dental implants
- textiles (clothing)
- customized hearing aid shells.

C.2.6 Describe a plotter cutter.

© IBO 2007

A plotter cutter is identical to a traditional vector-driven plotter, with the exception that the pen is replaced by a sharp knife used to cut shapes. Some plotters have pressure control to adjust the force applied to the blade allowing cuts to mark the surface only without fully penetrating. Cutting knives are mounted on ball-bearing assemblies to allow for direction changes.

Plotter cutters are often used in the sign-making industry using coloured, adhesive-backed vinyl to produce signage for application to posters, billboards, and car bodies. This technology has also found application in the textile industry for sailmaking, awnings, upholstery, clothing etc.

Figure C.2.6 Plotter cutter

C.2.7 Explain how CNC (computer numerical control) routers, milling machines, laser cutters and plotter cutter machines can be used to manufacture a variety of outcomes (subtractive).

© IBO 2007

Subtractive fabrication or wasting processes involve the removal of material from a solid block using processes such as lathing, routing and multi-axis milling. These procedures may be applied directly to materials such as polymers, stone, metals and timber. Figure C.2.7 shows a CNC router assembly.

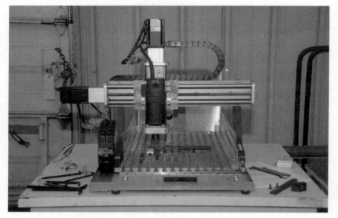

Figure C.2.7 CNC router
Image by Jon 'ShakataGaNai' Davis CC-BY-SA-3.0 unported (www.creativecommons.org/licenses/by-sa/3.0/) via Wikimedia Commons

Subtractive processes may also be used to machine moulds ready for injection moulding or casting of other materials, such as metals or concrete. Examples of products produced directly or indirectly by subtractive machining processes include:

- routed signs
- vacuum forming moulds
- moulds for casting, metals, polymers, concrete
- machined timber products - modular components.

C.2.9 Explain a situation in which it would be advantageous to use subtractive or additive manufacturing when making a product.

© IBO 2007

Examples of products more suitable for subtractive manufacturing include those requiring high quality surface finishes, greater precision, simple shapes and specific materials requirements. Subtractive processes

are also able to generate a range of surface finishes pertinent where friction may be an issue, the product may be employed in consumer trials or where cosmetic appearances are important. Subtractive processes are also required where ready-for-service parts (such as those required by biomedical industries) and where biocompatibility of materials is important.

Subtractive processes are most suited to generating large sized prototypes too big to be manufactured using additive processes.

If however, time, model complexity and the ability of the product to function are important, additive technologies are the most appropriate.

Rapid prototyping is finding applications increasingly in the field of biomedical engineering. Reproducing bone structures previously scanned are an ideal use for additive rapid prototyping techniques. The geometries involved and the number of inaccessible parts, make subtractive processes an inappropriate choice. Figure C.2.9 shows the complex surface geometries produced from a scan of patient's mouth.

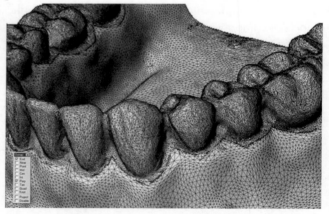

Figure C.2.9 Scanning of complex body parts ready for rapid prototyping

Image by WYSIWYG3D

C.2.10 Explain how a variety of tools can be used to make a complex outcome.

© IBO 2007

Multi-tool CNC machines are used where the outcome requires more than one cutting process. For example, a CNC lathe is able to drill, ream, thread, cut and part-off components. Figure C.2.10 shows a range of milling cutters including a ball end mill for finishing and end mills for roughing operations.

Figure C.2.10 Milling cutters

> **C.2.11** Discuss the advantages and disadvantages of using large or small-diameter tools when machining.
>
> © IBO 2007

Large-diameter tools remove greater amounts of material faster. They are often used for roughing cuts to define approximations of shape. Shapes produced in this fashion may, however, have uneven surfaces and exhibit 'stepping' across contours. Smaller diameter cutting tools operate at higher shaft speeds, but move at slower feed rates. These tools are often used for more accurate and detailed finishing cuts. Small diameter tools, however, are vulnerable to breaking if loaded too heavily and are not available in longer series sizes for this reason. Deeper finishing cuts may require a four or five-axis machine to finish fine details using shorter length small diameter bits.

> **C.2.12** Define machine tool step variable.
>
> **C.2.13** Outline how the machine tool step-over variables can determine the output quality of a product.
>
> © IBO 2007

Tool step-over is the distance the tool moves across the workpiece after finishing a pass. The horizontal distance between each path is called the step-over. The step-over is calculated as a fraction (generally 20% to 50%) of the diameter of the machine tool.

Too large a step-over may place extra pressure on the tool and raise heat, or even generate failure of the tool. Excessive heat from the tool also affects the material being machined, and, subsequently accuracy of the cut. Smaller step-over amounts allow time for the tool to cool and improve the surface finish of the object, but also increase the machining time. Commonly used values for a step-over are up to 50 % (of the cutter diameter) for roughing

cuts and down to 20% for high quality finishing cuts. Step-over distances are often determined after considering the material to be cut and the type of cutter employed.

After completing each successive layer, the tool plunges deeper (if required), partially overlapping the previous path. The vertical distance between each layer is called the step-down.

> **C.2.14** Describe raster, spiral and pocket cutting to manufacture.
>
> © IBO 2007

A raster approach to creating a 3D shape uses a straight tool path following the X, Y axes. The cutter makes multiple passes over the model to develop the final shape. The model may need a series of passes to improve the quality of the surface finish. Each set of passes would require a smaller step-over until the final run, which should have a step-over around 25% of the tool diameter. Raster machining is the most common operation in three-axis machining.

Spiral cutting uses a circular toolpath. By having one start point and one finish point, the spiral-cutting path keeps the tools on the job, without any retract move in between. Tool loading remains constant as the tool does not make any sharp direction changes and the amount of material being removed is also constant. This toolpath enables the machine tool to run at very high feed rates, eliminating the acceleration and deceleration caused by sudden changes in direction. Spiral cutting is particularly useful for round and curved components.

Pocket cutting is an action involving the creation of a tool path to cut an interior recess into the surface of a workpiece. Pockets may be circular or rectangular.

> **C.2.15** Discuss how machining paths alter the quality of a product and amount of time required in order to produce it (consider raster, spiral and pocket machining).
>
> © IBO 2007

CAM programmers have a great deal of flexibility when determining machining tool paths. The choice of tool, tool path, speed and sequence of operations affects cutting times and resultant surface finishes. Post-processing software allows programmers to simulate tool paths and predict cutting times using raster, spiral and pocket machining techniques.

As a rule, high quality and dimensionally accurate surface finishes require low feed rates and higher spindle speeds. Small step-overs, (and thus longer machining times), are regularly specified for hard or tough materials while softer substances can sustain larger step-overs and improved machining times.

Spiral finishing toolpaths prevent the formation of witness marks due to the tool's constant contact with the model surface.

C.2.16 Discuss the limitations of using three-axis machining when making a 3D product.

A disadvantage associated with three-axis milling machines is their inability to machine overhangs, undercuts or cavities in one operation. These features may be machined, but only through strategically breaking the design into parts, such that undercuts and cavities appear to have been removed. This process is complicated and requires a high degree of precision when sectioning and reassembling components.

Even when using more flexible five-axis mills, the size of the tool and its armature must be able to reach into the workspace when machining undercuts.

C.2.17 Define G code.

G code is a programming language used to impart instructions to CNC machines. G codes instruct machines to perform a particular function or move in a specified way. The information supplied by these codes relates to tool feed rates, spindle speeds, depth and direction of cut etc. Examples of some common G codes are recorded below. Note that these codes may vary between software packages and individual CNC machines. These codes are provided as a guide only.

G00 Rapid positioning
G04 Dwell
G21 Programming in mm
G28 Return to home position
G33 Thread cutting

C.2.18 Outline how a 3D CAD drawing is converted into a CNC file using G codes.

Translation of existing 3D drawings into G code involves the use of post-processing software. This low cost process converts CAD drawing files such as STL, IGES or DWF formats into CNC ready G codes.

C.2.19 Define feed speed.

C.2.20 Outline how feed speeds change depending on material and size of tool.

There are several variables to be considered when controlling cutting tools including cutting speed, tool materials, coolant, feed rate, depth of cut and approach angle. However, cutting speeds depend primarily on the material being cut i.e. the harder the work material, the slower the cutting speed. Cutting tool materials also influence optimal cutting speed selection i.e. the harder the cutting tool material, the faster the cutting speed.

Tools with larger diameters use slower spindle speeds and reduced feed rates. Figure C.2.20 shows approximate cutting speeds for materials determined for a specific set of conditions.

Depth of cut and feed rate also affect cutting speeds, but not to as great as an extent as workpiece hardness. These three factors, cutting speed, feed rate and depth of cut, are known as 'cutting conditions'. Cutting conditions are determined by the machinability rating, which compares the ease of materials to be machined.

Material type	Meters/minute
Mild steel	30—38
Castiron (medium)	18—24
Bronzes	24—45
Leaded steel (Leadloy 12L14)	300
Aluminium	75—105
Brass	600+

Figure C.2.20 Approximate cutting speeds for materials

Software is available to read G codes and automatically generate feed rates optimized against tool size, depth of cut and material selection.

C.2.21 Outline how limitations of tooling can affect the manner in which an object can be designed and manufactured.

Limitations of tool lengths and diameters affect the final design and manufacture of a product. Internal corners will often have radii and deep pockets that will not be easily cut by smaller diameter tools.

Five-axis machining allows all existing machining strategies to be used with the machine tool head inclined. This allows undercuts to be machined or shorter tools used in deep pockets. Shorter tools improve surface finish through reduced vibration and are inherently stronger.

Further reading

Beaman, J. J. (Chair), (2004). WTEC Panel on Additive/ *Subtractive Manufacturing Research and Development in Europe*, WTEC.

Heynick, M. & Stotz, I. (2006). *3D CAD, CAM and Rapid Prototyping*, LAPA Digital Technology Seminar Workshop 1: April 06, 07, & 08.

Lennings, L., *Selecting Either Layered Manufacturing or CNC Machining to Build Your Prototype*. Delft Spline Systems.

Nikam, P. E. (2000). *Application of Subtractive Rapid Prototyping to the Design and Manufacture of Rapid Solidification Process Tooling*, Maharashtra Institute of Technology, Pune, India.

Yang, Z., Wysk R. A., Joshi S., Frank M. C. & Petrzelka J. E. (2009). *Conventional Machining Methods for Rapid Prototyping and Direct Manufacturing*, International Journal of Rapid Manufacturing, Vol. 1, No. 1, Inderscience Enterprises Ltd.

C3 THE IMPACT OF CAD/CAM ON MANUFACTURING

C.3.1 Define numerical control.

Numerical control or control through numbers, refers to the automation of machining operations using programmed commands, as opposed to mechanical input such as hand-wheels, levers or cams. These commands are stored using a variety of media. These take the form of punch cards, magnetic tape and punch tape which are converted into output signals that directly control machine operations such as spindle rotation, tool type, tool movement, and cutting fluid flow.

C.3.2 Explain how a numerically controlled (NC) machine aids manufacturing.

Numerical control systems were developed in the 1940s and 1950s to meet the demands of mass production, uniformity and consistent part quality. This advance allowed for the automatic control of machines to perform repetitive operations continuously, to exacting standards and to operate in environments otherwise harsh or hazardous to humans.

C.3.3 Define computer numerical control (CNC).

In CNC systems, an operator generates a computer file that can be directly loaded into the CNC machine for manufacturing. In some cases, the computer file may be a drawing. The computer program then extracts the information required for manufacturing. CNC machining systems use a computer or machine control unit that calculates optimal settings and issues commands accordingly. These commands are issued in the form of numeric data to motors that position slides, select tools, adjust spindle speeds, manipulate tool paths and control coolant.

C.3.4 Compare numerical control and computer numerical control.

Numerical control (NC) machines are not connected to a computer and receive their instructions from punch cards or tape. These punch cards, made of paper, are fragile and have a limited life expectancy. The card reading technology (hard wired to the machine) can also be unreliable. NC controlled machines have no mechanism, such as display monitors or graphic user interfaces, to provide feedback to the operator. CNC machines offer greater flexibility than their NC counterparts.

C.3.5 Explain how a CNC machine further aids manufacture.

The major advantage of CNC machining is its ability to improve machining times, accuracy, efficiency, productivity and worker safety. In many situations, CNC equipment can continue to operate unmanned, 24hrs a day, seven days a week.

In conjunction with CAM technologies, digital images can be translated into pre-production pieces for testing, and later mass-produced through CNC equipment. Integration of CNC with CAD/CAM offers cost savings as significant as those achieved by integrating CAD and CAM. Data integration between different pieces of machinery, along with the merging of CAD/CAM systems, reduces programming and set-up costs. Data integration also saves machine and programming time, thus reducing costs.

Since the production of complex components may require a variety of machining operations and range of tooling, CNC machines can group multiple tools into a single 'cell'. As an alternative to single machine production, components can be machined by a variety of machines with automated transportation and positioning, all pre-programmed.

The generation of solid models using CAD packages and rapid prototyping is an example of the way in which new technologies merge to improve effectiveness and efficiency. Global computer networks allow for transfer of data to enable collaborative design and manufacturing.

C.3.6 Describe two- and three-axis machining processes.

Examples of two-axis machines include lathes, foam cutters, laser and plasma cutters. A two-axis machine, such as a lathe, uses a rotary motion to move the workpiece, while tool paths are created along the X- and Z- axes.

Figure C.3.6 Two axis machining

The number of axes available can determine a machine's capability. Three-axis machining, uses a router or vertical mill employing three linear axes along which movement is possible. Each of the axes is named for identification purposes. Machine table movements in the horizontal plane, (at 90° to each other), are designated 'X' and 'Y'. Vertical movement of the rotating cutting head is in the 'Z' axis.

C.3.7 Describe four- and five-axis machining processes.

Four-axis machining typically employs lathing operations, with the addition of a milling head attachment. This accounts for the X, Y and Z-axes plus the added rotating mill head. The fourth axis, (designated 'B'), is created through the addition of a rotary table to the machine bed, (Figure C.3.7). When linked to CAD software, four-axis mills can easily machine moulds for injection moulding operations, including complex features such as undercuts, manual slides and runner shutoffs.

Five-axis machining processes such as found in CNC milling machines, allow for simultaneous movement about five axes. These are typically comprised of a machine table that allows for movement in the X- and Y-axes, and a tool spindle that travels vertically in the Z-axis. The additional two axes come from the ability of the machine to rotate around the X- and Y-axes.

Five-axis machining is used for complex 3D profiles. It has the advantage of requiring only one set-up, yet produces high quality results and more flexibility when plotting tool paths. The process is widely employed where three- or four-axis machining techniques may cause collisions. The ability of this equipment to machine with inclined cutting tools allows for the use of shorter, more rigid, tools improving surface finish, reducing tool breakage and allowing for direct machining of undercuts. It also allows for machining of holes, pockets and tapping normal to complex surfaces.

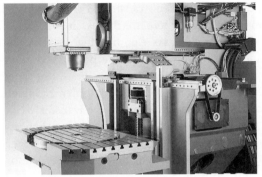

Figure C.3.7 Four-axis rotary table mill

Image by Gildemeister Aktiengesellschaft Davis CC-BY-SA-3.0 (www.creativecommons.org/licenses/by-sa/3.0/) via Wikimedia Commons

Using shorter tools, five-axis milling can:

- reduce vibration
- increase tool life
- machine more accurately
- produce higher quality surface finishes.

Typical applications for this type of machining include impellors or turbine blades Engine and fuel-system components typically feature complex surfaces at various angles, containing many holes of different sizes.

C.3.8 Outline how milling machines and routers can be interfaced in a CAD/CAM system.

A 'rectangular coordinate system' is used to accurately locate job positioning relative to the cutting tool using X, Y and Z-axes. Linear datum tolerances as small as one thousandth of a millimeter (.001mm) are commonly used. Plotting points relative to the axes allows for the accurate plotting of coordinates or points in space. These coordinates are used to relocate the cutting tool. Groups of coordinates can therefore be plotted to determine precise toolpaths. The tool is driven by a series of stepper motors to each of the coordinates.

CNC systems can therefore be used to drive any process where an operating head moves through space performing specific operations. These systems include laser cutting, welding, flame and plasma cutting, bending, routing etc.

Tooling selection criteria that were previously applied manually, including speeds/feeds, depth of cut are now imported automatically from the software package's database.

C.3.9 Discuss the issues faced by the designer and manufacturer when choosing CNC equipment.

Manufacturers and designers chose CNC equipment because of its ability to:

- reduce waste
- machine accurately
- improve cost per part
- take advantage of new materials
- improve accuracy and consistency
- improve workshop safety through automation.

Due to their initial high setup costs, manufacturers and designers are looking for a long-term return on their investment. Machines must therefore offer value for money. This value can be determined by considering the costs and benefits associated with a purchase. Considerations include:

- staff training needs
- tooling requirements
- speed and quality of finish
- flexibility and upgradeability
- equipment manufacturer support
- machine features and capabilities
- compatibility with existing equipment
- running costs or maintenance requirements.

C.3.10 Outline how a CNC lathe is interfaced in a CAD/CAM system to produce a 3D model.

CNC lathes driven by CAD software allows for horizontal or vertical lathing operations. Various tools are easily selected through graphic user interfaces from inbuilt tool libraries. Once selected, toolpaths can be automatically generated for machining operations including roughing, grooving, chamfering, boring and threading. These toolpaths can be verified through simulation of the machining operation(s) to ensure collision-free machining. NC codes are simultaneously generated (through post processing) as well as any workshop documentation that may be required. The main challenge of CNC systems for operators is the less-than-intuitive interface. Skilled artisans, operating manual machinery, develop a 'feel' for materials, speeds and feeds, based on past experience. None of this feedback is available to CNC machine operators.

> **C.3.11** Define computer integrated manufacture (CIM).
>
> **C.3.12** Describe how CAD/CAM can be integrated into a CIM system.
>
> © IBO 2007

CIM systems incorporate technologies or methodologies used to increase productivity through the integration of design, planning, engineering and processing operations in manufacturing plants using computer systems. CIM is a programmable computer-based manufacturing system linking design, engineering, manufacturing processes and industrial robots, using automated workstations. CIM systems can monitor operations from raw materials intake to final product marketing. CIM allows for the storage, retrieval and analysis of complex data providing manufacturers with valuable information relating to equipment maintenance scheduling, process optimization time and resource management. Major motivations for the implementation of a CIM systems approach is the need for manufacturing industries to quickly and efficiently respond to changes. CIM systems control and link the following components:

- personnel
- marketing
- materials handling
- product design (CAD)
- computer management
- machine tools and equipment (CAM).

A key consideration when implementing CIM is its compatibility with existing systems and infrastructure. Implementation of CIM may be best handled through a gradual or staged process instead of wholesale restructuring. Components of CIM may be added as deemed necessary as part of a plant overhaul.

> **C.3.13** Outline one example of a CIM system.
>
> © IBO 2007

Many automobile manufacturers have chosen CIM systems to manage and coordinate their already high level of automation. Integrating the ordering stage into the process involves taking into consideration customers with very specific requirements. Incorporating incoming orders with materials and third-party component inventories improves flexibility and reduces warehousing, allowing for JIT (just-in-time) manufacture. On the production floor, a variety of computer-controlled machines may be arranged to sequentially perform a range of operations. Components are often transferred automatically from station to station where machines, in teams, perform their programmed tasks e.g.; holding, rotating, welding, painting etc. These processes are performed along what are known as 'flow', or 'transfer', lines, the control of which is flexibly managed by a computer. Employing this networked system, components are transferred between stations using robot assistance. Movement of components through their various stages of assembly is managed by a computer 'hand off' system and assemblies are monitored for quality control at every stage, reducing wastage and improving consistency. Data from process control points is also logged and stored for reporting and review purposes.

> **C.3.14** Discuss the advantages and disadvantages of CIM to consumers and manufacturers.
>
> © IBO 2007

CIM systems provide many benefits to manufacturers including lower inventories and reduced warehousing requirements. Computer managed machinery improves machine utilization, offers greater scheduling flexibility and reduces manufacturing and lead-times. Labour and its associated on-costs should be reduced and have flow on effects to overall cost efficiencies. Improved access to production data allows managerial reviews for historical comparison and analysis. Manufacturers, however, may find initial setup costs high. The challenges of computerization and staff restructuring, however, may have negative affects on staff morale. Customers should benefit from price reductions, improved quality. Mass customization is easier within CIM production plants. Consumers may even be able to follow the production of their order through online interfaces with the plant.

Further Reading

Qi, R., Liu, W., Bian, H. & Li L. (2009). *Five-axis rough machining for impellers* Front. Mech. Eng. China.

Gunasekaran, A. (2001). *Next Generation Computer-Integrated Strategies and Techniques*, Journal of Computer Integrated Manufacturing. VOL. 14, NO. 2, pp. 137–139.

C4 RAPID PROTOTYPE MANUFACTURE

C.4.1 Describe stereo lithography.

Stereo lithography (as shown in Figure C.4.7) is just one rapid prototyping technology employed to build physical models, using only CAD data. In this process, computer software sections a 3D computer model into thin slices (0.05mm–0.15mm) before a computer-controlled laser beam 'builds' the model layer by layer.

The model building process involves the reaction between a bath of liquid photopolymer and a directed ultraviolet laser beam that 'prints out' the gradually solidifying object. As each layer is complete, the object, mounted on a moveable table, moves downwards to expose more photopolymer ready to create the next layer.

This technique allows the production of objects that may be too costly, time consuming or difficult to create, using traditional methods.

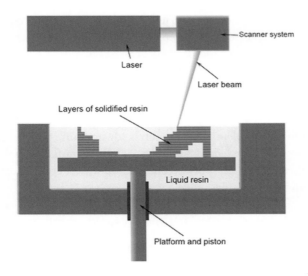

Figure C.4.1 Stereo lithography

Image by Materialgeeza [CC-BY-SA-3.0 (www. creativecommons.org/licenses/by-sa/3.0) or GFDL (www. gnu.org/copyleft/fdl.html)], from Wikimedia Commons

C.4.2 Describe wet rapid prototyping.

Wet prototyping technology employs photopolymeric materials sprayed in thin layers onto a moveable table. As each layer is complete, it is cured with an application of ultraviolet light. Manufactured in this fashion, no post-production curing of the resin is necessary. Complex geometry, fine detail or delicate structures formed using this technique may require support until sufficient layers have been deposited. A supporting gel holds all these features in place until the object is complete. This gel may be removed with water jets, or through use of an acid bath.

C.4.3 Describe dry rapid prototyping.

Dry prototyping builds models incorporating supports that secure any loose or overhanging elements of the design. These support structures are deposited simultaneously with the model. Once the model is complete, the build bed is raised, the model is cleaned and the supporting elements manually broken loose.

The support structures are typically made from a different, cost efficient material to that of the model. 3D printer software calculates where the support material would be most effective. Orientation of the model may even be suggested to minimize support structure requirements.

C.4.4 Describe laminated object manufacture (LOM).

Using a laser cutter, LOM technologies cut sheet material (pre-glued paper or plastic) based on data provided by CAD software that has sliced the original CAD model into layers. Once cut, these layers are glued together to form a physical model. Assembly of these layers may use locating pins or an automatic process conducted on a moveable table directly under the laser, (Figure C.4.4). Kraft paper, backed with a polyethylene-based, heat sensitive adhesive, is often used as the modelling material. This product is both cost-effective and environmentally friendly. Paper models are regularly sealed to prevent damage from moisture and improve their overall strength. Other modelling materials include acrylic, metal and ceramic 'felt"

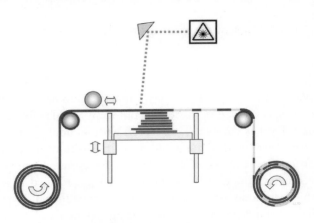

Figure C.4.4 Layered object manufacturing

Image modified from Laurensvanlieshout CC-BY-SA-3.0 (www.creativecommons.org/licenses/by-sa/3.0), from Wikimedia Commons

C.4.5 Describe solid object printing.

Solid object printing uses technology similar to inkjet printers. It employs a paraffin-based thermo-polymer that is applied in molten microscopic drops that solidify together on contact. This wax-based model is printed in layers to build its height and is suitable for use as an investment casting blank, (see 11.3.1).

Modifications may be carved directly on the printed model which, in turn, may be rescanned ready for a second modified 'print' run.

C.4.6 Describe fuse deposition modelling (FDM).

The fuse deposition modelling process works on a principle similar to a hot-melt glue gun, (Figure C.4.6). FDM uses ultra thin filaments, stored on a spool. These filaments are extruded through a heated chamber that converts them into a semi-liquid form, before being deposited. The fusion head travels horizontally across a moveable machine table. FDM modelling filaments include investment casting wax, polycarbonate, polyphenylsulfone, and durable polyester. Accuracies of + - 0.15% can be achieved. A second printer head delivers the support material in a different colour to allow for differentiation and ease of removal. Models may be manufactured in wax or, more commonly, ABS plastic. Surface finish of these models is not as accurate as some other processes, but models are strong and may be cleaned up later.

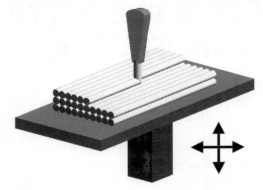

Figure C.4.6 Fused deposition modelling

Image modified from Zureks, GNU Free Documentation License, Version 1.2, from Wikimedia Commons

C.4.7 Describe select laser sintering (SLS).

Select laser sintering has its name derived directly from the manufacturing processes involved. A CO_2 laser selectively focuses on a section of a moveable table covered in a heat-fusible powder. The power of the laser is set to bind the powder without it melting (sintering). Repetitive scans of the table with the laser build up the model in layers.

Support structures are not required in this process. As each layer scan is complete, a new layer of powder is deposited over the top and pressed flat with a roller. The act of compressing the powder allows the model to be constructed without supporting structures. Models may even be manufactured with moving parts.

Once complete, the model is dusted off, with excess powder recycled. SLS powders can be manufactured from thermoplastics, polystyrene, sand, wax, ceramics, steel and even stainless steel.

C.4.8 Compare wet and dry rapid prototype techniques.

Wet prototyping techniques can be used for more detailed or delicate part designs. The nature of the supporting gel allows for its ease of removal through the flushing or jetting of fluids.

In dry prototyping, the use of more solid support structures leads to a removal process that is harsher on the model. Physically breaking away support structures may damage the model and leave difficult-to-trim remnants. Some supporting structures may even be inaccessible in the completed object.

Explain the benefits of being able to rapid prototype a product instead of using other CAM techniques.

Rapid prototyping technologies have allowed designers to now quickly manufacture prototypes, moulds or one-off originals that have already been:

- tested for interference and fit
- specified with appropriate materials
- examined for strength and serviceably.

They also incorporate relatively short build times without the need for custom tooling. Internal features for components may also be incorporated into the model and deposited simultaneously as the model is built layer by layer. This complexity has little effect on build times.

Additive processes may employ a range of materials e.g. polymers, paper products, metals, composites and even ceramics. Some additive technologies can even build models from a selection of materials and distribute them based on the CAD data supplied. Even with these options, material selection is still limited. This may result in models not exhibiting the desired physical properties required of a final product.

At this point, surface finishes continue to improve for additive processes, but they cannot match those achievable through machining. To this end, rapid prototyped models may require post-processing dependent on their final application.

C.4.10 Discuss the limitations of rapid prototyping for volume-produced products.

Due to high initial establishment costs, the use of customized tooling and lengthy setup times, conventional processes are less cost effective for low-volume produced products. Additive fabrication techniques have limited setup procedures and complex parts may be built directly from a CAD model through a computer interface. This makes additive processes the most appropriate choice for low-volume production runs.

Economies of scale come into play when high volume production is required. Machining, moulding and casting are still the preferred approaches when dealing with high production volumes. Cost per unit reduces as production quotas increase and cycling times are currently shorter for

traditional technologies than for additive processes. Also, additive processes are most suited to smaller components. Build times for additive processes also increase as model sizes get larger. Larger X- and Y-axes require greater time to complete each pass while an increase in the Z-axis requires more layers to be deposited.

Limitations in part size are not as critical for casting or machining. Cycle times for machining are more dependent on part complexity and material, while the determining factor for casting relates more to wall thickness.

C.4.11 Discuss how rapid prototyping (RP) benefits trials, testing and final part manufacture.

Rapid prototyping is a powerful tool used to shorten product design, development and testing times. Prototypes or models produced through rapid prototyping processes are playing an increasingly important role in achieving and improving design success by:

- allowing companies to quickly respond to design change requirements, evaluate components in context and introduce products into the market with speed and precision
- producing prototype models with the same features and surface textures as the finished product
- ensuring customers have a clear understanding of new and innovative concepts, by presenting clients with 3D visualizations or hands-on prototypes of product designs.

Dependent on the material used, final products manufactured using rapid prototyping technologies should have excellent repeatability due to the elimination of tool wear as a variable.

C.4.12 Compare SLS, LOM and FDM rapid prototype processes.

C.4.13 Describe different design contexts where SLS, LOM and FDM would be applicable.

Within the range of rapid prototyping processes available, stereo lithography, selective laser sintering and fused deposition modelling are the most common technologies employed.

FDM and SLS, (opposed to LOM), are selected when functionality of the model is a consideration. FDM modelled components are similar to injection moulded components.

SLS offers the ability to form complex geometries, is faster than FDM and has greater flexibility in its range of materials selection including investment casting wax, metals and thermoplastic composite materials. Recent advances provide materials that even simulate glass-reinforced nylon. Improvements in the technology have secured greater dimensional accuracy and see parts produced to finer tolerances. If necessary, minimal post-processing such as sanding may be adopted.

The most significant advantage of the SLS process lies in its ability to 'nest' designs and thus improve material efficiencies, reduce costs, lessen waste and improve whole-of-product processing times.

LOM is the most appropriate choice when cost is a factor. Particularly when developing larger models, the use of paper as the constituent material keeps costs low. Neither LOM or FDM use additional support structures in their construction however, FDM products can be limited in the depth of layering available, although work continues to develop larger machines.

Further Reading

Chua, C. K., Leong, K. F., Cheng, H. K. & Chow, L. M. (1997). *A Multimedia Approach to Teaching Rapid Prototyping Systems,* International Journal of Engineering, Great Britain, Vol. 13, No. 2, p. 108±116.

Ruffo, M., Tuck, C., & Hague, R. (2006). *Cost Estimation for Rapid Manufacturing – Laser Sintering Production for low to Medium Volumes,* Journal of Engineering Manufacture, Vol. 220 Part B.

Yang, Z., Wysk, R.A., Joshi, S., Frank, M.C. & Petrzelka, J. E. (2009). *Conventional Machining Methods for Rapid Prototyping and Direct Manufacturing*, International Journal of Rapid Manufacturing, Vol. 1, No. 1, pp.41–64. C5 CAD/CAM Products.

C.5 PACKAGING

> **C.5.1** Describe the use of CAD and rapid prototyping in the development of electronic product housing.
>
> © IBO 2007

Designs for the large range and variety of electronic product housings require flexibility in enclosure design, materials selection and manufacturing processes. Designers are faced with challenges ranging from sheet metal cases to enclosures requiring complex surface geometries demanding both completed injection-moulded parts and complex moulded internal configurations.

Using advanced CAD modelling software, housings can be designed, tested and evaluated in a virtual environment. Housings must be designed with external conditions in mind, allowing the product to fit precisely and match potential mounting points. This attention to detail reduces materials, testing and trial times. The same is true for the interior design of the housing. Electronics housings such as those requiring thin walls, reinforcing ribs, complex internal details, attachment points, pre-drilled holes and hinging, may all be designed and evaluated in virtual environments. Compatibility with internal components and third-party assemblies can also be examined.

Manufactured in a range of plastics, ceramics or metals, the choice of rapid prototyping technology may allow for physical testing of the housing and even client approval. If appropriate materials are within the range of the rapid prototyping process selected, housings may even be produced with specific electrostatic discharge requirements, including conductive, static, dissipative and anti-static materials and coatings.

> **C.5.2** Discuss the benefits of using CAD and rapid prototyping to the designer and manufacturer of electronic products.
>
> © IBO 2007

Product designers are able to design complex products while adding little to manufacturing times. A greater degree of artistic freedom is achieved where functional and/or aesthetic designs are easily accommodated and designs can meet very complex customer specifications. Rapid prototyping can reduce parts count and the need for associated fasteners and fixings, by combining several parts into single components that have previously been unable to be realized through the inaccessibility of tooling and other constraints. This process also minimizes waste from machining processes. Reduction in the number of components also assists with assembly and disassembly, tolerancing and alignment issues. Electronics products through rapid prototyping can be designed:

- with reduced part numbers
- incorporating thin walls
- involving complex shapes
- disregarding machining constraints.

> **C.5.3** Describe the use of rapid prototyping in the development of cosmetics packaging.
>
> **C.5.4** Discuss the benefits of using rapid prototyping to the designer and manufacturer of cosmetics products.
>
> © IBO 2007

The combination of CAD software and rapid prototyping allows for fast modification of complex design alternatives for presentation to manufacturers or clients. Some of this process may be automated as one change has automated flow-on affects to the overall design, leaving designers to concentrate on product form. Considerations for cosmetic products and packaging include:

- volume constraints
- fill-line requirements
- manufacturing costs
- product package wall thickness
- production methods and surface finishes.

Standardization of parts and component libraries for caps, threads, hinges, closures etc. speed the design process, reduce complications and give designers and manufacturers confidence.

3D computer models can produce files appropriate for rapid prototyping processing and the subsequent generation of physical prototypes for evaluation. Virtual testing, allows designers to minimize material usage without compromising strength or the integrity of packaging alternatives. Reviewing these digital designs through finite element analysis can also allow for material optimization by examining a variety of wall thicknesses and materials combinations.

Some software packages automatically generate mould designs (including split lines) or tooling designs for a range of appropriate processes and materials including blow moulding, injection moulding etc. Calculations may also include allowances for shrinkage, thus guaranteeing container volume.

While rapid prototyping may not produce models with production-quality surface finishes or allow for a wide range of materials, rapid injection moulding technologies produce fully functional, production-quality prototypes ready for evaluation, market trials or even pilot production. If approved, rapid injection moulding is suitable for up to 10,000 models without additional tooling costs. This process is much more economical than premature investment in expensive injection moulding equipment.

> **C.5.5** Discuss how CAD and rapid prototyping has reduced the life cycle of packaged products.
>
> © IBO 2007

Packaging is important because it:

- protects products
- groups multiple parts of a product
- provides assistance with marketing
- presents consumer information and legislative requirements about a product.

Within the cosmetics industry enclosure and packaging design can be the key discriminator for consumers when making a choice in the marketplace. Designers and manufacturers are forced to innovate in response to reduced product life cycles based on markets that may change not annually, but seasonally. Designers are always searching for new materials or better and cheaper ways to make products and packages. Shortened product life cycles due to the need to remain 'current' and therefore competitive require rapid response times and the high levels of flexibility offered through CAD/CAM and rapid prototyping technologies.

> **C.5.6** Describe how the use of CAD has changed the jewellery industry.
>
> © IBO 2007

Historically, jewellery design, model making and manufacturing of finished pieces has been craft-based. Designers create one-off unique pieces that are painstakingly manufactured by highly skilled artisans. The processes involved are time consuming, and ultimately add to the overall cost. Materials employed in jewellery making are also expensive and manufacturing errors or miscommunication with clients can rapidly escalate costs. The use of machinery or any form of automation was previously limited to specific stages of manufacturing such as grinding, polishing or cleaning.

The introduction of CAD and rapid prototyping technologies has revolutionized the industry. Designers are able to rapidly respond to client requests using an iterative design process involving adjustment to virtual designs or even wax prototypes printed on-site.

> **C.5.7** Discuss the benefits of using CAD/CAM to the designer and manufacturer of jewellery.
>
> **C.5.8** Explain how CAD/CAM has improved the type and range of jewellery products available to the consumer.
>
> © IBO 2007

CAD and the technologies associated with rapid prototyping of jewellery has a major advantage when developing complimentary or themed sets. Once an original design has been generated in CAD and checked for its ability to be manufactured, mirrored models may be created to produce a left or right identical match for the pair or copied into a bracelet or pendant blank. These operations can be very time consuming and rely on the expertise of the artisan when produced by hand. Variants of designs are easily generated once an original is established. In the design stage, virtual models of jewellery are created with CAD software, (Figure C.5.7), before being converted into STL files. The use of standard libraries or previously modelled items may be used for modification. 2D sketches or 3D scanned images may also be imported to start the design process. These models can include such features as undercuts, fine details, thin wires, beads and hollow areas hitherto unable to be produced by milling.

Through stereo lithographic processes, a wax master may be produced. Mould production, and subsequent casting of the piece, (through lost wax or investment casting processes), quickly generates clean, highly accurate designs that reduce gemstone breakage rates.

CAD software has in-built features to assist designers, manufacturers and consumers, including the ability to:

- rotate 3D designs
- account for shrinkage after casting
- preview costs as modifications are made
- view designs as pieces or sets assembled on screen
- incorporate a range of materials that are interchangeable
- dynamically calculate weights of designs as material selections change.

Figure C.5.7 CAD model of an intricate jewelled pendant

Image by http://www.alldzine.com Creative Commons Attribution 3.0 Unported, from Wikimedia Commons

> **C.5.9** Outline a piece of furniture that can be manufactured by CAD/CAM or by a more traditional process.
>
> **C.5.10** Compare the two manufacturing processes for a chosen piece of furniture.
>
> **C.5.11** Evaluate the product manufactured by the two manufacturing processes.
>
> © IBO 2007

Flat-pack furniture, in this case chair production, lends itself towards CAD/CAM processes. By its nature, flat-pack furniture is composed of modular profiles joined by industry-standardized fittings. This allows for repetitive manufacturing processes, ease of assembly, ease of storage and transportation and ease of disassembly. Precise location of components is produced using CAD/CAM technologies. Most departments in modern flat-pack industries involve automation through complex palletizing, warehousing of products, banding, polishing and coating of panels. Flat-pack furniture has found mass-market acceptance through companies such as IKEA.

Michael Thonet's 19th Century café or bistro chair is one of the most recognizable pieces of furniture ever made. Instantly identifiable by its simple design and bent wood construction, this chair is one of the best-selling pieces of furniture ever produced. What is not readily appreciated is that this may be the first example of flat-pack furniture.

Originally produced using only six pieces of steam-bent beechwood, formed in cast iron moulds, unskilled factory workers were able to mass-produce this design classic. Eight screws and a pair of nuts and bolts allowed the chair to be easily assembled and disassembled - a precursor to today's flat-pack designs. Figure C.5.9 shows an assembled and disassembled version of Thonet's design.

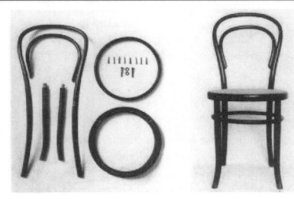

Figure C.5.9 Thonet chair

Today, companies like IKEA, market large parts of their furniture range based on flat-pack designs and the benefits they bring to manufacturers and consumers alike. Many styles of flat-pack furniture designs exist today catering for a range of preferences in styles, materials and cost.

Mass-produced flat-pack furniture has a market niche with consumers who wish to take advantages of savings gained through the scale of the manufacturers operation, reduced shipping, storage and transportation costs, plus the benefits of ease of transport and ready-to-assemble convenience.

CAD software packages coupled with sophisticated CAM machinery can now cope with not only mass-produced items, but also complex individual decorative pieces. This software targets skilled artisans rather than technicians. It allows craftsmen to import, rescale and position textures or decorative features, thus reducing hours of delicate and testing work.

Mass production, quality assurance programs, global networks, on-line ordering and reduced transportation costs make flat-pack furniture a cost-effective option compared to handcrafted alternatives. Mass-produced furniture of this type is generally purchased with a purpose in mind. It is not intended to 'last through the ages' and may in fact be part of a regular redecorating process. Factory made furniture mostly adheres to a standard, is cheaper and more easily accessed.

Handmade furniture introduces variations in skill levels of craftsman, quality of design, selection of and understanding of materials etc. Traditional furniture making practices involve handcrafting of individual pieces by skilled artisans. Handcrafted items are unique. No two pieces of wood are the same and craftsmen take great care in selecting exactly the right piece of wood for a particular use, taking into consideration colour, grain density. Even pieces crafted as parts of matched sets will have minor variations. While they may look similar, on closer inspection minor variations in grain, colour and ornamental detail will be evident. Figure C.5.11 shows an antique, highly ornate, handcrafted, chestnut, ceremonial chair.

Consumers may purchase expensive one-off, handcrafted pieces of furniture as an investment, with plans to keep the furniture for an extended period of time, or hand it down through generations, such as the case with antique pieces. Consumers often have a closer relationship with craftsmen manufacturers than their mass production counterparts. As such, consumers can have more say in the specification of their work and may even have input into the work at various stages of construction.

In terms of life cycle analysis, local artisans utilizing native timbers may have less impact on the environment than an overseas sourced mass-produced item.

Figure C.5.11 Carved ornamental chair

Image by Artist signature unreadable (Google Books) [Public domain], via Wikimedia Commons

> **C.5.12** Discuss the benefits of using CAD/CAM in the design and manufacture of flat-pack furniture.
>
> © IBO 2007

Flat-pack furniture designs are conceived with manufacturing in mind. The use of easy-to-assemble components combined with standardized hardware and knockdown fittings also allows designers to source standardized components from existing CAD libraries, manufacturers to easily source hardware and consumers to easily assemble the final product. The use of pre-drilled holes for these fittings means manufacturers can set CNC boring machines to follow simple repetitive patterns.

Cutting and shaping of timber furniture sections is easily accomplished through the application of CNC routers. Reading directly from original designs, the CNC router can not only cut timber to very precise tolerances, but also calculate and establish nesting groups to maximize materials use and minimize wastage.

Manufacturers benefit from the ability to set production lines in motion, turning out large numbers of identical components. Completed flat-pack designs are packaged into one or more boxes and allow for ease of warehousing, transportation for distribution and final delivery to consumers.

Limited, (assembly), tooling is required and can incorporate an opportunity to modularize the design, allowing for a range of alternative assemblies. Flat-pack furniture relies on its consistent sameness as a selling point. This sameness also assists the manufacturing process.

C.5.13 Discuss how CAD/CAM has affected consumer choice when purchasing furniture.

© IBO 2007

CAD packages offer consumers the opportunity to consider a range of design variations relating to proportion, materials selection and finish. When ordering, this allows for greater flexibility and mass customization of products. Selected combinations may be displayed in traditional catalogue form, in virtual environments to allow simulation for 'walk throughs' or may be electronically combined with clients' own photographs to produce photorealistic images.

C.5.14 Outline an area in which a single task robot could be used in the manufacture of flat-pack furniture.

© IBO 2007

The two most common applications of robots in the manufacture of flat-pack furniture are in the palletizing of raw materials and finished products and the edge treatment of manufactured boards and natural timbers. Specifically, robots are programmed to perform repetitive tasks helping to improve efficiency or maintain quality control throughout a factory. Tasks include such operations as:

- drilling holes
- edge banding
- reading barcodes (inventory)
- counting operations (components)
- inserting hardware (knock-down fittings)
- scanning for surface defects (quality control).

C.5.15 Discuss the issues associated with using manufactured boards and natural timber when using CAM to produce furniture.

© IBO 2007

When employing CAD/CAM processes the raw materials, in this case timber products, must meet specific requirements to be deemed suitable. Materials specified for flat-pack furniture are either engineered to specific requirements, or undergo rigorous selection criteria to guarantee their homogeneity. The use of manufactured boards, or supplied timber blanks of known size, allows for fast and convenient materials handling. Consistent and predictable material size is critical to placement and alignment of materials. These materials must exhibit consistency from piece to piece. This consistency refers to:

- security of supply
- high degrees of dimensional stability
- homogeneity throughout (individual pieces and job lots).

This consistency guarantees automated machinery will not misfeed or misalign components when manufacturing. It also guards against any movement of the materials during or after processing, causing inaccuracies in machining or displacement of connection points, making assembly difficult.

Manufactured boards offer a number of advantages over natural timber and are often specified by furniture designers and manufacturers. Also known as engineered or man-made boards, they incorporate a range of materials from particle boards to plywoods. They are all composite materials made by combining fibres, particles, flakes or veneers of wood or other materials, with a binding adhesive. Manufactured boards have the following properties. They are:

- defect free
- easily machined
- created to be homogeneous
- manufactured to precise sizes
- available in sizes larger than natural timber
- engineered to meet a required specification i.e. water resistant
- manufactured from waste timber or plantation timber thinnings
- available in a variety of surface finishes e.g. veneers, laminates etc.
- accept a range of surface finishes, e.g. paint, lacquer, two pack epoxy etc.

> **C.5.16** Outline how the increased use of CAD/CAM in furniture manufacture has developed the need for a wider range of knock down fittings.
>
> © IBO 2007

In an effort to deal with rising production costs, timber availability and a rising concern over the sustainability of timber products, manufacturers have turned to manufactured boards, composites, CAD/CAM and knock-down fittings. Combinations of these allow manufacturers to reduce costs, maintain or improve quality control and produce flat-pack alternatives to traditional designs. These flat-pack alternatives take up less space during storage, are less expensive when distributing to point-of-sale and are more easily transported by consumers to their homes.

Due to its increasing popularity, flat-pack furniture manufacturers continue to explore new materials and designs that are more complex. The design and variety of knock-down fittings is considerable and continues to develop to cater for this increasing demand as designers develop new ways to hold assemblies together.

> **C.5.17** Describe how exploded view CAD drawings have helped consumers when assembling components.
>
> © IBO 2007

Assembly diagrams often show a 3D view of components or parts separated as if suspended in space. The appearance is as if a small explosion has separated an assembled object into its constituent parts hence the name, exploded assembly drawing. These drawings assist with:

- sequence of assembly
- identification of parts
- tools and hardware required
- final appearance of assembled product
- viewing the appearance of the progressive assembly.

These drawings also provide assistance if disassembly is required.

Further reading

Carroll, T. (2007). *Then and now: Robot arms,* Servo. pp. 79-82.

Cleminshaw, D. (.1999) *Sea change, Visualizing Strategy, Innovation.* pp. 35-28.

Marinelli, O. (2008). *From Humans to Robots: The Consequences of Labor Replacement in the Automobile Industry Human Change* Paper.

Molinari, L.C., Megazzini, M.C., Bemporad, E., *The Role of CAD/CAM in the Modern Jewellery Business.* pp. 3-7.

Stone, R. J. (2000). *Haptic Feedback: A Brief History from Telepresence to Virtual Reality, Proceedings of the First International Workshop on Haptic Human-Computer Interaction.* pp.1-16.

Wannarumon, S. & Bohez, E. L. J. (2004). *Rapid Prototyping and Tooling in Jewelry CAD, Computer-Aided Design And Applications.* Volume 1 Numbers1-4 pp. 569-576.

Young, Y. Y., Yu, K. M. & Kwong, C. K. (2001). *Rapid Jewelry Manufacture Using Spatial Subdivision,* Engineering with Computers. 17: 386–392.

Furniture production - Materials and Technology, ABB Robots Assembles the Perfect Flat Pack. Issue 161 March 2007.

C6 MATERIALS - HL

Virtually any material can be CNC machined. Materials suitable for CAD machining are dimensionally stable and exhibit uniform structural and mechanical properties throughout i.e. they are homogeneous over the range of temperatures experienced during machining processes. Depending on the purpose of the final product, materials with such diverse properties as transparency, temperature resistance, low density, high strength or stiffness may be machined using this approach. Restrictions are only imposed based on the size and power of the equipment used.

During machining operations, friction between the workpiece and the cutting tool can generate high temperatures. Friction and heat generated vary and are dependent on the type of material being machined, severity of cutting operation and the cutting tool material. Nevertheless, the result of this heat can lead to:

- shorter tool life
- higher surface roughness
- degradation of tool edges
- reduced dimensional accuracy of workpieces.

A variety of methods may be employed to reduce this friction, moderate heat generated and improve surface finish. Most commonly employed is the use of cutting fluids to lubricate machining operations and cool toolpieces. The use of lubricants can allow for higher feed rates and thus faster machining times. Unfortunately, many of these fluids can have a detrimental affect on the environment.

The use of new materials for cutting tools sees the development of dry machining approaches as an alternative to the use of cutting fluids.

While initial investment in capital equipment for CAD/CAM operations can be high, these costs are recovered over time through the efficiencies gained by improvements in quality, productivity, efficiency, and reductions in wastage.

Environments for workers should improve as conditions change from the physical manipulation of tools and machinery, to the more technical requirements of maintenance and programming. Machinery can be isolated from workers, reducing exposure to dust and noise.

Finding skilled artisans and apprentices can be difficult. Equally difficult can be the constant upgrading of a CAD/CAM operator's skills, a requirement to effectively meet the needs of constantly evolving software and operating systems.

CAD/CAM gives manufacturers greater confidence in the quality and accuracy of finished components, within predetermined tolerances. A major advantage is the assured repeatability of these operations.

Materials for CAD/CAM modelling include card, standard plastics (ABS, TryCut), manufactured boards, modelling wax, woods (balsa), resins and foams. Depending on the process, materials may also include aluminium and zirconia-based oxide ceramics, titanium, acrylics and non-precious alloys. Sheet and block material are both usable.

Medium density fibreboard (MDF) is available in large flat sheets. It is dimensionally stable, homogeneous throughout and reliably consistent between construction batches, making it suitable for CAM operations. Alternative manufactured boards to MDF, such as chipboard, have low shear strength and variable properties throughout, while plywood has greater strength but a layered or lamellar structure.

Comprehensive research conducted across the globe indicates machining MDF generates dust particles similar to any machining operation performed on wood and produces the same health and safety issues associated with wood dust. There is some contention as to whether machining operations performed on MDF produce smaller dust particles, more easily dispersed in the surrounding environment. Dust extraction equipment and personal protection should be used when machining all wood products, including MDF.

The use of formaldehyde as a bonding agent in MDF has long been considered a health issue. Formaldehyde can cause eye, skin and throat irritation and trigger asthma attacks. Consideration should also be given to the fact that formaldehyde also occurs naturally in wood. Smoke and burn marks will appear if feed rates and spindle speeds are set too fast, causing the emission of formaldehyde fumes.

> **C.6.7** Discuss how modelling wax can be used in a CAM system to aid jewellery production.
>
> © IBO 2007

Lost-wax, investment casting or precision casting is most often applied to create small intricate castings like the one shown in Figure C.6.7a. It is used in the jewellery making process because it can create products with great precision and accuracy. Wax is often used to create a master pattern from which a mould is made. Modelling techniques in wax, allow for the casting of fine filigree or other extremely thin sections or objects with connecting pieces.

Figure C.6.7a Lost wax cast pendant

Image by Harry J. Smith, GFDL, GNU Free Documentation License, via Wikimedia Commons

A variety of processes may be employed to manufacture the wax master. Traditionally, hand carving allowed for the creation of unique pieces. Today CAD/CAM techniques are employed to create the wax master. 3D printers (such as the one shown in Figure C.6.7b) may be employed to produce wax models from digital STl files. The master is 'printed', layer-by-layer to produce a solid wax pattern. Objects produced in this fashion capture very fine details with an excellent surface finish.

Figure C.6.7b 3D printer

After printing, the wax pattern is coated with a ceramic and fired in a kiln to melt the wax, leaving behind a hollow shell ready for casting. The end result is a perfect casting produced quickly, without expensive tooling and time consuming setups.

As an alternative to 3D printing, the wax master may be machined with a CNC router similar to the one shown in Figure C.6.7c. The same process, as previously described, is employed after the production of the wax master.

Figure C.6 7c CAD router

> **C.6.8** Discuss the issues associated with using metals in a CAM system.
>
> © IBO 2007

Spindle speeds and feed rates not only affect the quality of surface finish but also tool wear and cutter damage. The following factors are representative considerations:

- coolant used
- material machined
- cutting tool condition
- type, size and material of cutting tool
- workpiece design and machining operation
- max. and min. spindle speed settings available.

Speeds and feed rates are always approximate and test runs prove invaluable in determining accurate settings.

C.6.9 Outline how surface modelling techniques let consumers test before they buy.

© IBO 2007

Surface modelling techniques allow designers to provide consumers with realistic looking models, parts or assemblies incorporating variations in materials, texture and colour. Photorealistic renderings can place a model in-situ with contextual lighting and the ability to view the model from any direction. Animation may also be included to simulate the interaction of moving parts.

Further reading

Çakīr, O., Yardimeden, A., Ozben, T., Kilickap, E. (2007). *Selection of Cutting Fluids in Machining Processes, Journal of Achievements in Materials and Manufacturing Engineering, Volume 25*, Issue 2.

Wannarumon, S., & Bohez E. (2004). *Rapid Prototyping and Tooling Technology in Jewelry CAD,* Computer-Aided Design & Applications.

Heynick, M., & Stotz I. (2006). *3D CAD, CAM and Rapid Prototyping.* LAPA Digital Technology Seminar.

HL

OPTION

C.7 ROBOTS

C.7.1 Define industrial robot.

© IBO 2007

The International Standards Organisation, (ISO), defines an industrial robot as, 'an automatically controlled, reprogrammable, multipurpose, manipulator programmable in three or more axes, which may be either fixed in place or mobile for use in industrial automation applications', ISO 8373. Figure C.7.1 shows a generic example of a fixed robotic arm. Typically, industrial robots are comprised of four basic components:

- power source – electrical, hydraulic or pneumatic
- tooling – fixed, multiple or interchangeable tools
- mechanical unit – structural arm, sensors, joints, actuators
- control system – computer or microprocessor driven controller.

Figure C.7.1 Typical robot arm

Image by Humanrobo Creative Commons Attribution-Share Alike 3.0 Unported, from Wikimedia

C.7.2 Describe the role of the robot in an industrial environment

© IBO 2007

Robots are not the answer to all of a manufacturer's problems. There are many tasks that will never be assigned to robots, yet they can still perform others with improved efficiency. These roles can be divided into three categories:

- quality control and inventory
- fabrication or assembly operations
- materials handling and transportation.

Materials handling robots transport materials, components and finished product throughout a plant. They may be used for complex palletising of products in a warehouse, retrieving multiple components ready for the assembly line or moving sub-assemblies between stations. Automated warehouses are an example of this application.

Figure C.7.2 Robotic materials handling and transport

Fabrication or assembly robots work in a variety ways i.e. single robot - single-task, multi robot - single-task or single robot - multi-task situations. Single-task robots perform one operation such as spot welding. In multi-robot situations a team of robots may work together to place components and hold them in place, while other robots drill, weld or rivet. Multi-task robots may perform a variety of operations within the one cell using interchangeable heads or multiple arms.

Quality control robots use sensors to inspect products for defects. These robots may be stationed throughout the assembly line and may be independent or programmed as part of a multi-tasking robot operation.

Improved management of robotic systems is achieved using flexible manufacturing or CIM systems, (see C.3.11), where computers monitor and control the entire process of manufacturing from scheduling each step of production to keeping track of parts inventories, tool use and warehousing.

> **C.7.3** Describe the use of robots in industrial conditions that would be unsuitable for humans.
>
> © IBO 2007

Robots are most often found in situations where any one or more of the 3Ds exist; dirty, dangerous or dull jobs. These types of jobs include repetitive assembly, spray painting, welding, deburring, machining, heavy lifting, materials handling, complex palletising etc. Harsh or remote environments may self-select the use of robots in such situations as foundries, space, undersea, toxic atmospheres, garbage handling, radioactive environments, high temperature and/or noisy conditions.

> **C.7.4** Describe how robots can perform new processes in extreme conditions.
>
> © IBO 2007

Extreme conditions may be associated with loading, heat, cold, dust, radiation or the need to maintain a clean or sterile environment. Applications range from clean rooms to foundries or oil rigs, to food processing and surgical procedures etc. Use of robots in hazardous or demanding environments reduces human exposure to risk, improves efficiency and improves productivity.

As robot capabilities improve, new applications and environments are found where their skills would be beneficial. Improvements in materials technologies, flexible joints and seals see new corrosion resistant alloys of steel and aluminium incorporated into designs. Secure moisture-resistant seals sufficient to maintain positive internal pressures create stable vapour-free environments for the internal housing of delicate instruments.

Extreme cold presents challenges to the deterioration of flexible cables, bearings and seals. In these environments, servomotors are also subject to electrical signal distortion.

Reductions in work envelope requirements also allow robots to move into areas they were previously unable to service. Robots are also not affected by issues associated with orientation, the way their human counterparts are and, as such, may operate at precarious angles or even upside down. Sophisticated collision avoidance systems also allow robots to work successfully in teams or independently near other equipment and increasingly humans.

> **C.7.5** Describe how robots can perform new processes in extreme conditions.
>
> © IBO 2007

Robots tasked to continuously perform repetitive operations, do not become bored or fatigued. This aids in the reduction of errors, as does the constant monitoring, (through sensors), for surface imperfections or scanning for internal defects.

The nature of robotic circuitry allows it to cycle at thousands of times a second. This gives robots the opportunity to scan components and assemblies while they are moving at speeds of several meters per second. The fitting of sensors to robots may also provide feedback on forces to allow for application of accurate torques when tightening bolts and completing assemblies. Robots may also auto-correct positioning of components and reduce misalignments or sense the distribution of loads on irregular geometry.

Each of these operations are able to be performed by the robot at a higher level than its human counterpart i.e. the tolerances for error are much reduced.

C.7.6	Discuss the issues associated with replacing the human workforce with robots.

© IBO 2007

The issues associated with the replacement of humans with robotic systems are a combination of social and technological considerations. While factory workers may not enjoy working conditions associated with dirty, dangerous or mundane and boring work, people still need to be gainfully employed. The introduction of robotic systems into manufacturing plants has seen significant job losses. However, from a manufacturer's perspective, the significant labour savings accrued from the introduction of robotics is used to offset high initial capital investment costs.

In many situations, the complete removal of the workforce along a production line is either not possible or desirable. Although robots may assume much of the production work, highly skilled human workers still have roles to play; monitoring, maintaining and repairing robot systems. The restructuring of the factory workforce from labour intensive to monitoring and programming operations requires careful planning and budgeting. Ongoing costs associated with robiticised production lines must include the provision for training, maintenance and eventually upgrading or replacement.

The freeing of a workforce from menial labour obviously has appeal, however, not everyone is suitable for retraining as a supervisor or programmer. As robots relieve factory workers from the tedium of boring and sometimes dangerous working environments, problems arise when attempting to find work for older or unskilled staff, qualified to find new employment.

C.7.7	Explain how robots have reduced waste in manufacture.

© IBO 2007

Once programmed to perform a task, robots have the advantage of consistently performing the same task automatically. It is this repeatability, with minimal variation, that provides a major advantage over human-

directed operations in situations such as spraying painting, welding or machining.

Robots work with a consistency unmatched by human operators. Their continuous work cycles, without loss of performance, producing higher quality parts faster, with fewer defects, minimizes scrap and rejected components resulting from inconsistent processing. Industrial robots are able to work continuously, constantly monitoring their output using quality assurance detectors. In terms of product life cycle, products assembled from robot–produced components are inherently more reliable, have less defects and, therefore, have fewer warranty claims. Relative to traditional manual systems, robots also perform these tasks at reduced operating costs.

C.7.8	Define artificial intelligence.

© IBO 2007

Artificial intelligence refers to the development of computer systems that mimic human thought patterns or exhibit problem solving skills, the capability to learn or some form of reasoning power.

C.7.9	Outline how feedback plays an important role in developing artificial intelligence.

© IBO 2007

In the 1950s, Norbert Wiener made the link between machines and artificial intelligence when he noted the principle of feedback. Wiener theorised that feedback mechanisms demonstrated intelligence or, at least, the makings of intelligent behaviour. This revelation influenced the earliest work on artificial intelligence.

Feedback is essential to self-monitoring/correcting systems. Feedback loops consist of devices constantly sensing physical parameters to determine the application of a pre-programmed action. Quantities measured could include displacement, pressure, velocity, temperature etc. The most quoted observance of feedback theory in action is the thermostat. Thermostats work by sensing environmental temperatures, compare them with a preset amount and make adjustments based on this information. The cycle continues and a feedback loop is created.

Machines have used the principle of feedback to automate control mechanisms for centuries. An early feedback-based control system developed by James Watt to regulate the speed of a steam engine was the fly-ball governor illustrated in Figure C.7.9. The governor consisted of a vertical spindle attached to the engine that rotated at a rate determined by engine speed. Two brass, or iron, balls suspended from the top of the spindle rotated such that they separated due to centrifugal force as speed increases. As the balls moved out or in due to changing engine speed, a ferrule attached to the ball suspension arms moved up and down the main spindle. A lever attached to the ferrule could be set to adjust steam supply to the engine, thus controlling engine speed.

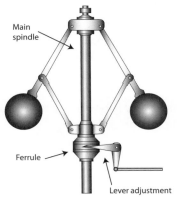

Figure C.7.9 Governor or fly-ball governor used to control steam pressure, developed by James Watt

In industry, manufacturers use feedback loops to assist their machines to 'think and respond', thus allowing machines to be self-correcting, maintain processes within set limits and comply with predetermined standards. These feedback systems are commonly employed to test, measure, count etc.

> **C.7.10 Discuss the advantages of replacing hydraulic robots with electrical robots.**
> © IBO 2007

Hydraulic robots have the advantage of mechanical simplicity (few moving parts), physical strength and high speed. Using oil under pressure, hydraulic robots are able to perform heavy lifting operations. However, hydraulically powered robots also need another energy source to pressurise the rams. Hydraulic systems also involve large masses and generate significant inertia making rapid changes in speed and direction difficult. Digital encoders and sensitive feedback controllers are required to give hydraulically controlled robots similar accuracy and repeatability levels comparable with electrically controlled robots. Oscillation or bounce (occurring when the arm is moving or decelerating to a predetermined stop) is another feature of robotic arms that must be dealt with to improve system accuracy.

Electrically actuated robots are mostly driven by DC stepper motors requiring little maintenance. These motors operate accurately, demonstrate good repeatability, are quiet and take up less floor space than their hydraulic

counterparts. In dangerous or emergency situations, electrically powered robots respond faster and more safely to 'power down' commands than their hydraulically driven counterparts. Compared to hydraulically driven systems, however, electrical actuators have a limited load bearing capacity.

> **C.7.11 Discuss the social and moral issues of using robots to manufacture goods.**
> © IBO 2007

Robots offer:

- reduced OH&S issues
- reduced costs (long term)
- greater hygiene in food & beverage plants
- greater ability to compete (faster to market)
- less staff issues (leave, working hours, breaks)
- better production efficiency, (better quality, faster, consistency, reliability)
- increased production efficiency (quality, consistency, greater reliability, less waste).

Western societies are concerned with ageing populations and the resultant socio-economic impact. The Lisbon Strategy for jobs and growth calls for European communities to improve industrial productivity by:

- developing of a more dynamic knowledge economy
- supporting innovation and investing in human capital
- moving away from the exploitation of natural resources to more sustainable models.

Robotics research, development and implementation is part of this planned approach to developing the knowledge economy.

Downsides associated with these developments include the rate at which standards of living are separating between advanced nations and those with developing economies. The production of cheap, mass-produced items can also lead to increased consumption and planned obsolescence with all the associated negative environmental impacts. In this scenario, dirtier primary industries, involving lower technological requirements tend to aggregate in developing economies. Products produced in these economies may then be shipped around the world for consumption.

C.7.12 Identify where robots can be used in automated car manufacturing.

The automotive industry is one of the largest employers of robots. Manufacturers view robot technology as robust, reliable and financially sustainable. They perform critical functions in three key areas including:

- quality control, counting
- assembling, welding, spray painting, edge smoothing
- palletizing, retrieving components, transporting, locating/holding.

Figure C.7.12 Automotive robots in car assembly line

Image by Mixabest, Creative Commons Attribution-Share Alike 3.0 Unported via Wikimedia

The most commonly used applications for robotics in auto manufacturing plants are in the fields of welding and spray painting. Both these fields fit the classic criteria for robot suitability, (as outlined previously) dirty, dull and dangerous. These operations involve complex tasks, yet are repetitive in nature and operate in environments hazardous to human health.

Auto manufacturers use robots extensively for quality control. This is especially true when they sub-contract components for use in their assembly lines. Pressed sections for car bodies produced for Porsche are now all closely examined through robot sensor systems, where previously they were only manually sampled or spot-checked. The use of a highly configurable automated holding system allows a range of body panels to be constrained while examined by a single robotic sensor arm.

Auto manufacturers also employ adaptable, flexible, welding lines capable of processing a variety of car bodies in random sequence. Manufacturers using this technology

enjoy the benefits obtained from the enormous flexibility robot-assisted systems offer. In extreme applications of the technology, large manufacturing plants producing over 1,000 units a day could potentially construct every vehicle differently, based on consumer preferences.

An effective and widespread use of robots in the auto industry is in the field of spray painting. Here robots work continuously in environments otherwise hazardous to humans. The quality and consistency of the work, the savings accrued through lack of overspray and cheaper running costs also make robots a popular choice with manufacturers in this area.

C.7.13 Explain why robots work in teams to complete an operation.

Robots work in co-operative teams where multiple functions are required. These include moving, locating, holding and fixing processes. These processes must be efficiently coordinated and programmed to ensure effective, accurate, repeatable and collision-free operations.

Assembly operations such as those associated with automobiles require robot systems not only to maneuver parts into place, but also to hold components precisely while they are being secured. In these situations, multiple robots may be required to strategically weld assemblies held in place by another robot. A clear example of this could be a car door panel. The door assembly must be quickly and accurately aligned with, and held against, the body shell while another robot welds the hinges in place. Once the routine is established and programmed, the robots can continue to repeatedly perform this function.

C.7.14 Outline the differences between single-task and multi-task robots.

Single-task robots perform specific operations. These robots are often limited in their ability to move e.g. left or right, up or down. Most commonly known as servo robots these machines use servomechanisms to control arms and grippers. This technology provides robot arms with greater flexibility i.e. 5 to 7 directions. These robots may weld joints, hold assemblies or paint parts repeatedly without variation, with a high degree of precision. This type of robot is particularly successful at relieving human operators of boring, repetitive or dangerous tasks. Single-task robots may also be employed in multi-robot situations to achieve the desired outcome within an operational cell.

Through their complexity, multi-task robots provide a greater degree of flexibility. Making use of priority controlled, pre-emptive scheduling or even artificial intelligence. Multi-tasking robots can handle both complex and parallel operations, employing independent secondary axes and using a variety of tools. Pre-programmed tool changes on one of the axes increase the robot's versatility, yet still allows the continued independent operation of the other axis.

> **C.7.15 Distinguish between robots that perform single tasks and reprogrammable robots that undertake a variety of tasks.**
>
> © IBO 2007

The advantage associated with reprogrammable robots opposed to the single task alternative is their ability to be reprogrammed and returned to new production lines with new skill sets, rather than being scrapped.

Reprogrammable robots may also have the flexibility to deal with multiple product types within a single production line. The ability to switch from one task to another without any downtime provides considerable productivity advantages through improved flexibility and reductions in retooling, time and costs. This makes reprogrammable robots albeit more expensive, a very cost effective alternative to single-task robots. In some situations, variations of products (mass customisation) or entirely different products may be able to be manufactured simultaneously using multi-tasking robots in one continuous production line.

> **C.7.16 Discuss how developments in robotics mean that robots are now used for small-scale production as well as volume production.**
>
> © IBO 2007

Originally, robot automation technologies were created specifically for complex systems, for use in capital-intensive large-volume manufacturing. The large capital investment was recouped over time through large production volumes reducing per part costs. In addition, due to the dominance of the automotive industry, their high uptake and subsequent demand for robotics, robot manufacturers have geared designs to large-scale continuous outputs. These standard, commercially available systems have proven to be too inflexible, too large or too costly for small scale production

New designs catering for small and medium enterprises, (SME), see the introduction of affordable, flexible robotic solutions with reduced setup times, suitable for smaller scale production runs involving frequent changes. The main goal for robot designers is to generate designs with the highest number of features and the greatest degree of flexibility at an affordable price.

New technologies, such as microsystem-based force sensors have enabled the development of much cheaper robots, with actuators developing high power-to-weight ratios. This development alone improves the flexibility of robotic solutions for precise, delicate manufacturing procedures.

Further Reading

Haegele, M., Et al, *Network of Excellence Information Society Technologies* DR.14.1 White paper - Industrial Robot Automation

Niemueller, T., Sumedha, W. (2003). *Artificial Intelligence – An Introduction to Robotics.*

ABB Robotics - 10 good reasons to invest in robots.

Robotics - Efficient robot-based automation for the wood industries, Robotics-Wood-brochure-ROB012SEN-A, 2009.

HL

OPTION

C.8 SOCIAL, MORAL, ECONOMIC AND ENVIRONMENTAL ASPECTS

C.8.1 Discuss how CAD allows for working 24 hours a day every day across time zones.

C.8.2 Discuss how CAD allows for flexible working in any location.

Early adopters of CAD technologies were able to reap many of the productivity benefits, including the ability to:

- create 2-D or 3-D presentations
- store data in a variety of formats
- present work as paper printouts or virtual models
- electronically distribute solutions for collaboration as part of a group project
- correct or alter designs very quickly based on design team or client suggestions.

Mobile computing offers all of the advantages of desktop digital counterparts, with the added advantage of portability. Laptops, scanners, digital cameras and portable printers, coupled with access to wireless global communication systems, the internet, research databases, email and video conferencing effectively become portable design offices. This frees designers up to collaborate when and where they choose: locally, nationally and internationally. These technologies:

- reduce the need for expensive travel
- increase real-time information exchange
- decrease time–to–market of product solutions
- link to CAD technologies for rapid manufacturing of 'proof of concept' prototypes
- allow collaborative design conferences potentially linking multiple remote locations.

C.8.3 Outline how CAD has changed the role of the designer in the design process.

Designers are tasked with the brief of bringing successful designs to market and meeting an identified need, using predetermined specifications, all as quickly as possible.

Designers create solutions in the hope of meeting a design challenge, adhering to explicit specifications. The time-to-market cycle can mean the difference between success and failure, considering the advantages associated with first-to-market designs.

Testing, and even market circulation, expose the difference between the predicted performance and actual performance of sometimes-complex designs. In layman's terms, this is often referred to as trial and error. Prototypes are used to reduce the incidence and severity of errors, while still within the design process. Gathering of data in this way provides valuable insights into how the next iteration of the design should proceed. It is at this point that CAD technologies are having their most impact. Modifications to designs occur in the hope they will solve problems, moving the design ever closer to the optimal solution.

Designers now have 3D CAD model databases at their disposal. These allow designers to choose already successfully tested components to be integrated into current designs, or at the minimum, provide a starting point for further development.

Using 3D scanners, designers can also replicate or modify existing designs once they have been captured digitally. This process allows designers to work even more closely with clients and involve them in real-time changes as the time between design conception, production and market availability is shortened.

Using CAD packages, designers are now able to conduct LCAs based on a varying range of materials and processes. Detailed reports can be generated to produce documentation explaining a design's relative sustainability compared to other selected alternatives.

C.8.4 Outline how CAD has changed the nature of the designer–client relationship.

Clients with specific ideas or concepts but without sufficient technical knowledge to implement or express their ideas can now provide designers with an incomplete brief, encouraging the designer to explore creative alternatives for approval. CAD packages allow designers to generate computer-based models, allowing them to explore fanciful 'what if' scenarios faster and more efficiently. Clients can see models incorporating design modifications and quickly respond. The ability to virtually examine models or rapid prototyped speculative designs with a client enhances communication, accelerates the design process and makes the entire procedure more cost effective.

C.8.5 Outline how CAD has changed the nature of design education.

Students of design now more than ever have access to fast, affordable computing with readily available advanced software of industry standard. Software manufacturers offer academic versions of software at significantly discounted prices to introduce their product into the marketplace. Training courses are available through traditional methods of instruction, online tutorials and DVD instruction. CAD has the opportunity to free students of the tedium of drawing, provide access to design libraries and allow for collaborative exchange of ideas real time over the Internet.

C.8.6 Discuss the effect of CAM on the labour force.

CAM technologies certainly reduce the number of employees required for supervising and running equipment. The nature of 24 hour automated workshops operating continuously has also shifted job requirements from the technicalities of manual machining or trade-based skills, towards CNC related software and hardware programming and management skills. Single machines no longer require individual attention. Machine technicians may be responsible for monitoring a number of machines at a time. This has lead to the creation of new manufacturing jobs, particularly as more advanced countries move from resource and manufacturing based to knowledge-based economies.

C.8.7 Outline how CAM has changed the type and range of product.

As additive and subtractive CAM technologies continue to develop, they are increasingly finding manufacturing applications. These processes can dramatically decrease the time-to-market for new products. Due to the inherent materials saving, quality and consistency of the processes, life cycle impacts of new and existing products are also being reduced. The flexibility associated with CAM technologies allows manufacturers to make the transition from mass-produced, generic products, to new highly customized products, rapidly responding to changing design trends and consumer demands. In this situation, consumers can more directly affect the design process.

C.8.8 Explain why some products are manufactured by CAM while others may be made using traditional manufacturing techniques.

There will always be a need for products manufactured using traditional technologies. One-off unique custom pieces priced at the premium end of the market, designed and crafted by artisans, will always command a small part of the overall market. However, products manufactured for mass consumption created using processes and materials that minimize costs will also have significant market appeal.

Mass produced products, consistently delivering quality at an affordable price meet the majority of the market's needs. The flexibility of mass-customization also provides consumers with the opportunity to personalize their choice.

C.8.9 Discuss how rapid prototyping and other CAM techniques reduce the use of natural resources.

Rapid prototyping and other CAM technologies construct physical models directly from CAD data. These virtual models have often been through numerous design iterations to find the optimal aesthetic, functional and engineering combination. Design may have even received pre-approval from manufacturers or clients prior to prototyping. Rejection rates of designs are low as the designer has a clear expectation of exactly what will be reproduced from the CAD model. This process also reduces waste when designers generate low volume runs or one-off items.

Materials employed for prototyping are often recyclable to the point where accepted models may even be recycled if not needed for the manufacturing of production moulds.

Rapid prototyping techniques may also be used to generate rapid tooling. A faster and less-expensive process than full production moulding, this technique may be used for limited volume runs, manufacturing production-quality finishes. Due to the quality of rapid manufactured items, consumer trials using these products may be able to be conducted.

Subtractive processes such as cutting sheet materials require complex nesting operations to be materials efficient.

These may be calculated automatically, using CAD/CAM software faster, and employing finer tolerances, than are possible with human operators.

Reduction in the amount of original material required, and waste, leads to reduced environmental impacts. The consumption of natural resources such as fossil fuels used for transporting raw materials and waste disposal is also reduced.

> **C.8.10** Discuss the implications of computerized manufacture on the infringement of copyright and patent laws.
>
> © IBO 2007

Computerized manufacturing techniques have made the copying of intellectual property considerably easier. Through the process of reverse engineering, an individual can easily analyze an existing product and then copy the product through rapid prototyping techniques to produce a fully functioning model ready for further development or direct manufacturing.

Using 3D laser scanning technology, every detail of an artifact can be precisely measured. The digitized information obtained in this way can then be transferred to a variety of forms of CAD technology, ready for manufacturing.

This approach is currently being used by manufacturers to recreate parts for vintage car enthusiasts. 'New' parts manufactured in this way exactly replicate the original, but do not breach patent laws, as the original equipment manufacturer (OEM) either does not exist or no longer finds production viable.

Other less scrupulous manufacturers may choose to apply the principles of reverse engineering to a successful product design to gain an understanding of how it works, to either construct similar or identical copies to sell in competition with the original design.

Reverse engineering may also be employed to determine copyright or patent infringements. A manufacturer may deconstruct a product suspected of unlawful copying of processes, products, components, designs or technologies.

Further Reading

Gunasekaran, A. (1998). *Agile Manufacturing: Enablers and an Implementation Framework*, International Journal of Product Research. Vol. 36, no. 5, 1223±1247

Exercises

1. Rapid prototyping systems may use:

   A. Liquids
   B. Solids
   C. Powders
   D. Any of the above.

2. Identify the properties that make MDF suitable for CAD processes:

   A. cost, grain, warp resistance
   B. durability, insect resistance, colour
   C. recyclability, surface finish, moisture resistance
   D. homogeneity, dimensional stability, standardized sizing.

3. Exploded view drawings assist:

   A. manufacturers when calculating costs
   B. consumers when assembling flat pack products
   C. designers when deciding on materials selection
   D. CAD technicians when designing machine toolpaths.

4. This type of CAD modelling allows a designer to add new parts to assemblies through the application of relationships, reducing the chance of error in complex assemblies.

   A. solid
   B. surface
   C. top down
   D. bottom up

5. When choosing between SLS, LOM and FDM rapid prototype processes. SLS may be chosen due to its:

   A. low cost and larger model options
   B. flexibility in materials selection and speed
   C. absence of the need for support structures
   D. production of parts requiring no additional finishing.

6. List four factors that affect surface finish when CNC machining.

7. Explain the benefits of CAM produced flat pack furniture to consumers.

8. Explain why drawing software packages now use 3D sketching as the basis for CAD drawing.

9. Explain how liquids are converted to solids during processes such as stereo lithography.

10. Describe how robots help with the process of mass customization.

11. Explain why the automobile industry has traditionally seen the largest uptake of robots.

12. Discuss the impact of automation and robotics on the factory workforce.

13. Describe the advantages of rapid prototyping to designers, manufacturers and consumers.

14. Discuss the relative merits of sketching and CAD for design development.

15. Explain the difference between virtual reality and animation.

16. Compare and contrast the advantages and disadvantages associated with hydraulic and electrically powered robot systems.

HL

OPTION

HL

OPTION

TEXTILES

CONTENTS

D

Evidence of weaving has been found in archaeological digs dating back to the Neolithic period, (about 5000 BC). The earliest use of textiles is believed to be the knotting and looping of threads to make fishing nets, while spinning, weaving and dying all took place across the globe in early cultures. While the Pharaohs of Egypt were wearing garments of cotton and flax, European Royalty was clothed in wool and linen and the silkworms of Asia and the Orient were spinning threads to make the finest fabrics to clothe the Siamese and Chinese courts.

It wasn't however until the Industrial Revolution that textile manufacturing was elevated above a craft and developed first into a mechanized and then later, an automated industry.

Today's challenges for the textiles industry revolve around the creation of relevant solutions to the opportunities presented by new materials. They process through the development of next generation fibre technologies (e.g. nanotechnology fibres) and smart textiles (incorporating micro computing systems), while at the same time improving the sustainability of the industry at every level.

D1 RAW MATERIALS

D.1.1 Define fibre and yarn.

© IBO 2007

Fibres are a group of materials consisting of elongated hair-like strands or discrete continuous filaments. A more technical definition defines fibres as continuous lengths of a material (either natural or synthetic) in which the length exceeds more than 200 times its diameter. The majority of natural fibres are short, however, very long fibres such as silk are termed filaments. Fibres may be used in the manufacture of felt, composite materials and paper-based products.

Most fibres cannot be used to make cloth in their raw form. For this purpose, they must be converted into yarns. Yarn represents a collection or bundle of fibres gathered into a continuous strand using a twisting or entangling process. This process results in an increase in the tensile strength, abrasion resistance and handling properties. These properties therefore depend not only on the properties of the individual fibres, but also on the angle of twist.

D.1.2 List two subdivisions of textile fibres.

© IBO 2007

Fibres are most commonly subdivided into two basic divisions:

- natural (organic) fibres that have either a plant or animal origin
- synthetic (man-made) fibres that have been created by chemical processes. Many are polymer-based while others are manufactured from glass, metal ceramic and carbon.

There are however a variety of classification criteria available including:

- fibre geometry
- spinning process
- animal, vegetable, mineral, artificial.

C.1.3 Define animation and virtual reality.

© IBO 2007

All fabric begins as natural or synthetic fibre. Natural fibres require some cleaning or refining before any processing can take place. Some mixing may also be required to homogenize the batch. Machinery is employed to draw out individual fibres and introduce a twist. Twisting increases strength by wrapping fibres around each other. This process is repeated, all the while lengthening the yarn. The yarn formed is called a 'single', i.e. a single strand of yarn.

Plying (with another strand of yarn) or setting the twist finishes the process. Plying involves twisting multiple strands of yarn together, generally in the opposite direction to which they were originally spun. This makes the yarn stronger, thicker, heavier and more stable. Figure D.1.3 shows a flow chart of the fibre spinning process.

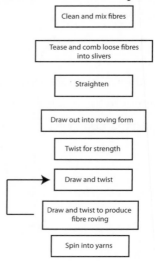

Figure D.1.3 Spinning fibres into yarn

D.1.4 Identify the characteristics of three natural textile fibres.

© IBO 2007

Purified, bleached cotton is nearly pure cellulose. It resists the action of alkalis well, but is harmed by hot, strong acids, or if acid is allowed to dry on the fabric. Untreated cotton has a very low ignition temperature (around 250°C) and burns intensely and rapidly. Very fine yarn can be spun from cotton because of the spiral character of the fibres. This twist of the fibres is peculiar to cotton, being present in no other animal or vegetable fibre. Because of this twist, cotton cloths are much more elastic in character than those woven from linen, the fibres of which are stiff and straight. Due to their molecular structure, cotton fibres actually attract water molecules giving cotton the ability to hold up to 25 times its own weight in water. Materials with this property are known as hydrophilic.

Wool fibre is distinguished by its scale-like surface which gives it its felting and spinning properties. The great value of wool as a fibre lies in the fact that it is strong, elastic, soft, susceptible to dyeing, easily woven and furnishes a great number of air spaces, rendering clothing made from it very warm and light. Wool has the remarkable property of absorbing up to 30 percent or more of its weight in water and yet not feel perceptibly damp to the touch. This is called hydroscopic moisture. This property makes wool a superior textile for underclothing. Wool has naturally low flammability and one of the highest ignition temperatures of commonly occurring fibres (570-600°C). At molecular levels, wool contains high levels of nitrogen, which is a common component of fire retardant compounds. Natural moisture contained in every fibre also improves wool's resistance to flame without any additional chemical treatment, the wool may char but will self extinguish. Wool fibre is quite elastic and can be stretched significantly when dry and wet.

Silk is nearly faultless, fine and continuous, with individual fibres often measuring from 300—1200 metres long, without a scale, joint, or blemish. Though not of the same diameter or fineness throughout its entire length, silk fibres become finer as the interior of the cocoon is approached. Silk differs from all other vegetable or animal fibres by being devoid of all cellular structure. Silk, however, like wool, has the property of absorbing considerable moisture without becoming perceptibly damp. Like wool and all the animal fibres, it is harmed by alkalis. The important physical properties of silk are its beautiful lustre, strength, elasticity and the readiness with which it takes dyes. Silk is an elastic material that can be stretched up to 20-25% of its original length. Silk is also more heat resistant than many other fabrics, including wool, for example, and is actually rather difficult to burn. Silk combines well with other animal and plant fibres. Figure D.1.4 shows comparative data for the three selected fibres in tabular form.

D.1.5 Describe the sources of the three natural textile fibres considered in D.1.4.

Cotton is a member of the Mallow family and the name refers to the white downy fibres surrounding small cottonseeds, called a boll. A native of many of parts of the world, several species of cotton plant exist. Columbus, Cortez and Pizarro found cotton growing in the West Indies, Mexico and Peru respectively.

Wool is an animal fibre harvested from the dense, soft, often curly, protective coat, or fleece of sheep, goats, alpacas, camels and certain other mammals. Consisting of cylindrical fibres of keratin covered by minute overlapping scales, wool is mainly obtained by shearing.

Silk is obtained from the cocoons of several species of insects. These insects produce a secretion of jelly-like substance that hardens as a thread on exposure to the air. The thread wound about the body of the silkworm forms a cocoon that may be harvested for fibre. It is very important that the moth should not be allowed to escape from the cocoon; the mere breaking of the cocoon greatly decreases the value of the thread. Killing the chrysalis by heat preserves the cocoon.

		Cotton	Wool	Silk
Tenacity or Breaking Strength grams/denier	Dry	2.1-4.2	1.23-1.59	4.3-5.2
	Wet	100-110% of dry	78-90% of dry	80-85% of dry
Elongation at break	Dry	5.6-9.6%	29-40%	23-31%
Elasticity (Elastic recovery)	Dry	45-75%	65-99%	10-25%
Effect of Heat		Chars without melting. Burns and smoulders		
Young's Modulus		1350 kg/mm^2	250 kg/mm^2	1000kg/mm^2
Specific Gravity		1.52	1.32	1.35
Moisture regain (%)		7 -8.5	11-18	12
Resistance to micro-organisms		Liable to attack when damp		

Figure D.1.4 Characteristics of selected natural fibres   *Adapted from Lewin M., Sello S., B., Handbook of Fibre Science and Technology, Hall A., J., Standard Handbook of Textiles, and Salamone J., C., Polymeric Materials Encyclopedia*

D.1.6 Define fibre and yarn.

D.1.7 Identify the characteristics of three synthetic textile fibres.

Cotton should be picked only when it is fully ripe - when the pods are fully burst and the fibres expanded. The unripe fibre is glassy, does not attain full strength and resists dyeing. Cotton harvesting is mostly done by machine. The cotton boll is stripped from the plant and any waste separated before baling. Cotton sourced from a variety of locations is mixed together in an attempt to enhance fibre uniformity. Separation of the small, sticky seeds from the boll is imperative to prepare the cotton for spinning and weaving. In a process called 'ginning', cotton is cleaned, de-seeded then carded, to align the fibres. A variety of spinning systems are available to process the fibre including ring, open-end, air jet and vortex. Spun yarn is wound tightly around tubes ready for weaving.

Wool, from sheep or other animals cannot be worked into yarn without being thoroughly cleansed of its impurities. In the case of wool from sheep, once shorn from the animal, the fleece is examined in a process referred to as skirting, where contaminated and undesirable wool is removed. Classing is then performed by grading the fibre according to fineness, length of fibre and strength. Some secondary cleaning may be required but essentially, once dry, the fibre may be carded (disentangled), combed, and finished into yarn.

Silk is harvested from the cocoon of the silkworm. The cocoon must first be soaked in heated water to kill the pupa inside and release the natural gum bonding the fibre together. Each cocoon consists of one continuous fibre and this must be teased out and wound onto a spinning frame. Fibres from several cocoons are processed at the one time through a twisting action that produces a fine silk thread. Separate threads may be later twisted together.

Nylon is a synthetic fibre. A macromolecule, consisting of long chains of repeating units of carbon, oxygen and hydrogen, originally made as a high strength fibre to replace silk. Untreated, nylons ignite easily (250 – 350°C) and melt readily. Nylon is also particularly prone to static build-up and is a recognized ignition source. It is essentially non-absorbent (hydrophobic), has a high tensile strength, is abrasion resistant, yet lightweight. Nylon is also resistant to alkalis, solvents, moulds and fungi.

The properties of polyester (Dacron®) include: high tensile strength, high resistance to abrasion and stretching, (wet or dry), and good resistance to bleaches and chemicals. Polyester also has a reputation as a wrinkle-free fabric, resisting water absorption and attacks from moths. While it does not absorb moisture, it does absorb oil; making polyester suitable for treatment with water-, soil-, and fire-resistant finishes.

Polyurethane fibres, are a family of stretch fibres originally developed as a replacement for rubber. Spandex is the generic name for this material, however, it is popularly marketed as Lycra® (a trademark of the DuPont company). Spandex has elastomeric properties, which give it the ability to stretch up to 600% and spring back to its original length. It combines well with other fibres (natural and synthetic) to produce fabrics with varying degrees of elasticity. Lightweight, durable, easily dyed, and abrasion resistant, Lycra® has the added advantage of moisture wicking (drawing moisture away from the wearer's body).

Figure D.1.7 Characteristics of selected synthetic fibres.

		Nylon 6	Dacron®	Lycra®
Tenacity or Breaking Strength grams/denier	Dry	4.5–5.5	4.4–5.0	0.6–1.5
	Wet	4.0–5.0	4.3–4.9	
Elongation at break (%)	Dry	20–25 %	18–22 %	520–610 %
	Wet	21–32%	18–23%	
Elastic recovery	Dry			
	Wet			
Effect of Heat		Can be safely ironed up to 356oF	Burns and melts	
Specific Gravity		1.14	1.38	1.20-1.25
Moisture regain (%)		4.5	0.5	0.8–1.2
Resistance to micro-organisms		Resistant	Resistant	Resistant

D.1.8 Describe the sources of the three textile fibres considered in D.1.7.

The synthetic fibres described above are all polymer-based organic compounds derived from by-products of oil.

Nylon 6 is manufactured from caprolactam, a derivative of coal tar and by-product of the petrochemical industry. This white flaky solid melts at 68°C and is soluble in water. Nylon forms when caprolactam is heated and mixed in a watery suspension of pigment, with acetic acid and an acid chain stopper. The molten mass is passed through spinnerets to form fibres. Polymerisation is controlled by temperature and the density of the molten polymer by the acid chain stopper.

Polyester is the generic name is given to all polymers containing the repeating ester group [-R-CO-O]. The major constituent of this long-chain polymer is ethylene. Polyester is formed from the condensation polymerization of Ethylene Glycol and Terephthalic Acid. In this reaction, two or more molecules combine to make a long chain molecule, whose structure repeats throughout its length. These molecules are very stable and strong. There are variations in the compositions and therefore in the properties of polyester fibres.

Spandex fibres are made from the long chain polymer, polyurethane. Structurally, fibres consist of a backbone with stabilizers and colourants. The polymer backbone is formed by the reaction of the pre-polymers, macro-glycol and diisocyanate. The macro-glycol can be a polyester, polyether, polycarbonate or polycaprolactone. These long chain molecules provide spandex with its flexibility and stretchability. The shorter stiffer diisocyanate gives the fibres greater strength. Antioxidants are added as stabilizers to protect the fibres from the damaging effects of heat, UV, mould, atmospheric contaminants, and chlorine.

D.1.9 Describe how each of the fibres considered in D.1.7 is produced and converted into yarn.

Most polymer-based, synthetic fibres are produced by a group of processes known as spinning (melt, dry and wet). The process involves two generic stages. Stage one is extrusion - where liquid polymer is forced through fine holes known as spinnerets, the number and diameter of which determine the type of yarn formed. Stage two involves fibre orientation where fibres are stretched or drawn to develop a degree of crystallinity and improve tensile strength.

Specifically, fibre manufacture may be classified according to the type of spinning that the polymer liquid undergoes. This may be melt spinning, dry spinning, or wet spinning. Of the three processes, melt spinning is the simplest and most widely used.

Nylon and Dacron® are mostly produced by melt spinning while spandex fibres may be produced by; melt dry or wet spinning.

Further Reading

DfS Quickstart 6, Product Ecology Pty Ltd and Sustainability, Victoria, 2006.

D2 FABRIC MANUFACTURING AND FINISHING TECHNIQUES

D.2.1 Define fabric.

A fabric consists of the interlacing of yarn by way of weaving, knitting or braiding, to produce a continuous sheet that has both a significant length and breadth.

D.2.2 Describe the knitting process for producing fabric.

The art and process of forming fabrics by looping a single thread, either by hand with slender wires, or by means of a machine provided with hooked needles, is called knitting. Knitting is carried on without making knots; thus, the destruction of one loop threatens the destruction of the whole web, unless the meshes are reunited.

The principle of knitting is quite distinct from that of weaving. In the weaving of cloth, the yarns of one system cross those of another system at right angles, thus producing a solid, firm texture. The great elasticity of any kind of texture produced by knitting is the chief feature that distinguishes it from woven cloth.

Two distinct variations of knitting occur: warp and weft knitting. Warp knitting, involves a series creating wales on the lengthwise direction of the fabric, while weft knitting uses one continuous yarn to form courses across the fabric.

D.2.3 Describe the weaving process for producing fabric.

© IBO 2007

The process of forming cloth, weaving, is done in a machine called a loom. Every woven piece of cloth is made up of two distinct systems of threads, known as the warp and filling (weft), which are interlaced with each other to form a fabric. The warp threads run lengthways of the piece of cloth, and the filling runs across from side to side. The manner in which the warp and filling threads interlace with each other is known as the weave. Today this process is fully automated for mass production.

The interlacing of the warp and weft can be accomplished in a number of ways. If a simple pattern of alternately passing the weft over and under the warp is used, a simple weave pattern is produced, as illustrated by Figure D2.3a. A twill weave pattern is produced by alternately passing under two and over one (Figure D.2.3b), while a sateen weave is obtained by passing (or 'floating') four warp strands over the weft stands, before passing under a weft strand (Figure D.2.3c). Because of the long distance that the yarn 'floats' a smooth satin finish is achieved. By using a warp yarn of different thickness to the weft, ribs may be produced in the fabric.

cotton. Lace may be made by hand with a needle, bobbins or machine and is created by looping and plaiting one thread with another, independent of any backing material. When the work is constructed with a needle, it is known as 'needlepoint lace.' When bobbins, pins, and a pillow or cushion are used, this is called 'pillow lace.' Machinery may be used when limitations of both point and pillow lace preclude the production of patterns.

Synthetic threads are often used for machine-manufactured lace and due to their high strength-to-weight characteristics intricately patterned sheer laces can be produced. Relatively cheaper synthetic threads create a ready market for these lace designs.

D.2.5 Describe the felting process for producing fabric.

© IBO 2007

The property of felting depends in part upon kinks in fibres, but mainly upon the scales with which the fibre is covered. These scales, or points, are exceedingly minute, ranging from about 450 to the centimetre to nearly 1200. The stem of the fibre itself is extremely slender, being less than 0.0254 millimetres in diameter. In good felting wools, the scales are more perfect and numerous, while inferior wools generally possess fewer serrations, and are less perfect in structure.

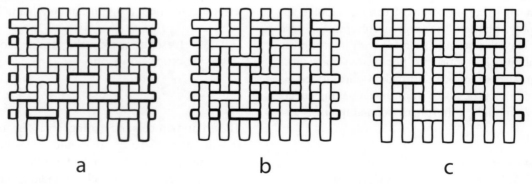

a   b   c

Figure D.2.3 Weaving styles

D.2.4 Describe the lace-making process for producing fabric.

© IBO 2007

Lace is an openwork, stitched fabric, patterned with holes. Originally made from linen, silk, silver or even gold thread, lace-work is now most commonly made from

In the process of felting, the fibres become entangled with one another, and the little projecting scales hook into one another and hold the fibres closely interlocked. The deeper these scales fit into one another, the closer becomes the structure of the thread.

Felt may be made from wool, rabbit or beaver fur. Felt made from wool is produced by progressively depositing layers of cleaned and combed fibres in to a large tray. Consecutive layers are deposited at 90 degrees to each

OPTION

other. Hot soapy water poured over the fibres assists with lubrication and reduces friction, allowing fibres to move and become entangled in the naturally occurring barbs on the fibre surface. The combination of heat, pressure, water, lubrication and friction bond the fibres to form a cloth. As an alternative, needle felting is a dry process involving combining fibres using specially barbed felting needles. Felting techniques are centuries old, with archaeological digs recovering remnants of felted tents and other products.

> **D.2.6** Describe the bonding process for producing fabric.
>
> © IBO 2007

Fabrics produced by interlocking and bonding fibres are known as non-woven fabrics. They are manufactured by one of two processes.

Melt blowing blows a spray of short fibres onto a moving screen where they cool to form a web as shown in Figure D.2.6a. Meltblown fibres are much finer than those in the spunlaid process and, as such, are not strong fabrics.

Flashspinning is a modification of the spunbond process that involves a polymer/solvent solution extruded under conditions so that rapid solvent evaporation at the spinneret occurs. The individual filaments are disrupted into a highly fibrillar form and are collected on a moving screen to form a web.

Both meltblown and spunlaid non-wovens have little mechanical resistance without thermal bonding or the use of a binding resin.

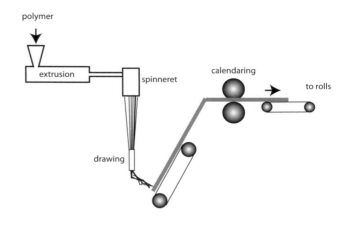

Figure D.2.6b Spunlaid technology

> **D.2.7** Identify the characteristics of the fabrics produced by each of the techniques listed in D.2.2–D.2.6.
>
> © IBO 2007

Dimensional stability of a fabric determines whether a fabric has the potential to retain its original shape and remain stable, indicating it will not bubble or sag over time, when applied over a substrate; it also indicates suitability for a specified use.

Dimensional stability is important when considering movement due to shrinkage or stretching that may occur during wet processing of the fabric when bleaching, dyeing, washing and drying. These changes occur due to the relaxation of stresses created in the yarn during manufacture. During the weaving process, the yarn is stretched, creating a tensile stress in the yarn, particularly in the warp direction. When exposed to moisture for the first time, the yarn relaxes and tries to return to its original length, the fabric therefore tends to pull together leading to fabric shrinkage. Compact weaves reduce the amount of contraction that can take place, impacting the amount of shrinkage observed. Poor dimensional stability can result in misshapen, ill-fitting garments ultimately unsuitable for their intended purpose. Poor dimensional stability will also affect other fabric characteristics such as feel and drape.

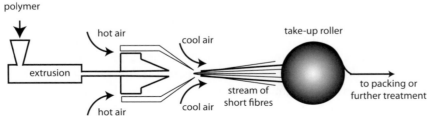

Figure D.2.6a Meltblow technology

'Feel' or 'Hand' is a subjective measure of fabric comfort and seeks to establish how a fabric will perform in relation to contact with the skin. It is therefore strongly associated with the aesthetics of the fabric. Factors that affect this characteristic are:

- density
- hardness
- thickness
- extensibility
- flexural rigidity
- bending length
- bending modulus
- compression modulus.

Some attempts have been made to standardise this measure in order to bring some objectivity into the assessment. The most widely used system is that developed by Kawabata that has since come to be known as the Kawabata Evaluation System (KES). This system, developed from the language and assessments of expert panels, seeks to categorize the feel of a fabric based on a combination of factors related to fabric stiffness, softness and roughness. This system also takes into consideration the end use of the fabric.

Drape is an important characteristic of fabrics, affecting both its aesthetics and the way that it moves. It can therefore be used as a means of describing how a fabric will perform when manufactured into clothing. At its simplest, drape is the way that a fabric falls or hangs under its own weight.

In order to establish a quantitative measure of drape, a number of methods have been developed over the years. One of the most widely used of these is the 'Drape Coefficient' (DC), as determined by the Cusick Drapemeter (British Standard BS5058). This test uses a circular fabric specimen of either 240mm, 300mm or 360mm diameter that is held horizontally and centrally between two small rigid support discs of 180mm diameter. The fabric specimen is then allowed to drape into folds over the edges of the bottom support disc. This assembly is then placed at a standard height above the centre of a paper disc of the same initial diameter as the fabric specimen and a light shone from above, in order to create a shadow pattern of the fabric onto the paper disc below.

Once a shadow has been created, the shadow pattern is then traced onto the paper disc and the disc weighed before (W1) and after (W2) cutting away the shadow perimeter. Because the paper is considered to be of constant weight per unit area, the measured mass is proportional to the area. The ratio of W1 to W2 is multiplied by 100 to give the 'Drape Coefficient' as a percentage.

$$DC = \frac{W2 \times 100}{W1}$$

Digital image capture technology is now often used to obtain a measure of the 'Drape Coefficient', by evaluating the difference in area directly.

$$DC = \frac{Ad - A1 \times 100}{A2 - A1}$$

Where
A2 = Total area of paper disc
A1 = Area of support disc
Ad = Area of drape shadow (includes A1)

This technology allows fast reproducible results, while also allowing the electronic storage of images. A low drape coefficient (<30%), indicates a fabric that is limp and easily deformed, while a high drape coefficient (>85%) indicates a relatively stiff material.

The ability of a fabric to drape is influenced by a number of things such as the weight of the yarn, weave type, weave tightness and finishing treatments. The Drape Coefficient can therefore be used as a quality control tool.

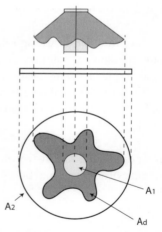

Figure D.2.7 Cusick Drapemeter method of measuring the 'Drape Coefficient' (DC)

In textiles, the strength-to-weight ratio is also known as specific strength or tenacity. The specific strength is a material's strength (force per unit area at failure) divided by its density, however, tenacity is the commonly used term for fibre or yarn strength.

The level of transparency of a fabric effects its ability to transmit light and the degree to which objects or images are visible through the fabric. In building or architectural situations, these fabrics are used to: control light and glare, reduce solar heat gain and act as acoustic dampeners. Weave structure affects; transparency, solar heat gain (or shading coefficient), texture and the appearance of the fabric.

As identified earlier, weave patterns affect the dimensional stability of woven fabrics. Weave patterns with a high number of interlacings have lower shrinkage values which are evaluated by ISO6330.

The construction of woven fabrics, made up of fibres that run straight and at 90° angles to each other, makes them generally stable, mostly only stretching on the bias (unless woven from elastic materials such as spandex).

Woven cotton fabrics usually show a greater degree of dimensional stability during laundering than those knitted. Mechanical properties such as the strength and elasticity of woven textiles are dependent on type of fibre, number of warp and weft yarns, yarn density and selection of weave structure. Strength is greatest in the warp and weft direction. In the bias direction, strength and shear values are lower, while elasticity is greater.

Knitting involves the use of a single yarn to form a series of interlocking loops using wires or needles. The interlocking loops allow the fabric to stretch in any direction. The amount and direction of stretch is variable depending on both yarn selection and knitting pattern. Knitted fabrics may stretch up to 500%, hence their choice for sock and hosiery applications. Knitted fabrics provide warmth because the looped construction provides air pockets. Knitted products have the disadvantage that because they are constructed from a single yarn if the yarn breaks, a hole is created which will 'run'.

Modern highly elastic garments often obtain their stretch from material selection, but may also achieve some stretch through knitting. Knitted fabrics are rarely coated because they are dimensionally unstable and too stretchable. On occasions, heavy-duty knitted fabrics may be back-coated to reduce excessive stretch.

Felt has no warp, filling or selvage and will not fray or unravel. It has little or no elasticity, low strength and cannot be draped but can be cut and blocked into shape.

Lace is a fabric that can be produced using an almost infinite number of construction variables i.e., type of fibres, fibre blends, yarn twist, yarn ply, chemical and mechanical finish. It is therefore difficult to establish a clear set of performance values for fabric of this type.

Bonded-fibre fabrics are not as strong as woven or knitted fabrics. Mostly used for interlining, they are easy to sew, crease-resistant, do not fray and are stable to washing and dry-cleaning.

D.2.8 Describe how cutting and machining are used for wasting fabric to produce components for textile products.

Fabric cutting is a critical process at every stage of textile manufacturing. Cutting operations occur for cloth manufacturing, distribution, pattern transfer, garment machining/assembly. Minimizing waste, quality of finish and material/weave type is critical to the approach selected.

Some fabrics will fray when cut with shears or blades. Repeatability can also be an issue with this level of technology.

Laser cutters are able to produce patterns involving complex detail with a high degree of repeatability, directly from vector files. Laser cutting also seals the edges of most fabrics, eliminating fraying while cutting in a one-step process.

D.2.9 Describe techniques for joining natural and synthetic fabrics.

Textile products and garments require joining. Methods include stitching, gluing, welding or thermal bonding and use of hardware and fasteners. The purpose of joining is to provide continuity by maintaining the same strength as the original or parent material. Many joining processes are limited to flat, straight joints. Some techniques are only applicable with specific fabrics (depending on the constituent polymers used in the textile).

Sewing is the most common joining method used for fabrics. In its simplest form sewing is a means of joining two pieces of fabric together with a single row of stitches. A very versatile and fast process, controlled variations in the stitching process include selection and type of thread, style and length of stitch. An integral part of the design process, stitching works with almost every fabric and can be used to join straight or complexly curved assemblies.

Welding and adhesive bonding are employed where a sealed or even watertight seam is required. Welding is a heat-based process causing the melting of the base fabrics, fibres, bonded surface or filler material. Welding processes include both ultrasonic and laser.

Adhesive bonding may be used to reinforce, seal, or replace stitched seams. Adhesives employ either a chemical or mechanical bond, infiltrating the weave and/or fibre of the textile. Adhesives have the added advantage of being able to join dissimilar materials. Fusible tape is also an option to compliment or replace sewing. In this process, a special tape melts, causing a glue-like bond to be formed between two pieces of fabric.

Fasteners are used in the textile industry for assembly or fixing components in place. They may be permanent (rivets, etc.) semi-permanent (buttons, snaps, zippers, etc.) or adjustable (velcro, buckles, D rings, etc.). Fasteners may be made from metal, polymers, textiles and ceramics.

D.2.10 Explain why the manufacture of some textile garments is still done by hand.

Handcrafted textiles are often produced by indigenous cultures to maintain contact with traditional techniques, tools and cultural values. These skills are proudly passed on from generation to generation, maintaining an historical link for many cultures. Handcrafted items include traditional clothing, carpets, lace work and soft furnishings e.g. pillow covers etc.

The craft industry also still exists in many cultures with interest groups determined to keep the skills of the past alive. At the other end of the spectrum, some exclusive fashion labels pride themselves on one-off unique creations, handcrafted to the highest standards. These products are priced at the premium end of the market.

D.2.11 Describe the coating process for finishing fabrics.

The first coated fabric was developed in the 19th C by Charles Mackintosh whose rubber-coated fabric produced a raincoat bearing his name. Fabric coating covers both the yarn and the spaces in between. The result is a new composite structure with very different properties.

The coating process involves the application of a polymer or resin to on one or both sides of a cloth substrate. A variety of procedures for coating are available including direct, calendaring, foam, transfer, hot-melt and coagulation.

D.2.12 Describe the embossing process for finishing fabrics.

The embossing technique uses the dual action of heat and pressure to create three-dimensional images and patterns.

Using two rotating rollers temperature, pressure, roller speed and gap (between the rolls) are all adjustable. The process is mostly performed on non-woven materials such as napkins, but it may also be applied to fabrics and even garments such as cotton T-shirts for subsequent printing.

D.2.13 Describe the dyeing process for finishing fabrics.

Dyes (synthetic and natural) are used for the colouring and decoration of fabrics. A variety of dyeing processes are employed dependent on the materials to be dyed, intended fabric use and colours required. Dyeing processes, categorized by chemistry include acid dyes, direct (substantive) dyes, azoic dyes, disperse dyes, sulfur dyes, fibre reactive dyes, basic dyes, oxidation dyes, mordant (chrome) dyes, developed dyes, vat dyes, pigments, optical/fluorescent brighteners, and solvent dyes.

A variety of dyeing systems and machines are employed in the dyeing process. Dyeing processes involve a range of variables including tension of fabric, dye transfer (aqueous, inorganic solvent or sublimation), weight limitations, batch or continuous systems etc. As a rule, hydrophilic fibres accept dyes easier than hydrophobic fibres. Steps involved in the dyeing process include:

i. dissolving the dye
ii. transferring the dye to the surface of the fibre
iii. spreading dye over the entire fibre surface
iv. absorbing the dye into the fibre.

Major dye classes and substrate fibres

Class	Fibres
Acid	Wool, silk, nylon
Azoic	Cotton, cellulose
Basic	Acrylic, certain polyesters
Chrome	Wool, silk, nylon
Direct	Cotton, rayon, other cellulosic
Disperse	Polyester, acetate, other synthetics
Fibre reactive	Wool, cotton, other cellulosic
Napthol (azoic)	Cotton, rayon, other cellulosic
Mordant (obsolete)	Natural fibres (pretreat with metals)
Pigment	All (requires binders)
Solvent	Synthetic (rarely used)
Sulfur	Cotton, other cellulosic
Vat	Cotton, other cellulosic

Table adapted from Best Management Practices for Pollution Prevention in the Textile Industry, USEPA Office of Research and Development, Washington, DC. 1996.

D.2.14 Describe the bleaching process for finishing fabrics.

Bleaching is a process employed to remove staining, whiten (or de-colour) fibres, yarns or cloth. The process of bleach involves oxidizing the elements that provide colour. Bleaching may be used to remove natural colouration of fibres or marks accrued as part of the manufacturing process. Bleaching can involve the use of chemicals or exposure to sunlight, air, and moisture.

D.2.15 Explain how each of the techniques identified in D.2.11–D.2.14 is used to modify the performance characteristics of textile fabrics.

Coated fabrics are engineered with the end use in mind. Selection of the fabric, coating material and production processes all influence the properties of the final product. Commonly requested properties include resistance to moisture or water, mildew, UV, chemical attack, soiling, cutting/puncturing and the addition of fire retardants.

Embossing can improve fabric strength, creates a smoother surface finish and also increases surface lustre.

Dyeing may account for a slight increase in fabric stiffness and a variance in shear values, but the dyeing process does not appreciably change mechanical properties in situations of low stress.

Bleaching is regularly used to remove stains from white garments; however, its use may yellow chemically finished cottons or affect colour-dyed cottons. It also has strong chemical properties that may appreciably weaken some textile fibres. Chlorine bleach may also reduce the effectiveness of some fire retardant treatments.

D.2.16 Explain how the desired characteristics are developed in textile products through treating the raw material, manufacturing and finishing.

From raw state to finished fabric, textiles are subjected to a series of chemical and physical processes including: fibre preparation and pre-treatment, spinning, dyeing and finishing. In general, synthetic fibres are engineered and manufactured with specific properties in mind. Natural fibres often require modification to produce the desired range of properties required, although some of this may occur as a direct result of manufacturing and processing. A few of these processes are detailed below.

Textile fibres in their natural state contain many impurities. Soil, twigs, pesticides and fungicides contaminate the fibres in their raw form. Scouring is the process of removing this unwanted matter. Scouring using wetting agents, alkalis other chemicals is the means employed to remove this unwanted matter. After scouring, the textile has improved wetting and therefore better dye uptake properties.

Mercerization is a chemical process, (most often used on cotton), employing a caustic solution to improve fibre strength, shrinkage rates and uptake of dyes. Once treated, the fabric is neutralised in an acid wash.

Sol-gel technology has recently emerged as a promising way to functionalize fabric surfaces. Cotton fabric surfaces have been successfully modified by this process to impart: antibacterial, UV protection, water repellence, and wrinkle free properties to the fabric.

Plasma technology is now being employed to surface-treat synthetic and natural textiles. By placing fibres or textiles in a reaction chamber to plasma treatments, the exposed surface may be restructured, coated or chemically functionalized depending on the gas atmosphere and manipulation of the process. Plasma treatment may assist with dye uptake, biocompatibility, colourfastness, UV and moisture resistance, degradation, toughness, strength, shrink or crease resistance.

Further Reading

Demboski G., Bogoeva-Gaceva G., *Textile Structures for Technical Textiles, II Part: Types and Features of Textile Assemblies*, Bulletin of the Chemists and Technologists of Macedonia, Vol. 24, No. 1, pp. 77–86, 2005.

Desal A., *Plasma Technology; A Review*, The Indian Textile Journal, January 2008.

Kulkarni S. V., Blackwell C. D., Blackard A. L., Stackhouse C. W., and Alexander M. W., *Textile Dyes and Dyeing Equipment: Classification, Properties, and Environmental Aspects*, United States Environmental Protection Agency, 1985.

Hu J., Chan Y., *Effect of Fabric Mechanical Properties on Drape*, The Institute of Textiles and Clothing, Textile Research Journal January 1998 vol. 68 no. 1 57-64.

D3 EVOLUTION OF TEXTILE PROCESSING

> **D.3.2** Outline the changes in textile production caused by mechanization.
>
> **D.3.3** Outline the changes to textile production caused by automation.
>
> © IBO 2007

> **D.3.1** Discuss craft production in relation to textiles prior to the Industrial Revolution.
>
> © IBO 2007

The English textile trade prior to the Industrial Revolution consisted of craft production involving individuals or families working in their own villages to produce small quantities of textiles to subsidize their incomes, additional to the agricultural activities they pursued to survive. The system of craft production was often referred to as the 'putting out' or 'domestic' system. Decentralized by its nature, merchants 'put out' raw materials to the village workers (spinners and weavers), for transformation into fabrics or clothing.

The textile manufacturing cycle from raw material to finished product was a multi-stage tedious process. For woollen articles, fleeces (supplied locally), required sorting, cleaning and dyeing before carding and combing. Thread was then spun before finally being woven into cloth. Women and children performed much of this work. Traditionally, weaving was man's work while spinning was done by women (hence the origin of the term 'spinster').

The raw materials for silk and cotton fabrics were obtained from overseas sources such as China, North America, Africa and the West Indies. Most of the cloth delivered to merchants was produced for export.

Once finished the product was retrieved by the merchant. The system suffered from organizational inefficiencies, inconsistencies in quality, variable rates of output and excessive transport costs due to unnecessary movement of goods. Prior to the Industrial Revolution, traditional energy forms for production-related purposes involved human and/or animal power.

These changes did not come without significant social upheaval. Anger over the displacement of skilled workers lead to the short lived Luddite revolution etc.

Mechanization refers to the replacement of human labour with machines. Automation consists of the use of machines and systems that are self governing and the integration of machines into self-regulating processes i.e. they perform tasks previously done by human labour.

The first major breakthrough in the Industrial Revolution involved the way textiles or cloth was manufactured. Before the Industrial Revolution, spinning was a time-consuming process. It took the work of many spinners to provide enough thread to supply a single weaver. Innovations by John Kay, Lewis Paul and John Hargreaves saw weaving efficiencies improve to the point where machines were able to spin dozens of threads simultaneously. These inventions and subsequent improvements reduced cloth production time and lowered costs. In 1769, Richard Arkwright developed a water-powered spinning device. Arkwright's water frame required more power than muscle could supply, yet spun thread faster than human hands could provide the carded and combed raw material. Arkwright's water-powered spinning frame was the first automatic textile device producing stronger threads for yarn production. This device was an integral part of the move from home-based manufacturing to factory style production.

Along with mechanization came the centralizing of manufacturing or the factory system. Large factories powered by steam or water appeared across the countryside. The use of running water to power these machines encouraged merchants to set up large textile mills (containing many spinning machines), near rivers and streams. These mills required large workforces, and thus, the transition from village to factory as a workplace, grew. Mass production moved the workers from their homes to factories. Independent home-based weavers were turned into dependant factory workers. Societal changes involved increasing numbers of women joining the workforce instead of being homemakers.

Early automated looms still required workers to raise and lower the warp threads and pass the weft. These steps too are soon automated, and 1805 marked the development of a fully automated pattern loom. Built by Frenchman Joseph-Marie Jacquard, this was the first 'programmable' machine. Pattern details were recorded on long strips of punched paper and 'read' by a needle. Holes in the paper strip indicated a raised warp thread and blank sections determined lowered warp threads. In 1840, the first fully mechanized cloth loom was tested.

With the power of flowing rivers to drive machinery, processing of textiles became faster and greater volumes of production were generated with improved repeatability. Looms became faster again as steam power replaced water as the major source of energy. This in turn drove the need to size the yarn to improve grip through greater friction. The introduction of electric lighting also enabled mills to increase operating times.

Where mechanization provided equipment for operators to improve their efficiency, automation greatly reduced the need for human input. In general terms, automation lead to optimizing costs through improvements in speed, efficiency, materials wastage and quality control.

More modern looms used compressed air to pass the weft at velocities well beyond the capabilities of human operators. Speeds of up to 800 moves per minute are achieved.

Today, numerical control technology allows for the design and manufacture of detailed patterns ranging in width from a few centimetres to five metres. These systems are capable of individually controlling width up to 12,000 warp threads.

> **D.3.4 Explain why the textile industry expanded significantly during the time of the Industrial Revolution.**
>
> © IBO 2007

Textiles industries grew significantly during the Industrial Revolution due to the confluence of a number of factors including:

- abundant unskilled labour, even child labour
- large market demand in England and abroad
- well-established trade routes made transportation easy
- many labour saving inventions appeared around the same time, circa late18th Century
- raw materials and finished products were non-perishable, light and easily transported
- water, then steam power, transformed production processes, reduced labour costs.

The major reason however was the growth of overseas trade. During the 18th century, exports rose, textiles still predominated, but cotton replaced wool. The biggest change was in their destination: America became Britain's biggest market.

> **D.3.5 Explain the further expansion of the textile industry due to automation.**
>
> © IBO 2007

Automation has taken place in all the processes involving textile manufacture i.e. cotton picking, ginning, spinning, weaving, processing and even to some extent in garment making, resulting in enormous gains in productivity and efficiency. In environmental terms, automation has resulted in machines being designed to use water more efficiently and, use less chemicals and energy.

As early as 1801, Joseph Jacquard developed a textile machine controlled by punch cards. This programmable loom is a precursor to modern day numerical control.

Weaving technologies have advanced through the introduction of automatic shuttle looms and even automatic shuttle-less looms using water jets or compressed air to transport the yarn with multi-colour weft insertion. Electronic control through computers in automatic looms has also simplified, customized and optimized operations.

To be effective in global markets, manufacturers must extend automation beyond the factory floor, to encompass their entire operation. The purpose of this automation is to reduce labour, wastage, energy, capital and engineering costs. Location of plant and equipment is determined by a complex mix of raw material sources, labour costs, government subsidies and transportation of part-processed or finished product. A well-researched business plan, in association with a carefully implemented process of automation, may have significant benefits in one or more of the aforementioned areas, providing a competitive edge in the global marketplace.

Further Reading

Agarwal S., *Automation in Global Textiles for Global Challenges,* Tex Tech, Ahmedabad, 2006.

D4 DESIGNING TEXTILES WITH CAD

D.4.1 Outline how the use of CAD has enabled the design of a wide range of textile products.

© IBO 2007

CAD has made textile designing easier, quicker and more precise. It has enhanced design possibilities and improved textile manufacturing productivity through the:

- ease of storing and transmission of data files
- ability to quickly duplicate and repeat patterns
- speed of modification of colours and complex designs
- adjusting of isolated parts of a design without 'global' change
- opportunities availed by 'what if' creativity and experimentation
- modification of weaves which can be seen on screen prior to production
- saving of digital swatches for ease of retrieval and conservation of resources
- opportunity to involve clients as the project develops and receive timely feedback
- importing of ideas from artwork, digital cameras, fabric samples for inspiration/modification.

All of the above reasons support the implementation of CAD software for use in the designing of textiles. CAD software has additional advantages such as the ability to link with CAM technologies and the opportunity for stress or performance testing of fibre selection or weave. Programs are currently available that simulate fabric draping characteristics to provide designers with a virtual idea of how a fabric will 'fall'.

D.4.2 Discuss how the use of CAD has increased choice for consumers.

© IBO 2007

The use of computers in the designing process has opened up opportunities for consumers to become more involved in the design process. Technologies such as online ordering using virtual manikins, 3D scanners and digital cameras all play their part in the process. Response times for consumers and manufacturers are both reduced with allowance for 'off the rack' or highly customized online purchasing.

3-D body scanning technologies enable rapid capturing of individual consumer's measurements for the production of made-to-measure garments, with a precision unmatched by more traditional methods. Captured data can be manipulated and adjusted to conform to the taste of individuals. Due to the type and quantity of data collected, garments can be manufactured moulded to the unique three-dimensional shape of an individual. Lastly, scanned data can be imported into CAD systems ready for automated production.

D.4.3 Describe the process of applying laser image transfer (LIT) to textile products.

D.4.4 Discuss the limitations and benefits of using LIT when designing textile products.

© IBO 2007

Laser image transfer is a colour printing process that easily prints on white or light coloured fabrics, as well as a range of surfaces. Using laser printers with modified fuser units, digital images are printed (in reverse) onto specially treated paper. The image is then transferred to the cloth by through pressure and the application of heat.

LIT printers use standard toner that may also be used for normal printing processes. The LIT process can be used on a wide variety of everyday materials and objects requiring no additional surface treatment.

The limitations of available print area, stiffening of fabric area where transfer is applied and some quality variability between fabric blends are considerations when evaluating this system.

D.4.5 Describe the sublimation printing process for textile products.

D.4.6 Discuss the limitations and benefits of using sublimation when designing textile products.

© IBO 2007

Dye-sublimation printing is mostly used to print on synthetic fabrics such as polyester. Sublimated images can only be transferred onto materials with a special polymer coating, or onto polyester textiles. The sublimation process requires special inks and a dedicated printer that cannot be used for normal printing. The original printers used an electrostatic process, but this has been replaced by water-based, pigment inks delivered through inkjet printers.

Once the reverse image has been printed onto a specially coated paper, the transfer process involves heat and pressure to complete the sublimation, where the ink is converted into a vapour before returning to the solid state upon cooling. Sublimation prints can not be washed out or worn away as they permeate the fabric. Sublimation technology can generate detailed and precise photographic-quality images at cost effective rates. It is mostly performed on white fabrics because the transparent dyes require a background to make the colours visible. White backgrounds do not clash with other colours and also improve their vibrancy.

Further Reading

Istook C. L., Rapid Prototyping in the Textile & Apparel Industry: A Pilot Project, Journal of Textile and Apparel, Technology and Management, Volume 1, Issue 1, September 2000.

Ujiie, H., Digital Printing of Textiles, Woodhead Publishing Ltd., 2006.

Ujiie H., Digital inkjet textile printing : *Status Report, The Center for Excellence of Digital Inkjet Printing of Textiles* School of Engineering and Textiles, Philadelphia University, USA

S Kiatkamjornwong, P Putthimai and H Noguchi, *Comparison of textile print quality between inkjet and screen printings, Surface Coatings International Part B:* Coatings Transactions, Volume 88, Number 1, 25-34, 2005.

D5 MANUFACTURING TEXTILES WITH CAM

> D.5.1 Outline the key areas in which CAM can be used to manufacture textile products.
>
> © IBO 2007

As in many industries, CAM technologies have improved quality, reduced production times, improved working conditions and generated greater efficiencies. Within the textiles industry, specifically, CAM has:

- employed optical scanning for improved quality control
- reduced waste, using lasers for accurate cutting of complex patterns
- increased the speed of production during weaving and assembly stages
- reduced weaving machine downtime through laser detection of warp break
- allowed for more flexibility in the design and production of complex patterns
- enabled machines to be controlled remotely from user-friendly graphic interfaces.

Embroidery has also been revolutionized through both software and hardware developments. Digital embroidery allows the user to design complex patterns and leave the machinery to do the rest. The operator has little to do other than change threads. Detailed lace patterns may also be produced in the same fashion.

> D.5.2 Outline how sewing and knitting machines and looms can be interfaced in a CAD/CAM system to produce textile products.
>
> © IBO 2007

CAD/CAM knitting technology has developed to the point where whole garments are able to be manufactured ready-to-wear straight off the machine. This innovative whole garment, or seamless, knitting technology generates a completed product directly on the knitting machine. Garment production times are reduced by 30-40% over conventional methods. This also translates into significant reductions in energy costs and labour savings through the elimination of postproduction garment assembly. The process also reduces fabric loss and cut-loss. Knitting techniques are more consistent, leading to higher quality fabrics.

Driven by designs generated on a PC, these knitting machines can access coded instructions via a USB interface. Digital stitch control via the computer provides precision control over loop length to allow for precision pattern-based knitting and 3-D shaping. Linked to databases of yarns, knit patterns, garment styles and templates the user has an enormous degree of creative control. Designs can be directly scanned into the system or drawn on the screen before post-processing by software into code to control the knitting operation.

> **D.5.3** Discuss how the use of CAM in the textile industry has helped to minimize waste.

Textiles-specific software is now available. This software determines how best to lay out the pattern in order to maximise the yield from fabrics. As with other CAD programs, nesting of pattern pieces minimizes waste. The integration of this software with automated textile-cutting machines guarantees accuracy, consistency and eliminates costly errors.

> **D.5.4** Describe how a CNC embroidery machine is able to convert a photographic image into a textile decoration.

Using digital images directly, or by scanning existing photographs, textural designs can be imported and manipulated into software programs ready to be reproduced as an embroidered pattern. Once digitized these images may be cropped, resized, recoloured or personalized with text. In addition to this, tools exist to vary stitch type, angle and size.

> **D.5.5** Describe how CAM has enabled the development of mass-customized textile products in the global marketplace.

Market demands for personalization, customization and quick response are influencing the adoption of sophisticated CAD/CAM systems. Microelectronics and their associated applications have penetrated all stages of garment production to some degree. From computerized weaving control, digital imaging and ink jet printing technologies to pre-assembly cutting systems and even

garment assembly, manufacturers now have the flexibility to rapidly customize production.

Linked directly to online systems receiving orders directly from individual customers, or larger distribution companies, manufacturers are also able to benefit from JIT processes, tuning their manufacturing directly in response to specific requests. It is this linking of CAD/CAM and computer management systems that plays a significant role in monitoring inventories, raw materials, order processing and communication with suppliers and customers.

Further Reading

Bae, J. (2005). *Customer Focused Textile and Apparel, Manufacturing Systems: Toward an Effective E-Commerce Model,* Journal of Textile and Apparel, Technology and Management, Volume 4, Issue 4, Summer.

Ng, F. *A Review of The Techniques of Knitting and Moulding Pertinent to Seamless Fashion Creation,* RJTA Vol. 5 No. 1.

Karabegović, I., Ujevic, D. (2006). *Applying Intelligent Systems as a Basis for Improving the Position and Competitiveness of the European Textile Industry,* Fibres and Textiles in Eastern Europe, January / March Vol. 14, No.1 (55).

D6 MEDICAL PRODUCTS

Textiles find wide application in the medical field and form a subgroup of textiles known broadly as technical textiles. Textiles have, of course, been used for centuries in medical applications, particularly as bandages to bind and protect a wound from continued blood loss or keep it clean. The use of textiles within the body as replacements for diseased or injured body tissues is, however, a much more recent development. Their introduction in this capacity dates from only the early part of the 20th Century but has rapidly become routine.

Today, textiles are used extensively in prosthetic devices, finding wide application in the field of vascular surgery, where tubing manufactured from textiles is used to replace sections of a blood vessel that have become blocked or diseased. These tubes are produced from synthetic fibres in either a woven, knitted, braided or veloured form.

Further Reading

Czajka, R. (2005). *Development of medical textile market*. Fibres & Textiles in Eastern Europe. Vol.13 (1), pp13-15.

D.6.1   Define prosthesis and biocompatibility.

© IBO 2007

A prosthetic device or prosthesis is an artificial part used to replace a damaged or diseased body part. These devices may therefore be attached to the body as either an external prosthetic, such as an artificial limb, or as an internal prosthetic, often referred to as an implant, such as an artificial hip joint.

Prosthetic devices have been used for centuries. Dentistry in particular has used gold for over 2,000 years to repair teeth, while teeth made of wood or ivory have an extensive history. Glass eyes and prosthetic limbs made of wood or ivory have also been common. Evidence of a prosthetic wooden toe has been found with an Egyptian mummy dated at approximately 1000 BC, shown in Figure D.6.1. This prosthesis was reported to have indications of wear, suggesting it had been used during the life of the owner and was not just part of the burial ritual

Biocompatibility covers a broad range of requirements, but basically means that the material must be compatible with the continued health and function of the body tissue, bone and fluids with which it may come in contact.

This includes not only the parent material, but also any corrosion product and wear debris that may form in service.

Figure D.6.1 Wooden toe prosthetic from Egyptian Mummy c1000 BC

The body represents a unique and challenging environment for any man-made product that is to be implanted. This is particularly true of applications where the implant materials must not only be biocompatible and resist degradation from exposure to body fluids, but must undergo cyclic loading and maintain mechanical integrity and resilience over a long period of time. Such requirements are imposed on textiles used as vascular grafts, involved in the replacement or repair of blood vessels that have been damaged or become diseased, and where the consequences of failure are life threatening.

D.6.2   Outline the importance of vascular prostheses.

© IBO 2007

Millions of people develop Cardiovascular Disease (CVD) each year and with over 17 million deaths a year due to CVD it is a major cause of death worldwide. While heart disease has undoubtedly been with us throughout history, studies have suggested that the prevalence of heart disease as a major cause of death only dates from the Industrial Revolution of the 19th Century.

This change has been attributed to a decrease in physical labour, with the increase in mechanization and an increase in the consumption of processed foods. In addition to these factors, advances in the biological and medical sciences leading to reductions in other causes of death prevalent at the time, due to disease and high infant mortality has meant that CVD continues to increase.

Until the early part of the 20th Century little was known about the causative factors leading to the development of

CVD and even less available by way of treatment. Today, the factors contributing to CVD have been described, many of which are indicated below.

Risk factors include:
- age
- diet
- gender
- obesity
- smoking
- diabetes
- family history
- lack of exercise
- high blood pressure
- cholesterol deposits

Treatment of Cardiovascular Disease has also improved greatly. The 19th century represented a watershed in the development of biological and medical knowledge. The demonstration of anaesthesia in surgery, first of Sulphurous Ether by William Warren of the USA in 1846 and then Chloroform by James Simpson of Scotland in 1847, ushered in a new era of pain free surgery.

Similarly, the development of the Germ Theory of disease in the 1860s by Louis Pasteur, supported by work by the German Robert Koch in linking bacteria to disease, led to the development of aseptic surgery by Joseph Lister in 1865, reducing post operative infection. These developments led to a proliferation of surgical interventions, including those associated with Cardiovascular Disease.

It was not until the 1950s however that suitable materials were available for use as vascular prosthesis to meet the ever-increasing demand for the replacement of diseased arteries. From their commercial introduction in 1957, the demand for these products has grown such that by 2005, European sales of vascular prosthetic grafts of the type shown in Figure D.6.2 had reached approximately $342.8 million with projected growth by 2011 to reach $478.6 million (Medtech Insight report #A242).

Today, over a million vascular implant operations are performed every year.

Vascular bypass surgery of the large arteries such as the aorta is usually performed using textile based prosthetic materials such as Dacron® or ePTFE.

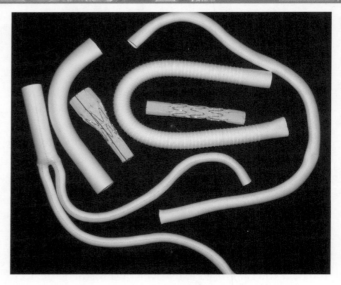

Figure D.6.2 A selection of textile vascular prosthetics

D.6.3 Outline the specification for the design of a textile vascular graft.

© IBO 2007

The success of vascular grafts is measured in terms of Patency, which relates to the amount of time an implant remains unblocked and operational. This can be further broken down into:
- Primary patency: graft material acts as required without further surgical intervention, and
- Secondary patency graft remains patent following additional surgical intervention.

Those materials that show the greatest patency are those that exhibit similarities in terms of the physical, mechanical and chemical properties, with the blood vessels to which they are to be attached. Materials that exhibit these characteristics are said to be compliant.

While the properties of the different materials and constructions used for textile vascular graft can vary significantly they all must satisfy a number of core requirements in order to remain patent, these include:

Dilation (expansion) resistance

Dilation relates to the bulging of a blood vessel. As the vessel expands, the wall thickness decreases, if the vessel wall is ruptured, sudden blood loss will occur resulting in an aneurism. A viable graft must maintain sufficient strength along its length to maintain its dimensions over a long period of time in an environment in which 90 beats/minute occur, cycling between a pressure of 80 mm and

120 mm Hg. This represents over 4.7 million cycles per year. Material properties required include:

- ability to stretch (elasticity)
- maintenance of long-term tensile strength
- circumferential strength sufficient to resist arterial pressures
- mechanical properties approximate to those of the native blood vessels to which they are attached
- compliance — although difficult to achieve due to the anisotropy of blood vessels.

Biocompatibility

The polymer must be nonreactive with respect to surrounding tissue and exhibit low thrombogenicity (i.e. the tendency to form a thrombus or blood clot).

All materials, with the exception of the thin layer of cells that line the blood vessels, known as endothelial cells, are considered to be thrombogenic. Textile vascular grafts, therefore, also represent a potential source of blood clots.

The formation of a blood clot can have serious consequences if it forms at, or moves to, a position where it can restrict blood flow.

Modern vascular grafts are designed with a small degree of porosity that allows a small leakage of blood into the fabric pores. This is designed to encourage a tightly adherent thrombus that allows tissue in-growth of fibrin and fibrous tissue, similar to that of the original blood vessel. If, however, the thickness of this fibrous layer is too great, blockage and failure of the implant can occur.

Operational or functional properties include:

- ability to withstand long shelf storage
- ability to resist kinking and squashing
- capacity for uniform volume production
- availability in a variety of sizes and configurations.
- flexibility to allow manipulation by the surgeon
- resistance to fraying at cut edges and tearing out of sutures
- ability to withstand sterilization without alteration in their physical and chemical behaviour.

> D.6.4   Outline the materials used in vascular grafts.
>
> © IBO 2007

While many individuals have contributed to the effective treatment of Cardiovascular Disease, several individuals standout, at least with respect to surgical intervention. One of these is the French surgeon Alexis Carrel who demonstrated the joining end-to-end of blood vessels (anastomosis) in 1902 and so began the field of cardiovascular tissue engineering. This work led to the award of the 1912 Nobel Prize for Physiology 'in recognition of his work on vascular suture and the transplantation of blood vessels and organs'. The ability to join blood vessels allowed the replacement of a diseased or blocked portion of an artery with a vein of similar size from another part of the patients' body (often the saphenous vein in the leg). This form of graft is known as an Autograft. A similar procedure, although involving the grafting of a vein from a donor is known as an Allograft (also known as a Homograft) and is performed if the patient does not have a vein suitable for grafting. This option has the disadvantage that immunosuppressant medication is required to prevent rejection.

The first prostheses used for the repair of the large blood vessels of the heart, such as the abdominal and thoracic aorta consisted of rigid tubes inserted into the artery and held in place by a ring. These tubes were manufactured from either metal (aluminium, gold and silver), glass, ivory or polymer. Blood clots, however, quickly developed within these materials leading to blockage and failure.

The use of textiles as a vascular prosthesis had its beginning with the pioneering research of the American surgeon Arthur Voorhees on dogs in the 1940s, who noticed that a misplaced silk suture became covered in tissue. This observation led Voorhees to experiment with textiles as vascular graft material. First using silk sewn from a handkerchief and fashioned into a tube, experiments were again performed on a dog. The dog survived for approximately one hour before dying of a hemorrhage through the pores of the cloth. The graft was however judged to still be patent. In 1948, Voorhees began experiments with woven Vinyon-N cloth produced by Union Carbide. Vinyon-N was a 60/40 mixture of vinyl chloride and acrylonitrile (also known as vinyl cyanide) and was used at the time for parachutes.

Again the grafts were found to be patent, although hemorrhage through the pores of the cloth remained a problem, emphasizing the importance of pore size in healing. In 1952, Voorhees performed the first textile graft of a Vinyon-N cloth tube on a human subject when no suitable allograft was available to repair a ruptured aortic aneurysm. Although the patient survived only 30 minutes the results encouraged further experimentation into the use of synthetic graft materials.

Influenced by the work of Voorhees, in 1953 Dr Michael DeBakey also experimented with the use of prosthetic vascular grafts using dogs as test subjects. Instead of Vinyon N, DeBakey used the polyester fabric Dacron® (Polyethelene Terephthalate), which he found in the hospital stores. Using his wife's sewing machine he manufactured a tube for implantation. Figure D.6.4a shows the surgeon making his Dacron® prosthetic tubes. These experiments were successful and, in collaboration with the Philadelphia College of Textiles, a circular knitting machine was developed to produce seamless tubes for implantation. By the 1957 Dacron® tubes were commercially available as prosthetic grafts, particularly for the repair of vessels of greater than 6 mm diameter in which blood flow rates are high and pressures low.

Figure D.6.4a Dr Michael DeBakey one of the pioneers of Vascular surgery sewing Dacron fabric to create a graft for animal experimentation in 1953

Courtesy of Baylor College of Medicine, Houston, Texas

Researchers also examined the use of other materials such as Orlon® and Nylon. The greater strength and stability of Dacron® over Vinyon-N, Orlon and Nylon (which were found lose up to 80% of their strength within the first 100 days of implantation) led to Dacron® becoming the preferred material for prosthetic vascular grafts.

PTFE has the advantages of high resistance to chemical, bacterial and fungal attack while maintaining long term strength and stability. It is however, much stiffer than Dacron and exhibits very poor compliance with blood vessels.

Today Dacron® and ePTFE are the most commonly used synthetic materials for vascular surgery.

Grafts made from these materials are available in woven, knitted or veloured form. The various processes offer differing advantages as vascular prosthesis vessels in terms of compliance and pore size. As previously indicated, pore size is of great importance to the success of the graft as,

they must be sufficiently small to limit the loss of blood through the graft walls, while providing sufficient sites to act as a scaffold to allow tissue ingrowth for healing.

Knitted Grafts

Knitted grafts provide long-term stability and resistance to dilation. The porosity of the knitted graft (typically 1500ml/cm^2/min) results in yarn mobility that imparts anisotropic characteristics, resulting in greater strength in the circumferential knit direction (known as the course) compared to the longitudinal knit direction (known as the wale). This anisotropy means that the knitted graft has greater compliance and is easier to handle than woven grafts. A knitted fabric is shown in Figure 6.4b in which the pores are clearly visible.

The porous nature of the structure also provides a scaffold for tissue ingrowth, which promotes healing and reduces dilation, but needs to be temporarily sealed to prevent blood loss. Sealing of the pores is performed in one of two ways: through the immersion of the graft in the patient's blood a few minutes before implantation to seal the pores with blood clots (pre-clotting) or with a resorbable material such as gelatine.

2009/10/14 14:15 L   1 mm

Figure D.6.4b Scanning Electron Microscope image of a DeBakey Elastic Knit

A knitted graft is produced by either the weft knitting or warp knitting process.

Weft knitted grafts involve the construction of a fabric from one set of yarns that are inter-looped as opposed to interlaced. Unfortunately they tend to lack dimensional stability and have a tendency to run (as with hosiery). Cut edges also curl up, making suturing difficult.

Warp knitted grafts use one or more sets of intermeshed fibres in a zig-zag pattern.

The compliance of warp knitted grafts is less than the weft knit. However they do not have the disadvantage of curling up at cut edges.

Knitted velour knits consist of knitted loops of differing height standing normal to the plane of the fabric. This vertical pile adds softness and promotes tissue in-growth. The most commonly used velour graft is the weft knitted Sauvage® Filamentous shown in Figure D.6.4c.

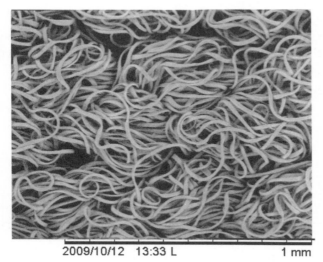

2009/10/12   13:33 L   1 mm

Figure D.6.4c Scanning Electron Microscope image of a Sauvage® Filamentous Velour

A woven fabric is a textile structure formed when two sets of yarns are interlaced at right angles to each other. Figure D.6.4d shows a Dacron® fabric woven in a plain weave, in which the warp yarns lie alternately over and under the weft. Early experimental and commercial vascular grafts belonged to the woven category and still account for a significant number of vascular grafts implanted each year.

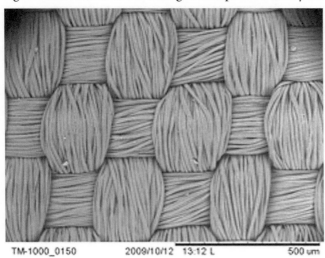

TM-1000_0150   2009/10/12 13:12 L   500 um

Figure 6.4d Scanning Electron Microscope image of a DeBakey Woven fabric

Because of the high number of interlacings, woven fabrics are the most dimensionally stable and can be manufactured with very low porosity making them impermeability to blood, although this also restricts tissue in growth. Woven grafts also exhibit good resistance to dilation. Unfortunately, woven grafts also exhibit very low compliance compared to knitted grafts and tend to fray at the end.

Recent development of a woven fabric with a velour surface created by the interlacing of extra threads has produced a softer more compliant material that encourages tissue ingrowth while maintaining strength.

Non woven fabrics are often made from synthetic fibres.

Teflon® (Polytetrafluoroethylene-PTFE) became available in the late 1950s and had advantages as a vascular grafts of the large vessels but was largely abandoned in favour of Dacron because manufacturers found it easier to handle. By 1975, an expanded form of PTFE, ePTFE became available under the brand name Gore-Tex and has gained a prominent place alongside Dacron® as a graft material.

Manufactured by heating PTFE and stretching it to form a micro-porous material. The structure of a ePTFE graft is shown in Figure D.6.4e, where the fibrils (pores) can be seen. The ePTFE grafts have excellent strength and stability, but are stiff and have poor compliance.

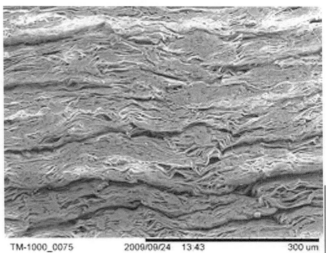

TM-1000_0075   2009/09/24   13:43   300 um

Figure D.6.4e Scanning Electron Microscope image of a Gore ePTFE

The ePTFE can also have a tendency to bleed at the suture line, potentially reducing the patency of the graft. In order to combat this tendency, a collar of PTFE felt is often added as a reinforcement of the suture line minimising blood loss. An example of PTFE felt is shown in Figure D.6.4f.

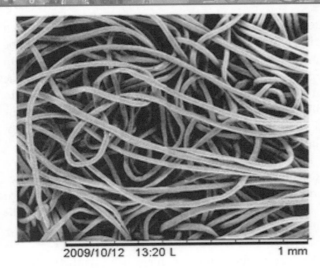

2009/10/12 13:20 L   1 mm

Figure D.6.4f Scanning Electron Microscope image of a Bard PTFE Felt

A summary of the characteristics of each method of vascular graft manufacture is presented in Figure D.6.4g.

D.6.5 Explain developments in the design and manufacture of textile vascular prostheses.

© IBO 2007

Today the pre-clotting of knitted grafts is no longer necessary as the pores are sealed with resorbable materials such as collagen, albumin or gelatine. The graft is then sealed in sterile containers to allow storage ready for use as shown in Figure D.6.5a.

Crimping of the tubes is also often performed to increase the resistance to dilation and kinking, through the creation of circumferential corrugations in the surface. A PTFE graft with a crimped surface is shown in Figure D.6.5b.

Characteristics	Non woven	Woven	Knitting		
			Weft	Warp	Veloured
Construction	ePTFE	Formed by interlacing two sets of yarn at 90°	One set of yarn inter-looped	One or more sets of yarn used to create separate loops that are intermeshed	Two or more yarns used of different loop height
Stability	Good	High dimensional stability, resists dilation	Long term Resists dilation	Long term resists dilation	Long term resists dilation
Porosity	Nil	Low	High 1200-1900ml/cm/min		Low-high
Strength	High	High	Lower than woven	Lower than woven	High
Pre-clotting required		No	Yes or gelatine sealed	Yes or gelatine sealed	No
Handling characteristics	Stiff	Poor	Good	Good	Excellent
Compliance compared with an artery	Poor	100 times less	30 Times less	Less than weft knitted	4-5 times less

Figure D.6.4g Summary of graft characteristics

OPTION

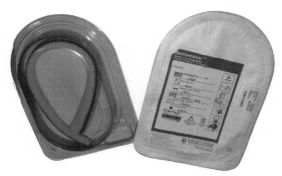

Figure D.6.5a Sterile packaging of textile vascular grafts

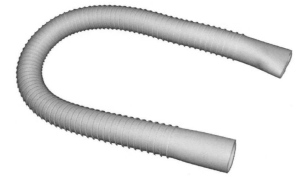

Figure D.6.5b Crimping in the surface of a graft to increase strength and resistance to kinking.

Vascular surgery of the small arteries, particularly those of less than 6mm in diameter and in areas of low flow rate, as in below the knee, typically involves the use autogenous grafts. The reason for this is that the traditional artificial graft materials, Dacron® and ePTFE, are relatively rigid compared with these smaller vessels. This difference results in what is known as a compliance mismatch. Recently polyurethanes have been introduced that possess an elastic modulus closer to that of the small vessels, improving compliance and increasing patency.

> **D.6.6** Explain the importance of biocompatibility in the development of textile vascular prostheses.

As with any material implanted into the body, biocompatibility is essential for the long term survival of the patient. If the prosthesis is not biocompatible, tissue reactions may occur that lead to failure of the graft through tissue inflammation and death.

> **D.6.7** Explain how implant materials are tested for biocompatibility.

A rigorous regimen of testing for toxicity and biocompatibility is undertaken prior to the acceptance of materials for implantation. These tests involve invitro testing in simulated biological solutions to determine chemical, physical and mechanical stability, as well as tissue exposure tests to confirm tissue compatibility. If such tests are satisfactory, further tests are performed invivo using animal subjects to again confirm compatibility and the absence of adverse effects, only then is the material considered to be biocompatible.

> **D.6.8** Explain why regulatory bodies, such as the Food and Drugs Authority in the US, do not approve materials in isolation but approve medical devices made from these materials for specific purposes.

Textile vascular grafts are more than just the materials from which they are constructed. The manner of manufacture greatly affects the properties that the graft displays and hence affects its performance. For this reason, the graft is considered in its entirety as a medical device, when an evaluation is performed for approval for implantation.

Further Reading

Alcántara, E. M. et al. (2005). *Mechanics of biomaterials: Vascular graft prostheses.* Application of Engineering Mechanics in Medicine, A1-A20.
[http://academic.uprm.edu/~mgoyal/materialsmay2005/a05graftmay.pdf]

Barros D'Sa, A.A.B, etal. (1980). *A healable filamentous Dacron® surgical fabric.* Ann. Surg, Vol.192 (5), pp645. [http://www.ncbi.nlm.nih.gov/pmc/articles/PMC1344947/pdf/annsurg00225-0065.pdf].

Blakemore, A.H. & Voorhees, A.B. (1951). *The use of tubes constructed from Vinyon 'N' cloth in bridging arterial defects-experimental and clinical.* Ol.140(3), Annals of Surgery pp 324-333.
[http://www.ncbi.nlm.nih.gov/pmc/articles/PMC1609759/pdf/annsurg01318-0067.pdf]

Campbell, G.R. & Campbell, J.H. (2007). *Development of tissue engineered vascular grafts.* Current Pharmaceutical Biotechnology, Vol 8 (1), pp43-50.

Greenwald, S. E., & Berry, C. L. (2000). *Improving vascular grafts: the importance of mechanical and haemodynamic properties.* J Path, 190 (3), 292-299.

D7 RECREATIONAL PRODUCTS

D.7.1 Define biomimetics.

Biomimetics is the imitation of biological systems. Biologically inspired textiles are those that take ideas from nature and implement them in new fibres and fabrics

D.7.2 Outline the use of biomimetics in the development of sports clothing.

Innovative developments in biomimetic fibres, yarns and fabrics have been the differentiating feature in the high-performance sportswear market. Equipped with more powerful technology allowing scientists to examine natural systems in greater detail, technologists can now appreciate how nature has evolved its own efficiencies.

At the synthetic fibre level, hollow fibres, or those with an irregular cross-sectional area have been engineered to improve thermo-physiological properties, while fabric development has imitated naturally efficient designs and applied them to fabric surfacing.

Manufacturers have developed fabric surface technology to imitate the hydrodynamic properties of sharkskin. One fabric of this type, marketed as Fastskin®, (mimicking the skin of a shark) reproduces a shark's small individual scales called dermal denticles. It is this surface, ribbed with grooves, that reduces eddy formation and provides efficiency.

This technology also has other benefits associated with the health, maritime and transport industries.

D.7.3 Explain the advantages and disadvantages of using biomimetics in sports clothing.

New developments in textiles used by athletes require testing and review by the relevant governing authorities to ascertain whether they confer unfair advantages. Critics of performance enhancing textiles and garments claim sporting competitions are skewed in favour of those maintaining a technological advantage over their competitors. Groups promoting the use of advanced textiles to assist athletes make the counter claim that these garments do not add to an athlete's natural talent but simply allow them to perform to the best of their ability through mechanisms such as reducing drag, improving athlete comfort, lighter weight fabrics etc.

D.7.4 Outline how the development of textiles has contributed to the improved performance of athletes.

D.7.5 Discuss the impact of textile developments on improved athletic performance.

Originally, all athletic clothing was manufactured from natural fibres such as cotton and wool. In the 1970s, physicist Karl-Heinz Umbach demonstrated the physiological benefits gained from using synthetic fibres for athletic apparel. This development led directly to the Austrian women's team at the 1980 Winter Olympics using underwear made from Transtex®, a dual layer textile with an inner layer capable of 'wicking' (effectively drawing away sweat from the skin), while the outer cotton layer of cotton provided insulation and evaporation.

Dutch athletes competing in the 2010 Winter Olympics benefited from the development of a new suit for short-course skaters. Through the combination of Dyneema®, (an ultra-high-molecular-weight polyethylene gel-spun fibre) with other fibres, a Dutch company has created a tighter fitting single layer skinsuit. Improved performance is expected from the lighter weight fabric that keeps skaters cooler and is more comfortable than the multi layer alternatives.

Speedo's Fastskin FS II is fitted to an individual's biometrics. Employing the same surface technology as the FS I, the new swimsuit has improved shape retention and a better fit meaning greater muscle compression, less fatigue and reduced muscle vibration. Passive drag tests show an overall 7.75 % improvement over other swimsuits.

Gore-Tex™ Comfort Mapping fabric was developed for mountaineers whose clothing required high levels of insulation and heat retention combined with breathability and stretch. Nike has used this lamellar fabric technology to incorporate combinations of these properties precisely into those parts of their 'Nike Sphere React' fabric range of the jackets as required. Sensors may also be embedded into these jackets to assist athletes in improving their skills.

In Australia, the Commonwealth Scientific and Research Organisation, (CSIRO), is working in conjunction with the Australian Institute of Sport to develop garments that actively map the position of selected body parts. Using an 'interactive sleeve', athletes practising netball skills are able to receive feedback through the fabric when the correct series of movements are performed characterising a successful action. The system provides real-time feedback, reinforcing the athlete's learning. See unit: D11 for further information relating to smart clothing, wearable computers and haptic interfaces.

Another approach uses a 'responsive fibre' woven into garments. This uses compression technology to return energy emitted from the body back to the skin, increasing oxygenated blood flow and boosting athletic performance. This technology, used outside of competition, is designed to allow athletes to perform for longer, train harder and recover quicker. One of these garments, marketed as sleepwear, is designed to enhance the recuperative effects of sleep by maintaining body temperatures and promoting more even blood circulation over the entire body.

Greater worldwide interest and participation in active sports and outdoor leisure pursuits has seen strong growth in the development and demand for textile materials in competitive and social sporting situations. The pace of innovation in the fields of fibre and fabric development, plus the effects of globalisation and the shift away from a rigid two-season year has also contributed to market strengthening. The development of manufactured fibres and coatings has largely replaced the use of natural fibres in performance textiles. Innovations in sportswear continue to be based around improving functionality designed to improve performance of the wearer.

Further Reading

Gasi F., Bittencourt B., *Evaluation of Textile Materials in Physical Activity*, Chemical Engineering Transactions, Volume 17, Brazil, 2009.

Marculescu, D. Marculescu, R. Park, S. Jayaraman, S., *Ready to Ware, Spectrum*, Oct. 2003, Volume: 40 Issue: 10, 28 - 32.

D8 TRANSPORTATION PRODUCTS

> D.8.1 Outline the use of smart and technical textile materials in vehicles.
>
> © IBO 2007

Technical textiles are manufactured primarily to meet a technical specification that defines the functional properties of the textile rather than aesthetic, tactile or decorative features. Technical textiles are mostly synthetic, regenerated or inorganic fibre polymers because of their inherent strength and versatility. Natural fibres, such as cotton, jute and sisal, while still comprising a significant portion of the market are not as dominant. The use of technical fibres in vehicles includes applications in the aircraft, road transport and maritime fields.

Textiles contribute about 20-25kg of an automobile's mass. Textiles appear in such areas as carpets, upholstery, seat belts, airbags, filters, firewalls, sound proofing, thermal insulation, vibration mitigation and reinforcing in fibreglass panels, tyres and hoses. Fibres commonly used include polyester, nylon, polypropylene, wool, carbon and glass. Individual fibre types find application in such areas as:

- polypropylene - low specific gravity
- nylon - excellent wear resistance for use in carpets and bearings
- polyester - widely used for upholstery, door panel lining and radial-ply tyres
- felt - employed as sound and vibration damping as well as dust sealing properties
- carbon fibre and GRP cloth - excellent strength to weight and stiffness values for lightweight body shells.

An example of the development of technical textile application in vehicles is the seat belt. Woven from either nylon or polyester continuous filament yarn, the fabric must exhibit the following properties:

- light weight
- dye-fastness
- soft and flexible
- high tensile strength
- energy absorbing
- extension of 25%–30%
- static load bearing capacity of 1500 kg
- high abrasion, heat, chemical, shrink and UV resistance.

Smart textiles in vehicles in the future are expected to perform a range of functions including the ability to generate energy, recover shape, sense and respond to the environment and actively self-clean.

> **D.8.2** Discuss the advantages of the use of smart and technical textiles in vehicles compared to more traditional materials.
>
> © IBO 2007

The multi-functional properties of smart and technical textiles make them a popular choice over materials of a more traditional nature.

Technical textile products must not only meet specific functional requirements, but must also be lightweight. Approximately 75% of a vehicle's fuel consumption can be attributed to the weight of the vehicle. The remaining 25% is generated by the aerodynamics of the vehicle shell and the resultant drag. Lighter textiles mean not just improved fuel economy but also reduced emissions to better meet 'clean air' legislation.

The merging of new and existing technologies with the textile design industry has led to the development of fabrics with the ability to generate light, self-repair and transmit power. Even though the level of uptake is currently low, development is still underway, making vehicles themselves smarter through the integration of smart textiles. Examples of smart textiles applicable for vehicle use could include upholstery that repels moisture, bacteria or dirt. Others may regulate heat, assisting with passenger comfort. Light emitting textiles are being tested for door linings, bonnet and boot interiors. Fabrics that provide electromagnetic or radio frequency shielding capabilities and/or embedded conductivity have the ability to act as wires and are now being considered to replace electrical cabling.

Further reading

Jul L., *Adding Values Smart Textile Options for Automotive Applications*, Textile Journal.

Dubas S., Mahaveer B., Mahaveer N., *Automotive Textile*.

David Rigby Associates, *Technical Textiles and Nonwovens: World Market Forecasts 2010*.

D9 MARKETS

> **D.9.1** Discuss the diversity of end-users of textile products.
>
> © IBO 2007

Collectively textiles play an important global role in a diverse range of fields and applications. These may be roughly grouped into: industrial, home or soft furnishing and apparel, textile categories.

Industrial fabrics are designed and manufactured for their functional characteristics such as: strength, durability, serviceability, flexibility, permeability, resistance to chemicals and UV radiation. Industrial textiles are often used in the: building and construction, civil engineering, horticulture, forestry, mining, fishing, sanitation, transport, packaging, medicine, military and space environments. Geo-textiles as a sub-group are used in ground or soil based structures such as road building, dam construction, erosion control and agriculture.

Fashion is a major determining factor in the development of textiles for the home and apparel market sectors.

Home products including: soft furnishings and components of furniture, (including bedding, lampshades, cushions, lounges etc.), table linen, towels, curtains, floor coverings and fibrefill.

Apparel loosely covers: clothing and garments for a range of purposes including: outerwear, underwear, sport and leisure, headwear, footwear, parasols and accessories.

> **D.9.2** Outline the purpose of the information provided on textile labels.
>
> **D.9.3** Discuss the impact of health and safety legislation governing textile product labeling.
>
> © IBO 2007

Textile and apparel labeling is provided to allow consumers to make an informed choice. Fibres used in construction, care of fabrics, shrinkage rates and flammability are all basic pieces of information consumers may require to make decisions based on; materials, care, durability, allergies, ethics, sustainability, country of origin/manufacture and appropriateness for use.

In the USA, manufacturers are required to list generic class names for textiles rather than trademark names.

These names are vetted by the Federal Trade Commission (FTC) or the International Standards Organization (ISO). The ASTM permanent care label system also assists the consumer with information for laundering of the fabric. These standardized symbols are shown in Figure D.9.2. Trademarked finishes to fabrics to reduce shrinkage or soiling information may also appear on labels.

wash   bleach   tumble dry   press or iron   dry clean   do not

Figure D.9.2 ASTM Permanent care label symbols

Flammability legislation and labeling is directed towards keeping dangerously flammable materials from inappropriate use. Products such as children's sleepwear, mattresses, and carpets are regulated by stringent government flammability standards. Items not meeting these criteria may not be sold, advertised or imported.

> **D.9.4** Describe how packaging materials and display methods affect the promotion of textile products.
>
> **D.9.5** Discuss the impact of alternative packaging on product cost and the environment.
>
> © IBO 2007

Packaging serves a number of purposes including protection (during shipping and or display), promotion, description of contents (including any legislative requirements) and, on occasions, theft deterrence or tracking technologies. Packaging may create the vital first impression a consumer has of a product. It is an integral part of a company's business marketing strategy to attract buyers and persuade them to make a purchase. Quality package design and manufacture is regarded as an essential part of successful business practice. Marketing plans may also employ packaging as a way to inject new life into maturing products.

Labeling on packaging is also an important component of the overall marketing mix and can help support advertising campaigns, reinforce brand identity and enhance product recognition. When designing packaging, associated costs of manufacturing, shipping, displaying and disposing of the package must be considered.

Packaging in the textiles industry can be modified to be more environmentally friendly at every stage of the product life cycle, i.e. from supply of raw materials to presentation of the final product. Alternative environmentally friendly

packaging systems employ the use of recycled materials, materials that are easily recycled or materials that may be reused. Wherever possible, the amount of packaging required may be reduced or multiple items are packaged in bulk to conserve materials.

Environmentally friendly fashion designers recognized the power of public feeling about green design when they developed lines of goods promoting an eco-friendly agenda, while still encouraging consumption. Bags of all description soon appeared bearing the printed message: 'I am not a plastic bag' and trend-conscious shoppers proudly displayed their green credentials through their purchase. Environmentally friendly materials for packaging may include:

- reed fibre - packaging made from fast growing sustainable plant
- palm fibre - palm oil by-product similar to paper, but coarser in structure
- hemp - fast growing plant able to be processed into string or woven into bags
- green polythene - ethanol-based product making both flexible and hard packaging
- PLA - plastic based on corn starch and used for thin, transparent packaging or bags
- bagasse - sugar by-product, similar to compressed paper when processed - decomposes in 45-60 days.

Figure D.9.4 Bagasse fibre

Image by David Monniaux Creative Commons Attribution-Share Alike 3.0 Unported

Innovative or alternative packaging may provide ancillary benefits such as:

- recyclability
- tamper-proof seals
- value-adding to overall reusability
- easy-open, easy-store, easy-carry functionality.

D.9.6 Outline the positive and negative impacts of male and female modelling of textile garments on the behaviour and health of adolescents.

© IBO 2007

Young people exposed to a flood of print and electronic media will be influenced either directly or indirectly. The predominance of skinny models employed by the fashion industry only reinforces the notion, to be beautiful and successful you must be skinny. Eager to identify with these role models, adolescent girls become dissatisfied with their body image and explore ways to approach this 'ideal'. An entire industry is ready to promote the latest fad diet, eating or exercise plan. Fashion magazines blur the lines between reality and the glamorous life of a model. Approached in the right way, a healthy diet and exercise is an appropriate way to maintain good health and well being, however, impressionable adolescents (boys and girls) are more vulnerable to marketing and peer pressure. The result may be unhealthy diets and eating patterns that may lead to eating disorders. Most adolescents are unaware of the long-term health affects associated with eating disorders such as bulimia and anorexia.

D.9.7 Explain how shopping outlets code and mark their stock to help protect against theft.

© IBO 2007

Many of the more traditional methods for antitheft protection are single function devices and thus require a variety of additional processes or technologies to manage product movement.

Barcodes are binary codes constructed from fields of lines and gaps arranged in a parallel configuration. The sequence of these lines and gaps can be read, interpreted and translated into numerical and alphanumerical data using optical scanning devices. Reading devices may be hand-held or flush mounted in counter tops requiring a single pass at any orientation to read the barcode. These scanners may be directly linked to data systems recording stock movement, inventory and cash registers to assist with sales. Barcode readers located within stores also allow customers to check pricing that can be flexibly changed through centralized data input. Barcoding may be used to identify missing or stolen inventory at the stage of stocktaking or well after the garment has been lost.

Radio frequency identification (RFID) tags use microchip technology to manage a range of functions relative to the garment to which it is attached. These devices store data electronically and allow information exchange using magnetic or electromagnetic fields. The RFID label is incorporated into the swing tag of the garment, (similar to barcoding) and assists not only with theft prevention at point of sale but may also be installed well back in the supply chain and used to track garments from manufacturing through to wholesale and distribution networks. RFID information can be gathered and analyzed to produce statistics and reports at every stage of a garment's presale life. Using 'read gates', RFID technology security is fully automated and requires no swiping of magnetic strips by sales staff when processing legitimate purchases.

D.9.8 Explain the impact of the lack of international standardization of clothing labels on marketing strategies.

© IBO 2007

Due to the lack of standardization or the uptake of available standards, many countries have enforced their own standards on manufacturers and importers of textile products. Through the Trade Practices Act in Australia the government constantly reviews and updates its policy on care labels for textiles, garments and associated goods. The schedule includes:

'Clothing, household textiles, apparel (including articles such as wedding dresses, christening gowns, and promotional, sample and flawed articles), furnishings, upholstered furniture, bedding, (including sleeping bags), mattresses, bed bases, piece goods and yarns made from textiles, plastics, plastic coated fabrics, suede, skins, hides, grain leathers and/or furs'. Consumer Protection Notice No.25 of 2010.

This comprehensive document requires adequate care instruction labeling to consider:

- fibres
- fasteners
- dyes and finishes
- design and construction
- padding, interfacings and linings
- decorative items (embroidery, lace, beading, trim, decals) .

In an attempt to provide better information for consumers the EU is enforcing standardized fibre labeling and associated textiles terminology. Only products meeting this directive will be allowed to be sold in the EU.

D.9.9 Define brand.

Branding is designed to create product differentiation in the mind of the consumer. It most often consists of a symbol, (logo/trademark), word or image placed on a product. Successful branding is designed to manage how consumers feel about a product. Consumers buy well-known brands based on previous experience and reputations of quality or performance. A company's brand may be considered its most valuable asset. It has the capacity to both promote the company and generate sales.

D.9.10 Explain how the packaging of textile garments contributes to the development of brand loyalty.

Companies that consistently deliver on 'brand promise' develop a strong consumer following or customer loyalty. Packaging and presentation must match the image and quality of the product. Poor package development may result in negative consumer experiences, which can quickly translate into negative brand equity and potentially, reduced sales.

D.9.11 Discuss branding as a global marketing strategy.

Globalization is leading towards one big market. The textiles industry in particular is characterized by great competition, however, maintaining low costs is simply not enough to be competitive, particularly when threats associated with unauthorized copying and misuse of trademarks make trading for legitimate brands difficult. In this situation, more than ever, branding must clearly reinforce and promote product differentiation. This process encourages the consumer to make a purchase based on the assumption that buying the garment will give the consumer some satisfaction.

Global brands are seen as successful, having beaten off the competition. This success is seen by consumers as product validation and is also associated with quality. Global brands trade on an imagined cultural ideal or global identity. With ownership, they generate a feeling of belonging to a larger community. Product branding

conveys to the consumer the company identity that may relate concepts of quality, status, uniqueness, desirability etc. Branding is an essential part of a company's overall marketing strategy. Well-planned and executed brand strategies drive a company's reputation and are designed to craft how the market views a brand. Managing a brand, responding to the market and developing innovative products are key strategies to maintaining a competitive advantage.

A major advantage associated with globalization is the economy of scale benefits associated with packaging, labels, brand recognition, market acceptance, marketing, promotions, and advertising. While branding and brand management is of paramount importance in the global textile industry, non price-factors such as variety, response times, quality, personalization and differentiation all influence demand for one product over another. In a market that no longer follows the traditional seasonal trends, and where frequent materials and production innovations are routine, whole product ranges may change as rapidly as monthly.

D.9.12 Discuss the positive and negative effects of product branding on adolescents.

Clothing brands, through clever marketing strategies, sell not only garments but an image. Purchasers are persuaded that with the product, the brand will convey on them status, success, prestige, freedom etc. This message is particular strong amongst adolescents who are still developing their own identity and may seek to transplant values from a coveted brand and project them by owning and wearing the garment. Unfortunately, many of the most prized brands come at a premium cost due to high demand (and in some cases exclusivity of the product).

Positive effects accrued from the ability to purchase and wear clothing seen as desirable can be feelings of 'inclusion', an improved self image and greater confidence. Peer pressure may be one of the larger forces driving consumption of global brands. Those who cannot afford the cost of owning these prized consumer brands may also feel outcast or devalued.

D.9.13 Discuss the global impact of branded textile products.

Through the joint strategies of permeation and saturation, market leaders like Billabong and Nike have achieved global product recognition and market dominance. Their products abound in shopping malls across Europe and America, while at the same time peppering market stalls across Asia.

Market leaders dominating particular fields tend to build on their success, not only by improving sales but also by acquiring other companies with appropriate technology, expertise and market share. This has the affect of increasing distribution networks, sales outlets and market share. It also has the affect of reducing competition and giving companies stronger control over pricing and availability. An example of this was the acquisition and integration of Reebok into the Adidas Group for US$3.8 billion. While this acquisition strengthened Adidas' market share, Nike was still the global leader in the sports industry, with enormous exposure and purchasing power across the globe.

Another example of a market leading, global brand, Billabong International Ltd. sell their branded merchandise at sporting shops throughout Australia, Europe, Japan, South America, and North America. Manufacturer and distributer of surfing, skating, and snowboarding apparel and accessories, Billabong has built its business through its Australian base and has spread from there. Billabong executive Paul Naude, is quoted in the August 2000 issue of WWD as saying, 'Up until two years ago, Billabong had numerous licensees around the world, but in the last couple of years, our focus has been on becoming a truly global brand. We are moving much more to wholly owned subsidiaries and taking control of key markets and secondary markets and setting ourselves up to maximize the brand's potential in those areas.'

Further Reading

Bruer S.M., Cassill N, Jones M., *Branding to Compete: Applications to Textiles and Apparel,* Journal of Textiles and Apparel, Technology and Management, Volume 4, Issue 3, Spring 2005.

Holt D. B., Quelch J. A., & Taylor E. L., *How Global Brands Compete,* Harvard Business Review, September, 2004.

Kweon H., *The Effect of Fashion Media on Young Women's Body Image,* International Journal of Beauty Industry, Vol. 3, No. 1, pp.19-21, 2008.

Malinowska-Olszowy M., *Brand Strategy in the Clothing and Textile Market,* Fibres & Textiles in Eastern Europe, January / March 2005, Vol. 13, No.1 (49).

D10 SILK

D.10.1 Describe the silkworm.

D.10.2 Outline the key stages in the life cycle of the silkworm.

Silkworms are a Northern China native moth, (Bombyx mori) that spins a cocoon made of silk. The adult moths only live a few days, during which they breed and lay around 200-500 tiny eggs. Once the larvae hatch. they eat almost constantly for 4 -6 weeks and grow to about 75 mm in length. Over this period, the larvae change their skins a number of times. Larvae only eat the leaves of the mulberry tree and, when larger, can consume up to six leaves per day. They require no other food or additional water. In the pupa, the silkworm twisting in a 'figure 8' motion, will spin silk threads around itself until it is completely enveloped and enclosed in a cocoon. Spinning cocoons takes three to four days, while another two to three weeks is required for the larva to pupate and emerge as a moth from the cocoon, fluttering, albeit flightless. The newly emerged adult moths (a mixture of male and female) survive for about 5 days during which time they mate in preparation for laying a new batch of eggs for the cycle to restart.

In short silkworms have a life cycle consisting of four stages: egg, larva or caterpillar, pupa, and adult.

D.10.3 Describe the cocoon of the silkworm.

Produced in the head of the caterpillar and laid down as a continuous fibre, cocoon silk is composed of two proteins: fibroin, and sericin. The fibre itself is made from the long-chain fibroin while the sericin acts as a binder to hold the cocoon together. Cocoons can have an individual fibre length of up to 15,600 metres. Silk cocoons (coloured by the sericin) may be yellow, pink or orange. Once the sericin is removed the colouring disappears.

Figure D.10.3 Silk cocoons

D.10.4 Describe how silk fibres are harvested from silkworm cocoons.

Silkworm cocoons are cleaned and placed in boiling water to kill the pupa inside and loosen the sericin holding the cocoon fibre in place. The loosened fibres from a number of cocoons are teased out, twisted together and wound onto a revolving frame to form a fine silk thread.

Some cocoons are left aside to allow the pupae to mature into moths and continue the lifecycle for another generation.

Figure D.10.4 shows the silk harvesting process. Raw silkworm cocoons are placed into boiling water to kill the pupae and release threads from the outside of the cocoon. Loose threads (300—900m long) from cocoons are gathered together and wound onto a reel. During this process the individual filaments combine together to form a single 'thread'. The individual threads are bound together by a gum found on the outside surface of each thread. This process produces a single continuous thread of raw silk.

Figure D.10.4 Harvesting silk - Cambodia

D.10.5 Explain why silk production using silkworms has remained a craft industry.

The growing and harvesting of silk has defied mechanization. The process of producing silk thread has changed little in thousands of years. Silkworm food, available as a commercial preparation may be used where mulberry leaves are not available and plastic may have replaced the more traditional timber trays, but the process is still essentially labour intensive. This is due to the somewhat lengthy process, constant monitoring, tedious requirements of handling ultra fine filaments of silk (of inconsistent diameter) and the delicate nature of dealing with live creatures.

D.10.6 Explain that silk production was kept a carefully guarded secret by the Chinese, who maintained a monopoly on silk production for about 3,000 years.

The discovery of the process for harvesting silk is the subject of Chinese legend from thousands of years ago. Silk, its production, use and trade were central to the Chinese economy. Silk became more than a valued commodity and soon became a currency for trade. Taxes were paid in grain and silk and traders substituted lengths of silk instead of measures of gold.

The cultivation of silk worms and the production of the fibre was a well-guarded secret. Exporting of live silk worms was forbidden and was regarded as a capital crime. These actions were taken to maintain a monopoly on the production of silk fibre. In spite of their secrecy, however, the Chinese were destined to eventually lose their monopoly on silk production.

D.10.7 Describe the 'Silk Road'.

The 'Silk Road' marks the shifting trade route from east to west, stretching from China to the Mediterranean. The route was first established when the Han Dynasty Emperor instructed one of her generals to investigate military alliances to the north and west. On return, the general reported his inability to establish any alliance but relayed his discovery of a number of commercially viable kingdoms prepared to trade Chinese silk for horses. Estimates vary but the first caravans traveled to Persia around 100 BC. The 'Silk Road' flourished until sea routes established between homeports and European colonies established in Asia became the preferred alternative.

D.10.8 Explain why the 'Silk Road' can be considered as the information superhighway of its day.

The 'Silk Road' provided more than just a conduit for silk and other goods for traders like Marco Polo. They transferred knowledge, technologies, philosophies and religious ideas. The fields of medicine, warfare, engineering, printing, food and others were all beneficiaries of the two way exchange. Unfortunately the spread of the Black Plague to Europe is also attributed to 'Silk Road' travelers.

D.10.9 Explain why silk substitutes, for example, nylon and rayon, marginalized but never replaced silk as a fibre.

© IBO 2007

Rayon and nylon, both synthetic fibres, were developed and used as silk substitutes. Available at a significantly lower price, nylon replaced silk for stockings around 1940 and, as part of the American WWII military campaign, silk for parachutes, braided parachute cord and tenting were substituted with nylon alternatives. This was also seen as patriotic act as nylon was an American discovery and Japan was the leading producer of silk in the world.

The superior properties of silk have maintained its position as a premium fibre. This moisture absorbent, warm, strong, lustrous and drapeable fabric compares favourably with nylon. Nylon's properties include pilling, static charge, non-absorbency and retention of body heat in garments. Rayon, while absorbent, shrinks, wrinkles, has low abrasion resistance, loses strength when wet and also retains body heat in garments. Silk remains in demand due to its eco-friendly credentials and sustainability of its production methods, this is in direct contrast to the petro-chemical basis of nylon production.

D.10.10 State that silk spiders also produce silk.

© IBO 2007

Some spiders have the unique ability to spin webs of silk fibre, secreted through several spinneret glands located on the spider's abdomen. Consisting of an amorphous polymer and chains of two simple proteins, this biopolymer fibre has exceptional mechanical properties.

D.10.11 Describe why silk spiders cannot be commercially reared like silkworms.

© IBO 2007

Commercial farming of spiders for silk has been attempted and failed due to the territorial, aggressively predatory and cannibalistic nature of the spiders. If kept in close proximity the spiders attack, kill and eat one another.

D.10.12 Describe the characteristics of spider silk ('bio steel').

© IBO 2007

Spider silk is considered to be the strongest of all fibres, naturally occurring and synthetic. Rated at five times the strength of steel and twice as strong as Kevlar®, spider silk

is also highly elastic, waterproof, resistant to bacterial breakdown and around 10 times tougher than cellulose and collagen.

D.10.13 Explain how artificial spider silk is produced from goat's milk through genetic engineering.

© IBO 2007

Genetically engineered goats have been developed to excrete milk containing spider silk proteins. These transgenic animals are created through the insertion of a gene from one animal into another's genome. While spiders and goats are very different creatures, they share similar systems i.e. protein production and storage organs such as silk and mammary glands.

Spider genes spliced into goat DNA are activated in mammary gland tissues to the point where the genetically modified goats produce milk containing silk proteins, ready to be extracted and spun into thread. Processing involves alignment of the protein chains by forcing them through a narrow die before stretching. This technique imitates the spider's natural processes, creating a zigzag pattern in the protein chains. After processing, just one gram of silk generates up to 9 km of thread. Fibre produced in this fashion is termed BioSteel®.

D.10.14 Describe why artificial spider silk protein cannot be spun into a fibre.

© IBO 2007

The artificial production of spider silk continues to improve, but many hurdles have prevented scientists from replicating the physical properties of the natural fibre. Current efforts to produce spider silk have resulted in a product of inferior strength, with a much larger diameter than its natural counterpart. Scientists have yet to bridge the technology gap to make this material viable.

Further Reading

Ko F. K., Kawabata S., Inoue M., Niwa, Fossey S., and Song J., *Engineering Properties of Spider Silk.*

Gole R. S.,Kumar P., *Spider's silk: Investigation of Spinning Process, Web Material and its Properties,* Department of Biological Sciences and Bioengineering, Indian Institute of Technology Kanpur,

Datta K., Nanavat D., Nanavaty M., *Global Silk Industry: A Complete Sourcebook,* Universal Publishers, Florida, USA, 2005.

D11 SMART CLOTHING AND WEARABLE COMPUTING

D.11.1 Define intelligent fabric and haptic technology.

© IBO 2007

Intelligent fabric or 'smart textiles' are those that interact with, and respond to, environmental stimuli. The stimulus or response can be driven by electrical thermal, chemical or magnetic means. Also known as electrotextiles, these materials are fabrics made from yarn performing the function of electronic components and weaves, acting as circuits. This technology offers the opportunity to integrate technology into everyday life by the introduction of items such as smart clothing through to intelligent furniture

Haptic technology provides feedback through the sense of touch. This technology appears in the field of textiles through the development of touch sensitive fabrics where applications are found using embedded proportional control or pressure sensing switches.

D.11.2 Describe smart clothing.

© IBO 2007

Smart clothing incorporates intelligent systems through technologies embedded within the fabric. New materials such as conductive, or so-called e-textiles, incorporate computing functionalities directly into garment fabrics. These fabrics allow sensing and data communication of the wearer's condition and the external environment. Communication may be in electrical, mechanical, magnetic or chemical form.

Wearable computing is distinguished from smart clothing in that wearable computing is designed around the connecting and attaching of conventional digital technologies to clothing or individuals.

One application of smart clothing uses conductive elastane sensors placed strategically at body joints. This allows for the tracking of body movements and has applications in the fields of ergonomics, sports medicine, biomechanics, robotics, athlete training and animation. Garments may be in the form of shirts, pants and gloves.

Dupont announced the latest offering in advanced fibres 'Nomex on Demand'. This smart fibre technology gives fire-fighters up to 20% more thermal performance when encountering emergency conditions. The fibre automatically expands to trap more air for greater thermal insulation. The fibre has been specifically engineered to react and expand when temperatures reach 250 F or higher. Under routine conditions, the fibre remains thin and flexible, providing good mobility and thermal protection.

LifeShirt, developed by Sensatex, is marketed as an undershirt. Optical fibres are spirally plaited into its structure. The whole undershirt has been made with a special weaving technique, in one piece, without any cuttings or seams. The main task of this intelligent shirt is to monitor human physiological parameters such as temperature and heartbeat. It can be used with different textile sensors, not only optical sensors. It is also possible to include sensors into the textile structure to measure the presence of poisonous gases in the air. The sensors collect data into a central unit, and send it to the information centre wirelessly.

D.11.3 Describe wearable computing.

© IBO 2007

Bulky in form, limited levels of usage and high power requirements are often cited as drawbacks to the use of hand-held or portable electronic devices. Wearable computing is designed to address these issues through the development of devices that are:

- small
- light-weight
- fashionable
- energy efficient
- large in memory
- network connectable
- environment/activity aware
- fast in computational performance.

Wearable computers most often consist of a CPU, battery, input/output devices and wireless internet connectivity. They are designed to be worn on the body during use and may be integrated into the user's clothing or can be attached to the body by other means. For example, as a wristband, belt, head mount or glove. Three distinct advantages of wearable computers include hands free operation, unobtrusive portability allowing for the conducting of normal activities by the wearer and 'always on' accessibility.

HL

OPTION

Devices such as the apple iPod allow for direct connectivity to exercise machines or, through chips concealed in shoes, to transfer information about training or exercise routines. Heads up displays such as those in helmets or in eyeglasses also fall into the category of wearable computers. The EyeTap, (shown in Figure D.11.3), is a device worn in front of the eye acting as a camera and also as a display device that superimposes computer-generated imagery on the original scene, making this augmented reality available to the eye.

D.11.3 Wearable computer - EyeTap

By EN:Glogger [GPL (www.gnu.org/licenses/gpl.html)], via Wikimedia Commons

Other products include bluetooth communication gloves, jackets with in-built GPS and/or solar collectors and shirts that log vital signs and sporting performance. Applications exist in the fields of: in-patient monitoring, injury rehabilitation, sports training, navigation etc.

> D.11.4 Identify key areas of research required to promote wearable computing.
>
> D.11.5 Identify the key challenges for wearable computing garments.
>
> © IBO 2007

Wearable computers are faced with many of the same problems beset by their less portable counterparts as well as additional difficulties peculiar to their context. Miniaturization, weight, portability, ergonomics, comfort, user friendliness, training requirements, interface design, security of data transmission and storage, power consumption and battery life are all issues requiring specific attention to make the product viable.

To overcome the issues associated with hard-wired input and output devices on wearable computers, infrared (IR), wireless (bluetooth) or radio frequency (RF) technologies are recommended. Signals must be generated on unique frequencies to allow multiple input devices to be individually identified. It here that issues of power, size, security and weight distribution can be challenging.

Wearable computers often require precise placement, particularly where pressure on the skin is required.

Battery technologies, size, weight, heat dissipation and power consumption of mobile devices are all important design considerations. Advances in Lithium-Polymer battery technologies present new possibilities through the production of flat, lightweight, robust batteries without an enclosing case. These designs allow for the embedding of power cells directly into garments.

Head-mounted displays traditionally consume large amounts of power, developments such as such as 'static electronic paper' and other robust display technologies offer reduced power consumption alternatives. Additionally, the range and frequency of garment deformation, plus the operational environments and cleaning regimes that are required of clothing, cause design problems and restrict both technologies and applications.

Finally, countries traditionally associated with textiles such as China and India, contemplating the development of wearable computers are challenged to transform from a production or manufacturing approach to a more knowledge based economy.

> D.11.6 Identify alternative input and output devices for use with wearable computing.
>
> D.11.7 Identify the advantages and disadvantages of a range of input/ output devices for wearable computing applications.
>
> © IBO 2007

Performance and development goals for wearable computers include:

- improved operator/employee efficiencies
- easy to use, intuitive, non-intrusive interfaces
- fast, reliable, real time data access and response times.

Designers and manufacturers are looking for the 'killer application' that will launch their technology into mainstream usage. While the technology is available, market penetration has yet to see this field expand significantly. Users still require better guarantees of privacy and security when using real-time wireless communication. Safety issues around ergonomics, but more importantly EMI and RFI, still plague this industry.

Figure D.11.7 shows the results of a survey documenting the responses of consumers to features that will influence future usage/purchase of wearable computing devices.

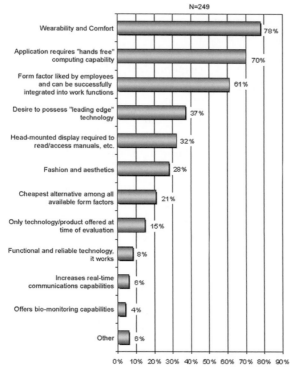

Figure D.11.7 Survey results documenting consumer opinions of future wearable computer features

Image by Ziff Davis

D.11.8 Describe an intelligent fabric.

Intelligent fabrics are textiles demonstrating technology-enhanced performance. Used in smart clothing these fabrics respond to stimuli to improve moisture resistance, heat transfer, or anti-wrinkling properties. They may or may not include input sensors

An example of this approach, using shape memory polymer (SMP) technology, is seen in the production of the intelligent, waterproof, breathable fabric diAPLEX This textile either restricts or allows the loss of body heat and moisture dependent on ambient conditions. DiAPLEX is a layered textile consisting of a SMP sandwiched between two layers of fabric. Under cooler conditions, the particles in the SMP form a solid film, creating an insulator and preventing the loss of thermal energy or the ingress of the colder atmosphere. As body temperature increases, (maybe due to exercise or strenuous activity), the SMP

responds to a predetermined 'trigger point' that causes tiny openings to vent excess moisture and heat.

D.11.9 Explain how the design of wearable computing garments brings together multidisciplinary teams.

Clothing and fabric design requires a very different skillset to product or electronics design. The design of intelligent textiles and smart clothing merges the two fields. Both of these areas have different knowledge bases, but also vastly different modes of designing.

New products will require new ways of working and involve collaborative multidisciplinary teams. These design teams will require expertise in a variety of fields including:

- computers – computing device, network and software engineers
- garment construction – fashion consultants and textiles technologists
- ergonomics and anthropometrics - physiology, biomechanics technicians
- engineering – electronics, embedding, battery and materials technologies.

D.11.10 Compare the markets for fashion garments and consumer electronics and the implications for wearable computing garments.

Fashion and consumer electronics developers identify and target their markets very differently. While the consumer electronic market is broader, fashion designers tend to identify their customer base very specifically. The fashion market targets customers and therefore designs their product very specifically, based around aesthetics, ethics, protection, brand perception, prestige, comfort and value. The design characteristics of electronic devices, however, tend to be centred around usability, functionality, durability and safety.

The merging of these two disparate fields will require psychological and physiological consideration of fashion and its implications for wearable computing garments, potentially promoted in a lifestyle way to access wider markets.

HL

OPTION

D.11.11   Discuss how technology push and market pull impact on the wearable computing market.

© IBO 2007

Technology push in the field of wearable computing arises from gains in miniaturizing of processors and sensors, storage capacities, wireless networking and the availability of high quality, low cost components. As the aforementioned developments have occurred, manufacturers have sought to exploit their use in fields such as wearable computing. Once a market demand is established, designers then approach the problem from an application or need basis, developing the product around the application and creating innovative ways of packaging the product to attract consumers.

Over time, manufacturers have attempted to predict future trends using these innovations and, through this, the development of applications in a wide variety of fields from medical to sports, professional and social uses. While the original development may have been technology push the further modification and tailoring of devices is market pull driven.

D.11.12   Identify obstacles to the expansion of the wearables market.

D.11.13   Discuss the benefits of aligning the wearable computing market more closely with the fashion market.

© IBO 2007

Price will always be a determining factor, as will the perceived benefit gained from the use of the product. Outside of military applications, medical or sports associated devices seem to be the most prevalent. The use of medical related technologies, however, require more stringent testing and certification than their commercial counterparts, thus the greater development in the domestic personal use sector.

The fashion-driven market for wearable computing may still be the most powerful motivator for the consumer (see topic D.11.16). Until these devices are also seen by the public as 'must have', either through function or fashion trend non-wearable devices will still prevail.

D.11.14   Discuss the benefits of laser welding as a joining technique for the manufacture of wearable computing garments.

© IBO 2007

The manufacture of garments with added functionality requires viable joining techniques for fabric and connectors. There is conflict between micro-joining of electronics and macro-joining used for clothing. Stitching is the most common joining method for clothing manufacture, but is labour-intensive, which is cost-prohibitive in most parts of the world, and it makes holes in the fabric, which disrupts the worn connectors, impairs the strength of the garment and reduces the performance of the seam. Advantages of laser welding include the ease of automation, high performance, aesthetic appearance, durability and that the seams are effectively sealed.

Technical textiles are often welded if their structures contain thermoplastic materials that can be fused without destroying their polymeric structure. Air bag fabrics made of either nylon 6.6 or polyester are good examples of the use of laser transmission welding.

Laser welding is particularly suited to the manufacture of waterproof garments. A major advantage being the generation of seams without perforating the material. Buttonholes and pleats may also be produced using this approach.

D.11.15   Explain the potential contribution of the automation of manufacture of wearable computing garments.

© IBO 2007

Many of the new technical textiles required for computing garments employ automated processes and, in some cases CAM technologies, in their manufacture. Modern processes, such as flexible laminating, electrospinning of nanofibres, extrusion of bicomponent conducting fibres, plasma treatments and the use of nanotechnologies and smart materials, all necessitate automated manufacturing.

D.11.16   Evaluate a range of wearable computing garments.

© IBO 2007

The rapid development of electronic textile and nanotextile materials, manufacturing technologies and computers see the field of wearable computing rapidly changing. This requires the consumer to be adept at assessing quality, fitness for purpose and value for money.

One of the early forays (1996), into the world of wearable computing was the Georgia Tech Wearable Motherboard or 'Smart Shirt'. Originally developed for the US Navy to monitor vital signs of combat troops, the product was further developed into a multi-purpose system with applications in sport, medicine and emergency services. Based on optical fibre technology woven into the garment fabric, the shirt was made from one piece of fabric with no seams or discontinuities. Detachable sensors made the product customizable to individual environments.

Released in 2002, to mixed reviews, the North Face MET 5 climber's jacket was an insulated soft shell jacket that has additional heating elements providing warmth on demand with adjustable heat levels, powered by lithium ion battery technology that can boost the wearer's core temperature for six hours. Evaluated by some as a lightweight multi-purpose jacket, the product has, however, also been criticised as an over-engineered and overpriced electric blanket.

Awarded as one of the best inventions for 2006, (TIME Magazine), The Hug Shirt™ uses embedding technology to send people hugs over distance. Using Bluetooth technology linked to the wearer's mobile phone, sensors measure a range of inputs for transmission to a designated recipient. These sensors 'feel' strength of touch and skin warmth, while measuring heart rates of the sender. Actuators recreate these sensations in the wearer of an identical product. Using this technology, sending hugs can be as easy as sending an SMS text.

Nike has developed monitoring technology linking a portable computing device with a sensor implanted into the sole of its running shoes. One of the market leaders in this application, data sent from the running shoe sensor provides feedback to the wearer, encourages him/her to sign up for challenges, both virtual and real events and also offers coaching, all through an iPod interface. Latest developments of this technology allow the athlete to automatically 'tweet' a message through the twitter service and/or post a status update on Facebook. The technology works seamlessly, having been developed and tested over a number of years. Criticism appears to be around the proprietary nature of the sensor technology that only fits Nike shoes.

Figure D.11.16 Nike Sensor and shoe

Further reading

Ajmera N., Dash S.P., Meena C.R., *Smart Textile.*

Baurley S., *Interactive and experiential design in smart textile products and applications,* Pers Ubiquit Comput (2004) 8: 274–281.

Post E. R., Orth M., *Smart Fabric or Wearable Clothing: Proceedings of the First International Symposium on Wearable Computers,* Cambridge, MA, pp. 167-168, October 13-14th, 1997.

Starner T., *The Challenges of Wearable Computing: Parts 1 & 2,* IEEE Micro, July-August, 2001.

Finger S., Terk M., Subrahmanian E., Kasabach C., Prinz F., Siewiorek D. P., Smailagic A., Stivoric J., and Weiss L., *Rapid Design and Manufacture of Wearable Computers,* Communications of the ACM, February 1996/Vol. 39, No. 2.

Cho G., (editor), *Smart Clothing Technology and Applications,* CRC Press Taylor & Francis Group, Florida, 2010.

D.12 SUSTAINABILITY IN THE TEXTILES INDUSTRY

> **D.12.1** Discuss the impact of the introduction of mechanization in the textile industry on the workforce.
>
> © IBO 2007

The changes in the textile industry brought about by mechanization were not limited to the technology alone. In the latter part of the 18th Century, spinning and later weaving 'putting out', was replaced by the more centralized 'factory system'. Originally located around rural water-powered sites, these factories housed workers numbered in the tens. Steam technology liberated factories from their remote river-based locations and by the 1830s manufacturing moved to urban centres closer to the coalfields of Lancashire and Yorkshire. Because the technological changes either appeared or were applied to the textile industries first, manufacturers were able to exploit the availability of the large and unskilled workforce before any of the other industries started to reap the benefits of the Industrial Revolution. Without competition, textiles manufacturers had free reign over working conditions, hours and salaries. Working conditions were largely unregulated. Many factory jobs were repetitive and boring. Poorly lit, dusty and dangerous environments were the norm, with women and children the preferred workforce due to lower rates of pay. Management closely supervised workers during working days, often extending past 12 hours within a six day week.

> **D.12.2** Explain the changes in working conditions that have occurred with the introduction of automation in the textile industry.
>
> © IBO 2007

The introduction of mechanized systems and processes, along with innovations in technology enabled many industries to automate their systems to improve quality, consistency and cost-effectiveness.

Automation refers to any process or function that reduces or eliminates the need for human intervention. The textiles industry is no different to any other and as levels of automation rise in labour-intensive workplaces, job prospects diminish. Reductions in jobs and restructuring of workforces are just two effects of automation. The impact of these changes brings about a series of changes with mixed results for workers:

- unemployment
- higher paying jobs
- improved productivity
- safer, better work environments
- education and vocational training programs
- shifts from 'blue collar' to 'white' collar employment.

Technological developments in mechanization, automation and, more recently, numerical control, make new processes of manufacturing and new products possible. While price is always a determining factor, speed of production, innovation and fashion trends drive the industry. Automation provides the means to maintain a competitive advantage through the production of consistently high quality products on schedule.

> **D.12.3** Discuss sustainability issues in relation to the use of natural fibres.
>
> © IBO 2007

Green fabrics, ecotextiles, organic fibres; all these names speak to the environmentally friendly nature of textiles and their manufacture. The real question is whether these industries are truly sustainable in their practices and whether the products themselves are economically sustainable in an industry driven by fashion and transient trends.

Significant legislation has been passed in many countries around the world, attesting to long-term governmental commitments to sustainability. This legislation provides a legally enforceable framework, requiring manufacturers to take environmentally responsible and ethical manufacturing practises seriously.

Even the textiles industry associated with the production of natural fibres, such as cotton and wool, has environmental issues that go directly to sustainability including:

- use of pesticides, fungicides, herbicides and cleaning of raw fibres (removal and disposal of fats, oils and grease)
- water requirements and wastage (1 kg of cotton fabric requires 4,500 litres of water, 1kg of wool fabric uses 1,666,000 litres of water)
- energy costs (energy accounts for approximately between 10% – 15% of total textile production costs)

- use of hazardous chemicals for dyeing and finishing (chlorine for 'anti felting' wool)
- land use issues (inappropriate site choice for cultivating cotton – Aral Sea etc.).

Man-made fibres are almost exclusively sourced from petroleum, however, even manufacturers using synthetic fibres see the market demand for green fabrics and have responded by producing and promoting their use of recycled materials, such as polyester, in the manufacture of new product lines.

Carbon previously derived from finite petro-chemical sources is now being refined from plants. Processing corn and wheat (through fermentation and distillation) these new fibres compete with traditional natural products like cotton and wool. Generically known as PLA (polylactide) this series of fibres is promoted as combining all the best properties of natural and synthetic fibres.

> **D.12.4** Describe the links between global communication systems and the growth of multinational textile companies.
>
> © IBO 2007

The globalization and the interconnectedness of international economies continues to impact on textile industries. Historically the industry has been constrained by various agreements and quotas, protecting manufacturers by limiting or restricting imports from developing nations. Increased liberalization of trade was originally thought to solely benefit developing countries, as production rates increased. However, as multi-national industries have established their own manufacturing plants in developing nations, improved communications and transport infrastructure have made it viable for companies to have a location presence based on the role required within the company as whole.

> **D.12.5** Outline the advantages and disadvantages of multinational textile companies establishing manufacturing outlets in developing countries.
>
> © IBO 2007

While textiles industries and clothing manufacturing sub-sectors are closely linked, there are variations to their infrastructure and requirements. Garment assembly mostly involves lower levels of technology and can be labour-intensive. Textile industries, however, tend to be more capital-intensive and require a skilled or semi-skilled workforce.

In developing nations, where labour is both cheap and abundant, these activities are still commercially viable. Local environmental legislation that may not be as stringent as developed nations also allows practices to continue that would be outlawed elsewhere. Employment and working conditions also allow manufacturers to exploit local circumstances. Location of textiles factories in these locations can address, price, infrastructure, speed and quality issues, the final determining factor is distribution. Companies have now created sophisticated, highly connected, international, 'value chains'. This transportation network connects distributors, major brand manufacturers and retailers to small scale, low-wage subcontractors (often in developing countries). The process of garment assembly remains labour intensive due to the:

- varied nature of fabrics
- rapid changes in fashions
- constant demand for new product
- complexity of assembly processes.

> **D.12.6** Discuss the advantages and disadvantages for developing countries when large multinational companies establish textile manufacturing plants in their country.
>
> © IBO 2007

Developing countries are more attractive to manufacturers in the garment assembly industry where they can take advantage of labour conditions, relatively low wages and greater productivity. This generates considerable local employment, however, the financial benefits tend to be with the manufacturers selling their product in affluent global markets at the expense of the workers. The majority of garment assembly workers in developing nations are women and children who work long hours in poor conditions for small financial return.

> **D.12.7** Outline the effects of import and export quotas (fair trade regulations) on the commercial development of the textile industry.
>
> © IBO 2007

The world economy has seen a rise in the volume and value of trade. Most countries recognise the long-term benefits of free trade in goods and services between nations although there are disputes about what free trade actually means! Trade is widely regarded as a catalyst for growth both on the demand and supply-side of their economies.

But frequently there are trade disputes between countries – as often as not because one or more parties believes that trade is being conducted unfairly, on an uneven playing field, or because they believe that there is an economic or strategic justification for some form of import control.

Countries who feel they are not benefiting from free trade agreements tend to respond with import restrictions or some sort of protectionist strategy. These protectionist measures may take the form of:

- tariffs - import taxes
- quotas – imposition of quantitative limits
- embargoes - banning specific imported goods
- intellectual property laws – enforcing copyright and patents to restrict copying
- export assistance - subsidies encouraging domestic production
- import licensing - limited granting of licenses to import goods
- exchange controls - limiting the amount of foreign exchange between countries.

Governments seeking to control imports may impose quotas such as those found in the Multi-Fibre Agreement which expired in January 2005 and which led, in 2005, to a trade dispute between the EU and China over the issue of textile imports.

Protectionist policies are often imposed as a reaction to 'import dumping'. Dumping is illegal and occurs when one country exports product at a price below product costs. Dumping is often cited in the textiles industry as a means to protect local manufacturers, but is difficult to prove when attempting to calculate costs outside of a domestic market. Dumping may be claimed in an effort to protect more developed economies and their textile industries from those in developing nations with lower infrastructure costs, less mandatory legislation and lower wages. Protectionist policies are often claimed as supporting high levels of poverty in many of the world's less developed economies.

While protectionist barriers designed to protect local manufacturers, maintain employment and retain skills they maintain higher prices, penalise foreign manufacturers and allocate resources inefficiently locally and internationally. They may also lead to retaliatory action by governments in the form of 'trade wars'. The inherent concern over protectionist policies is that they become entrenched and maintain and support inefficiencies in production.

D.12.8 Discuss corporate social responsibility and 'triple bottom line' (social, economic and environmental) sustainability of a rapidly growing and developing textile industry.

© IBO 2007

Manufacturers and consumers both have responsibilities when it comes to sustainable practice. Director of the Textile Exchange, David Bennell, makes this clear in his comments on the textiles industry when notes:

- textile waste occupies nearly five percent of all landfill space
- the average U.S. resident throws away 31 kilograms of clothing every year
- twenty percent of industrial fresh water pollution comes from textile treatment and dyeing
- one trillion kilowatt hours are used every year by the global textile industry, which results in 10 percent of total global carbon impact
- 700 gallons of fresh water are used to make one cotton T-shirt and in 2009, three trillion gallons of fresh water were used to produce 60 billion kilos of fabric.

Apparel Technology and Business Insight – from Concept to Consumer, 2010.

Consumers have continued to support eco-friendly textile industries employing sustainable practices even in times of economic hardship. Manufactures have also found some eco-practice to be more efficient. Waste is the equivalent of lost value, so any system or process that reduces waste is more efficient. Manufacturers adopting eco-friendly practices are using the change as one of their marketing strategies. New practices are certified using stringent international guidelines such as the Global Organic Textile Standard (GOTS) for organic fibres, and bluesign™ for synthetic fibres, to substantiate their claims. While design has a major impact on the sustainability of a product, manufacturers can also take steps towards sustainable practice by:

- auditing energy needs
- developing a raw materials sourcing strategy
- assessing waste, effluent and use of toxic chemicals
- measuring company footprints and researching opportunities for change
- guaranteeing product integrity through environmental certification and transparency of operation.

The development of new textiles and related technologies needs to consider sustainability issues such as use, recycling and disposal. In the design phase the development of reusable or multi-use items instead of single use products can extend product life and usefulness. Extracting the maximum benefit from materials resources makes social, economic and environmental sense. The triple bottom line mantra of, 'people, profit, planet' applies directly here.

Wastage from textiles may be categorized as either pre- or post-consumer. Pre-consumer textile waste consists of those materials generated as part by-products of production processes. Recycling of waste and by-products can yield large volumes of material suitable for use in soft furnishing, automotive, construction and paper industries. Post-consumer waste refers to clothing or household textiles reused or recycled instead of being disposed. Reuse of fabrics and garments may take the form of form of eco-fashion, re-tasking or redistribution (through second hand outlets and charities).

Recycling involves the reprocessing of used clothing, fibrous material, fabric scraps and waste from the manufacturing process. Textiles made from both natural and man-made fibres can be recycled. Besides natural fibres such as wool, cotton, silk and linen, popular synthetic fabrics such as polyamides, polyesters and acrylics, can all be recycled. Once collected, cleaned and sorted, recyclable textiles may be processed mechanically, where fibres are separated before re-spinning into yarn or chemically, through repolymerizing fibres to again spin into yarn.

Knitted or woven woolens are 'pulled' into a fibrous state for reuse in applications such as: insulation, padding or raw material for felting. Cotton can be re-tasked as rag, compost or form a constituent of high-quality paper. Garment, buttons, zippers and hardware may be recovered for reuse. Waste reduction, reuse and recycling results in:

- lowering purchase prices
- reducing use of virgin materials
- reduces disposal costs and landfill
- generates less air and water pollution
- keeping materials out of the waste stream
- preserving the 'embodied energy' used in manufacturing.

Solid wastes can be reduced by up to 95% if all methods of recycling and reuse are exploited.

While a company's global identity delivers it much strength in the marketplace, consumers still prefer brands that reflect the country of origin, particularly those countries whose national identities are associated with specific traits or products e.g.:

- Turkey - rugs
- Thailand - silk
- Italy - fashion design
- Australia - woollen products
- America - cotton and denim.

Examples of the relationship between culture, history and textile design can be found in most cultures. Influences on African textile development in one tribal area is outlined below.

African clothing is known for its colourful fabrics and distinctive designs. Colours in the cloths of African people posses important meaning. Meanings vary from people to people and cloth to cloth. For example, the Akan people in West Africa use dark colours such as red, black, and brown for funerals, while the Akon use white for joyous occasions, such as naming ceremonies.

The kente cloth made by the Asante people of Ghana, (who are also Akan), displays golden colours representing status and serenity. Yellow represents fertility (like the ripeness of an egg yoke or a fruit) and vitality. Green signifies renewal and growth. Blue represents the presence of God and the omnipotence of the blue sky. Red indicates passion, Asante also believe that red holds protective powers. Finally, black denotes seriousness and a union with ancestors. It implies spiritual awareness.

Different styles of African fashion have evolved from the mixture of African and western cultures. African designers create clothes of western design using traditional African cloth. Hence, ones sees kente ties and coats made from indigo cloth. Clothes of traditional African cut are also fashioned using a combination of western and African cloth.

Figure D.12.10 shows kente cloth sewn together from many narrow kente stripes. The image depicts three different typical Ewe kente stripes.

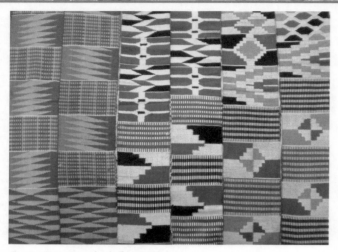

D.12.10 Kente cloth from Ghana

Further Reading

Sustainability: can it last?, The Apparel Analyst No: 9.

Lunt J., *Textiles and the Environment: a more sustainable solution*, Cargill Dow, USA.

Petry F., *Environmental Protection and Sustainability in the Textile Industry*, Melliand English, 7-8/2008.

D13 COTTON AND THE 'EU FLOWER': CASE STUDY OF AN ECOLABEL

> D.13.1 Describe the significance of the 'EU Flower' as an environmental quality mark covering a range of product categories.
>
> © IBO 2007

Based on life cycle analysis the EU ecolabel, shown in Figure D.13.1, is awarded to products and services that limit their impact on the environment (see 3.2.12). The environmental impacts of products and services are examined in detail incorporating such areas as energy consumption, materials selection, waste generation and emissions. The value of the EU ecolabel program lies in its holistic approach to assessment.

The EU flower program provides a coherent framework for product development. It allows manufacturers to integrate environmental considerations at the design stage, which is arguably the most effective and efficient means of improving the environmental impact of products throughout their life cycle.

The EU Ecolabel program continues to evolve. On January 30th 2010, new regulations made provision for:

- addition of new product categories
- lowering fees and simplifying criteria
- liaising with other national environmental label programs across the EU
- targeting products with greatest potential for environmental improvement
- reducing bureaucracy, allowing for faster criteria development and revision of existing procedures.

Currently, the program covers 26 product categories including; cleaning products, electronic equipment, textiles, tourist accommodation, incorporating in excess of 24,000 products and services.

Figure D.13.1 EU ecolabel

D.13.2 Outline the key benefits of the 'EU Flower' system.

The EU flower systems meets a strong community demand for eco product certification. Environmentally conscious consumers are looking for guarantees on performance, quality, environmentally responsible production methods and sustainable use of material resources, without the use of toxic or harmful processes and materials. Companies wishing to import their products into the EU must also comply with these Ecolabel requirements, such as full life cycle assessment. Because the EU Flower program is independently verified, consumers can make purchases based on manufacturers claims, with confidence.

D.13.3 Explain how manufacturers would achieve the 'EU Flower' label for their products.

The EU Ecolabel, or flower program, is managed by the European Commission and other selected member State bodies. A life-cycle based multi-criteria assessment determines the environmental impact, effectiveness and efficiency of the product. These criteria are regularly reviewed and updated to incorporate new products and technological developments. Manufacturers hoping to have their products accepted into the program must follow a standardized procedure involving the following steps:

- Apply for the award of an EU Ecolabel. After selecting the appropriate product group manufacturers contact the appropriate Competent Body responsible for supporting and administering the scheme at a national level.
- Gather documentation ready for submission. Manufacturers consult with the Competent Body to determine an appropriate testing regimen. Testing laboratories must be certified under ISO 17025 or equivalent.
- Approval or rejection is based on the ecological and performance documentation submitted. Competent Bodies may visit manufacturing sites to ensure compliance with the criteria.
- Award of the EU Ecolabel allows companies to use the Ecolabel on products, packaging and advertising.

D.13.4 Identify the range of textile products covered by the 'EU Flower' label textiles product category.

Textiles are a significant group within the EU flower program. An audit conducted in November 2007, revealed textiles as the second largest group after tourist accommodation. Textile products included in this group range from fibres, yarns and fabrics, to home textiles, clothing and accessories.

D.13.5 List the key benefits of the 'EU Flower' system in limiting the environmental impact of a textile product at all stages of its life cycle from manufacture through use to disposal.

The EU ecolabel on textile products informs consumers testing has been conducted to verify:

- maintenance of shape over time
- risk of allergic reactions has been minimized
- shrinkage is no more than expected from conventional products
- colour resistance relative to perspiration, washing, drying and exposure to sunlight
- materials and processes harmful to the environment have been limited during fibre production.

HL

OPTION

D.13.6 Discuss the key environmental issue involved in the cultivation of cotton products.

© IBO 2007

The United States cultivates and produces the majority of the world's cotton and, as such, bears the majority of the environmental concerns associated with its production. The key environmental issues most identified with the cultivation of cotton relate to damage caused through inappropriate use of pesticides, water and land.

Conventionally cultivated cotton uses more insecticide than any other crop. Many of these pesticides are also hazardous to humans, wildlife and the environment. As recently as 2000 the US Environmental Protection Agency rated seven of the top fifteen pesticides used for cotton cultivation as possible, likely, probable, or known human carcinogens. PANNA, the Pesticide Action Network of North America has warned, 'these pesticides can poison farm workers, drift into neighbouring communities, contaminate ground and surface water and kill beneficial insects and soil micro-organisms.' Waste cotton straw used for livestock feed can also transfer these chemicals directly into the food chain. Indiscriminate spraying or crop dusting also distributes pesticides beyond the target crop. Cotton is an exceptionally demanding crop in terms of its water needs (3.6 litres of water are needed per cotton bud). Polluted run-off from cotton fields can wash into local waterways and leach into groundwater.

The Aral Sea in Uzbekistan was drained for cotton production aiming to make the Soviet Union self-sufficient in cotton. Pesticide use, poor irrigation practice and rising salt levels have left this once fertile area barren. Once a large body of fresh water the Aral sea has been significantly reduced in size to a saline, contaminated environment, unable to support fish life. The United Nations described the environmental damage caused as one of the 'most staggering disasters of the 20th century'.

In recent years, cotton producers have to reduced environmental impact through:

- increasing crop yields
- improving water efficiency
- practising conservation tillage
- reducing the number of pesticide applications.

Some large retailers in the U.S. and U.K. are encouraging farmers to use more eco-friendly and socially acceptable practices. These corporations also recognise the market benefits obtained from 'greening' their product lines.

D.13.7 Discuss the key environmental issues involved in the ginning process.

© IBO 2007

Once harvested, raw cotton is processed by ginning. Cotton ginning involves passing the raw cotton through a series of rollers that separate the seed from the cotton fibre. Leather covered rollers are used to extract the seeds from the fibre. The leather-clad rollers contain chromium, a material hazardous to human health. During the ginning process, the cotton lint absorbs some of this chromium, as do seeds and other by-products, due to the rubbing against the rollers. Gin workers may be exposed to this material through airborne cotton dust and chromium poisoning has been recorded amongst animals consuming cottonseed feedstock. Separated seeds may be recovered for future sewing, converted into oil processed for use as feedstock or edible oil. To minimize this problem, rubber coated rollers have been developed.

In some countries the feeding of by-products from the ginning process (leaves, stems and short fibres), is also prohibited due to the high concentration of harmful pesticides.

D.13.8 Discuss the key environmental issues involved in spinning, knitting and weaving of cotton fibres.

© IBO 2007

Cleaning and processing cotton fibres into yarn ready for cloth production can involve a range of numerous toxic chemicals including petroleum scours, ammonia, and formaldehyde.

Spinning, weaving and knitting are mechanical processes. Their environmental impacts relate to energy use, production of dust, noise pollution and generation of solid waste. All three processes require the addition of chemical lubricants (spinning), oils (knitting) or size (weaving) to protect or strengthen fibres during processing. In general, the environmental impact of weaving is higher than that of spinning due to the use of sizing agents, but all of these additives must be removed before dyeing. Due to their poor biodegradability, many of these agents damage the environment. Large amounts of water can be used in this stage as well as more chemical additives to remove sizing etc. The recovery of some sizing agents is possible, thus significantly reducing the polluting effects of the effluent. Along with sizing agents and lubricants, any biocides previously applied to the cotton leach out at this point, producing highly toxic waste. Emission of these materials is outlawed in the EU and US, due to their carcinogenic properties.

Limiting environment impact at this stage may be achieved through:

- recycling of sizing agents
- use of biodegradable lubricants
- combining de-sizing and scouring (cleaning) stages to reduce use of chemicals, energy and water.

> **D.13.9** Discuss the key environmental impacts associated with the dyeing and printing of cotton and how these might be minimized.
>
> © IBO 2007

Cotton, by its nature, does not accept dyes easily. The preparation of cotton for dyeing involves the stripping of minerals, waxes and other contaminants from the fibre. Frequent bleaching and rinsing cycles are also often employed. Effluent associated with dyeing processes may be heavily coloured, contain high concentrations of salts, and exhibit high biological oxygen/chemical oxygen demands.

Alternatively, cotton may be also be prepared by bleaching with non-toxic hydrogen peroxide and dyed with low-impact dyes that are gentler on the environment.

> **D.13.10** Discuss the key environmental issues involved in cutting cotton fabrics and how these might be minimized.
>
> © IBO 2007

Optimal arrangements of patterns and templates on cloth can minimize waste and improve resource use. CAD programs can efficiently layout cutting schedules and in conjunction with CAM reduce wastage, improve quality and reduce errors.

> **D.13.11** Discuss the implications of the care and maintenance of textile products in the home on health and the environment.
>
> © IBO 2007

Health experts and consumers have become increasingly aware of the health risks textiles may pose. Textile fibres, plant contaminants, dyes, finishes, formaldehyde, latex, detergents and fabric softeners used to wash your clothes have all been found to cause dermatitis or other allergic reactions in sensitized individuals. Permanent press treatments containing formaldehyde-releasing resins have been used in the past. The treatment of textile fibres, or their raw materials, with pesticides has also caused consumer concern to the point where the industry has established certification through the introduction of 'eco seals' and seen the increased uptake of organic products.

Rashes most often occur at friction points where fabrics and bodies come into contact. Under arms, waists, inner thighs, elbow and knee areas are most susceptible. New technologies improving functionality to protect against UV radiation, creasing, staining, fading etc. may also cause allergic reactions in sensitized individuals.

Asthma and allergies may also be caused by biological pollution through the multiplication of bacteria and dust mites in bedding, soft furnishings, curtains and carpets. Washing, (particularly in hot water) and dry cleaning will kill dust mites. Heating will minimize dust mite populations and air conditioning will dry out interior environments and reduce the food supply for dust mites.

> **D.13.12** Discuss the key environmental issues involved in the reuse and recycling of cotton products.
>
> © IBO 2007

As with other textiles, recycling and reuse addresses issues surrounding:

- landfill
- embodied energy
- use of raw materials
- environmental pollution
- greenhouse gas generation.

Research, conducted through the application of a streamlined LCA, has shown that over 97% of energy can be saved through reuse of cotton clothing opposed to manufacturing from virgin materials. The major consideration for reuse is the quality of the fabric and garment construction.

Cotton can be re-tasked as: absorbent rags, polishing cloths, clothing patches quilting squares, compost etc. Cotton fibres may also be recycled into absorbent cotton wool or form a constituent of high-quality paper.

Reuse can be also incorporated into the design stage of new products. Durable and reusable, calico bags manufactured from woven cotton are becoming increasingly popular as many countries legislate to reduce the use of disposable plastic bags.

HL

OPTION

Further reading

Elsner P., Karger Gazette, *Textiles and the Skin, No. 67*, August 2004.

Woolridge A.C., Ward G.D., Phillips P.S., Collins M. Gandy S., *Life Cycle Assessment for Reuse/Recycling of Donated Waste Textiles Compared to use of Virgin Material: An UK Energy Saving Perspective*, Resources, Conservation and Recycling 46 (2006) 94–103.

Resource Guide for Garment and Textile Care Professionals, United States Environmental Protection Agency, September 1997.

EPA, Textile Industry, *Doing What it Takes to be Waste Wise,* February 2002.

HL

OPTION

Exercises

1. Which of the following is a principle of applying colour to yarns?

   A. warping
   B. bleaching
   C. immersion
   D. digital imaging

2. What is a major factor affecting the consumer call for eco-fabrics?

   A. cost
   B. legislation
   C. globalisation
   D. environmental concern

3. Which fibre would be most suitable for children's nightwear due to its high moisture absorbency, comfort and fire resistance?

   A. lycra
   B. nylon
   C. cotton
   D. polyester

4. How have knitting machines impacted on production of textiles?

   A. stretch
   B. increasing yarn
   C. design possibilities
   D. increased job opportunities

5. How could the life cycle of a textile product be extended:

   A. introduce a new product
   B. increase product price
   C. decrease product quality
   D. modify and update the product

6. Classify the following fibres as man-made and natural: Nylon, Wool, Cotton, Silk, Polyester, Rayon, Silk.

7. Describe the difference between a filament and a fibre.

8. State whether the following are true or false and correct the false statements:

(i) Fibre is the basic unit of all fabrics.

(ii) Filaments are short fibres.

(iii) Silk is prepared from the stem of a plant.

(iv) Polyester is a naturally occurring cellulose fibre.

(vi) Lycra is the trade name for spandex.

9. Identify and evaluate three properties that make spandex a suitable choice of material for the production of swimsuits.

10. Explain how work was organized before the Industrial Revolution?

11. Define these terms; hydrophillic, hydroscopic and hydrophobic. Identify materials with these properties, how they occur and why they may be advantageous.

HL

OPTION

HUMAN FACTORS

E

CONTENTS

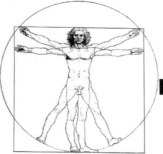

One of the defining characteristics of humanity is its use of tools. From prehistoric times tools have been shaped in order to facilitate and extend human action. Early measurement also made use of human dimensions with measures such as the cubit, hand, foot, yard, fathom, etc., being based on anthropometric measurements.

Leonardo da Vinci's famous drawing, The Vitruvian Man, is named after the 1st Century BC, Roman engineer Vitruvius who studied human form in order to develop buildings of appropriate scale. da Vinci took extensive measurements of two subjects to explore the relationships outlined by Vitruvius. This sketch could then be thought of as a representation of the average dimensions of the male form. Many investigators over the years since Da Vinci have examined the dimensions of the human body. However, it was not until the 20th Century and the need to simplify aircraft controls and indicators that the field of human factors design began to develop in earnest. This was in order to take into consideration the wide variation in individuals' measurements.

E.1 HUMAN FACTORS DESIGN

E.1.1 Identify the objectives of human factors design.

© ISO 2007

Human factors design, also known as ergonomic design, is a design process that strives to understand the interactions among humans, and with systems and equipment, in order to provide efficient, and effective engagement. In order to accomplish this, a number of disciplines are called upon, outlined in Figure E.1.1. Design objectives include:

- reduce errors
- increase safety
- increase ease of use
- reduce stress and fatigue
- enhance operational comfort
- improve system performance, reliability and maintenance.

OPTION

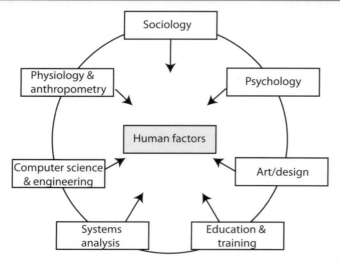

Figure E.1.1 Dimensions of human factors design

Sociology: social and cultural sensitivities and assumptions regarding designs and operations (population stereotypes).

Psychology: Cognitive, psychological factors that impact operations including effects of environmental conditions such as stress, lighting, temperature, humidity, noise, vibration, etc.

Education and Training: Training and understanding of the various interactions between humans, systems and equipment.

Physiology/Anthropology: Understanding of human movement and dimensions.

Systems Analysis: Systems employed to organise and implement effective human-artifact interactions.

Art/Design: the artifacts and systems developed to both facilitate use and satisfy requirements of style and aesthetics.

Computer Science/Engineering/Manufacturing: The selection of suitable materials and their manufacture into artifacts and/or development of computer software that provide functionality with both safety and security.

E.1.2   Describe why visibility is an important consideration in human factors design.

© IBO 2007

For normally sighted individuals, visual information is often the most important. For this information to be useful it needs to be clear and unambiguous, conveying relevant information when and where it is needed in a manner that is meaningful and free of distracting clutter.

It is the designer's job to ensure that considerations of visibility are taken into account with regard to how the operator is to use the information. For example, visual clues should be provided that indicate how equipment should be used. If a door opens in only one direction, push or pull should be clearly displayed. Figure E.1.2 shown a commonly used L-shaped door handle on a door on which a sign indicates the action required to open the door.

Figure E.1.2 Sign indicating action required to open the door

E.1.3   Describe why feedback is an important consideration in human factors design.

© IBO 2007

Feedback allows the results of an action (input) to be monitored for conformance with expectations (output), allowing a change in the input to be made in order to modify the output. A simple feedback system is shown in Figure E.1.3.

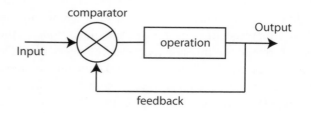

Figure E.1.3 Simple feedback system

We routinely use our senses of sight, hearing, touch, smell, taste and balance to monitor the world around us. It is through this feedback that we navigate our way through the world. In human design, the feedback could be something as simple as the positive click or tone accompanying the pressing of a keypad or an indicator light illuminating in response to the operating of a switch. The provision of such feedback in human factors design is important if the confident, efficient and safe operation of equipment is to be achieved.

> **E.1.4** Describe why mapping is an important consideration in human factors design.
>
> © IBO 2007

Mapping relates to the establishment or mapping of the connections between human capabilities and limitations to system requirements and affordances. This process aims to improve perceptual cues and ease of interpretation in order to improve comfort and efficiency of operation. Such mapping allows the design of equipment displays and operations in the most efficient layout for operators.

> **E.1.5** Describe why affordance is an important consideration in human factors design.
>
> © IBO 2007

Affordance is a term coined by the psychologist James J. Gibson in 1977 to describe all actions possible in an environment, even if not recognised by an individual. Donald Norman later modified this definition. When applied to human factors design, Norman adjusted affordance to be the perceived property of an object that indicates how it is to be used. Typical examples include:

- chairs are for sitting
- switches are toggled
- knobs are to be turned
- buttons are to be pressed
- mating plug and socket can be connected.

Where confusion exists additional information needs to be supplied. For example, a doorknob will be turned to release the door latch, but the direction the door opens may be ambiguous and need signage to clarify whether pushing or pulling actually opens the door. This example illustrates a division between perceived affordance and actual affordance, in that the perceived affordance of the doorknob does not in and of itself supply the additional actual affordance information, that to open the door the doorknob needs to be turned and the door pushed (or pulled) for it to be opened.

> **E.1.6** Describe why constraints are an important consideration in human factors design.
>
> © IBO 2007

Constraints limit the interactions that are possible and by so doing, act to reduce errors. A constraint can be a physical limitation, such as a key and lock, or software such as limiting the type and form of data to be entered, or cultural such as the computer page scroll bar on the right hand side of the screen. Designs that limit incorrect connection due to incompatibility are an example of a design constraint. Several such examples are shown in Figure E.1.6.

Figure E.1.6 Physical constraints represented by different connection designs

> **E.1.7** Explain why consumers misuse many products due to inappropriate human factors considerations in their design.
>
> © IBO 2007

Misuse of many products can be attributed to the lack of clarity with respect to the operation of the various functions available. This includes factors of poor definition of affordance and appropriate constraints, along with an understanding of how users would interact with the product.

> **E.1.8** Explain why the aims of human factors may conflict with other design aims.
>
> © IBO 2007

Any product design will represent a number of compromises between form, function, reliability, manufacturability, cost and safety. It is the relative importance that has been placed on these various factors during the decision making phases of the design process, that leads to the wide range of competing products available on the market.

OPTION

E.1.9 Explain that the ergonomic data required in systems design depends on the role of people in that system

© IBO 2007

The ergonomic data required for a systems design must take into account the various activities and requirements of each role within the system. The design must therefore accommodate the range of anthropometric variability that could exist within the user population.

Further Reading

Kirwan, B. et.al. (1997). *Human Factors in the ATM System Design Life Cycle*. FAA/Eurocontrol ATM R&D Seminar, 16 – 20 June, 1997, Paris, France
http://www.atmseminar.org/seminarContent/seminar1/papers/p_007_CDR.pdf

Human Factors
http://www.slideshare.net/mschongkong/human-factors-presentation

Affordances
http://www.interaction-design.org/encyclopedia/affordances.html

Darnell, M.J. Bad Human Factors Designs.
http://www.baddesigns.com/examples.html

Don Norman's jnd.org
http://www.jnd.org/dn.mss/affordances_and_design.html

Mann, D. (2000). *Design without compromise, design for life*
http://www.triz-journal.com/archives/2000/05/d/index.htm

Parmee, I.C. (2001). *Poor-definition, uncertainty, and human factors-satisfying multiple objectives in real world decision-making environments*. In Proceedings of EMO'2001. pp.52-66.
http://www.dss.dpem.tuc.gr/pdf/Poor-Definition,%20Uncertainty,%20and%20Human%20Factors%20-%20Satisfying.pdf

E.2 HUMAN FACTORS DATA

E.2.1 Define user population.

© IBO 2007

Population is defined as the group expected to make use of or 'use' an item, instrument, product or data.

E.2.2 Outline how large user groups may be defined.

© IBO 2007

Large groups can be defined in terms of common characteristics such as age, gender, physical condition, handedness, ethnicity etc.

Any of these, or other group definitions, can be used to identify a user population.

E.2.3 Outline the importance of sampling to gain information about potential users.

© IBO 2007

While some products can be used by almost everyone, many designs acknowledge that some people within a population may not be able to use a product for one reason or another. Within any group, variation will exist. Because of this, statistical methods are used to collect data from a large number of people in order to describe the population. A survey of a large population typically results in a Gaussian distribution, also known as a Normal Distribution of measurements, in which the highest numbers correspond with the mean or average value and the other members of the population are distributed evenly about the mean in an ever decreasing amount. The distinctive shape of the distribution results in its common description as a bell curve. The distribution is defined by two basic measures the Mean, described above, and the Standard Deviation. The standard deviation is a measure of the dispersion of values about the mean and is represented by the Greek letter sigma (σ). The Normal Distribution presented in Figure E.2.3 is shown with the standard deviation divisions on the x-axis. As indicated, the area bounded by ±1 standard deviation represents approximately 68% of the population, while approximately 95% of the population is bounded by ±2 standard deviations.

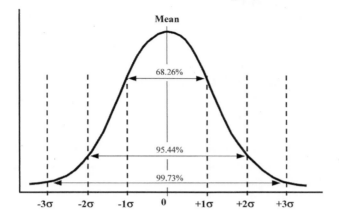

Figure E.2.3 Normal population distribution

When considering a product designed for mass use, sufficient sampling of the target population needs to be performed, in order to accurately define that population. Information collected from just a few people, will give an inaccurate picture, as it is unlikely to be representative of the whole range of users.

> E.2.4 Describe how a user group sample is based on the factors considered in E.2.2.
>
> © IBO 2007

Depending on the requirements, the defining characteristics of a user group may be very broad or very narrow. In determining the size of seating for a general audience in a theatre or passengers on a commercial airliner for example, consideration needs to be given to accommodating body sizes from that of children through to obese adults. Designs in this instance are often based on the requirements of the 95% percentile, to ensure the seats are wide enough to comfortably accommodate the largest number of customers.

> E.2.5 Discuss how the factors in E.2.2 are further defined to determine the exact nature of a user group sample.
>
> © IBO 2007

Many professions place anthropometric restrictions on the selection of their members, considered necessary to fulfil their role.

The Police Force of NSW Australia among other things requires applicants to be over 18 years of age and to be physically, fit with a BMI <30 with good hearing and sight.

A basketball team will recruit players from the taller end of a population, while a jockey will typically be from the lower end. A ballerina, in addition to being technically proficient, is generally required to conform to the body shape and height requirements of a company.

> E.2.6 Outline the use of the concept of 'methods of extremes' to limit sample sizes.
>
> © IBO 2007

As the name implies the 'methods of extremes' looks at the extremes of the user population distribution. These positions along with the mean are used to design equipment used for general use.

Doorways, ladders, escape hatches are based on the 95th percentile of males while the forces required to operate control panel buttons are based on the 5th percentile of females. By adopting these extremes, the greatest number of users are accommodated.

By its nature this form of design will not include those members of the population that lie beyond the extremes chosen.

> E.2.7 Define population stereotypes.
>
> © IBO 2007

Assumptions and associations are made by the population of a particular culture, regarding how equipment and products operate. Such assumptions include the direction a handle should turn to open or close, or the direction a switch moves for on or off. These are not associations that are intrinsic to the machine, but are established as a factor in machine standardization within a society. Because of this, it is often the case that different paths to standardisation have been taken leading to different population stereotypes. In the UK and Australia, for instance, a light switch is pushed down for on and up for off while, in the USA, it is the reverse.

> E.2.8 Describe the relevance of the use of population stereotypes in the design of controls for products.
>
> © IBO 2007

If population stereotypes are incorporated into the design of product controls, operation feels more intuitive and conforms to the users' expectations, based on past experience.

E.2.9 Discuss the problems of displacing population stereotypes in the design of controls for products.

© IBO 2007

The displacement of a population stereotype means that an operation does not conform to expectations of how it should work based on previous experience of the user. Such a displacement might be the turning of a knob clockwise for ON rather than anti-clockwise. With a little effort, the alternate operation can be learned, however under conditions of stress or tiredness reversion to the population stereotype can emerge.

Under conditions of stress working memory is occupied and the patterns of action learned over a lifetime reassert themselves and the chances of an error increases, or an increased delay in response can occur. One such situation can arise if a motorist has learnt to drive in a vehicle in which the turn indicator control is on the right hand side of the steering column, and the windshield wiper controls on the left. If this motorist then occasionally drives a European vehicle in which these controls are on the opposite sides of the steering column, confusion will result in the wipers being activated when a turn signal was intended.

E.2.10 Discuss how the use of converging technology in product design may lead to confusing control layout.

© IBO 2007

Converging technology offers the benefits of the incorporation of a variety of technologies into a single device, providing increased functionality. Where these technologies are incorporated without rationalisation of the controls into a uniform solution however, confusion can arise regarding operation particularly under conditions of stress.

E.2.11 Discuss how the concepts of 'range of sizes' and 'adjustability' affect the design of products.

© IBO 2007

Designing for adjustability means that provision is made within the design for adjustments to accommodate the anthropometric variability between members of the user group. In other words, adjustability avoids anthropometric mismatch. These adjustments can be performed using mechanical, electrical, pneumatic or hydraulic means. Most cars for example incorporate systems to adjust seat height and steering wheel position. Similarly, many office chair designs allow height and back rest tilt adjustment.

Domestic equipment, such as the ironing board, are also manufactured with several height adjustment positions to increase the population that can use it in an ergonomically appropriate position.

Figure E.2.11 represents a population distribution curve, in which the broad population range is possible because of device adjustability.

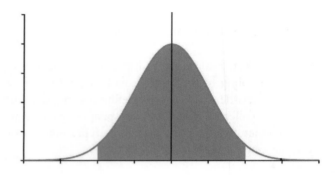

Figure E.2.11 User group accommodated by designing for adjustability

E.2.12 Compare the collection of static anthropometric data with the collection of dynamic anthropometric data.

© IBO 2007

Anthropometry is the study of human body properties such as height, mass and volume, and is used extensively in the design of consumer goods.

Static data is easy to collect because the subject is not moving. Measurements are made between joints using standardised equipment such as callipers, as these hard bony points are well defined.

Dynamic data is obtained while the subject is moving and while quantitative data is more difficult to obtain, is often of greater use because it demonstrates the range and ease with which movements can be made.

E.2.13 Describe the instruments used in the collection of anthropometric data.

© IBO 2007

A number of instruments are used to obtain anthropometric data. The main criteria for such instruments is that they are calibrated and are of sturdy design to ensure they provide reliable results.

Sliding calliper: Sliding calipers, also known as Vernier calipers, allow measurement to an accuracy of 0.01mm. The calipers, shown in Figure E.2.13a, have two arms, one fixed and the other a moveable arm that slides along the scale. Accurate measurement is provided by a second scale (the Vernier scale) on the moveable arm.

Figure E.2.13a Sliding calipers

Flexible tapes: Circumferential measurements of the body can be made with a flexible tape. Cloth tape, also known as tailor's tape can be used for such measurements, although these can be subject to stretching, so that flexible metal tapes are preferred. These tapes do not have the curved profile typically seen with builder's tape measures, as this would prevent the even flexing of the tape during measurement.

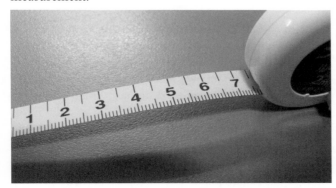

Figure E.2.13b A flexible metal tape

Stadiometer: The stadiometer, shown in Figure E.2.13c, is used to measure vertical distance from the floor to the top of the head of a person standing. A horizontal headboard is attached to a vertical track. The subject to be measured is placed against the vertical scale and the headboard moved down until it touches the head. Height is then read from the scale or recorded from a digital read-out.

Sitting height table: This instrument is a modification of the Stadiometer and is used to measure the vertical distance from the floor or the seat to the top of the head of a person seated in an upright position. The subject is seated such that the shank of the leg is vertical and the head is such that the Frankfort line is horizontal. The Frankfort line is a line connecting the ear hole with the bottom of the eye socket. A horizontal headboard is lowered onto the head and measurements recorded.

Figure E.2.13c Height measurement using a Stadiometer

Skinfold Calipers: The skinfold calipers shown in Figure E.2.13d are used to determine the amount of subcutaneous body fat by gently pinching a fold of skin. Although skin thickness is generally uniform over the body, the pattern of fat deposition is not. Two regions have been standardized for testing, the triceps and subscapular skinfold (on the back just below the scapular).

Figure E.2.13d Skinfold calipers

Torso callipers: These instruments are available in a number of forms as indicated in Figure E.2.13e. The torso calipers allow measurements of parts of the body such as the torso, where a chest depth measurement might be required.

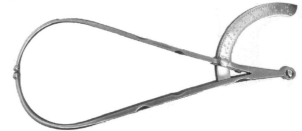

Figure E.2.13e Torso calipers

Harpenden anthropometer: The Harpenden anthropometer, shown in Figure E.2.13f, consists of set of measuring instruments that contains a measuring beam with extensions, along with straight and curved arms. Depending on the measurements to be performed, the selected arms are secured to the beam. One arm is fixed while the other can slide along the beam and is accurate to the nearest millimetre. With the beam extensions in place, measurements of up to two metres can be made.

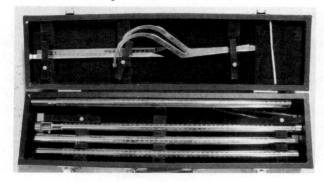

Figure E.2.13f Harpenden anthropometer kit

Laser: New technology now allows the scanning of objects and conversion of data into computer data that is three-dimensional.

Using 3D computer modelling programs, 3D-scanned objects can be rotated, manipulated, tested in virtual environments and even animated on a computer screen. Once an object has been 3D scanned, the 3D computer model can be converted into industry standard computer formats. These files of digitised objects can be viewed and manipulated in a variety of different programs. Almost anything can be 3D scanned.

Examples of objects that can be 3D scanned include large buildings, mine sites, vehicles, people, household products, tooling, toys, archaeological artifacts, room interiors, art works and body parts.

> **E.2.14** Explain why it is difficult to obtain accurate anthropometric data using the equipment described in E.2.13.
>
> © IBO 2007

Anthropometric data is intended to represent the measurements of the nude body. Cultural restrictions however may prevent the ability to obtain data from unclothed subjects. In order to adjust for this situation, investigators make allowances for the type and thickness of the clothes worn.

Perhaps of even more importance is the need for measurements to be undertaken in a methodical, standardised manner that allows confidence in the data collection.

> **E.2.15** Identify an appropriate percentile range for the design of adjustable equipment.
>
> © IBO 2007

The percentile range generally considered appropriate is the 5th percentile of females and the 95th percentile of males. Because of the overlap in dimensions of the male and female population, this regime would account for approximately 95% of the user population if human dimensions were always in the same proportion. That is, that only 5% of the population would not be accommodated within the adjustable range of the equipment. Unfortunately human dimensions are not always in the same proportion, and a tall person can have short arms and a short person may have proportionately longer arms. Multivariate analysis is used to account for all variations and means that more than 5% of the population may be excluded on one or more dimension using the 5th to 95th percentile range described above.

However, the cost of accommodating all possible combinations increases dramatically past this range and in most situations is not justified. Figure E.2.15 shows an operator sitting on an adjustable chair in front of a computer screen that is also adjustable. While the desk may be of a standard design and height, the other elements in the arrangement together should accommodate most of the user population.

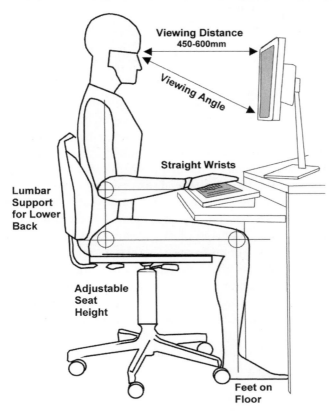

Figure E.2.15 An operator sitting at a workstation after adjusting equipment appropriately

Labels in figure:
- Viewing Distance 450-600mm
- Viewing Angle
- Straight Wrists
- Lumbar Support for Lower Back
- Adjustable Seat Height
- Feet on Floor

E.2.16 Explain how designers use primary and secondary anthropometric data in solving a design problem.

Primary data: collected by the designer, who performs anthropometric measurements on the proposed user group. Because they are performed on user group, it relates directly to the intended population.

Secondary data: collected from a database of anthropometric measurements. Such databases are often national in nature.

E.2.17 Define biomechanics.

The study of the mechanical laws relating to the movement of living organisms particularly in relation to animals and the human body.

E.2.17 Discuss the importance of biomechanics to the design of a given artifact.

Within the design of any device or product are a number of assumptions made by the designer regarding the biomechanical capacities of the user population. That is to say, that successful operation assumes that sufficient pressure will be able to be brought to bear to push and activate a button, or toggle a switch on a control panel, or that sufficient force can be applied to turn the handle of a can opener or corkscrew.

While assumptions are made in designs, these assumptions are based on anthropometric measurements establishing the population distributions for capabilities such as strength, dexterity and fine motor control.

Age related muscle weakness and a number of medical conditions such as Arthritis, Parkinson's disease, Multiple Sclerosis, etc exist that significantly impact on the assumed capabilities. In order to accommodate these groups of users, special adaptations or modifications may be required, either to the original design, or through the development of adaptive technologies that amplify biomechanical capabilities, such as those shown in Figure E.2.17.

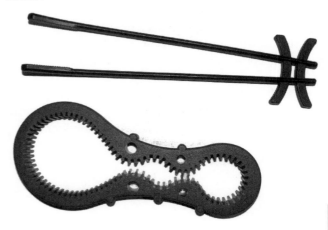

Figure E.2.17 Two examples of biomechanical aids, represented by chopsticks, and a rubber grip for undoing tight lids of various sizes

Further Reading

Human Scale Ergonomics
http://www.youtube.com/watch?v=S_F-yaQ4Xqc&feature=related

Taking Measurements
www.fantaproject.org/downloads/pds/anthro_5.pdf

OPTION

E3 RESEARCH AND TESTING

E.3.1 List four types of data scales.

American psychologist, Stanley Smith Stevens developed the theory of scales of measurement in 1946. He proposed four types of data measurement scales:

- nominal
- ordinal
- interval
- ratio data.

These four data scales may be further categorized into two groups; categorical and continuous. Nominal and ordinal scales are categorical data, while interval and ratio scales constitute continuous data.

E.3.2 Describe nominal scale.

Nominal means 'by name'. As such the nominal scale deals with the classification or division of objects into discrete groups each of which is identified with a name.

The scale does not provide a measure of magnitude within or between categories. An example of a nominal scale would be organisation into: plant, animal or mineral.

E.3.3 Describe ordinal scale.

The ordinal scale is one that deals with the order or position of items. An ordinal scale can consist of words, letters, symbols or numbers arranged in a hierarchical order. The difference between the items on the scale is not indicated so a quantitative assessment cannot be made. An example of an ordinal scale would be a ranking such as: 1st, 2nd, 3rd, 4th, etc. The Mohs hardness scale also represents an ordinal scale.

E.3.4 Describe interval scale.

An interval scale is organised into even divisions or intervals such that the difference between the divisions or intervals is of equal size although there is no natural zero. This means that measurements using an interval scale can be subjected to numerical or quantitative analysis although the zero is arbitrarily defined. An example of an interval scale would be the Celsius temperature scale where the temperature divisions are equal, although the use of the freezing temperature of water is arbitrarily defined as zero (0°C). Because of this, a meaningful statement of the ratio of one value on the scale relative to another cannot be made. For example a temperature of 40°C is not twice as hot as 20°C. The Lickert scale commonly used in consumer surveys is another example of an ordinal scale.

E.3.5 Describe a ratio scale.

A ratio scale is similar to the interval scale although a true zero exists. Height and weight are examples of a ratio scale since a zero measurement is possible. The Kelvin temperature scale is also a ratio scale because a natural zero exists. The Richter scale of earthquake intensity is also an example of a ratio scale, in which zero represents no earth movement. In this case each unit on the scale represents a order of magnitude on a base 10 logarithmic scale.

E.3.6 Explain the relevance of using the different rating scales to design contexts.

Human interaction with the environment occurs on a spectrum from the precise and quantitative at one end to the more qualitative experiential at the other. It is often necessary within this spectrum to assess and rank experiences and to measure outcomes using different scales.

In the design of a car for instance, an ordinal scale might be used to assess preferences on stylistic or aesthetic grounds among a number of alternative designs, while a ratio scale would be used to assess differences in fuel economy. A nominal scale would place the car designs into categories such as small, medium, large or SUV.

E.3.7   Describe the human information
         processing system.

Information about our surroundings is continually being supplied by our senses of sight, hearing, touch, smell and taste. This information is sent to the brain for integration and processing. The brain then provides signals to the body's muscles to take the required action. An example of this would be when driving a car; operations such as such as changing gears, braking or accelerating are a direct response to external stimuli. Given sufficient time, an experienced driver often performs these processes without conscious effort. It is this level of familiarity with the vehicle controls that is called upon in times of emergency to manoeuvre the vehicle to safety.

E.3.8   Explain that the human information
         processing system can be represented by
         an information flow diagram.

In the flowchart below, Figure E.3.8, the arrows represent the flow of information through the system. The boxes represent functional elements in the processing chain, where information is processed.

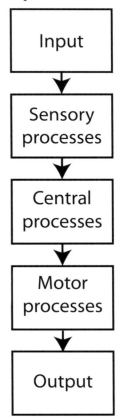

Figure E.3.8 Flow chart representation of the human information processing system

E.3.9   Apply the information flow diagram to
         particular contexts.

When using a mobile phone, the information flow diagram to make a telephone call the process might be represented as shown.

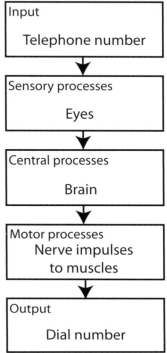

Figure E.3.9a Mobile phone call information flow diagram

When asked a question, the information flow diagram demonstrating the process might be represented as shown.

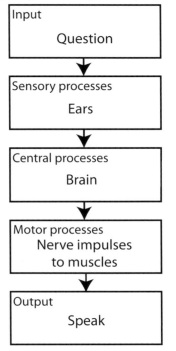

Figure E.3.9b Question information flow diagram

E.3.10 Outline how the flow process described in E.3.9 may break down.

A breakdown in the information processing chain could occur at any stage.

The information input could be incompatible with the sensory receptors. In the processes given in E.3.9 for example, the input may be too high in frequency to be detected.

Sensory receptors may have degraded, as occurs with macular degeneration.

At the central processing stage, the incoming information may be incorrect, no suitable responses to it may be available or damage to the central processor may prevent processing, as may arise through damage associated with a stroke.

The motor output stage may be unable to perform the actions specified by the central processing unit.

E.3.11 Outline how motor outputs may be inhibited if the physical fit between the person and the environment is wrong.

If the motor outputs required from a process are incompatible with the capacities and capabilities of an individual due to age, skill level, disability, infirmity or frailty they will be severely impeded.

Young children may not have the size, strength, fine motor control, or skill to perform some tasks, while those at the other end of the spectrum in old age may have similar problems. People with disabilities, such as arthritis and Parkinson's disease, may also not have the fine motor control required.

Further Reading

Scales of Measurement
http://people.math.sfu.ca/~cschwarz/Stat-301/Handouts/node5.html

E.4 MODELLING

E.4.1 Define manikin, ergonome, appearance prototype and functional prototype.

Manikin: A life-sized 3D human doll used for modelling, education and testing. Manikins may be a physical models such as a fashion manikin and the crash test dummy or a 3D computer model.

Ergonome: An ergonome is a physical model of a human body usually in 2D form such as a cut out paper pattern, although a 3D form, such as a 'Barbie™' doll, can be used. The ergonome must have moveable limbs that allow it to be posed. The dimensions of the ergonome should correspond with an anthropometric percentile and the surroundings scaled appropriately.

Appearance prototype: This physical representation closely resembles the product in appearance but is not functional. It may be made from a variety of materials e.g. clay, wood, plaster, foam or plastic.

Functional prototype: This type of physical model is capable of operating in a manner expected of the finished product and is used to test the functionality and usability of the product.

E.4.2 Outline the use of manikins to represent human factors data.

E.4.3 Discuss advantages and disadvantages of the use of manikins to represent human factors data.

Advantages: Fashion outlets routinely use manikins to display clothing because it allows customers see how an outfit will look. Similarly, architectural spaces and products can more easily be assessed for issues such as access, reach, size etc. Manikins can also be relatively cheap and easy to use. Computer generated 3D manikins can be used to model a wide range of body proportions, allowing designs to be checked quickly against unusual combinations.

Disadvantages: Because manikins are based on a certain body size and shape they can only give an approximate, and perhaps idealized, indication to a customer of how clothing will look on them. Some limitations also exist with regard to adjustability, in order to model a range of anthropometric percentiles.

Ergonomes are useful for assessing the relationship of body parts to spatial arrangements, such as to a chair or desk. Because they are relatively small, they are easily moved and can be quickly adjusted. They may even be employed to investigate equipment layout in relation to human movement.

Because ergonomes are quickly constructed and cheap, a range of anthropometric percentiles can be investigated in relation to a proposed layout. This allows many adjustments to be considered in a short space of time, eliminating unnecessary costs if full scale models were used. The small in scale, measurements and adjustments performed at this level however, give only an approximation of the final solution.

Because an appearance prototype looks like the final product, assessments of aesthetic factors such as size, shape, colour, texture and even weight can be made and since it is not intended to be functional, it can be made from a variety of cheap materials such as foam.

Such models are often used in advertising and marketing roles to give customers a look at an upcoming product.

The appearance prototype also gives others in the product development chain a chance to evaluate the product. Production engineers, for example, are able to examine the design and begin assessing manufacturing methods and materials which feed into calculations of tooling, production rates and costs.

Functional prototypes allow testing of the product with members of the potential user population to assess issues of usability and functionality.

Because the user population interacts with the prototype, designers are able to assess whether the prototype functions operate as intended under realistic conditions and that users are satisfied with that functionality. Issues of potential misuse and ambiguity of instructions and controls can also be determined, allowing adjustment before the final product is released.

Cardboard modelling is a fast, inexpensive way to see how something will look, it allows an initial assessment of aesthetics and user interfaces. Because it is made from cardboard there is not a large financial or emotional investment in the model. The Dyson company reportedly built 5000 cardboard prototypes before being satisfied with their original Dual™ Cyclone Technology vacuum cleaner.

Figure E.4.10a Prototype Dyson vacuum cleaner

Once the fundamental layout of the product has been established with a cardboard model, detailed Computer Aided Design (CAD) drawings are prepared.

OPTION

Clay has been the traditional medium for the production of appearance models and allowed issues of aesthetics to be evaluated. Models may be sculpted by hand or machine. Figure E.10.4b shows a full scale clay model of a Series 3 BMW. Some actual parts such as wheels, exhaust pipes or door handles may be added for realism.

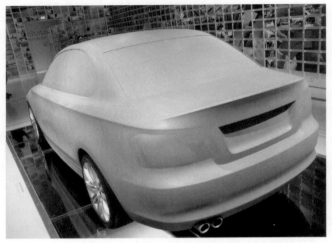

Figure E.4.10b BMW 3 series clay prototype

Image by Biso (Own work) [GFDL (www.gnu.org/copyleft/ fdl.html) or CC-BY-3.0 (www.creativecommons.org/ licenses/by/3.0)], via Wikimedia Commons

While such models are still sometimes manufactured, newer materials and processes have emerged. These include moulding from the thermoplastic known as Polymorph. This plastic is supplied in granular (pellet) form. The pellets soften with the application of heat and become pliable at a temperature around 62—65°C. Hot water is sufficient to soften the pellets. In its flexible form, polymorph may be moulded into any shape. It hardens at room temperature and once cooled, the Polymorph model becomes a tough, machinable solid with the consistency and colour of nylon. Being a thermoplastic, the model may be reformed again and again, through renewed applications of heat.

A more expensive, but increasingly attractive, method of producing an appearance prototype is through rapid prototyping by Selective Laser Sintering (SLS). In this process, sometimes called 3D printing, a thin layer of thermoplastic powder is sprayed over a moveable table and a laser used to fuse parts of the powder, based on computer instructions derived from a CAD drawing. Once a layer has fused, the bed lowers slightly and another layer of powder introduced ready to be fused. This process continues until a 3D model has been produced.

Further Reading

Akaoka, E., Ginn, T. & Vertegaal, R. (2010). *DisplayObjects: Prototyping Functional physical interfaces on 3D styrofoam, paper or cardboard models.* [http://tei-conf.org/10/uploads/Program/p49.pdf]

Designing success from failure [http://www.innovationmagazine.com/innovation/ volumes/v7n2/spotlight1.shtml]

FG Clay Model Falcon Ute http://www.forddiscovery.com/news/fg-clay-model- falcon-ute.htm

Heat/Voltage Reactive Materials [http://www.mindsetsonline.co.uk/images/ catalogue2011/1.Materials.pdf]

How to prototype http://www.inventor-strategies.com/how-to-prototype

James Dyson Foundation. *Build it, break it* [http://media.dyson.com/downloads/JDF/Poster_9_ Build_It_Break_It.pdf]

James Dyson Foundation: *Teachers Pack* http://media.dyson.com/downloads/JDF/JDF_Teachers_ Pack.pdf

Modelling ECT Products http://www.ectinschools.org/page. php?m=249&ps=212&p=758

Polymorph Design [http://www.polymorphdesign.com/ ProductDevelopment.html]

Richardson, S. *Designing Modern Britain: Key Stage 2 Teachers Pack.* Design Museum, London, UK. http://designmuseum.org/media/item/608/0/Designing_ Modern_Britain_KS2_pack.pdf

Young Technologist's Handbook, Version 1.1 : Ergonomics http://www.newbattle.org.uk/Departments/CDT/ Resources/PD/Introduction%20to%20Product%20 Design%204%20-%20Ergonomics/TEP%20Ergonomics. pdf

E5 HEALTH AND SAFETY LEGISLATION

> **E.5.1** Describe the objectives of product safety testing.
>
> © IBO 2007

Safety tests are conducted to ensure products comply with existing standards, regulations and legislation. The overall aim of safety testing is to reduce opportunities for accidents to occur. Testing may also provide products with certification that allows them access to markets. Certification also provides evidence to consumers that a product meets or exceeds certain requirements and may give consumers more confidence to purchase one product over another.

> **E.5.2** Identify the general human factors contributing to accidents.
>
> © IBO 2007

An accident may be generally described as an event that happens unexpectedly and unintentionally, as a direct result of human activity, typically resulting in damage or injury. Human factors that are contributory to accidents may be categorized into three interrelated criteria: the job, the individual worker and the organization.

The job, including elements such as the:
- type of task
- workload or time constraints
- design of signage and controls
- difficulty or complexity of tasks
- repetitive nature of some tasks causing boredom or apathy
- physical working environment (noise, dust, dirt, temperature, ventilation, lighting etc.).
- equipment type and design (ergonomic design, hazards, guards etc.).

The individual, including personal traits such as their:
- perception of risk
- general attitude or behaviour
- decision making requirements
- level of training or competence
- physical or mental limitations and strengths.

The organization, incorporating factors affecting individuals and groups including:
- policies and procedures
- patterns of work (e.g. shift work)
- pressures of time and or resources
- workplace culture and staff morale
- quality of communications and leadership
- certification, risk assessments, levels of supervision.

> **E.5.3** Outline the factors that contribute to thermal comfort in office and other working environments.
>
> © IBO 2007

The British Standard BS EN ISO 7730 defines thermal comfort as: *'that condition of mind which expresses satisfaction with the thermal environment.'*

From this definition it can be seen thermal comfort is a psychological state of mind i.e. whether an individual feels hot or cold. Thermal comfort, particularly in office spaces, can be a critical factor in determining staff morale and productivity. Thermal comfort for office spaces can be difficult to achieve however, considering there would be a range of psychological responses to the environment. It is generally considered that when 80% of a given population feels comfortable, then a situation of 'reasonable comfort' is achieved.

Air temperature alone is not a valid indicator of thermal comfort. Many factors influence thermal comfort and are essentially grouped into either environmental or individual factors including:

Environmental factors:
- air temperature
- radiant temperature - has the strongest influence on humans due to absorptive nature of the human body, measured with a globe thermometer
- air velocity – movement of air
- humidity – amount of water vapour in the atmosphere.

Personal factors:
- clothing – acting as insulation
- metabolic heat - this is produced by individual's burning calories to produce energy, given off as heat even while at rest. Body weight, sex, age and state of health, all influence an individual's metabolic rate.

OPTION

E.5.4 Discuss the legislative requirements for temperature in the workplace.

© IBO 2007

The HSE, (Health and Safety Executive), is Britain's national independent regulator of occupational health and safety, given the mandate to monitor and act in the interest of public safety to reduce workplace accidents and injury.

Regulations developed by the HSE do not state a maximum or minimum temperature. The Workplace, (Health, Safety and Welfare), Regulations 1992 Approved Code of Practice states: *'The temperature in workrooms should provide reasonable comfort without the need for special clothing. Where such a temperature is impractical because of hot or cold processes, all reasonable steps should be taken to achieve a temperature which is as close as possible to comfortable. Workroom means a room where people normally work for more than short periods.'*

Previously the HSE has determined thermal comfort zones for workers generally lie between 16°C and 30°C. It clarified this range, indicating that greater physical exertion could be tolerated at the lower end of the spectrum, while the upper end would require more sedentary activities.

The current legislation only enforces the lower value of 16°C as a minimum, but quotes research indicating discomfort, reduced productivity and the potential for an increase in accident rates at temperatures over 24°C. The legislation, however, provides no right for workers to vacate the workplace in conditions of extremes of heat or cold, unless conditions exist where there is: *'serious, imminent and unavoidable danger'* (Management of Health and Safety at Work Regulations, 1992).

The World Health Organisation, (WHO), provides similar guidelines to the HSE and uses a figure of 25°C for maximum workplace air temperatures.

E.5.5 Outline the legislative requirements for decibel levels for working with machinery.

© IBO 2007

The aim of noise regulations or legislation is to protect the long term hearing of workers' by limiting their exposure to excessive noise. Excessive noise in the work place can also cause permanent ringing in the ears (tinnitus).

In the UK, the level at which employers must provide hearing protection and hearing protection zones is now 85 decibels (daily or weekly average exposure) and the level at which employers must assess the risk to workers' health and provide them with information and training is now 80 decibels. There is also an exposure limit value of 87 decibels, taking account of any reduction in exposure provided by hearing protection, above which workers must not be exposed. Figure E.5.5 shows personal protective equipment that may be specified for use in noisy environments.

In Europe, the legislation calls for noise risks to be eliminated at their source or reduced to a minimum. This legislation is designed to make manufacturers of equipment reduce noise risks. Directive 98/37/EC, states that machinery should be, 'designed and constructed (so) that risks resulting from the emission of airborne noise are reduced to the lowest level'. This document also establishes daily exposure limits to 87dB.

Figure E.5.5 Ear protection - ear muffs

E.5.6 Discuss the legislative incentives to incorporate human factors into product design.

© IBO 2007

Legislation requires the incorporation of human factors into product design, enforcing the meeting of specific standards and regulations for manufacturers to:

- incorporate elements of universal design to cater for users with a disability
- meet legislative requirements on materials, manufacturing and quality for the granting of import/export licenses
- minimize their exposure to litigation as an outcome of cases filed against poorly functioning or faulty products, compromising the safety of users.

E.5.7   Describe the methods used for identifying hazards and evaluating risks.

© IBO 2007

Methods for detecting, evaluating and assessing risks include scenario analysis, fault tree analysis and risk assessment.

Scenario analysis is commonly employed as a predictive approach to determining future sales of a new product. It has also proved useful when assessing risks associated with introduction of new products. The approach analyses, human behaviour, usage, context and product design. Employing this approach, researchers can gather human factors data identifying accident patterns. These patterns may then be inform questionnaires, strategically targeting users, the task, the product, and the context. Where appropriate, decisions can be made to modify the product or the usage of the device to prevent accidents, injuries and product failure.

Postma and Liebl (2005), state; 'we have found this approach particularly useful for technology and product assessments when the risks and opportunities of innovations have to be evaluated. For example, one would ask in which contexts a product would have to be used in order to provide maximum utility or damage. For a brand, one would investigate in which contexts, including functional aspects and aspects of use as well as the symbolic aspects, it would develop optimally or would be damaged most seriously, etc.'

Fault tree analysis, (FTA), is a widely used method in system reliability and failure probability analysis. A graphical representation similar to a flowchart is generated to show failures and their causes.

The process allows designers to concentrate on safety critical areas of design and produce solutions to minimize or remove incidence or impact. For a small investment in time, FTA can provide the extra assurance required of safety-critical projects.

When used in conjunction with the traditional functional verification techniques, the end product is a system with safer operational characteristics than prior to the application of the FTA technique.

Figure E.5.7 shows the series graphic symbols used in FTA including:

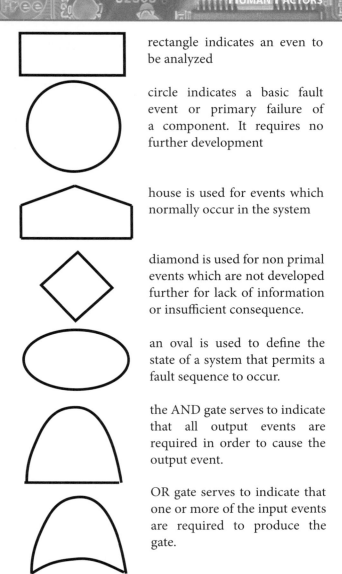

rectangle indicates an even to be analyzed

circle indicates a basic fault event or primary failure of a component. It requires no further development

house is used for events which normally occur in the system

diamond is used for non primal events which are not developed further for lack of information or insufficient consequence.

an oval is used to define the state of a system that permits a fault sequence to occur.

the AND gate serves to indicate that all output events are required in order to cause the output event.

OR gate serves to indicate that one or more of the input events are required to produce the gate.

Figure E.5.7a Fault tree analysis symbols

Image and accompanying text modified from NASA Software Safety Handbook

Risk assessment matches frequency of events against their potential harm to produce a matrix which, when coupled with a hierarchy of controls, provides designers with to opportunities manage safety and risk within product design. Figure E.5.7b shows a typical risk assessment matrix, where the green colours indicate lower risk potential leading to the red sector of potentially dangerous events.

Where a risk assessment has been conducted and a matrix plotting severity against frequency produced, a hierarchy of controls may be applied to guide designers in appropriate means of dealing with the risks. The hierarchy of controls documents actions to be taken ranging from most severe to least severe.

OPTION

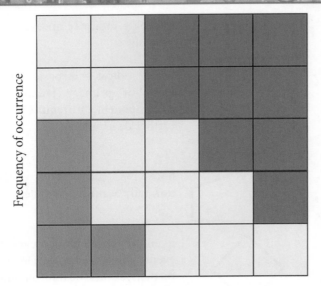

Severity of consequence

Figure E.5.7b Risk assessment matrix

Risk assessment hierarchy of controls

Eliminate: This requires designers to remove toxic or hazardous materials or redesign the product to perform safely

Substitute: Where hazards cannot be removed, substitution of a less hazardous material or feature may be required e.g. substituting natural-based pigments for lead-based paints.

Reduce: Use of smaller quantities such as lower voltages in electrical appliances, reduction of soldered joints.

Engineering controls: such as introduction of alarms or auto shutdown for appliances such as earth leakage circuit breakers, guards, ventilation etc.

Administrative procedures: operational advice/training, manuals and product usage warnings.

Personal protective equipment (PPE): such as safety glasses, gloves, footwear etc.

> E.5.8 Explain how human factors specialists determine adequate product safety.
>
> © IBO 2007

Human factors specialists work to design products to fit users rather than users adapting to products. They use a variety of testing procedures to determine if products firstly meet government legislation, standards and requirements, before conducting human factors evaluations.

Usability and safety tests: These emulate the device in use. In this situation, target market subjects, selected across a range of different ages, genders and demographics perform common or safety critical operations. Evaluation of these tests may be through observation by experts, post-test interviews, questionnaires or focus groups. Users are often encouraged to speak while they are interacting with product so researchers can gather information on the total user experience. Most regulatory bodies require manufacturers to conduct some form of usability testing to validate product safety prior to approval or certification.

Figure E.5.8a User trials - space suit safety and functionality

Image by Bandgirl807 (Own work) [CC-BY-3.0 (www. creativecommons.org/licenses/by/3.0)], via Wikimedia Commons

Focus groups: Most often involving an interviewer guiding a small group discussion on product experiences, designers gather both negative and positive evaluations.

Bench testing: This technique is often a precursor to engaging actual users. It provides an analytical assessment of performance characteristics conducted by human factors experts. This stage is designed to identify usability problems in terms of severity, frequency of occurrence and potential consequences. Identified problems assist in refining designs before releasing for target market user trials. Bench testing would also be performed on returned products, warranty claims or failed devices.

Multiple rounds of testing using a variety of procedures may be employed as various product iterations are generated.

Figure E.5.8b NASA's Virtual Airport Tower Ames Research Center California

NASA's Virtual Airport Tower shown in Figure E.5.8b, is a highly sophisticated, full-scale, simulation facility that emulates Level 5 air traffic control towers and the busiest airports. It provides the platform to conduct in-depth human factors studies.

Further reading

Jordan, P. W. (2001). *An Introduction To Usability 1st edition.* CRC Press. Taylor & Francis Ltd. London.

E6 DESIGN FOR USABILITY

> E.6.1 Identify three characteristics of good user–product interfaces.
>
> © IBO 2007

Good user-interface design exhibits the following features:
- low user error rate
- high levels of user satisfaction
- easy to learn - simple uncomplicated, uncluttered interfaces
- easy to use - intuitive design, controls appear where anticipated and actions perform as expected
- easy to remember - functions and operation are performed over time with an ease of repeatability and high level of competence retention.

> E.6.2 Explain the disadvantages of user–product interfaces that are not well organized and cannot be learnt intuitively and remembered easily.
>
> E.6.3 Discuss the impact of memory burden on the user-friendliness of a product.
>
> © IBO 2007

Most consumers want to use a product 'straight out of the box.' Easy to use intuitive interface design allows new operators to quickly become competent in the basic operations. Good user interface design can be the discriminating factor for consumers Levels of customer satisfaction or frustration in their interactions with the interface can tarnish the reputation of an otherwise sound product. This can be the contributing factor between product acceptance and failure in the marketplace.

Poorly designed, less intuitively organized interfaces place a high level of learning through trial and error. They also increase the memory burden placed on consumers who may use the product intermittently and be destined to repeat the learning process over. When simple operations require higher levels of concentration or memory, the full feature set of a product would tend to less well exploited. An easy to use interface with high levels of success generates confidence in the user and encourages further use of the device.

Good user-interface design exhibits the following features:

- low user error rate
- high levels of user satisfaction
- easy to learn - simple uncomplicated, uncluttered interfaces
- easy to use - intuitive design, controls appear where anticipated and actions perform as expected
- easy to remember - functions and operation are performed over time with an ease of repeatability and high level of competence retention.

Figure E.5.8c A modern 'glass cockpit' - a state-of-the-art user interface.

E.6.4   Explain why it is difficult for designers to develop simple intuitive user–product interfaces.

© IBO 2007

Product designers have a complete and intimate knowledge of the device and interface design. It is difficult for them to understand the experience of a novice user or someone who may be less familiar or less confident with typical interface configurations.

Redevelopment of products through the introduction of improved or additional features may also only serve to exacerbate the situation as interfaces receive upgrades that may only add greater levels of complexity along with the intended increased functionality.

E.6.5   Define paper prototyping.

E.6.6   Explain that paper prototyping is one example of participatory design.

© IBO 2007

Paper prototyping is a method for quickly and cheaply designing, testing, and refining user-product interfaces. Paper prototyping is also known as low-fi (low-fidelity) prototyping. The paper prototypes may be hand-drawn sketches or printed screen shots. This low technology response to designing allows for rapid construction and quick changes or design iterations. Participants in the design process more easily focus on design features and functionality rather than being distracted or intimidated by the technology of a more detailed high-fidelity mock-up.

Because the testing is process based and technology independent, multi-disciplinary teams can easily collaborate.

E.6.7   Explain the roles of the facilitator, the user, the computer and the observer in a paper prototyping session.

© IBO 2007

Usability testing is designed to provide an opportunity to gather realistic, independent data from potential users. The process can be less intimidating than reviewing a mock up of highly technological interface, and provides fast, inexpensive feedback.

Facilitator: someone specifically trained to conduct usability trials. Their role is to settle the participant and explain the expectations of the session and how to operate the paper user interface. The facilitator may sit with the user to provide any necessary clarification.

Computer: a person manipulating the paper interface to simulate the responses of a real interface. This person cannot assist the user nor provide any additional explanations.

Users: individuals representative of the target market.

Observers: mostly members of the design team, quietly observing the user while taking notes. They may ask questions after the test has been completed.

E.6.8   Explain the advantages of paper prototyping.

© IBO 2007

The advantages of paper prototyping include:

- inexpensive
- ease of implementation
- fast to develop and modify
- no technology or coding required
- realistic feedback provided by target market
- promotes communication between members of the development team.

Further Reading

Rudd, J., Stern, K. & Isensee, S. 1996. *Low vs. high-fidelity prototyping debate.* Interactions. January:76-85.

Säde, S., & Battarbee, K. 2001. The third dimension in paper prototypes. Design by people for people: Essays on usability, ed R. Branaghan, pp. 203-212. Chicago: UPA.

E7 CONTEXTS

E.7.1   Outline three elements of anthropometric data used in the design of a mobile phone.

© IBO 2007

Product: mobile phone

Elements requiring anthropometric data for mobile phones fall into three general fields and are associated with:

Vision: This dimension concerns itself with data relating to visual acuity, (the ability of the eye to observe detail), viewing angles and on-screen glare

Hearing: Includes speaker volumes, vocal clarity, and the ability to discriminate frequencies

Physical contact: Refers to hand sizes, finger dexterity and range, and the ability to detect tactile sensations from keystrokes or vibration notifications.

Figure E.7.1 shows a small mobile phone and the relationship between keys, hand and finger sizes. It also illustrates the graphical nature of the screen and prioritization of images and data presented.

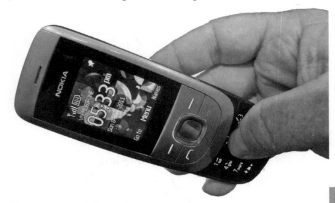

Figure E.7.1 Mobile phone

Image by Scottie Macquarie

E.7.2   Outline one design factor related to ease of use of the mobile phone that has compromised the use of human factors data.

© IBO 2007

Mobile phones have continued to shrink in size as improved technology allows more powerful configurations in smaller packages. Concerns have been raised over both the size of buttons and screens. Dexterity issues, relating to the use of thumbs, have been noted by experts in ergonomics. Smaller phones have enabled consumers to adapt their usage of the device to use their thumb instead of the forefinger, using the phone in a one-handed fashion. This in itself breaks the principles of ergonomic design. The design should adapt to the user, not the other way round.

A British newspaper, The Observer, (March 24th 2002), reported on a University of Warwick study: '..*carried out in nine cities around the world, shows that the thumbs of the younger generation have overtaken their fingers as the hand's most muscled and dexterous digit. The change affects those who have grown up with hand-held devices capable of text messaging, emailing and accessing internet services.*'

Unfortunately, research by the American Society of Hand Therapists also shows an increased incidence in patients presenting with a swelling at the base of the thumb attributed to the playing of video games and mobile phone usage.

E.7.3 Outline psychological human factors data that could be used in the design of a mobile phone.

© IBO 2007

It should come as no surprise that psychological human factors data would be used in the design and improvement of mobile phones. There is historical precedent for the use human factors data to develop telephones as precursors to mobile phone design.

Dr Alphonse Chapanis, (an industrial and human factors psychologist), worked on the development of push button phones while employed at Bell Telephone Laboratories in the early 1950s. Chapanis proposed a series of arrangements using buttons to replace the rotary mechanism in use at the time. He designed a 'population stereotype' test to find the preferred arrangement of numbers and letters on keys.

Today mobile phone design is carefully considered when targeting specific markets. Design variations in colour, shape, materials, use of backlighting and surface finish are all carefully combined to be attractive to different consumer groups. It is not just the functions and services available that sell mobile phones. Figure E.7.3 shows physical design variations that attempt to meet an individual's psychological needs.

Figure E.7.3 Variety of phone designs

E.7.4 Discuss the relationship between fashion and human factors in the design of the mobile phone.

© IBO 2007

Fashion is the cyclic change in style and appearance that is employed to increase the appeal of a product. Fashion trends should not affect the functionality of the product and should be carefully introduced after the gathering of human factors data. Stylistically, fashion trends determine the overall dimensions of phones, keypads and screens. They also influence colours and surface finishes. Trends in miniaturization can make phones more portable, however, this can also effectively make the technology more difficult to use.

E.7.5 Define aesthetic-usability effect.

© IBO 2007

Users may prioritize aesthetics over usabilty. They may perceive a desirable or pleasing design and translate or confuse this with ease of use or they may simply make a purchase based on brand power and social trends.

E.7.6 Discuss how the aesthetics of a mobile phone make it look easier to use and increase the probability of it being used, whether or not it is actually easier to use.

© IBO 2007

Marketing strategies often include endorsements from celebrities extolling the virtues and features of products. Many of these claims may be spurious, particularly for products that require very precise fits to human factor constraints. In these instances, individual consumers would be best served testing or trialling a product in a range of situations before making a purchasing decision.

System: kitchen

> E.7.7   Describe the concept of a work triangle in relation to kitchen layout.

In 1843, Catherine Beecher, authored, '*A Treatise on Domestic Economy.*' In her publication, she established guidelines for kitchen design. Mostly focussing on storage space for food, she also allocated separate spaces for food preparation. The cooking area was actually removed from the kitchen and often placed in an adjacent alcove. This design was clearly an attempt to maximize use of the workspace, but also was heavily influenced by food preservation, storage and transport technologies of the day.

Figure E.7.7a Beecher's 'model kitchen' bringing elements of ergonomics to kitchen design

In the 1950s, the Building Research Council School of Architecture, University of Illinois, remodelled industry experience to suit kitchen layout. Using practises adopted by Henry Ford, researchers took his 'workspace triangle' model and examined its functionality in a kitchen setting.

The 'workspace triangle' principle was used to arrange team members in such a fashion as to allow them to accomplish designated tasks within as small an area as possible. University of Illinois researchers determined kitchens revolved around the three basic functions of storage, preparation, and cooking. The kitchen work triangle concept appeared as a direct consequence of these basic functions. The outline defined by connecting standard appliances associated with each of these functions, (refrigerator, stove (cooktop) and sink) is a triangle.

Kitchen work triangles may be used to plan future designs or test the efficiency of existing kitchens.

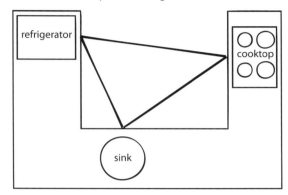

Figure E.7.7b Kitchen work triangle

> E.7.8   Explain the principles of the work triangle in relation to safety issues in a kitchen.
>
> E.7.9   Discuss the 'sequence of use' design principle as applied to kitchen design.

As with Ford's 'work triangle,' the kitchen triangle is designed to keep the three major workstations near the cook. Through-traffic should not cross this zone and placement of the apex of each triangle should be in a fashion that facilitates ease of movement and safety without being cramped.

The sequence of use in a kitchen triangle starts with food storage, proceeds to food preparation and completes with cooking. In this situation, placement of the refrigerator is most often the first to take place. The refrigerator is the most visited appliance in the kitchen and is used for many purposes, apart from those associated with kitchen triangle.

Once located, the refrigerator constitutes the food storage component of the triangle and as such should be associated with other food storage units such as cupboards. Foot traffic, entry and egress paths should be considered when placing this appliance.

The sink provides water for cooking and washing food, dishes or utensils. Many sinks are placed under windows and some compromises may be made here depending on the architecture of the building. Work surfaces and those associated with food preparation should be nearby the sink. The final consideration is the placement of the stove or cooktop. Here, movement may be with hot and/or heavy items, most often towards the food preparation area. Kitchen safety guidelines and modern health regulations preclude stoves or cooktops being placed under windows, or next to doors, to reduce potential fire hazards.

> **E.7.10** Outline three examples of the use of anthropometric data in kitchen design.
>
> © IBO 2007

Kitchens provide unique environments, workspaces and tasks. These require more information than may be found in traditional anthropometric databases.

Data is required measuring a range of kitchen activities including:

- bending or kneeling down to lower placed cupboards bench or preparation surface and heights for chopping, dishwashing or cooking
- reaching towards higher cupboards (potentially over workbenches) and shelves.

All of these tasks may also include lifting or carrying activities and in some circumstances hot and/or heavy items.

> **E.7.11** Outline psychological human factors data that could be used in kitchen design.
>
> © IBO 2007

Choice of materials, colours, surface textures and decorator items may also convey a stylistic impression. For example, stainless steel, shiny surfaces, downlighting, polished concrete and glass may be used to provide an industrial or commercial environment while use of warmer colours, textured surfaces and natural materials such as earthenware or brick may suggest a more bucolic feeling.

Colour theory may be used to enhance natural light, delineate spaces or provide a visual focus.

> **E.7.12** Discuss the differences in human factors data that may be relevant for a domestic kitchen compared to a commercial restaurant kitchen.
>
> © IBO 2007

There are many factors that discriminate between a domestic and a commercial kitchen. The kitchen space may have a large number of people, (kitchen assistant(s),

kitchen hand(s) and a Chef or Cook), all working within the one, often small environment. Constant movement of people and trolleys occurs both within and through the kitchen. Frequent direction changes and task-focused staff must negotiate this limited space with care.

Human factors data required in a commercial kitchen would revolve around the following areas;

Reaching or stretching: Extended forward reach over worktops or overhead reaching to cupboards/storage areas.

Reading/operating controls and displays: Variety of knobs and levers mostly located around waist/bench height, including stovetop or ovens, taps.

Traffic patterns: economical/efficient and safe movement of staff around confined space arranged around work patterns and predetermined rules.

Force exertion/lift: lifting of food buckets from floor to benchtop and large pots from preparation areas to stoves.

Postural requirements: long periods of standing and walking

Strength, grip, handling and dexterity: range of grip styles for carrying a variety of shapes, sizes and masses of implements and tools from knives to heavy saucepans. Frequent fine motor manipulation use of utensils for food preparation.

Air movement and ventilation: removal of heat, steam and oil vapours.

Other physical demands: disrupted patterns of work and

Figure E.7.12 Commercial kitchenImage by David Monniaux Creative Commons Attribution-Share Alike 3.0 Unported

E.7.13 Discuss how the layout of labeling information for kitchen appliances can be misleading to the user.

Labels on appliances should be both user friendly and reliable. Markings and scales for switches and controls should be placed near these components, however, care must be taken with placement of these markings particularly when controls may be moved or repositioned relative to the advice, potentially rendering the marking(s) useless or misleading.

Energy labels, assisting consumers with information relating to appliance efficiency also need to be informative without being overly technical. Consumers requiring more in-depth information relating to energy efficiency should be able to access it in a supplementary form, (pamphlets or users manuals) rather than having it directly incorporated into labeling.

Labels and markings should be designed through consumer usability trials.

E.7.14 Outline physiological human factors data that could be used when designing kitchen products.

Touch – When designing knobs, handles and switches forces relative to grip strength, torque required, textured or smooth surfaces, sensitivity to temperature, non-slip surfaces for floors or handles.

Sight – Legibility of instruction. Lines of sight for placing markings and size of fonts assisting readability over a distance

Hearing – audibility of appliance alarms, bells and buzzers

Further reading

Kishtwaria, J., Mathur, P. & Rana, A. (2007). *Ergonomic Evaluation of Kitchen Work with Reference to Space Designing*. J. Hum. Ecol. India. 21(1): pp. 43-46

E.7.15 Outline the influence of the psychological human factors of noise and temperature on the design of an open-plan office.

Environment: open-plan office

Open-plan office designs were popularized in the 1970s, when they were perceived to improve worker communication and productivity. Worker comfort and or satisfaction with the environment has been linked to productivity, so reaching an optimal solution in office design is not only a personnel imperative, but can also be a financial one. Considering salaries and staff training comprise the majority of costs in an office environment, it is important that businesses develop the most cost-efficient office design, considering the needs of their employees. The Lawrence Berkeley National Laboratory, Indoor Air Quality Resource Bank, (2010), claims; '*Work performance may be improved from a few percent to possibly as much as 10% by providing superior indoor environmental quality (IEQ).*'

Environmental psychology studies the relationship between an environment and how it affects its inhabitants. In this case, the environment under study is an office space. Typical psychological human factors in an indoor office environment include:

- lighting
- acoustics
- air quality
- temperature
- worker densities.

Open-plan offices are often developed to allow for greater worker density. This increases the need to deal with the pollutants generated by occupants. This may be in the form of air conditioning, which may present its own set of problems to be solved such as, air movement, optimal temperature, noise etc.

Open-plan offices allow for larger amounts of unrestricted space. This may be in the form of reducing the number of interior walls and replacing them with partitions or in some cases reducing the size of partitions themselves.

The purpose of removing or lowering walls is to remove barriers to communication and provide people with the feeling or perception of space. Partitions of reduced size also allow freer movement of air and distribution of light from windows. The disadvantages associated with this, however, include the reduction of barriers to general noise transfer, reduced personal privacy and the opportunity for greater visual distraction.

467

E.7.16 Discuss how the final design of an open-plan office is a compromise between individual space preferences and standardized design.

Standard space allocations in offices are often based around the requirements of job specific tasks, seniority or status within an organization. While open-plan offices free up communication and provide more public space there also exists a need for individuals to have their own personal space. The amount of personal space an individual requires varies and may be influenced by culture or upbringing. This comfort zone, or personal space, is also known as 'defensible space,' a termed coined by John Calhoun in the 1940s.

Defensible space is incorporated into office design to overcome the sense of overcrowding and the negative behaviours or feelings this may create. Through the judicious use of barriers or partitions, personal spaces may be created while still maintaining an open plan. The creation of areas such as this allows employees to customize their space within an office space improves the individuals feeling of comfort, safety and control.

Office space designers may use the; 'Physical Work Environment Satisfaction Questionnaire,' (PWESQ), to measure worker satisfaction and better inform their designs. This tool takes into account human factors relative to a worker's occupational health and safety including physical demands, work systems, environmental considerations, tools and equipment.

E.7.17 Discuss safety considerations that impact on the design of an open-plan office.

Like any other workplace, office spaces require a risk management approach to design and ongoing safety management. There are, however, a number of considerations that are more pertinent to office spaces than general safety provisions including:

Physical hazards include a range of considerations such as desk or monitor placement to reduce glare, chair design that is supportive and encourages good posture and even filing cabinets designed not to become tipping hazards when full.

Chemical hazards, including selection of paints and carpet with low VOC emission values. Placement of photocopiers and laser printers must also be considered due to production of airborne particles and vapours such as, ozone, selenium, carbon monoxide and carbon black.

Electrical hazards, such as damaged electrical cords are repaired by licensed electricians and checked regularly. Sufficient power access points are located conveniently, removing the need for power boards and overloading. Power and data points are located to remove the risk of cables creating a trip hazard.

Foot traffic areas and walkways must remain clear for ease of movement, while stairs and egress points are required to be well signposted and remain free from encumbrances for emergency evacuations.

Organizations such as the UK Health and Safety Executive offer online assessment of workplaces for individuals to review their current work environment.

E.7.18 Identify psychological and physiological factors that influence the design of office furniture.

Office furniture design and layout affects workers by addressing their physical and task needs, privacy needs, and need for recognition. The degree of fulfilment of these needs influences environmental satisfaction and therefore worker performance.

Arrangement of workspaces to provide a measure of private space also encourages workers to personalize their own area, improve their levels of comfort and make workers feel more secure.

When considering chair design, poor posture or protracted activities can cause back strain and/or fatigue for workers. The longer a worker is to remain seated, the more important chair design becomes. A chair that facilitates a natural body posture allows the body's muscles, ligaments and tendons to relax. Vertebrae are also better aligned and spaced, thus reducing pressure on discs. As a direct consequence both breathing and blood circulation are improved. Furniture such as chairs designed to replicate or support the body in maintaining a natural posture will better accommodate the users' physiological needs.

Adjustability also accommodates a range of user sizes, allows for customization to an individual's preferences and provides an opportunity for users to readjust the chair when seated for long periods.

E.7.19 Outline three examples of the use of anthropometric data in the design of office furniture.

© IBO 2007

One of the most frequently referenced anthropometric databases is the Natick studies (or ANSUR database) developed over two decades in the 1970s and 1980s using American military personnel. The Society of Engineers has since collected their own civilian-based data in 2000. Known as the Civilian American and European Surface Anthropometry Resource (or CAESAR), this document contains anthropometric measurements and 3D body scans of thousands of non-military, civilian individuals from the across the US and Europe.

In the US, the Business and Institutional Furniture Manufacturers Association (BIFMA) performance standards reference the Natick (military) studies for design purposes and have used these to develop standards for office furniture. Reviewed every five years by the American National Standards Institute (ANSI), these standards are intended to provide manufacturers and users with a common basis for evaluating furniture safety, strength and suitability.

Using these standards, work surfaces, chairs and reach envelopes are all examined using anthropometric data. Each of these categories may be divided further in subgroups requiring specific attention.

Some companies, providing customized furniture, use online services to gather anthropometric data from individuals. Below is listed typical information requested to design an ergonomic chair:

- desk height
- widest part of hips/thighs
- height/weight of occupant
- top of seat to top of shoulder
- top of seat to middle of lumbar curve
- top of seat to slightly under bent elbow
- from buttocks to back of knee (when seated)
- behind knee to under heel (wearing work shoes).

While the Natick studies are still used by BIFMA, CAESAR data is proving to be increasingly popular.

Further Reading

Sandom, C. & Harvey, R. S. (Editors) (2004). Human Factors for Engineers. The Institution of Engineering and Technology, London, United Kingdom.

Environment: car

E.7.20 Outline how the location and layout of car controls influence efficient use.

© IBO 2007

In the field of automotive engineering, the purpose of ergonomic design is to assure the highest degree of comfort, enhancing both efficiency and driver safety. Standard ISO CD 9242 defines usability as *effectiveness, efficiency and satisfaction with which specific users reach specific objectives in given environments*.

Vehicle controls do not have an intrinsic quality of usabiity but create this affect through their relationship to the user, the environment and the specific task.

Specific primary and secondary vehicle control considerations include accessibility, visibility, complexity, configuration and functionality. In the final analysis, the controls should be reachable and operable through simple and natural movements.

The image of the Ferrari F355 GT F1 dashboard, shown in Figure E.7.20, shows the layout of a modern dashboard with a significant number of features. Ergonomically, all of the displays necessary for driving are located within the driver's cone of vision. What is not readily apparent is the Formula One technology behind the redesign of the gearbox controls. While still using a manual gearbox, favoured by enthusiasts, it operates without a clutch pedal. Replacing the clutch pedal are sophisticated electronics, allowing the driver to change gears through the use of steering wheel mounted levers. Changing gears using this technology is done without the driver taking a hand from the wheel or manipulating a foot pedal.

Figure E.7.20 Car dashboard and controls

OPTION

E.7.21 Discuss how designers have used new technology to redesign the interiors of cars to improve human factors issues.

E.7.22 Discuss how designers have redesigned the interiors of cars to the benefit of passengers and drivers.

© IBO 2007

Designers and automotive engineers are employing human factors data and ergonomic studies in multi-disciplinary approaches using rapid prototyping, virtual reality or mechanical simulators.

Rapid prototyping reduces the design cycle time and allows for multiple design iterations to be tested. Physical models may be created to test for aesthetics or functionality.

Virtual reality technologies allow designers to simulate the performance of an object in a range of environments and contexts. Human factors may be examined at this point before the object physically exists. Computer models can be quickly constructed to test vehicle controls and displays for: accessibility, visibility and usability for a range of users.

Mechanical simulators most often consist of a driver's seat, steering wheel and pedal assembly. The device may use human models or manikins to test the efficiency of the design. In some instances haptic (force feedback) technology may be incorporated to replicate tactile sensations. These devices allow designers to test for fatigue, comfort, posture, reach etc. They may be modified or adjusted to test a range of alternatives.

Figure E.7.21 shows a military vehicle simulator employing a physical mechanical model in conjunction with virtual reality and force feedback.

E.7.21 Military vehicle simulator

Car interiors are often designed with modular or replaceable components to allow for mass customization and even after-market personalization provided by suppliers other than the original equipment manufacturer.

Development of synthetic fibres and technical fabrics assist designers to solve problems particularly associated with car interiors. Specific requirements including wear resistance, sound absorption, stain and moisture resistance on a range of surfaces such as door panels, boot liners, seat covers, head liners etc. These materials may also allow for variation and be used to tailor car models to specific markets.

Designers have not only created more interior space with careful selection of materials, but also incorporated a range of built-in storage opportunities for drivers and passengers alike.

Electronic device interfaces provide for opportunities to connect media players, DVD units and mobile phones for hands free operation. Trip computers or GPS navigation devices are now also commonly included, or may be specified as options.

Driver comfort is imperative, particularly for long distance driving to reduce fatigue and assist the driver to maintain focus. To this end, designers and vehicle manufacturers have developed multi-adjustable, body contoured seating, with ergonomically designed door and centre console armrests. Cabins are also equipped with climate controls to maintain comfortable levels of temperature and humidity.

E.7.23 Discuss how designers may overlook the implications for human factors when designing multifunctional electronic controls in cars.

© IBO 2007

The design of electronic devices can sometimes be overshadowed by the technology itself. Designers may become so focussed on what the technology is capable of that they lose sight of their overall goal – producing a usable device. On other occasions technology is developed simply because it can be done, rather than responding to a market or users' needs

E8 DIGITAL HUMANS

E.8.1 Define digital human and motion capture.

E.8.2 Explain how motion capture is used to digitally represent motion.

© IBO 2007

E.8.3 Identify the advantages of motion capture for digitally representing motion.

E.8.4 Explain how motion capture contributes to the development of a digital human.

© IBO 2007

Digital humans are computer-based models designed to assist researchers to simulate human biomechanics and predict how a real human body would react in a variety of situations and environments. The use of digital humans allows for the gathering of information relative to the range human motion, forces, fatigue, potential injury etc.

Motion capture technology is used to record, track and analyze movement. The process records movement through a series of snapshots generated many times per second. Special markers may be applied to strategic points of a moving human body to identify key pieces of geometry. The resultant changes in position of the figure(s) are recorded and easily digitized for playback or analysis.

Once recorded, motion animation such as in filmmaking, (as shown in Figure E.8.2), may be generated. The information may also be used directly for the purposes of motion study, or the interaction of human motion with the natural or built environments.

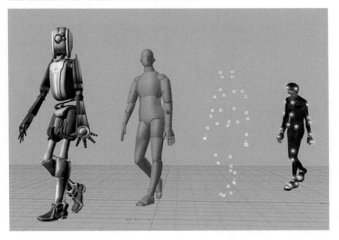

Figure E.8.2 Motion capture technology

Motion capture has been employed to assist with the understanding of human factors, physical limitations of users and product evaluation.

Motion capture saves time and creates more natural movements than the alternative, manual animation, but is limited to motions that are anatomically possible. Motion capture can reduce the cost of animation, which otherwise requires the animator to draw either each frame or key frames, that are then interpolated.

A motion capture session records the movements of the actor, not his or her visual appearance. The captured movements are mapped to a 3D human virtual model created by a computer artist. This process allows the computer model to replicate the movements and actions of the original human model.

E.8.5 Discuss how digital humans can enhance human factors research.

© IBO 2007

Digital humans, using software with an underlying physics engine may be used to replicate and calculate muscle force, efficient muscle action or fatigue. They may also identify effects of clothing on performance, model the dynamics of walking patterns and utilize the mathematical relationships between energy produced, heart rate and oxygen uptake. It is also possible to derive physiological indices such as the heart rate, breathing rate, carbon-dioxide production rate, and core temperature.

All of this data can be gathered automatically and simultaneously in a range of simulated environments, what if scenarios or hazardous situations that would be either too expensive or dangerous to reproduce using a human model.

Using statistics and data gathered from anthropometric tables and motion capture, digital humans employ complex algorithms to generate motion, posture, joint force etc. to predict responses to new situations or environments, previously untested.

HL

OPTION

E.8.6 Explain how digital humans enable the consideration of human factors early in the design cycle.

© IBO 2007

Digital human models are increasingly used early in product design to reduce product development time and costs. Manufacturing industry demands that products be designed for the comfort and accessibility of consumers as well as workplaces and the health and safety of employees. Digital human models assist manufacturers to examine designs from an ergonomic perspective. They allow designers to test virtual models and evaluate the performance of future products prior to the construction of a prototype.

Using digital humans early in the design cycle, designers can:

- save time and expensive resources
- test and evaluate products based on ergonomic factors
- take into account the range of sizes and shapes of users
- consider user safety factors in a range of environments
- establish physical use requirements and product serviceability
- review human factors in design before building physical prototypes.

E.8.7 Explain how digital humans can increase the speed of the product development cycle.

© IBO 2007

Digital human modelling, (DHM), can reduce the need for the production of physical prototypes. A range of parameters may be modelled and tested during product development, not only to optimize individual design factors, but to allow for the evaluation of the complex interplay between multiple modifications and their 'knock on' effects.

DHM and simulation in product design enables products to be developed more quickly, i.e. more design iterations in less time. This results in higher product quality, and meets human requirements more accurately. Products are safer as a result of more thorough analysis of safety aspects and improved productivity results from enhanced automation of the development process. Digital prototypes are also cheaper and faster to produce, test and modify than physical prototypes.

E.8.8 Explain the benefits of using digital humans in developing manufacturing plants and processes, maintenance and training.

© IBO 2007

Digital humans enable manufacturing plants to be developed more quickly and manual workflow to be optimized. They improve worker safety and reduce compensation costs resulting from accidents. Machines and other equipment can be positioned to optimize cycle time and avoid hazards. Manufacturing processes can be designed to eliminate inefficiencies and ensure optimal productivity. They can be used to ensure that people can access the parts and equipment needed to assemble products; check that workers can effectively use any hand tools needed to perform manual tasks; and check that all tasks can be performed safely without requiring inordinate strength or exposing people to risk of injury.

Using digital humans enables designers to ensure that there is sufficient space to perform maintenance tasks, including space for hands, arms and tools, as well as space to install and remove parts. Designers can check that technicians can see when they do specific maintenance tasks and that they can use the requisite hand tools. Digital humans enable people to be trained in multiple locations without the need for physical prototypes or actual equipment, and so reduce the cost of training manufacturing and maintenance personnel.

E.8.9 Explain the advantages of using digital humans in product marketing.

© IBO 2007

Digital humans can be used in e-commerce to model clothing products. A customer can produce a model corresponding to his or her body shape, size and look. The model can then try on clothing so that the customer can see what it might look like, for example, www.landsend. com.

Further reading

Faraway, J. & Reed, M. P. (2007). *Statistics for Digital Human Motion Modeling in Ergonomics.* University of Michigan Ann Arbor, Michigan. USA.

Zhang, X. & Chaffin, D. B. (2005). *Digital human modeling for computer-aided ergonomics.* In: Karwowski, W., Marras, W.S. (Eds.), Hand- book of Occupational Ergonomics. Taylor & Francis. CRC Press. London. Boca Raton.

E9 DESIGN FOR DISABILITY

Wheelchair-related design

To assist designers, manufacturers and consumers, standards, such as the Australian AS 3696, have been developed. The standards focus on the physical and mechanical requirements of wheelchair design. To match these guidelines, researchers need to test a range of individuals for the appropriate sizes, forces, pressures, joint positions and postures of users. This standard encompasses a series of separate, focussed regulations documenting tests and measurements for wheelchairs determining:

- efficiency of brakes
- obstacle climbing ability
- static and dynamic stability
- environment or climate tests
- coefficients of friction on test surfaces
- static impact and cyclic fatigue strength
- overall dimensions, mass and turning space
- energy consumption, power and controls - electric wheelchairs
- maximum speed, acceleration and retardation - electric wheelchairs.

Early wheelchairs are an example of 'industrial design'. This style is a legacy from the days of the Industrial Revolution, when engineers and designers were charged with developing functional products that were gradually improved over time.

Today, with a vast array of data available for materials and processes, plus the opportunities afforded by the deconstruction of existing market alternatives designers can turn their attention to fine-tuning the process not only for groups, but customizing products for individuals.

Anthropometric primary data gathered from individuals or retrieved from databases or tables, would be the starting point of any researcher.

User research trials produce valuable in-service data providing information about, functionality, efficiency and even maintenance. This data may be examined either in physical or virtual, computer-simulated environments.

Wheelchairs date back as far as 16th Century. Over time they have improved, mostly through the application of new materials and technologies. Wheelchairs have been consistently made lighter and more flexible. In the 19th Century, open weave wicker replaced solid timber. Unfortunately the wicker proved to have insufficient strength and designers returned to timber. In the 20th Century a lightweight folding design was developed and today we see electric wheelchairs with disc brakes commercially available. Human factors reviewed to develop and improve wheelchair design would include measurements relating to:

- strength and grip – strength values to move the chair, operate controls
- turning circle - ease of navigating confined spaces, dexterity required for control
- storage - ease of folding , unfolding, forces required, locking mechanisms
- weight – rolling friction, motive force required, static and dynamic stability
- reach envelopes – for controls, brakes, wheel rims and turning handles
- safety – stability, centre of gravity for different weights and heights of individuals, use of restraints such as seatbelts, comfort, ease of securing and opening buckles
- comfort and fatigue - force/time relationships, posture, adjustability
- environmental considerations - inclement conditions, stability, traction, force requirements, affects of water ingress on operational forces.

Wheelchair access legislation is enacted to ensure individuals with a disability are able to participate as fully as possible in the community. This includes providing access and the ability to navigate through; buildings and offices, schools, public spaces and amenities.

This legislation requires building owners to take all reasonable steps to change structures, policies and procedures to facilitate wheelchair access. While this legislation must be accommodated for new building to be approved, at the planning stage it can be difficult to modify existing premises.

In the simplest cases, it may simply require removal of barriers or restrictions to wheelchair access, while in others it may require the fitting of ramps, wheelchair lifts or elevators. Considerations of cost and space availability can make meeting the requirements of this legislation difficult.

> E.9.5 Evaluate the requirements for wheelchair access in the school environment.
>
> © IBO 2007

Every school must have an accessibility plan that documents how the physical environment has been adjusted to improve student access. The provision of lifts and ramps helps wheelchair-bound students access otherwise impassable steps and stairs. Improvement of the physical environment also involves widening of some doorways, adjusting opening mechanisms and providing modified toilet facilities. Modifications are aimed at improving access of students with a disability to all areas and aspects of school life.

> E.9.6 Identify human factors issues for those with limited hand movement.
>
> © IBO 2007

Design for limited hand movement

Individuals can have a limited range of hand movement as a result of an injury or disease. Alternatively, they may have been born with this restriction. Common causes of limited hand movement may be due to:

- arthritis
- amputation
- severe injury
- spinal injuries
- multiple sclerosis
- muscular dystrophy
- carpal tunnel syndrome.
- fibromyalgia, a widespread pain affecting the muscles.

Designers must consider not just the flexibility, reach and dexterity of hand and finger movement, but also the fact that, in some situations, these conditions are degenerative or have variable impact, depending on the situation or physiological conditions. The disability may also be exacerbated, or accompanied by pain, under physical stress. Pain itself may be the limiting factor in hand movement. In this case, the accompanying forces associated with stretching or pressure are the required measurements, not primarily the ability to physically extend or manipulate the hand and fingers.

> E.9.7 Explain the methods that designers would use to research human factors for those with limited hand movement.
>
> © IBO 2007

User trials would be the most effective way to gather information to assist designers. Data required would depend on the operation performed, but both qualitative and quantitative information obtained in this fashion would better inform design improvements. Some of the general interactions and operations performed would include where applicable:

- safety
- reaction time
- precision of movement
- required sensitivity of touch.

> E.9.8 Identify kitchen appliances that could be modified for greater ease of use for people with limited hand movements.
>
> E.9.9 Explain suitable modifications to the kitchen appliances identified in E.9.8 to enhance ease of use for people with limited hand movements.
>
> © IBO 2007

It has been recognized for some time that people with a range of disabilities may have difficulties using some kitchen appliances.

'Using standard kitchen and laundry appliances can be a major challenge for people who work from wheelchairs, who are crippled by arthritis or who are blind. In many instances, a special tool, control or installation may be needed so someone with disability can use an appliance most conveniently. While most of these modifications are made by the user, some manufacturers do offer special aids to help *owners adapt their appliances to meet the needs of a specific disability. Such aids include soft adapter knobs for those with arthritic hands and Braille controls and instructions for blind consumers. Some manufacturers and retailers offer these aids at no charge or at a very moderate cost.'*

(Whirlpool Corporation,1986)

People with arthritic hands or hand deformities find it difficult to grasp round knobs and controls; they may be unable to grasp handles on refrigerators, ovens and microwave ovens. Slip-on adapters are available for many round controls; they can be fitted on to provide a soft, enlarged surface for those with limitations of grip.

Refrigerators

Refrigerator doors can be heavy and difficult to open. Continuous tubular door handles placed vertically on the door offer infinite grasping positions. Unfortunately, most handles, have a shallow grasp area and are difficult for people with hand problems or those who have larger hands to operate. Some refrigerators come with foot pedal operated doors to facilitate opening. While not yet available, motorized door openers, powered by electricity would also assist those who have difficulty opening doors.

Cooktops

As with other appliances round knobs can be difficult to grip and maintain sufficient force or precision to use effectively. Even able-bodied operators have difficulty with round handles if their hands are wet or oily. Ergonomically shaped control, designed to facilitate turning would prove more effective.

Cookware

Holding a traditional straight-handled saucepan causes the user to bend his or her wrist at an awkward and sometimes painful, upward angle. Holding the saucepan in this fashion can reduce grip strength by around 45%.

For individuals with poor grip strength or pain associated with grasping, the award winning saucepans shown in Figure E.9.9 may provide some assistance. They have been specifically designed to be easier to use. The ergonomically designed, silicon coated, bent handle allows the user to hold a hot, heavy pan in a strong, neutral, (straight), wrist position assisting muscles and tendons to work more efficiently. The handle's overall effect is to place much less strain on hands, wrists and lower arms, while providing a greater degree of control. The saucepan bowl is also made from high quality hard-anodized aluminium to minimize weight.

Figure E.9.9 Ergonomic cookware design

> **E.9.10** Outline the forces involved in unscrewing the lid of a jar.
>
> © IBO 2007

To open a jar successfully, sufficient force must be generated at the perimeter of the lid to create enough turning force, or torque, to break the seal between the jar and the lid. At the same time, grip strength must be maintained to create enough frictional resistance between the user's hand and the lid, stopping any slippage that might occur.

> **E.9.11** Describe a range of products designed to assist people to unscrew the lid of a jar.
>
> © IBO 2007

Figure E.9.11a shows a plastic covered metal device designed to open a range of jar lids. The force required to open a jar has been lessened through the mechanical advantaged produced by the length of the utensil lever arm. The frictional grip force required by the hand has also been enhanced through the introduction of a serrated metal contact strip

Figure E.9.11a Metal bottle opener

The cone shaped flexible rubber moulding shown in Figure E.9.11b, fits a range of lid sizes and relies on the frictional resistance generated between the lid and the rubber utensil. The soft grip material improves the user's 'feel' of the lid.

Figure E.9.11b Rubber moulding

This four-in-one jar opener, pictured in Figure E.9.11c, uses a second order lever to supply a mechanical advantage. The rubber-lined metal construction provides a strong body with a high coefficient of friction.

Figure E.9.11c Lever based opener

E.9.12 Discuss the issues of human factors research in developing and developed countries.

The application of human factors research, methodologies and resulting recommendations is critical to the development successful products in emerging economies. In 2005, the 'UN Millennium Development Goals' documented the importance of making the benefits of new technologies and materials available to developing economies. It has become apparent, however, that it is not just a technological fix that is required, but a unique approach to developing countries, taking into account social considerations and cultural contexts. It is the consideration of these human factors, neglected in the past, that researchers believe is the key to sustainability in cross-cultural environments. Greater consideration is therefore required when transferring goods and technologies from developed nations to emerging economies. Human factors

requiring additional consideration in these situations include:

- social context and cultural setting
- suitability and relevance of the perceived need
- use of appropriate technology and infrastructure.

E.9.13 Explain the social responsibility of designers to design for all impaired groups.

The term Universal Design was originally used by Ron Mace, (1998), and was coined to meet the needs of people of all ages and abilities.

The Centre for Universal Design defines the term as, '... *the design of products and environment to be useable by all people, to the greatest extent possible, without the need for adaptation or specialized design. The intent of universal design is to simplify life for everyone by making products, communications, and the built environment more useable by as many people as possible at little or no cost.'*

Center for Universal Design, 2005.

Universal design takes into consideration people of all ages, genders and abilities, and, through design, attempts to improve the life of all people. In the past it has been misconstrued 'one size fits all'. This is clearly less than its full intention. Through legislation and public education campaigns, designers have come to realize their social responsibilities and the recognition that good design reflects the needs of a variety of users and makes accommodation for this range. The main features of Universal Design may be interpreted as:

- equity in use
- flexibility in service
- allow tolerance for error
- simple and intuitive operation
- communicate palpable information
- need low physical effort to function
- provide space for operators and use.

In many industrialized nations legislation exists covering and enforcing consideration of people with a disability.

E.9.14 Discuss the role of legislation in ensuring inclusive design for community facilities.

Human factors research drives and informs designs based on these legislative requirements. Just some of the countries with legislation requiring consideration of individuals with a disability include:

- UK, the Equality Act 2010
- Australia, the Disability Discrimination Act 1992
- Canada, the Ontarians with Disabilities Act of 2001
- US, under the Americans with Disabilities Act of 1990
- South Africa the Promotion of Equality and Prevention of Unfair Discrimination Act 2000
- India, Persons with Disabilities (Equal Opportunities, Protection of Rights and Full Participation) Act, 1995.

In developing countries, formal legislation may not be enacted, but through a series of informal guidelines and international standards promoted by NGOs and government agencies, disability issues may be addressed to some degree.

> E.9.15 Identify the opportunities presented by the global marketplace for design for specific impairments.
>
> © IBO 2007

Economies of scale can be generated when centralized production takes place to fill orders of significant size. Price reductions can be large, particularly when small markets are combined. Smaller individual markets scattered over the world pay for duplication of tooling and capital equipment. Combining markets into larger groups enables manufacturers to reduce prices and generate greater revenues for research and development. It also enables the production of more variety at lesser cost.

> E.9.16 Describe the benefits of increased access to product information by impaired consumers.
>
> © IBO 2007

Improved access to product information allows consumers to make better informed choices. People with a range of disabilities and mobility issues now have a range of tools and opportunities to better educate themselves and thus make more informed choices.

Further Reading

Design for Independent Living: Kitchen and Laundry Designs for Disabled People (Whirlpool, 1986)

Crews, D. E. & Zavotka, S. (2005). *Aging, Disability, and Frailty: Implications for Universal Design.* Journal of Psychological Anthropology. 25: pp.113–118. The Ohio State University. USA.

E10 DESIGN FOR PURPOSE

> E.10.1 Identify design contexts that have been purposely designed to provide only basic comfort for short periods of time.
>
> E.10.2 Explain considerations that may conflict with human factors in the seating design for a fast-food restaurant and an airport.
>
> © IBO 2007

Design for discomfort

Design for discomfort is a recent approach in design to improve productivity or efficiency. The basic premise is to create a situation or environment that feels either uncomfortable or provides comfort for a limited period of time.

Airports and fast food chains are quoted regularly as providing limited comfort. This is designed to facilitate movement of customers and discourage long-term use of facilities.

Shopping malls, supermarkets and bus stations have experimented, (with some success), playing classical music to discourage anti-social behaviour and loitering of young people around their premises. The purpose is to create a soundscape that is unpleasant or unwelcoming to targeted groups.

While designers have carefully constructed seating to provide comfort for limited periods of time, this approach is not always appropriate. In airports, early check-ins, extended stopovers, flight delays and even cancellations, can cause passengers to need seating to provide comfort for extended periods of time.

Maturing fast food chains have also retargeted their marketing towards families and the provision of sit-down meals, aiming to attract restaurant clientele. This naturally extends purchases and improves the company's bottom line, but without appropriate seating return customers may be difficult to attract.

HL

OPTION

E.10.3 Identify ways in which designers reconcile conflicting design considerations.

© IBO 2007

Good design is always an exercise in compromise. To be successful, however, the accurate identification of a detailed and comprehensive design specification is imperative. The prioritization of this specification, to determine which features dominate in importance over others, ultimately determines the direction the design will take. These priorities have to be identified considering: design principles (aesthetics), manufacturing methods, materials, cost, waste, environmental impact, clients, target market, end-of-life disposal etc. To be successful this complex interplay of elements must be considered holistically, as adjustments in one area have effects on others.

E.10.4 Discuss the importance of international standards in airport signage.

© IBO 2007

Design for discomfort

Airports are large, complex, congested places. They are filled with people enroute elsewhere. The airport and all of its facilities should be designed to facilitate the fast and efficient transfer of these people.

Travellers are often visiting the airport for the first time and have no knowledge of the building layout or conceivably even the local language. It is imperative that airport signage be designed to cater for all of these potential needs, maintain terminal efficiency, improve safety and limit the stress and frustration of the flying public.

The International Standards Organization (ISO) has developed a standard set of symbols to assist travelers around the world. Through the use of standard graphic symbols, without the need of language support to assist travelers wayfinding

E.10.5 Identify the shape and colour standards for road signs.

© IBO 2007

Since the introduction and growth of automobiles for transport, the need for road sign standardization has increased. With greater degrees of personal vehicle ownership, cross-border and international travel, this need has only grown. Attempts occurred as early as 1895. Over time a number of systems have been proposed. In

1968 as part of the Vienna Convention on Road Traffic Treaty, European countries agreed to identify precise colours, sizes and shapes for road signs.

Both Britain and the United States have developed their own road signage standards, many other nations in their respective spheres of influence have adopted these protocols.

European traffic signs have been designed to be clear and easily interpreted at a glance. Most of the signs use symbols, as opposed to text, for better clarity and international understanding. Figure E.10.5a shows a typical European warning sign accompanied by an acceptable and identifiable variation. The guiding principle of the European road sign standard is to maintain shapes and colours of groups of signs with the same purpose for example:

* prohibition signs are round with a red border
* informative or secondary signs use a rectangular shape
* warning signs are triangular with a white or yellow background.

The road sign standard continues to develop. In 2003, provisions regarding legibility, priority at roundabouts and tunnel safety were introduced.

Figure E.10.5a Shows a typical European triangular warning sign as defined by the convention standards accompanied by an acceptable variation

Figure E.10.5b shows just some examples of shape and language variation in stop signs around the world. Note the readily recognized octagon is not universal nor is the convention to use English, local or bilingual signs. These signs demonstrate some of the variations that may occur in countries that are not signatories to international standards.

Figure E.10.5b Language and shape variation in signs

HL

E.10.6 Identify human factors issues in the design of freeway/motorway signs.

E.10.7 Describe the methods designers would use to research human factors in signage.

© IBO 2007

Roadside signs provide directions, instructions and information. At a minimum they have to be perceived, comprehended and acted upon. Horberry, (1998), noted, ' *in some cases poor acquisition and interpretation of the information conveyed by traffic signs can increase accidents.*' Roadside signs are designed with the following features in mind:

- driver age
- driver visual acuity
- legibility of information
- environmental conditions
- conspicuity of placement - visibility
- comprehensibility - amount of information
- acquisition variables - speed, time distance
- graphic elements – shape, colour bordering
- symbology – recognition factors and standardization.

Quantitative testing of road sign design may be done through mechanisms such as:

- shape detection
- age-based visual acuity
- interpretation of information
- recognition of standard sign shapes.

E.10.8 Discuss the human factors advantages in LED signs.

© IBO 2007

LED signs have the advantage of allowing for the flexible delivery messages which may be changed as conditions or circumstances require. They are easier to read and brighter than conventional incandescently lit signals. Low power requirements and less heat generation mean the signs are more reliable and need less maintenance.

Unfortunately the visibility of an LED sign can be directional in its nature. Angles of viewing or movement in signs can also reduce reader legibility.

E.10.9 Identify the human factors that are paramount in the design of neon signs.

© IBO 2007

In 1910, Georges Claude displayed the first modern neon sign at the Grand Palais in Paris. Over time they have become very popular for promoting and advertising businesses, due to their durability, resistance to failure from shock, vibration, or frequent cycling and long life.

Human factors most important to neon sign design include:

- legibility – text size, font, spacing within and between letters
- graphic distortion – consider effects of distance and viewing angles
- appropriateness – aesthetic impact on surrounding visual environment
- size – matching building scale and allow for image recognition and text legibility
- illumination - considering long distance clarity, colour retention, daylight viewing and shadowing
- prominence – optimizing sign location for unobstructed viewing from a variety of angles and distances considering target audience.

Figure E.10.9 Neon signs Picadilly Circus London

Image by Billy Hicks (Own work) [GFDL (www.gnu.org/copyleft/fdl.html), CC-BY-SA-3.0 (www.creativecommons.org/licenses/by-sa/3.0/) or CC-BY-SA-2.5-2.0-1.0 (www.creativecommons.org/licenses/by-sa/2.5-2.0-1.0)], via Wikimedia Commons

OPTION

E.10.10   Define work-space envelope.

© IBO 2007

Personal space

Work-space envelope is defined as the three dimensional space required by an individual to perform a set task or tasks. The measurement of the work-space envelope for different occupational activities is an important aspect of ergonomic design.

Reliable data obtained from measurement of workspace envelopes is an important tool used to assist with ergonomic design. Traditionally measurements were taken manually, but in recent years video has proven to be an effective tool.

Accurate workspace envelopes must be carefully designed for robotic systems to guarantee the safety of nearby human workers.

E.10.11   Identify and measure the anthropometric data relevant to the design of a student's workspace envelope when studying at a desk.

© IBO 2007

Data collected should range from the 5th percentile female to the 95th percentile male. In this situation, the most important limiting factors relate to the reach of the individual's arm. Data may be gathered from anthropometric tables, dynamic measurement or through the use of software simulations. This data can be affected by such restrictions such as clothing or the provision, and angle of any backrest. Care should be taken here to consider the range of users across countries and cultures, where applicable.

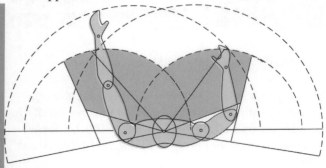

Figure E.10.11 Work space envelope

Image by Bolumena (Own work) GFDL (www.gnu.org/copyleft/fdl.html), via Wikimedia Commons

E.10.12   Discuss cultural differences in the sense of personal space.

© IBO 2007

Edward Hall, (1966), established the field of proxemics, or the study of personal space as a function of culture. Viewed as a virtual 'bubble' surrounding the individual, researchers propose people manage personal space as a consequence of social relationship, situation and culture. Appropriate spatial management is a learned behaviour and individuals only become aware of its presence when boundaries are crossed.

Quantifying personal space can be difficult as it varies from individual to individual. However, in some Asian cultures, people are more accustomed to crowds and shared communal living and, as such, often have smaller requirements for personal space.

As a generalization, personal space can be determined by the type of interaction, the more negative the interaction generally the greater the distance and conversely the more amenable the relationship, closer distances prevail.

'... studies have shown that negatively toned situations precipitate larger spatial zones.'

Bell, Greene, Fisher & Baum 1996

E.10.13   Suggest how a designer could consider cultural diversity in personal space in the design of a railway carriage.

© IBO 2007

Design of interiors of railway carriages are as much a feature of cultural design as purpose of journey, distance and ticket price.

Depending on the 'carriage class,' designs between carriages on one train could be entirely different. Carriages may be arranged for standing room only, serving meals, conducting business or transporting livestock, families and belongings.

Figure 10.13a shows the interior of a British rail carriage used for intercity journeys. An Indian intercity rail carriage shows reductions in space, aisle-ways and sleeping provisions above, including blankets.

Figure E.10.13a Interior of a Grand Central Railway standard class carriage operating between London Kings Cross and Sunderland, UK.

Image by Zzrbiker (Own work) [CC-BY-SA-3.0 (www. creativecommons.org/licenses/by-sa/3.0) or GFDL (www. gnu.org/copyleft/fdl.html)], via Wikimedia Commons

Figure E.10.13b Interior of train carriage India

Image by Agnes Chase

E.10.14	Explain how a designer may incorporate intimate areas into the design of a hotel lounge bar or a cafe.

Small, well-defined areas may be created with the addition of walls or screens to create intimate spaces and improve privacy within larger expanses. The use of warm or neutral tones, accompanied with heavily textured, soft fabrics can also create a cosier space.

The use of darker colours for flooring or ceilings gives the illusion of a smaller, more human scale. Incandescent lighting, rather than halogen or florescent lamps, provide a warmer, less harsh glow. These should be directed downwards from the ceiling or emanate from down-shaded strategically placed lamps.

Furniture, placed away from walls may be used to even further separate and divide spaces within a room.

Further Reading

Bell, P.A., Greene, T.C., Fisher, J.D. & Baum, A. (1996). *Environmental Psychology*. Fort Worth: Harcourt Brace College Publishers.

Conventional vs LED Traffic Signals; Operational Characteristics and Economic Feasibility. (2003). A Project Sponsored by Arkansas Department of Economic Development. Traffic Engineering Division Department of Public Works City of Little Rock.

Freyssinier, J.P., Narendran, N. & Bullough, J. D. (2006). *Luminance Requirements for Lighted Signage*. Sixth International Conference on Solid State Lighting, Proceedings of SPIE 6337, 63371M.

Freyssinier, J. P. (2004). *Evaluation of light-emitting diodes for signage applications*.

Herron, R. E. *Anthropometry: Definition, Uses and Methods of Measurement*. State University, CO 80525, USA

Low, S. M. (2003). Embodied Space(s) : *Anthropological Theories of Body, Space, and Culture Space and Culture*.

E11 BEYOND USABILITY— DESIGNING FOR PLEASURE

E.11.1 Describe the 'four pleasure framework'.

E.11.2 Define physio-pleasure, socio-pleasure, psycho-pleasure and ideo-pleasure.

© IBO 2007

In 1992, anthropologist Professor Lionel Tiger, proposed a system describing the range of positive, human, pleasurable experiences. This framework became known as the, 'four pleasure framework' and incorporated four areas including:

- physio-pleasure involves physical pleasures of the body and senses including taste, touch and smell. It also includes pleasure associated with achievement of physical tasks
- psycho-pleasures relate of the psychology of the mind, cognitive challenges and positive emotional responses to stimuli
- socio-pleasure deals with interpersonal and social relationships such as families, workmates, sense of community and social status
- ideo-pleasure incorporates personal taste, values and ethics, attitudes, belief systems and self image.

E.11.3 Identify ways in which products promote physio-pleasure.

© IBO 2007

Physio-pleasure is derived in variety of ways dependent on the product, for example:

- taste of a dessert or fresh fruit
- smell of perfume or fragrance of soaps
- weight, shape, fit and solid feel of a drinking glass in the hand.

E.11.4 Identify ways in which products promote socio-pleasure.

© IBO 2007

Socio-pleasure may be obtained from services that ease or facilitate communication such as phones, email, skype etc.

Other physical items that assist with social interaction or promote positive feelings of identity, status or community include clothing, team uniforms, jewellery, designer clothes, works of art, antiques etc.

E.11.5 Identify ways in which products promote psycho-pleasure.

© IBO 2007

Psycho-pleasure deals with pleasure derived from cognitive challenges and successful use of products. Successfully negotiating a complex manual for a new piece of equipment, or facilitating the efficient use of a new product through trial and error, would both produce positive psych-pleasure reactions.

E.11.6 Identify ways in which products promote ideo-pleasure.

© IBO 2007

Products that embody an individual's values and attitudes promote positive ideological belief responses. 'Green' or sustainably designed products would promote ideo-pleasure responses in those with a strong commitment to the environment. Companies that support charitable organizations would also solicit positive ideo-pleasure responses from consumers.

E.11.7 Explain how the 'four pleasure framework' promotes a holistic view of product design and marketing.

© IBO 2007

The 'four pleasure framework' provides a structure to support design and marketing staff when attempting to meet the needs of consumers. Taking into consideration all of the positive psychological elements associated with produce purchase and use, designers and marketing personnel become more successful at enhancing the overall experience of consumers. In this fashion, a greater understanding of the consumer brings with it a product that fulfills both practical and emotional needs. Companies successfully employing the 'four pleasures' principle include Harley Davidson, Starbucks and Loreal.

Further Reading

Jordan, P.W. (2002). *Designing Pleasurable Products,* Taylor and Francis: London.

Norman, D.A., *Emotional Design. (2005).* Basic Books: New York.

Exercises

1. Human factors design is also known as:

   A.   ergonomic design
   B.   ergonome design
   C.   workplace design
   D.   anthropometric design.

2. Positive responses to a product that are generated by human senses are examples of:

   A.   ideo-pleasure
   B.   socio-pleasure
   C.   physio-pleasure
   D.   psycho-pleasure.

3. Four types of data scales are:

   A.   nominal, ordinal, interval and ratio
   B.   normal, ordinary, scattered and ratio
   C.   natural, ordinal, relative and comparative
   D.   categorical, continuous, nominal and ordinal.

4. The kitchen triangle is based around:

   A.   sink, stove, refrigerator
   B.   reaching, bending, standing
   C.   wall colour, lighting, ventilation
   D.   entries, foot traffic, bench space.

5. Digital human modelling allows human factors designers to improve products by:

   A.   reducing product lead times
   B.   using motion capture technology
   C.   producing product animations for consumers
   D.   simulating human biomechanics in a range of environments.

6. Discuss how virtual reality and motion capture technologies may be used to inform human factors investigations.

7. Explain how the term 'universal design' includes more than 'one size fits all.'

8. Explain how a risk assessment strategy may be used to assist designers of consumer products.

9. Identify environmental factors that may affect worker performance.

10. Discuss how fashion can affect design and even override human factors research.

INDEX

Index

Symbols

A

Abrading 103

Adaptation 6

Additive manufacturing processes 364

Adjustability 448   454   473

Aeration 269

Aesthetic-usability effect. 464

Affordance 445

Agar-Agar 267

Airport signage 478

Algorithm 11   12

Alloy 47

Alternating current 308

Analogue signal 313

Analogy 6

Animation 356   396

Anorexia nervosa 252

Anthropometrics 114   115   121

Anthropometry 448   469   481

Antioxidants 260   268   283

Antisense technology 292

Appearance prototype 454

Appropriate technology 215

Archimedes 173

Arkwright, Richard 138

Assembly-line production 105

Atom 47

Attribute listing 7

Audiogram 327   328

Automation 106   406

Automotive robots 388

B

Bagasse fibre 421

Balanced diet 253

Bandwidth 328

Barcol hardness test 56

Bardeen, John 345

Barlow, Peter 139

Batch production 106

Bauhaus School of Design 120

Beam 162

Beecher, Catherine 465

Bellagio principles 218

Bell, Alexander Graham 19

Bell Telephone Laboratories 464

Bending moment 159   160

Binary code 313

Biocompatibility 405   411   417

Biological value 240

Biomechanics 451   471   483

Biometric iris scanning 339

Biomimetics 418

CORE

CORE

CORE